ECONOMICS
OF WATER RESOURCES
PLANNING

McGRAW-HILL SERIES IN WATER RESOURCES AND ENVIRONMENTAL ENGINEERING

Ven T. Chow, Rolf Eliassen, and Ray K. Linsley, Consulting Editors

GRAF   Hydraulics of Sediment Transport

HALL AND DRACUP   Water Resources Systems Engineering

JAMES AND LEE   Economics of Water Resources Planning

WALTON   Groundwater Resource Evaluation

ECONOMICS OF WATER RESOURCES PLANNING

L. DOUGLAS JAMES
Associate Professor in the Environmental Resources Center
Georgia Institute of Technology

ROBERT R. LEE
Director, Idaho Water Resource Board

McGRAW-HILL BOOK COMPANY
New York St. Louis San Francisco Düsseldorf
Johannesburg Kuala Lumpur London Mexico Montreal New Delhi
Panama Rio de Janeiro Singapore Sydney Toronto

ECONOMICS OF WATER RESOURCES PLANNING

Library of Congress Catalog Card Number 79-115146

32263

234567890 MAMM 798765432

This book was set in Modern by The Maple Press Company, and printed on permanent
paper and bound by The Maple Press Company. The designer was Edward A. Butler;
the drawings were done by John Cordes, J. & R. Technical Services, Inc. The editors
were B. J. Clark and M. E. Margolies. Sally Ellyson supervised production.

PREFACE

In a world where an expanding population and an even more rapidly expanding urban-industrial development are intensifying the pressures for a better planned water resources management program, the engineer involved in water resources planning recognizes he must maintain a planning methodology capable of producing a viable resource development program. At the same time, he wonders how he can do it. How can he better structure his design to meet current human needs? How can he make his design flexible enough to accommodate future human needs, the nature of which he can scarcely anticipate? How can he devise a management system for adequately sensing changes in human need as they occur and quickly adjusting management policy and even system design as is necessary?

The hydrologic cycle is the vast natural water resources system. Water falls on the earth, travels downward, over, or under the surface of the ground, reaches the ocean, and returns to the atmosphere through evaporation induced by solar energy. But nature picks its own times and places. The water resources planner seeks to modify the natural cycle by structural measures that force the movement of water to times and places better meeting known human needs. He also seeks to modify, by non-structural measures, the activities of man, so as to better conform to known movement patterns. He considers a flood control channel and flood plain management. He considers water supply systems to existing cities and the development of new cities closer to available supplies. The best management selects the best possible combination of measures.

The concept of the optimum program is changing as men recognize the wisdom, if not the necessity, of taking additional factors into consideration. Pressures from many groups and disciplines have contributed to the expanding awareness of relevant considerations. Business management has long been concerned with decision making to maximize returns to the firm. Engineering economy provides the procedures for the cost analysis of alternatives for the purpose of finding the least-cost approach, irrespective of viewpoint. Studies in microeconomics examine benefits produced as well as costs incurred, and provide rules for maximizing benefits minus costs as a step in optimization to enhance the welfare of the general public. The other social sciences provide further insight into how the welfare of man, as an individual being and as part of a group, can be improved. The biological sciences extend the analysis to all life systems. The institutions responsible for actual resource development draw from all of these sources in formulating their plans, and improvise to supplement the available procedures where action cannot wait for research. As the state of the art now stands, the concepts and procedures required for planning are scattered through the literature of many disciplines, some in journal publications but many in otherwise unpublished research reports and conference proceedings. The purpose of this book is to consolidate into a single volume the basic economic concepts required in water resources planning.

In one companion volume, "Water Resources Engineering,"[1] Linsley and Franzini present the basic physical system and survey the available structural measures for engineered water resources development. In another volume, "Water Resources Systems Engineering,"[2] Hall and Dracup present the procedures for analysis of how water resources systems may be designed to function together as a whole to better achieve specific objectives. In this book, we are seeking to examine how relevant objectives can be specified as well as the reasoning needed to apply rather abstract concepts of social welfare to specific design choices.

The reader should approach the material contained in this book from the viewpoint of developing a philosophy of planning. The detailed procedural steps as presented are intended to illustrate basic concepts, rather than to finalize a method to be followed by rote. These concepts and the written material describing them have been presented by the authors in teaching courses on water resources planning and have been applied by the authors in their planning experience.

The material in this book has been used as the basic text for a one-year course sequence dealing with the economic, social, and institutional issues involved in water resources management. Parts 1, 2, and 6 plus Chapters 8 and 9 can be adopted to a one-semester senior or one-semester first-year graduate course in public works economics (appropriate within programs in transportation, air pollution, and civil engineering management as well as programs in water resources). The remaining portions can then be covered in a second-semester course for those specifically interested in water resources. Although the material is covered in a manner

[1] Ray K. Linsley and Joseph B. Franzini, "Water Resources Engineering" (New York: McGraw-Hill Book Company, 1964).
[2] Warren A. Hall and John A. Dracup, "Water Resources Systems Engineering" (New York: McGraw-Hill Book Company, 1970).

requiring no specific prerequisites, owing to the diversity of background among students interested in resource development, some background in one or more of the areas of engineering economy, sophomore microeconomics, hydrology, water resources engineering, and systems analysis may add depth to the understanding of selected sections.

The authors gratefully acknowledge the contributions made indirectly to the book through discussion with numerous colleagues. Particular thanks are extended to Professors Ray K. Linsley and Eugene L. Grant of Stanford University and Dr. Charles W. Howe of Resources for the Future for their review of and contribution to various parts of the manuscript. Mrs. Betty Bradshaw and Mrs. Alice Taylor spent many hours typing preliminary drafts, and Miss Pat Miller typed much of the final manuscript.

L. DOUGLAS JAMES
ROBERT R. LEE

CONTENTS

ECONOMICS
OF WATER RESOURCES
PLANNING

1
ENGINEERING
ECONOMY

Engineering economy is the science of applying economic criteria to select the best of a group of alternative engineering designs. A design if implemented will produce a time pattern of consequences which must be predicted, evaluated, and compared. The method of comparison might more appropriately be called decision economics since the principles may just as well be used to select among the choices available to other disciplines. For example, the same type of analysis could be called business economics, education economics, or medical economics depending on the skills needed to define the choices. Although the approach emphasizes comparison in economic units, it also includes identification, for comparison to the fullest extent possible, of those consequences which do not relate to economic goals or cannot be expressed in money terms.

Arthur M. Wellington pioneered modern engineering economics through its application to the analysis of alternative railway locations in 1877.[1] Wellington was prompted by the neglect of economic factors in selecting railway location at a time when capital investment in railroads exceeded that in all manufacturing endeavors. The approach has been more thoroughly developed and applied to many other kinds of choices through the years, and current techniques are presented in a number of recent works.[2]

[1] Arthur M. Wellington, "The Economic Theory of the Location of Railways," 1st ed. (New York: John Wiley & Sons, Inc., 1877).
[2] For example, see Eugene L. Grant and Grant Ireson, "Principles of Engineering Economy," 5th ed. (New York: The Ronald Press Company, 1970); and E. P. DeGarmo, "Engineering Economy," 4th ed. (New York: The Macmillan Company, 1967).

The principles and techniques of engineering economics are not always clearly understood nor correctly applied in water resources planning. In separate books, Eckstein and McKean examined federal practices for analyzing water resources projects and suggested numerous revisions.[1] Hirshleifer, DeHaven, and Milliman received two large water resources projects, one in New York and the other in California, and found serious conceptual errors in official economic feasibility studies.[2] Lee produced similar findings in an examination of procedures used in analyzing water projects on the local government level.[3] These failures demonstrate the need for the water resources planner to thoroughly understand the principles and techniques of engineering economics. Part 1 reviews the basic principles of engineering economics as applied to public works in general and water resources development more specifically and presents the mathematics required in their application. Part 2 builds on this foundation by examining some of the more knotty conceptual problems in economic analysis.

[1]   Otto Eckstein, "Water Resource Development: The Economics of Project Evaluation" (Cambridge, Mass.: Harvard University Press, 1958); Roland McKean, "Efficiency in Government through Systems Analysis" (New York: John Wiley & Sons, Inc., 1958).
[2]   Jack Hirshleifer, James C. DeHaven, and Jerome W. Milliman, "Water Supply: Economics, Technology, and Policy" (Chicago: The University of Chicago Press, 1960).
[3]   Robert R. Lee, "Local Government Public Works Decision-Making" (Stanford, Calif.: Stanford University Institute in Engineering Economic Systems, 1964).

CHAPTER
ONE

PRINCIPLES
OF ENGINEERING
ECONOMICS

The principles of engineering economics guide the structuring of alternatives so they may be compared to determine which should be selected. The evaluation process requires prediction of the consequences expected to result from picking the alternative, estimation of the magnitude of each consequence, and conversion of each consequence magnitude into commensurable units. The purpose of this chapter is to review the conceptual problems and basic principles involved in the process.

1-1 EQUIVALENCE OF KIND The major obstacles to expressing the consequences of alternative courses of action in commensurable units are differences in kind and differences in time. The two differences may be illustrated through the example of comparing two alternative irrigation projects. One project provides irrigation water for peaches. The second provides water for cotton. Construction of the first project will produce x tons of peaches. Construction of the second will produce y bales of cotton. If the two projects can be constructed for equal cost, selection depends on whether x tons of peaches or y bales of cotton is more valuable.

As long as the two outputs are expressed in these diverse units, the projects cannot be compared. Only when common units are used is comparison possible. The first step in economic analysis must be to find a common value unit. One might use tons of peaches. A farmer selling y bales of cotton might receive the same price as if he had sold y' tons of peaches. The decision could then be based on whether x or y' was the larger. One might use bales of cotton as the common unit, express the value of x tons of peaches as x' bales of cotton, and make the decision. As a third approach, farmers grow both peaches and cotton to buy bread for their families. A farmer could sell x tons of peaches and buy x'' loaves of bread. A farmer could sell y bales of cotton and buy y'' loaves of bread. The decision could be based on a comparison between x'' and y''.

However, such approaches are uncommon because society has established a system of units for comparing relative value. Tons of peaches, bales of cotton, and loaves of bread may all be evaluated in monetary units. The use of monetary units in economy studies is based solely on convenience and does not imply a materialistic approach of considering only monetary profit while ignoring the many values of life, health, and happiness which can not be expressed in money terms. Handling intangible values will be discussed later (Sec. 1-6).

The simple fact is that diverse values are understood by more people when expressed in monetary terms than when any other kind of unit is used. Far more people can visualize worth in dollars than in tons of peaches, bales of cotton, or loaves of bread. The proper approach for comparing the two irrigation projects is to convert both tons of peaches and bales of cotton into dollars, compare the dollar totals, and (provided intangible values do not indicate otherwise) select the project producing the greater total.

1-2   EQUIVALENCE OF TIME   An irrigation project will provide water for many years. In evaluating the example project, should peaches produced this year be reckoned as having equal value to those expected to be produced 30 years from now? Most people would be more inclined to invest a dollar to produce 5 lb of peaches now than to invest the dollar to produce 5 lb of peaches 30 years from now.

An earlier realization of investment returns is desirable for the investor because it gives him greater flexibility for future action. If the returns are needed for consumption, they become available with less waiting. If they are to be reinvested, an earlier reinvestment will speed subsequent returns and result in a more rapid expansion of capital. To fail to differentiate returns by date is to say all economic expansion rates are equally desirable.

In order to make realistic investment decisions, each monetary value must be identified by both amount and time. Amounts at different times should not be directly compared or combined. They are not in common units. Amounts in different time periods may be made equivalent by multiplying future amounts by a factor becoming progressively smaller into the more distant future. The discount rate is the time rate of decrease in this factor expressed in percent per time period. An investment of a dollar at an annual rate of return of 5 percent would yield $1.05 a year hence. Similarly, $1.05 available a year from now is equivalent to $1.00 now when discounted at 5 percent.

The discount rate used has a great influence on the project selected. Future benefits and costs receive less weight with higher, and more weight with lower, discount rates. High discount rates favor projects with little initial investment, while low discount rates favor capital intensive projects. Determination of the proper discount rate for water resources planning is discussed in detail in Chap. 6.

1-3 *WHOSE VIEWPOINT?* Monetary value depends on the viewpoint taken in the evaluation. The grower who produces a ton of peaches will equate value with sale price. The community will add to this the gains accruing to food processors, farm workers, farm suppliers, and other individuals who profit indirectly. However, from the national viewpoint, committing resources to one community to grow more peaches may deny investment capital to another. Furthermore, peaches grown in different communities are competing goods.

The above description thus pinpoints the three viewpoints possible in an engineering economy study.[1]

1 That of the group sponsoring or financing the project. Consider only consequences affecting this group.
2 That of all the people in a specific area such as a state, county, or special district. Consider only consequences affecting those living in this defined area.
3 That of the entire nation. Consider all consequences to whomsoever they may accrue.

Viewpoint 1 is based on the premise that the sponsoring group should promote its own welfare. It is a legitimate viewpoint for private enterprise, but one of the primary justifications for action by government is to avoid the adverse consequences of individuals' putting personal above public welfare. Therefore, there appears to be no justification for a public agency's taking anything less than the public viewpoint. When a planning group ignores conflicting viewpoints, a higher level of government must bring about any adjustments necessary to protect the public interest.

[1] Eugene L. Grant and Grant Ireson, "Principles of Engineering Economy," 4th ed. (New York: The Ronald Press Company, 1960), p. 445. For a parallel discussion, see Tillo Kuhn, "Public Enterprise Economics and Transport Problems" (Berkeley: University of California Press, 1962), pp. 13–16.

Practical realities may restrict the freedom of a local government to take the national viewpoint.[1] First, the cost of tracing the consequences of proposed alternatives beyond its jurisdiction may be excessive. Secondly, a local government is subject to much political pressure from the taxpayers who support it but little from those living outside its jurisdiction. The tendency is to ignore these outside consequences. Higher levels of government must be responsible for making sure local planners adequately consider project consequences occurring in other areas.

Viewpoint 3 should, in principle, be taken by every level of government to maximize aggregate national welfare in the long run. Where federal programs, such as the reclamation of the arid West or the economic development of Appalachia, are designed to achieve regional goals, project consequences should be evaluated from both the national and regional viewpoints. Regional interests may try to influence federal agencies to select projects producing regional benefit, where they must repay only a fraction of project costs.[2] The decision maker needs to know if such a project can be justified from the national viewpoint and weigh the national sacrifice required to achieve local goals.

1-4 SUNK COST   The justification for following a course of action depends on the events occurring with it being better than those occurring without it, by an amount exceeding its implementation cost. An engineering economy study need analyze only differences between alternatives and differences between resulting consequences. All costs and benefits unaffected by which alternative is chosen should be disregarded. Obviously, past events have already occurred and cannot be retracted by future action. Past expenditure, or sunk costs, are past events and thus should have no influence on deciding among alternatives except as they affect future cash flows.

Despite their economic irrelevance, sunk costs have often been allowed to influence decisions for two main reasons. The decision makers may have a psychological, political, or even a legal commitment to continue a past policy so that past efforts are not wasted. Secondly, accounting records indicating an undepreciated book value for assets having no economic worth may restrict freedom to make new investment. However, in no case are past mistakes a legitimate excuse for continuing a policy which cannot be justified by future benefits.

[1]   Roland N. McKean, Costs and Benefits from Different Viewpoints, "Public Expenditure Decisions in the Urban Community" (Washington: Resources for the Future, 1962), pp. 148–151.
[2]   See Kuhn, *op. cit.*, p. 18. Kuhn would have the decision-making authority set at the highest level so that the broadest view of the public interest is observed. McKean, "Costs and Benefits from Different Viewpoints," p. 147, sees central planning as too often leading "to planning of the people, by the few, and for the few."

The sunk-cost principle is illustrated in the following example. Suppose $5 million have been spent on a hydropower installation ultimately costing $10 million. A steam plant costing an estimated $3 million is subsequently found to be capable of supplying the same energy. Which facility should be selected, assuming all other future costs to be the same? The $5 million already spent on the hydropower facility is a sunk cost, hence is irrelevant. Since the cost of the steam plant is less than the remaining cost of the hydropower installation, the steam plant should be selected. Continuing the initial project is not in the economic interest of the public.

1-5 INCREMENTAL COST   According to the incremental-cost principle, the change in benefits and the change in costs resulting from a given decision determine the merit of that decision. Each project segment should be judged on its own merits. The decision to enlarge a project should be justified by the enlargement's increasing benefits more than it increases cost.

For illustration, consider a 10,000 acre-ft reservoir which a city has determined to build for $1 million. Before construction begins, increasing the storage to 20,000 acre-ft and the cost to $1,500,000 is found to achieve $600,000 in downstream flood control benefits. The incorrect average-cost approach would preclude flood control on the basis that half the storage means half the cost, and $750,000 exceeds $600,000. The correct incremental-cost approach would include flood control because the additional expenditure of $500,000 is exceeded by the benefit of $600,000.

By the same token, an element costing $50,000 but producing only $20,000 in benefits should not be justified by inclusion in a large project with costs of $2 million and benefits of $3 million. The maximum net benefit is achieved with that element excluded.

1-6 INTANGIBLE VALUES   Even though an economy study seeks to evaluate all consequences in commensurable monetary units, many values defy such quantification. Unique or extremely rare items such as species of plant or animal life or sights of unusual beauty have no acknowledged money value. Neither have direct effects on human beings physically through loss of health or life, emotionally through loss of national prestige or personal integrity, or psychologically through environmental changes. Nor do monetary values serve to measure the achievement of such extra economic goals as income redistribution, increased economic stability, or improved environmental quality (Sec. 5-1). Each value which cannot be expressed in monetary terms is called an *intangible* or *irreducible*.

Inability to express a value in economic units does not necessarily preclude evaluation in other units. All intangible values should be quantified as precisely as possible. Vague statements on threat to human life are not nearly as helpful as a precise statement on the number of lives expected to be lost. In weighing whether a given sacrifice in economic value is worthwhile to achieve a goal, the decision maker should have access to the best possible information on the nature of the intangible consequences as well as the magnitude of the economic consequences.

1-7 PREDICTIVE UNCERTAINTY Because economic analysis compares future consequences of engineering alternatives, the reliability of each conclusion depends on the ability to predict future events. A project may only appear to be economically feasible because of incorrect predictions. No matter how much data or experience one has, predicting the future is inherently uncertain.

Uncertainty with respect to water resources project evaluation has been described by McKean as "inherent in the nature of things and is not necessarily evidence of lazy or careless estimation."[1] He gives five classifications:

1 *Uncertainty about objectives.* Even though planning objectives as currently conceived may be perfectly clear, future developments may significantly alter social goals.

2 *Uncertainty about constraints on the system.* It is computationally infeasible to plan all economic decisions simultaneously. A particular analysis must be performed in the context of constraints imposed by outside events. The price of steel may be taken as given in an economy study without attempting to determine an optimum price through industry analysis. However, future developments may produce unpredictable price changes.

3 *Uncertainty about public response.* Even though a thorough analysis may indicate the need for project-produced services, public inertia against learning new ways or psychological commitment to established procedures will affect their use in an often unpredictable manner.

4 *Uncertainty about technological change.* Even though a project currently produces a needed output at low cost, innovations or technological changes may cause the output to be no longer needed or introduce an even less costly production process.

5 *Uncertainty about the chance element in recurring events.* Even when the probability of occurrence of random events can be established statisti-

[1] Roland N. McKean, "Efficiency in Government through Systems Analysis" (New York: John Wiley & Sons, Inc. 1958), pp. 65–68.

cally, the precise time of occurrence (of flood peaks, for example) is never known in advance. Furthermore, the many random elements in any system cumulatively increase overall uncertainty.

Widely used approaches to treating uncertainty include (1) applying preselected percentages to increase costs or reduce benefits, (2) limiting the period of analysis, or (3) adding a risk increment to the discount rate. However, because each of these approaches requires selection of a numerical factor without providing any help on how a specific value is to be selected, Eckstein has well argued:

> These crude adjustments are intellectually not very satisfying and one should try to derive better adjustments from explicit objective functions and from the probabilistic nature of benefits.[1]

A more satisfactory approach is to recognize explicitly that project effects should not be predicted as single fixed values but rather as variables having some probability distribution of possible values. A more detailed description of specific approaches is found following Sec. 8-16, and decision-theory techniques are presented in a number of works by other authors.[2]

1-8 PLANNING HORIZONS   The planning horizon is the most distant future time considered in an engineering economy study. The inherent uncertainty of predicting the more distant future favors short planning periods, but the need for analysis of the long-run effects of plans to meet immediate needs favors a longer period. Actually, four different periods of time must be considered in any economic analysis: (1) the economic life, (2) the physical life, (3) the period of analysis, and (4) the construction horizon.

The *economic life* ends when the incremental benefits from continued use no longer exceed the incremental cost of continued operation. Economic life is usually shorter for such project elements as pumps and canal linings than for a water resources project as a whole.

The *physical life* ends when a facility can no longer physically perform its intended function. While the economic life never exceeds the physical life, it may be shorter because of obsolescence and changing demands for services. As an example, electric generation by nuclear power may become

[1] Otto Eckstein, A Survey of the Theory of Public Expenditure Criteria, in National Bureau of Economic Research, "Public Finances: Needs, Sources, and Utilization" (Princeton, N.J.: Princeton University Press, 1961), p. 470.
[2] See H. Chernoff and L. Moses, "Elementary Decision Theory" (New York: John Wiley & Sons, Inc., 1954).

so inexpensive as to make electric generation by fossil fuels uneconomical while such plants still function perfectly well.

The *period of analysis* is the length of time over which project consequences occurring are included in a particular study. The period of analysis for comparing alternative project designs has the project economic life as its upper limit but may be shortened arbitrarily to exclude the highly uncertain events of the very distant future.

The *construction horizon* is reached when the constructed facilities are no longer expected to satisfy the future demands. For example, the water supply alternatives for a community may be studied for a period of analysis of 40 years even though the original facilities may be planned large enough to supply the water usage predicted for only 20 years. The longer period of analysis helps integrate present action into the long-run solution. The shorter construction horizon adds flexibility to deal with unforeseen changes.

Regular maintenance and periodic replacement of worn parts may extend the life of a water resources project almost indefinitely, but a period of analysis of 50 or 100 years is generally used.[1] The optimum construction horizon for individual project components is often a shorter period and may be determined by economic analysis (Sec. 9-10). For example, tunnels may be economically built to maximum capacity because of the high cost of subsequent enlargement, whereas channels may be economically enlarged in 10- or 20-year stages.

When alternative schemes of water resources development are being compared, all must be evaluated over the same period of analysis. If a short economic life causes some alternatives to require periodic replacement, the most common assumption is that each cost will be repeated in a fixed cycle over a series of economic lives until the total project life is reached. However, this assumption should not be used automatically without considering, with respect to the cost or desirability of cyclic replacement, the effects of differential inflation (Sec. 9-8), the development of new production techniques through technological advance, and the changing nature of demand with time. Uncertainty with respect to any of these tends to favor short-lived alternatives.

If the period of analysis is not an even multiple of element lives, an adjustment must be made through a negative cash flow or salvage value equal to the value of the element at the end of the period of analysis. A refined value estimate is seldom warranted because of the relatively small present worth and the difficulty of predicting cash flows in the distant

[1] The President's Water Resources Council, *Policies, Standards, and Procedures in the Formulation, Evaluation, and Review of Plans for Use and Development of Water and Related Land Resources,* 87th Cong. 2d Sess., Sen. Doc. 97, 1962.

future. Straight-line depreciation may be used for a quick estimate of the value of unused life as

$$S = \left(1 - \frac{X}{L}\right) K \qquad (1\text{-}1)$$

where X is the years of unused life, L is the years of total life, and K is the initial value (Ex. 1-1).

EXAMPLE 1-1
A certain type of pump is estimated to require replacement every 20 years and is to be used in a project where the economy study is based on a 50-year period of analysis. What salvage value should be used if the initial cost is $15,000?

   The third pump will be installed in year 40 and thus will have 10 years of useful life remaining at the end of the period of analysis. Thus, $X = 10$ years, $L = 20$ years, and $K = \$15,000$. From Eq. (1-1),

$$S = \left(1 - \frac{10}{20}\right) \$15,000 = \$7,500$$

1-9 STRUCTURING ALTERNATIVES   Recognition of the full spectrum of potential alternatives for analysis is of paramount importance if the most efficient course of action is not to be omitted at the outset. All reasonable possibilities should be considered. The analyst must be imaginative in defining courses of action which will attain designated objectives. One of the most useful treatises on structuring and handling alternatives is found in the pioneering work of E. L. Grant[1] and is used as a basis for summarizing this chapter with the following points:

1   All alternatives physically capable of achieving the design objective should be clearly defined. One alternative is to "do nothing" if none of the other proposals is economically feasible. Limitations of time and funds often prevent a complete analysis of all alternatives. Before extending the study, the costs of additional information must be compared with the potential savings from better project selection.

2   The physical consequences of each alternative should be identified and evaluated in money units. Benefits and costs which cannot be evaluated in monetary terms should be explicitly identified.

3   The difference between alternatives should be the basis for comparison. Sunk costs are irrelevant in choosing between alternatives except as

---

[1] Eugene L. Grant, Concepts and Applications of Engineering Economy, in "Special Report 56, Economic Analysis in Highway Programming, Location, and Design" (Washington: Highway Research Board, 1960), pp. 8–14.

they affect the future. Allocated costs or average costs should not be used in economy studies; incremental or marginal costs should be used. Each separable increment of investment must return at least an equal increment of benefits in order to be justified.

4 Weight should be given to differences in intangibles as well as to differences in market consequences when comparing alternatives. Arbitrary monetary values should not be placed on intangibles since they distort the economic analysis. Economic analysis should not be ignored even if decisions must be based largely on intangibles. The decision maker should be aware of the cost of achieving other values when projects are justified on extraeconomic grounds.

5 The alternatives should be compared on a uniform basis. Such values as discount rates, period of analysis, and unit costs must be the same.

SELECTED REFERENCES

American Telephone and Telegraph Company: "Engineering Economy" (New York: 1963).

Chernoff, H., and L. Moses: "Elementary Decision Theory" (New York: John Wiley & Sons, Inc., 1954).

DeGarmo, E. P.: "Engineering Economy," 3d ed. (New York: The MacMillan Company, 1960).

Grant, Eugene L., and Grant Ireson: "Principles of Engineering Economy," 5th ed. (New York: The Ronald Press Company, 1970).

Kuhn, Tillo: "Public Enterprise Economics and Transport Problems" (Berkeley: University of California Press, 1962).

Wellington, Arthur M.: "The Economic Theory of the Location of Railways," 1st ed. (New York: John Wiley & Sons, Inc., 1877).

PROBLEMS

1-1 Costs and revenues for a particular project having alternate possible levels of investment have been estimated on an equivalent basis and found to be

| Cost: | 39 | 83 | 117 | 155 | 194 |
| Revenue: | 100 | 150 | 175 | 185 | 190 |

Which project level should be selected?

1-2 To develop a new water supply, an industry will have to spend $1 million. The resulting increased production is predicted to increase net income to the company from sales by $900,000. Associated economic development will benefit the community by $400,000 and other nearby communities in the same state by $250,000. However,

$500,000 of the increased state income represents transfers from other states. The river on which the industry is located flows into another country. The new industrial development is expected to deteriorate water quality sufficiently to cause $250,000 worth of damage downstream from the border.

a Would the project be economically justified from the viewpoint of the industry?

b The community?

c The state?

d The nation?

e What kinds of intangible factors might be weighed by each of the four viewpoints?

f Should the project be built from the overall viewpoint?

1-3 A community has spent $50,000 developing a new well and has not yet obtained water. The geological consultant estimates another $50,000 will be required to guarantee a good supply but admits sufficient water may be obtained after spending only $10,000. As an alternative a spring exists several miles away from which an equivalent supply could be pumped for $40,000. What course of action would you recommend and why?

CHAPTER
TWO

MATHEMATICS
OF ECONOMIC ANALYSIS

Formulating the Analysis

Economic analysis is performed in a series of steps. Each alternative must be explicitly defined and the resulting physical consequences must be predicted. A monetary value must be placed on each physical consequence. A discount rate must be selected and applied to convert the predicted time stream of monetary values into an equivalent single number. Only then can the alternatives be directly compared. Each step is developed in the following pages.

2-1 DEFINING THE ALTERNATIVES An engineering alternative is a course of action physically capable of achieving the design objective. Structural alternatives (a dam, for example) characteristically involve a large first cost for project construction to produce benefits throughout the project life. Nonstructural alternatives (flood-plain zoning, for example) involve benefits and costs which are both fairly well distributed over project life. A properly defined alternative must be specified by the engineer with sufficient clarity for its economic and intangible consequences to be evaluated and its nature understood by those responsible for the final selection. Properly defined alternatives are an evidence of clear thinking and a necessity for adequate consequence prediction.

A properly formulated set of engineering alternatives includes all possibilities for action (including taking no action at all) which have a realistic chance of proving optimum. Special care is necessary to include nonstructural alternatives with which engineers may be less familiar. The alternatives are called *mutually exclusive* if only one of a set can be selected. Alternatives may be mutually exclusive because of conflicting space requirements, limited financial resources, limited resource inputs (water, for example), or limited demand or need for resulting output. At other times, it may be practical to implement two or more of the alternatives.

2-2   PHYSICAL CONSEQUENCES   Each engineering alternative will if implemented produce a series of physical consequences occurring at various times into the future. For example, a project built to irrigate peaches, tomatoes, and alfalfa will produce a number of results. The project will have to be constructed. After construction is completed, the project will have to be maintained. Certain elements may wear out and require periodic replacement. Each such cost-associated event needs to be predicted by nature and date.

The water delivered by the project will be used to irrigate peaches, tomatoes, and alfalfa. The first year water is delivered, the acreage and increased yield of each crop can be used to predict a project output of X tons of peaches, Y tons of tomatoes, and Z tons of alfalfa. In a similar manner, X, Y, and Z may be predicted for each subsequent year of project life. The outputs can be expected to increase steadily in the early years as more and more land is irrigated. Later, they may be expected to fluctuate with changing weather and other factors which influence crop yield.

2-3   CASH FLOW DIAGRAM   Having identified the physical consequences of each alternative, it is necessary to decide which ones are relevant to the analysis. Some may not be because of the viewpoint taken in the study, a neutral effect which is neither desirable nor undesirable, a tenuous connection to the project, their small magnitude, or some other reason. Other consequences may be dropped from further evaluation because they are identical for each alternative and an economy study is concerned only with differences (incremental costs). The relevant consequences can be separated into two groups. Some can be assigned a reasonable monetary value. The others may have some monetary value but also require supplemental determination of the intangible factors (Sec. 1-6).

The assignment of a monetary value to physical consequences is a very complicated process having many ramifications which will be discussed throughout the remainder of the book. However, for the time being we will assume that meaningful monetary values can be assigned to the major project consequences. Economic analysis becomes a less reliable guide to decision making as more consequences fall in the intangible class. For the sample project, the cost of installation, the cost of maintenance in each year, replacement cost for each short-lived item, and the benefit resulting from the increased yield of each crop in each year would have to be determined.

The graphic presentation of each value plotted by time is called a *cash flow diagram*. The standard representation for a cash flow diagram is that receipts (benefits) are represented by arrows pointing upward, while costs are represented by arrows pointing downward. Arrows pointing toward the centerline indicate cash flows which may be taken either way in a general diagram (see Fig. 2-2). The length of the arrow is made proportional to the cost or benefit. The horizontal axis denotes time. For convenience in analysis and with little loss in accuracy for long-lived projects, all cash flows during a year are by convention combined into lump sums occurring at the end of the year. Figure 2-1 is a cash flow diagram which might be predicted for our hypothetical irrigation project. Annual benefits and costs will not in fact be constant every year but will vary around average values in an almost random fashion with crop production and maintenance needs. However, only expected average values are normally predicted in advance, even though the random component could conceivably be introduced through simulation (Sec. 20-10). Drawing of the cash flow diagram can be greatly simplified by use of envelope curves as a substitute for the many arrows.

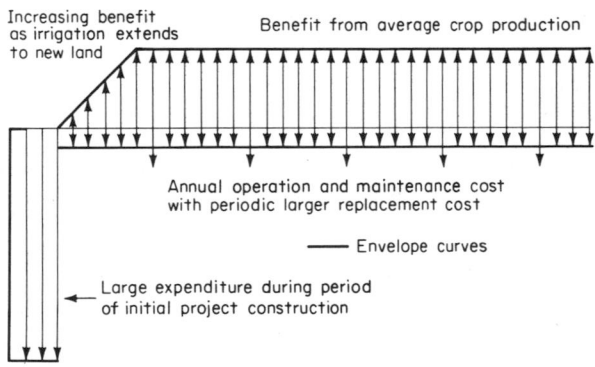

FIGURE 2-1   Cash flow diagram for hypothetical irrigation project.

Discounting Factors[1]

2-4 SINGLE-PAYMENT FACTORS In applying discounting to convert cash flows to a single number suitable for use in comparing alternatives, the basic objective is to convert a value at one date to an equivalent value at another date. Two single-payment factors are available for this purpose (Fig. 2-2).

Single-payment Compound-amount Factor The single-payment compound-amount factor indicates the number of dollars which will have accumulated after N years for every dollar initially invested at a rate of return of i percent. The functional notation is $(F/P,i\%,N)$,[2] where F implies a future and P a present amount. If one were to deposit P dollars initially, after 1 year

$$F = P(1 + i) \tag{2-1}$$

Each year the amount must again be multiplied by $1 + i$ to account for that year's interest; therefore after N years

$$F = P(1 + i)^N \tag{2-2}$$

The desired factor becomes

$$\left(\frac{F}{P}, i\%,N\right) = (1 + i)^N = \frac{F}{P} \tag{2-3}$$

Single-payment Present-worth Factor The single-payment present-worth factor indicates the number of dollars one must initially invest at i percent to have \$1 after N years. It will be abbreviated by $(P/F,i\%,N)$. The factor is the inverse of the previous factor, or

$$\left(\frac{P}{F}, i\%,N\right) = \frac{1}{(1 + i)^N} = \frac{P}{F} \tag{2-4}$$

[1] Standardized notation for discounting formulas has been suggested by the Ad Hoc Committee for Study of Standardization of Engineering Economy Notation, *Eng. Economist*, vol. 12 (Summer, 1967), pp. 253–263. Committee recommendations are followed for the most part in the subsequent development.

[2] The alternative mnemonic notation has been widely used, but it creates a group of rather artificial symbols which make it more difficult to learn and follow.

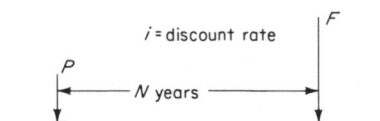

i = discount rate

P

N years

F

FIGURE 2-2 Single-payment factors. (*a*) Single-payment compound-amount factor = F/P; (*b*) single-payment present-worth factor = P/F.

Interest Tables Selected values of both single-payment factors are presented in Table A in the Appendix. When a discounting factor is needed for a combination of N and i not found in the tables, an approximate value may be found by interpolation. The error from interpolation becomes increasingly severe with higher discount rates. For precise values or values outside the range covered by the tables, one must substitute values for i and N in the appropriate formula.

2-5 UNIFORM-ANNUAL-SERIES FACTORS All discounting problems can be solved by applying the two single-payment factors. However, additional factors can be developed to greatly reduce the required work. As an example, one may take the irrigation project of Fig. 2-1. If it were to produce crops having equal value for each of 50 years, fifty separate single-payment present-worth factors would have to be applied to find the present worth of this uniform annual cash flow. The task is made much shorter by developing uniform-annual-series factors.

Uniform-annual-series factors indicate equivalence between the value at an earlier date, P, and equal amounts A at the end of each of the N years or between the N equal values of A and an accumulated amount F (Fig. 2-3).

Sinking-fund Factor The sinking-fund factor indicates the number of dollars one must invest in uniform amounts at i percent interest at the end of each of N years to accumulate \$1. The functional notation is $(A/F, i\%, N)$. If one were to apply the single-payment compound-amount factor individually to each of the N values of A in Fig. 2-3 and sum the

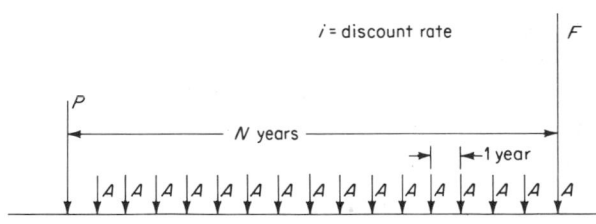

Figure 2-3 Uniform series factors. (*a*) Sinking-fund factor $= A/F$; (*b*) compound-amount factor $= F/A$; (*c*) capital-recovery factor $= A/P$; (*d*) present-worth factor $= P/A$.

results to obtain F, the result would be

$$F = A[1 + (1 + i) + (1 + i)^2 + \cdots + (1 + i)^{N-1}] \tag{2-5}$$

where the last value of A accumulates no interest because it is withdrawn immediately upon deposit and the first value of A accumulates interest for $N - 1$ years. Multiplying both sides of Eq. (2-5) by $1 + i$ gives

$$(1 + i)F = A[(1 + i) + (1 + i)^2 + (1 + i)^3$$
$$+ \cdots + (1 + i)^N] \tag{2-6}$$

The relationship may now be converted from a series to an explicit expression through term-by-term subtraction of Eq. (2-5) from Eq. (2-6) to give

$$iF = A[(1 + i)^N - 1] \tag{2-7}$$

The desired factor becomes

$$\left(\frac{A}{F}, i\%, N\right) = \frac{i}{(1 + i)^N - 1} = \frac{A}{F} \tag{2-8}$$

Capital-recovery Factor The capital-recovery factor indicates the number of dollars one can withdraw in equal amounts at the end of each of N years if \$1 is initially deposited at i percent interest. The functional notation is $(A/P, i\%, N)$. Because

$$\frac{A}{P} = \frac{A}{F}\frac{F}{P} \tag{2-9}$$

One may substitute Eqs. (2-8) and (2-3) in Eq. (2-9) to get

$$\left(\frac{A}{P}, i\%, N\right) = \frac{i(1 + i)^N}{(1 + i)^N - 1} = \frac{A}{P} \tag{2-10}$$

Series Compound-amount Factor The series compound-amount factor indicates the number of dollars which will accumulate if exactly \$1 is invested at i percent interest at the end of each of N years. The functional notation is $(F/A, i\%, N)$. The factor is the inverse of the sinking-fund factor, or

$$\left(\frac{F}{A}, i\%, N\right) = \frac{(1 + i)^N - 1}{i} = \frac{F}{A} \tag{2-11}$$

Series Present-worth Factor The series present-worth factor indicates the number of dollars one must initially invest at i percent interest to withdraw \$1 at the end of each of N years. The factor $(P/A, i\%, N)$ is the inverse of the capital-recovery factor or

$$\left(\frac{P}{A}, i\%, N\right) = \frac{(1+i)^N - 1}{i(1+i)^N} = \frac{P}{A} \tag{2-12}$$

Interest Tables Values for all four uniform-annual-series factors for selected values of i and N are tabulated in Table A in the Appendix.

2-6 UNIFORM-GRADIENT-SERIES FACTORS The uniform-annual-series factors can be applied to an equal cash flow in each year. Often cash flows will not be equal but will follow some definite pattern. The simplest pattern is the uniformly increasing gradient series, a series in which the cash flow increases by some constant amount between each pair of years.

Uniform-gradient-series Present-worth Factor The uniform-gradient-series present-worth factor indicates the number of dollars one must initially invest at i percent interest to withdraw \$1 one year later, \$2 two years later, to N dollars N years later. The functional notation is $(P/G, i\%, N)$.

   If one were to apply the single-payment compound-amount factor individually to each value, beginning with the last, in the gradient series of Fig. 2-4 and sum to obtain the accumulated amount just after the last deposit, the result would be

$$F = G[N + (N-1)(1+i) + \cdots$$
$$+ 2(1+i)^{N-2} + (1+i)^{N-1}] \tag{2-13}$$

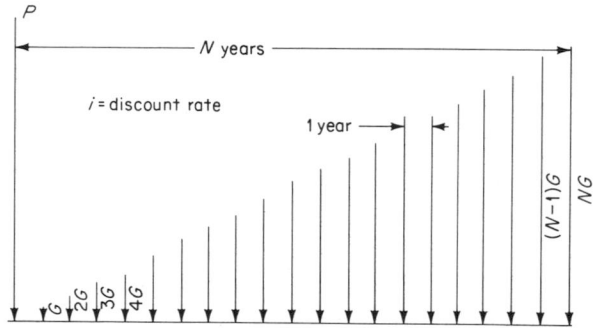

FIGURE 2-4   Gradient-series present-worth factor $= P/G$.

Multiplying both sides by $1 + i$ gives

$$(1 + i)F = G[N(1 + i) + (N - 1)(1 + i)^2 + \cdots$$
$$+ 2(1 + i)^{N-1} + (1 + i)^N] \tag{2-14}$$

Term-by-term subtraction of Eq. (2-13) from Eq. (2-14) gives

$$iF = G\{-N + (1 + i) + \cdots + (1 + i)^N\} \tag{2-15}$$

Multiplication of both sides by $1 + i$ gives

$$(1 + i)iF = G[-N(1 + i) + (1 + i)^2 + \cdots$$
$$+ (1 + i)^{N+1}] \tag{2-16}$$

Term-by-term subtraction of Eq. (2-15) from Eq. (2-16) then gives

$$i^2F = G[N - N(1 + i) - (1 + i) + (1 + i)^{N+1}] \tag{2-17}$$

Rearranged, Eq. (2-17) becomes

$$\frac{F}{G} = \frac{(1 + i)^{N+1} - (1 + Ni + i)}{i^2} \tag{2-18}$$

When Eq. (2-18) is combined with Eq. (2-4) to convert from F to P, the final result is

$$\left(\frac{P}{G}, i\%, N\right) = \frac{(1 + i)^{N+1} - (1 + Ni + i)}{i^2(1 + i)^N} = \frac{P}{G} \tag{2-19}$$

Interest Tables   Values of the uniform-gradient-series present-worth factor for selected values of i and N are tabulated in Table B in the Appendix.

Conversion from Present Worth   Whenever the uniform gradient series needs to be converted to an equivalent uniform annual series, Eqs. (2-10) and (2-19) can be combined to give

$$\frac{A}{G} = \left(\frac{P}{G}, i\%, N\right)\left(\frac{A}{P}, i\%, N\right) \tag{2-20}$$

Similarly, the uniform gradient series may be converted to a single lump sum at the end [as an alternate to direct substitution in Eq. (2-18)] by combining Eqs. (2-3) and (2-19) to get

$$\frac{F}{G} = \left(\frac{P}{G}, i\%, N\right)\left(\frac{F}{P}, i\%, N\right) \tag{2-21}$$

Uniformly Decreasing Series Conversions   The gradient series used to derive the expression for $(P/G, i\%, N)$ increases in value from year to year. When the present worth of a gradient series that decreases in value from year to year is needed, it may be determined by subtracting a uniformly increasing gradient series from a uniform annual series in the manner shown in Ex. 2-1.

EXAMPLE 2-1

An individual invested the following amounts of money at 4 percent interest. How much would he have at the end of year 25?

Year	Investment	Year	Investment	Year	Investment
1	5	8	40	15	25
2	10	9	45	16	20
3	15	10	50	17	15
4	20	11	45	18	10
5	25	12	40	19	5
6	30	13	35	20–25	0
7	35	14	30		

The present worth of the pyramid-shaped series can be found by subdividing it into three portions to which factors from the tables can be directly applied. (Cf. Fig. 2-5.)

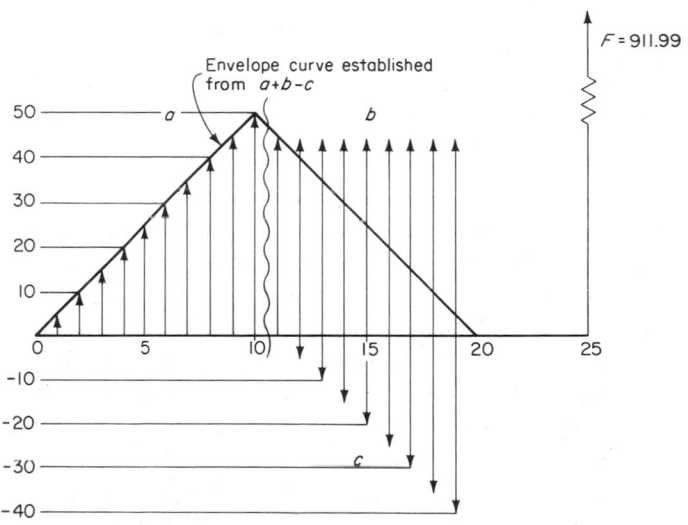

FIGURE 2-5   Cash flow diagram for Ex. 2-1.

1.   Present worth of series 5, 10, . . . , 45, 50 in years 1 through 10.

$$5\left(\frac{P}{G}, 4\%, 10\right) = 5(41.99225) = \$209.96$$

2. Plus present worth of series of 45 per year in years 11 through 19,

$$45 \left(\frac{P}{A}, 4\%, 9 \right) \left(\frac{P}{F}, 4\%, 10 \right) = 45(7.43533)(0.67556) = \$226.04$$

3. Minus present worth of series 5, 10, . . . , 35, 40 in years 12 through 19,

$$5 \left(\frac{P}{G}, 4\%, 8 \right) \left(\frac{P}{F}, 4\%, 11 \right) = 5(28.91333)(0.64958) = -\$93.92$$

The three values sum to a \$342.08 present worth, which can be converted to a value in year 25 by

$$342.08 \left(\frac{F}{P}, 4\%, 25 \right) = (342.08)(2.66584) = \$911.99$$

2-7 NONUNIFORM-GRADIENT-SERIES FACTORS

Project planning often requires determination of the present worth of some monotonically but not uniformly increasing time stream of benefits. Typical situations involve benefits increasing by a uniform annual percentage, benefits increasing rapidly in the early years of project life but more slowly later, benefits increasing most rapidly near the middle of project life, and benefits increasing most rapidly toward the end of project life.

Uniform-percentage-gradient-series Present-worth Factor This factor indicates the present worth at i percent interest of investment of \$1 at the end of the first year and an amount increasing by j percent from year to year until the N years are completed. While there is no standard functional notation for this factor, the notation $(P_j, i\%, N)$ will be used.

As shown in Fig. 2-6a, the deposit at the end of the last year would amount to $(1 + j)^{N-1}$. Since this last value is withdrawn immediately after deposit, no interest is added to it. The next to last deposit would be smaller by an amount found by dividing by $1 + j$, but accumulated interest would increase its worth by the factor $1 + i$. Summing each term backward through the series of Fig. 2-6 gives

$$F = (1+j)^{N-1} \left[1 + \frac{1+i}{1+j} + \cdots + \left(\frac{1+i}{1+j} \right)^{N-1} \right] \qquad (2\text{-}22)$$

Multiplication of both sides by $(1 + i)/(1 + j)$ gives

$$\frac{1+i}{1+j} F = (1+j)^{N-1} \left[\frac{1+i}{1+j} + \left(\frac{1+i}{1+j} \right)^2 + \cdots + \left(\frac{1+i}{1+j} \right)^N \right]$$

$$(2\text{-}23)$$

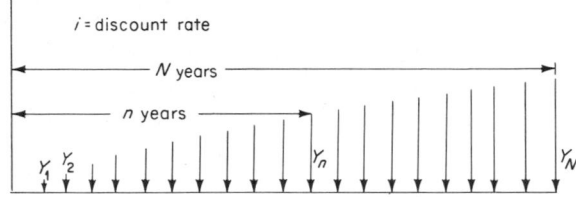

FIGURE 2-6   Nonuniform-gradient-series present-worth factors. (*a*)   Percentage-gradient-series present-worth factor $(P_j, i\%, N)$; $j =$ growth rate, $Y_1 = 1.00$, $Y_n = (1 + j)^{n-1}$. (*b*)   Accelerated-growth-curve present-worth factor $(P/F_a, i\%, N)$; $N = 50$ years, $F_a = Y_N$, $Y_n = [\ln (n + 1)/3.93183]F_a$. (*c*)   Normal-growth-curve present-worth factor $(P/F_n, i\%, N)$; $N = 50$ years, $F_n = Y_N$, $Y_n = (0.0012n^2 - 0.000016n^3)F_n$. (*d*)   Deferred-growth-curve present-worth factor $(P/F_d, i\%, N)$; $N = 50$ years, $F_d = Y_N$, $Y_n = (0.0004n^2)F_d$.

Term-by-term subtraction of Eq. (2-22) from Eq. (2-23) produces

$$\left(\frac{1 + i}{1 + j} - 1\right) F = (1 + j)^{N-1}\left[\left(\frac{1 + i}{1 + j}\right)^{N} - 1\right] \tag{2-24}$$

wherein the left-hand term may be transformed to $[(i - j)/(1 + j)]F$. Substituting $P(1 + i)^N$ for F [Eq. (2-2)] and simplifying gives

$$(P_j, i\%, N) = \frac{(1 + i)^N - (1 + j)^N}{(i - j)(1 + i)^N} \tag{2-25}$$

The right-hand side of Eq. (2-25), the uniform-percentage-gradient-series present-worth factor, is tabulated for selected values of i, N, and j in Table B in the Appendix.[1] Factors for negative growth rates can be found by substituting negative values of j in Eq. (2-25).

Accelerated-growth Present-worth Factor   This factor indicates the present worth at i percent interest of an annual investment pattern in which deposits begin by increasing very rapidly, but increase at a progressively slower rate in later years. Such a series is represented by an equation suggested by the Corps of Engineers[2] and indicated in Fig. 2-6b. The

[1]   In the special case where $i = j$, Eq. (2-25) is indeterminate, but $(P_j, i\%, N) = N/(1 + j)$.
[2]   U.S. Army Corps of Engineers, *Eng. Manual* EM 1120-2-118, (Washington, June, 1960), app. 2, change 1.

present-worth factors $(P/F_a,i\%,N)$ found by summing the present worths of the individual yearly values are tabulated in Table C in the Appendix. Each tabulated value should be multiplied by the fiftieth value in the series F_a to get the present worth. For example, the 10-year factor gives the present worth of the first 10 values in the series as a multiple of the fiftieth value.

Normal-growth Present-worth Factor This factor indicates the present worth at i percent interest of a series of deposits which increase at a progressively faster rate until the midpoint of project life and then increase progressively more slowly through the later years. Its typical use would be in finding the present worth of a benefit series realized in an area where development is expected to be most rapid 20 to 25 years after project construction. Such a series is represented by a curve suggested by the Corps of Engineers[1] and depicted in Fig. 2-6c. The present worth factors $(P/F_n,i\%,N)$ are found in Table C in the Appendix.

Deferred-growth Present-worth Factor This factor indicates the present worth at i percent interest of a series of deposits which increase slowly throughout most of the project life only to increase very rapidly in the last few years. Such a series is represented by another curve suggested by the Corps of Engineers[2] and shown in Fig. 2-6d. The present-worth factors $(P/F_d,i\%,N)$ are also found in Table C in the Appendix.

2-8 OTHER CASH FLOW PATTERNS Cash flow patterns for economy studies are based on projected future events, cannot be known with any real certainty, and thus can normally be approximated with sufficient accuracy by one of the above patterns. Sometimes it may be better to approximate a future cash flow pattern by using different gradients over different time periods as illustrated in Ex. 2-2.

EXAMPLE 2-2
A particular water resources project produces benefits which amount to $12,000 in year 1 and increase on a uniform gradient to $120,000 in year 10. Thereafter, they increase on another uniform gradient of $5,000 per year to $200,000 in year 26, at which point they remain constant at $200,000 each year until the end of project life in year 50. What is the present worth of these benefits at a 4 percent discount rate?

The present worth of the given benefit series can be found by sub-

[1] *Ibid.*
[2] *Ibid.*

dividing it into four portions to which factors from the tables can be directly applied.

1. Present worth of 12, 24, . . . , 108, 120 in years 1 through 10

$$12{,}000 \left(\frac{P}{G}, 4\%, 10 \right) = 12{,}000 \times 41.99225 = \$503{,}900$$

2. Present worth of 120 per year in years 11 through 25

$$120{,}000 \left(\frac{P}{A}, 4\%, 15 \right) \left(\frac{P}{F}, 4\%, 10 \right) = 120{,}000 \times 11.11839 \times 0.67556$$
$$= \$901{,}400$$

3. Present worth of 5, 10, . . . , 70, 75 in years 11 through 25

$$5{,}000 \left(\frac{P}{G}, 4\%, 15 \right) \left(\frac{P}{F}, 4\%, 10 \right) = 5{,}000 \times 80.85389 \times 0.67556$$
$$= \$273{,}100$$

4. Present worth of 200 per year in years 26 through 50

$$200{,}000 \left(\frac{A}{P}, 4\%, 25 \right) \left(\frac{P}{F}, 4\%, 25 \right) = 200{,}000 \times 15.62208 \times 0.37512$$
$$= \$1{,}172{,}000$$

The total present worth is the sum of these four values, or \$2,850,400.

If use of more complicated series is justified, an exact solution may be obtained by individual application of single-payment factors. For approximate results, a graphic solution may be used.[1]

Discounting Techniques

The procedure in which discounting factors may be systematically applied to compare alternatives (either different projects or different sizes of the same project) is called a *discounting technique*. The four conceptually correct discounting techniques are (1) the present-worth method, (2) the rate-of-return method, (3) the benefit-cost ratio method, and (4) the annual-cost method. Each method, if used correctly, leads to the same evaluation of the relative merit. However, each has advantages and disadvantages.

[1] George E. Ribble, Graphical Methods for Discounting Future Benefits in Feasibility Studies, *Civil Eng.*, vol. 35, no. 11 (November, 1965), pp. 86–87.

2-9 PRESENT-WORTH METHOD   The present-worth method selects the project with the largest present worth PW of the discounted algebraic sum of benefits minus costs over its life.

$$PW = \sum_{t=1}^{n} \left(\frac{P}{F}, i\%, t \right) (B_t - C_t) \tag{2-26}$$

where C_t is the cost and B_t the benefit in the subscripted year, n is the period of analysis in years, and i is discount rate. When the annual net benefits $B = B_t - C_t$ are constant over the project life except for the initial first cost K, the formula may be simplified to

$$PW = -K + B \left(\frac{P}{A}, i\%, n \right) \tag{2-27}$$

When the net benefits vary according to some regular gradient, the appropriate gradient factor should be used.

Calculation of present worth from a cash flow diagram is a purely mechanical process. However, certain rules must be followed in comparing the calculated present worths to make correct choices.

RULE 1 *Figure all present worths to the same time base.* Whether or not alternatives are to be initiated at the same time, each present worth must be discounted to the same base year (1970, for example) because sums of money at different times are different economic goods.

RULE 2 *Figure all present worths by using the same discount rate.* Whether or not alternatives are to be financed from the same funds, each must be discounted at the same rate if the result is to be an index of intrinsic project merit.

RULE 3 *Base all present worths on the same period of analysis.* Whether or not alternatives have a common economic life, the comparison must be based on a service provided over a common period of time. This may be done either by evaluating the cost of extending the service past the termination of the shorter-lived alternatives or by calculating the value of the unused life of the longer-lived alternatives (Ex. 1-1).

RULE 4 *Calculate the present worth of each alternative. Choose all alternatives having a positive present worth. Reject the rest.* This ends the procedure if no sets of mutually exclusive alternatives are involved. The choice among alternatives in such a set is made by Rule 5.

RULE 5 *Choose the alternative in a set of mutually exclusive alternatives having the greatest present worth.*

RULE 6 *If the alternatives in the set of mutually exclusive alternatives have benefits which cannot be quantified but are approximately equal, choose the alternative having least cost.*

A single example based on the two mutually exclusive alternative water supply projects described in Table 2-1 will be used to illustrate all four discounting techniques. Project A provides an initial investment large enough to meet the demands for water for 40 years, and project B uses investment in two stages to meet the same demand. The present worths are calculated to be

$$PW \text{ of } A = -\$40,000,000 - \$160,000 \left(\frac{P}{A}, 5\%,40\right)$$
$$+ \$2,500,000 \left(\frac{P}{A}, 5\%,40\right)$$
$$= -\$40,000,000 - \$160,000(17.159) + \$2,500,000(17.159)$$
$$= \$153,000$$

$$PW \text{ of } B = -\$25,000,000 - \$30,000,000 \left(\frac{P}{F}, 5\%,20\right)$$
$$- \$100,000 \left(\frac{P}{A}, 5\%,20\right) - \$220,000 \left(\frac{P}{A}, 5\%,20\right)\left(\frac{P}{F}, 5\%,20\right)$$
$$+ \$2,500,000 \left(\frac{P}{A}, 5\%,40\right)$$
$$= -\$25,000,000 - \$30,000,000(0.377) - \$100,000(12.462)$$
$$- \$220,000(12.462)(0.377) + \$2,500,000(17.159)$$
$$= \$4,308,000$$

Therefore we should choose *project B* since its present worth is greater. If the rule of analyzing only differences were strictly applied, the equal annual benefits could be deleted from the evaluation of each alternative to provide the same conclusion with less work.

Project B would appear even more favorable were an adjustment made to account for the economic life of the second stage lasting 20 years past the period of analysis. The adjustment according to Eq. (1-1) would add a $15

TABLE 2-1   Data for Sample Problem

	Project A	Project B
Construction cost	$40,000,000	$25,000,000, 1st stage
		$30,000,000, 2d stage
Operations and	$160,000 per year for	$100,000 per year for 1st 20 years
maintenance	40 years	$220,000 per year for 2d 20 years
Economic life	40 years	40 years for each stage
Period of analysis	40 years	40 years
Annual benefits	$2,500,000	$2,500,000
Discount rate	5 percent	5 percent

million salvage value in year 40 or \$15 million $(P/F,5\%,40) = \$2,130,000$ to the present worth.

If the time value of money is neglected, A seems preferable to B because of its smaller total cost. However, at a 5 percent discount rate, B is definitely preferable. Sensitivity analysis shows the cost of B's second stage could increase to \$41 million, and B would still be preferable! This example dramatically illustrates the desirability of postponing costs until further investment is actually needed so as to free capital for alternative productive investment.

Capitalized worth is defined as the present worth of perpetual service. The present worth may be converted to a capitalized worth by assuming an equivalent reinvestment at the end of each economic life and multiplying by the ratio of the capital-recovery factor to the discount rate. The multiplier is close to 1 with long lives or high discount rates. Appropriate discount factors may be used to estimate capitalized worth where cash flows for reinvestment are expected to differ from those for initial investment. The decision rules used for present worth also apply for capitalized worth.

2-10   RATE-OF-RETURN METHOD   The rate of return is the discount rate at which the present worth as defined by Eq. (2-26) equals zero as found by trial and error. Other decision rules apply when comparing alternatives by the rate-of-return method.

RULE 1   *Compare all alternatives over the same period of analysis.* Rates of return over different economic lives cannot be meaningfully compared because investment opportunity for the returns from the shorter-lived alternatives must be considered in determining whether capital should remain committed to the longer-lived alternative.

RULE 2   *Calculate the rate of return for each alternative. Choose all alternatives having a rate of return exceeding the minimum acceptable value. Reject the rest.* If sets of mutually exclusive alternatives are involved, proceed to Rule 3.

RULE 3   *Rank the alternatives in the set of mutually exclusive alternatives in order of increasing cost. Calculate the rate of return on the incremental cost and incremental benefits of the next alternative above the least costly alternative. Choose the more costly alternative if the incremental rate of return exceeds the minimum acceptable discount rate. Otherwise choose the less costly alternative. Continue the analysis by considering the alternatives in order of increased costliness, the alternative on the less costly side of each increment being the most costly project chosen thus far.*

The rate-of-return method will not lead to the same decisions as the present-worth method unless the incremental analysis of Rule 3 is used in place of selecting the mutually exclusive alternative with the highest rate of return. The rate-of-return method must be applied with caution because more than one rate of return exists when annual costs exceed annual benefits in years after annual benefits first exceed annual costs, but Heebink has shown that the rate-of-return method using Rule 3 still gives consistent answers even when dual solutions exist.[1] The water resources planner needs to be alert to this problem in comparing stage construction or non-structural alternatives by the rate-of-return method.

In the example of two alternative water supply projects, each has been found to have a positive present worth when discounted at 5 percent and thus must have a rate of return exceeding the minimum acceptable value. Therefore, the difference between alternatives ($A - B$ in Table 2-2) is used to compute the incremental rate of return as directed by Rule 3.

The procedure is to assume discount rates until the present worth, or

$$PW = \$15,000,000 - \$30,000,000 \left(\frac{P}{F}, i\%, 20\right) + \$60,000 \left(\frac{P}{A}, i\%, 20\right)$$

$$- \$60,000 \left(\frac{P}{A}, i\%, 20\right)\left(\frac{P}{F}, i\%, 20\right)$$

equals zero. For $i = 5\%$, $PW = \$4,155,000$ indicates the trial discount rate to be too high and the extra cost of A over B to be not justified at a minimum acceptable rate of return of 5 percent. Therefore, project B is chosen. Had the present worth at 5 percent been negative, the incremental rate would have been greater than 5 percent. A complete solution provides

[1]   David Heebink, "A Critique of Compound-Interest Models Used in Decision-making for Capital Budgets," Ph.D. thesis, Stanford University, Stanford, Calif., 1960, app. B, pp. 87–94.

TABLE 2-2   Incremental Data for Sample Problem

IN MILLIONS OF DOLLARS

	Project A	Project B	$A - B$
First cost	40.0	25.0, first stage	+15.0
		30.0, second stage	−30.0
Operations and maintenance	0.16 per yr	0.10 per yr, first 20 yr	+0.06 per yr, first 20 yr
		0.22 per yr, second 20 yr	−0.06 per yr, second 20 yr
Benefits	2.5 per yr	2.5 per yr	

an incremental rate of return of 3.39 percent and indicates project B to be favored only as long as the minimum acceptable rate of return exceeds 3.39 percent.

2-11 BENEFIT-COST RATIO METHOD The benefit-cost ratio PW_b/PW_c is the present worth of the benefits PW_b divided by the present worth of the costs PW_c. Annual values can alternatively be used without affecting the ratio. The present worth PW_b of annual benefits B_t is

$$PW_b = \sum_{t=1}^{n} \left(\frac{P}{F}, i\%, t \right) B_t \tag{2-28}$$

The present worth PW_c of the costs C_t is

$$PW_c = \sum_{t=1}^{n} \left(\frac{P}{F}, i\%, t \right) C_t \tag{2-29}$$

Series discounting factors may be used in either summation as appropriate.

The decision on whether particular cash flows should be considered costs or negative benefits is sometimes arbitrary (Sec. 8-4) and affects the benefit-cost ratio. While it does not affect project selection by the procedure described below, it is important to recognize that the best project has the greatest net benefits, not the largest benefit-cost ratio. Several authors have suggested that the benefit-cost ratio method leads to different decisions than the other techniques do.[1] However, this conflict only occurs when the incremental-cost principle of Rule 4 is neglected.

Four rules must be followed to apply the method correctly.

RULE 1 *Figure all benefit-cost ratios by using the same discount rate.*
RULE 2 *Compare all alternatives over the same period of analysis.*
RULE 3 *Calculate the benefit-cost ratio for each alternative. Choose all alternatives having a benefit-cost ratio exceeding unity. Reject the rest.* If sets of mutually exclusive alternatives are involved, proceed to Rule 4.
RULE 4 *Rank the alternatives in the set of mutually exclusive alternatives in order of increasing cost. Calculate the benefit-cost ratio by using the incremental cost and incremental benefit of the next alternative above the least costly alternatives. Choose the more costly alternative if the incremental benefit-cost ratio exceeds unity. Otherwise, choose the less costly alternative. Continue the analysis by considering the alternatives in order of increased costliness, the alternative on the less costly side of each increment being the most costly project chosen thus far.*

---

[1] Roland N. McKean, "Efficiency in Government through Systems Analysis" (New York: John Wiley and Sons, Inc., 1958), pp. 108–112; and Otto Eckstein, "Water Resource Development: The Economics of Project Evaluation" (Cambridge, Mass.: Harvard University Press, 1958), pp. 53–54.

From our previous calculations on our sample problem, we know that each project has a positive present worth at a 5 percent discount rate; therefore, each project has a benefit-cost ratio greater than 1 and Rule 3 is met. As with the rate-of-return method, differences between alternatives (Table 2-2) are taken to see if the incremental costs are justified. The incremental net cost found in Sec. 2-10 when coupled with the zero incremental benefit indicates a zero incremental benefit-cost ratio. Therefore, project B is chosen.

While project B has the higher overall benefit-cost ratio (1.11 instead of 1.00), the preferred project sometimes has a lower one. This may be illustrated by considering a project whose benefits equal 3 and whose costs equal 1 and which has an increment of investing an additional 4 to increase benefits to 10. The smaller project has a benefit-cost ratio of 3, while the larger one has a ratio of 2. Because the incremental ratio is 1.75, the larger investment should be chosen even though it has a smaller benefit-cost ratio.

2-12 ANNUAL-COST METHOD   The annual-cost method converts all benefits and costs into equivalent uniform annual figures. Decision rules resemble those for the present-worth method because each annual cost is a present worth times a constant capital-recovery factor.

RULE 1   *Figure all annual costs by using the same discount rate.*
RULE 2   *Base all annual costs on the same period of analysis.*
RULE 3   *Calculate the net annual benefit of each alternative. Choose all alternatives having a positive net annual benefit. Reject the rest.* If sets of mutually exclusive alternatives are involved, proceed to Rule 4.
RULE 4   *Choose the alternative in a set of mutually exclusive alternatives, having the greatest net annual benefit.*

TABLE 2-3 Summation of Annual-cost Method

	Project A	Project B
Present worth of benefits	$42,898,000	$42,898,000
Present worth of costs	42,745,000	38,590,000
Net present worth	153,000	4,308,000
Capital-recovery factor (A/P,5%,40)	0.05828	0.05828
Annual benefits	$ 2,500,000	$ 2,500,000
Annual cost	2,491,200	2,249,000
Net annual worth	8,800	251,000

RULE 5   *If the alternatives in the set of mutually exclusive alternatives have benefits which cannot be quantified but are approximately equal, choose the alternative having the least annual cost.*

Since the present worths for projects *A* and *B* are calculated in Sec. 2-9, they may be multiplied by the appropriate capital-recovery factor to get the equivalent annual figures shown in Table 2-3. Rule 4 says to choose project *B* as having the greater annual worth. Since the benefits are the same for each project, Rule 5 could be used to find the project accomplishing this benefit at least annual cost.

2-13   EVALUATION OF DISCOUNTING TECHNIQUES   Each of the four discounting methods will when used correctly select the same project, given the same data. However, each technique has advantages and disadvantages associated with ease of calculation or presentation and understanding of the results. These need to be considered in selecting the method to apply in a given analysis.

Because it does not require an additional set of computations to apply the incremental-cost principle, the present-worth technique has been described as "simpler, safer, easier, and more direct."[1] Others have said this method is "logically prior to others, and we recommend its use."[2] The simple, direct expression of net present worth is conceptually straightforward and easily presented. However, one is working with larger numbers which may be harder to visualize and lead more frequently to numerical errors. Furthermore, the present-worth method cannot be used to rank projects in order of economic desirability unless all require equal investment.

The rate-of-return technique has been recommended because it does not require a preselected discount rate, rates of return are intuitively meaningful to many investors, and the resulting rates can be compared with those for many other types of investment.[3] On the other hand, it has been criticized (1) as giving ambiguous answers because of dual solutions, (2) because of the necessity of calculating incremental rate of return for interdependent projects, (3) the danger of people's accepting overall as contrasted with incremental rates of return as indicators of rank, and (4) the complexity of the required trial-and-error solutions.[4] Some have gone

[1]   H. Bierman and S. Smidt, "The Capital Budgeting Decision" (New York: The MacMillan Company, 1960), p. 46.
[2]   Jack Hirshleifer, James C. DeHaven, and Jerome W. Milliman, "Water Supply: Economics, Technology and Policy" (Chicago: The University of Chicago Press, 1960), p. 152.
[3]   C. H. Oglesby and Eugene L. Grant, Economic Analysis—the Fundamental Approach to Decisions in Highway Planning and Design, *Highway Res. Board Proc.*, vol. 37 (1958), pp. 48–49.
[4]   Bierman and Smidt, *loc. cit.*

so far as to suggest the technique *never* be used.[1] However, the cited advantages are important enough to make the rate-of-return method a valuable analytic tool.

The benefit-cost ratio method is almost universally used by federal and state water resource agencies and can be expected to remain in this position into the indefinite future. Moreover, Krutilla and Eckstein[2] base their analysis on benefit-cost methods, and Marglin's work shows it to be consistent with economic theory.[3] On the other hand, the use of the benefit-cost ratio without applying the required incremental benefit-cost analysis can lead to serious errors. Interdependent projects cannot be ranked according to their benefit-cost ratios because each enlargement must pass the *incremental* benefit-cost ratio test. Nevertheless, the fact remains that the benefit-cost ratio method can lead to the same results as other correct discounting techniques.

The annual-cost method uses constant multiples of the present-worth method and has the same advantages and disadvantages (except for the use of smaller numbers). However, the annual cost is sometimes preferred because more people are accustomed to thinking in terms of annual costs than of present worths.

Which method should be used? The answer depends primarily on the purpose of the analysis. Where benefits cannot be evaluated, it is not possible to use benefit-cost or rate-of-return techniques. Costs alone must be compared by using the present-worth or annual-cost method. There are more calculations for the rate-of-return or benefit-cost ratio methods and more opportunities for errors of interpretation, but computational work is never more than a minor part of the total analysis.

Other Approaches

2-14 UNRELIABLE TECHNIQUES Of the many other decision criteria in use, which do not give consistent, reliable results, the three most commonly found in the analysis of water resources projects are urgency ratings, standards, and least total costs.

The urgency-rating technique rates proposals on their postponability, those being least postponable getting priority. Since this method is highly subjective, the selection process tends toward a political content because

[1]   Hirshleifer et al., *op. cit.*, p. 156.
[2]   John V. Krutilla and Otto Eckstein, "Multiple Purpose River Development" (Baltimore: The Johns Hopkins Press, 1958), pp. 76–77.
[3]   Stephen A. Marglin, Objectives of Water-resource Development, in Arthur Maass et al., "Design of Water-resource Systems" (Cambridge, Mass.: Harvard University Press, 1962), pp. 17–87.

no firm figures are available to assess relative merit. If projects are truly nonpostponable, this will be reflected in the efficiency calculations.

Standards are expressions of minimum acceptable project quality often made prior to, and thus without the benefit of, economic analysis. Engineers are familiar with standards for structural design, water quality, street widths, design freeboard, etc. No matter what standard is used, it should be based on economic analysis unless intangible factors can be demonstrated to be overriding. Unfortunately, standards which reflect the ultimate goals of professional groups rather than the relative needs of the local community are sometimes taken as a valid representation of community needs to the neglect of other important services. No standard can be achieved without cost, and costs incurred should be commensurate with utility achieved. Standards are a poor substitute for a searching appraisal to obtain a balanced level of public services.

Least-cost methods are used when the benefits are estimated to be the same. Two common variations are (1) the least-total-cost method and (2) the least-total-annual-cost method. The least-total-cost method merely sums the estimated investment, operations, and maintenance costs over the life of the project and thus obviously ignores the timing of costs required by the discounting concept. The least-total-annual-cost method adds an interest cost to the total cost. Those using this method confuse financial analysis with economic analysis by including interest as a cost without determining time equivalence by discounting specific cash flows.

SELECTED REFERENCES

Bierman, H., and S. Smidt: "The Capital Budgeting Decision" (New York: The MacMillan Company, 1960).

Brown, W. H., Jr., and C. E. Gilbert: "Planning Municipal Investment" (Philadelphia: University of Pennsylvania Press, 1961).

Grant, Eugene L., and Grant Ireson: "Principles of Engineering Economy" (New York: The Ronald Press Company, 1970).

Savage, L. J., and J. H. Lorie: Three Problems in Rationing Capital, *J. Business* (October, 1955).

Smith, Gerald W.: "Engineering Economy: Analysis of Capital Expenditures" (Ames: The Iowa State University Press, 1968).

Thuesen, H. G., and W. J. Fabrycky: "Engineering Economy" (Englewood Cliffs, N.J.: Prentice-Hall, Inc., 1964).

PROBLEMS

2-1   A writer on the subject of the determination of the costs of public hydroelectric power projects included the following items as costs: (1) interest on the first cost of the project; (2) depreciation by the straight-line method based on the estimated life of the project; (3) an annual deposit in an amortization sinking fund sufficient to amount to the first cost of the project at the end of 50 years (or at the end of the life of the project if that should be less than 50 years); (4) where money is borrowed, the annual disbursements for bond interest and bond repayment; (5) all actual annual disbursements for operation and maintenance of the project.

Do you believe that annual cost should properly be considered as the sum of these items? Explain your answer.[1]

2-2   A project to be evaluated at a 4.25 percent discount rate cost $1 million and has a $20,000 annual cost. Project benefits are expected to be $20,000 in the first year, increase to $100,000 in the fiftieth year following an accelerated growth curve, remain constant at $100,000 annually until the ninetieth year, and then decline on a uniform gradient to nothing in the hundredth year. What is the benefit-cost ratio?

2-3   An industry which requires 10 percent return on its capital has an opportunity to invest in a business estimated to be profitable for 10 years. Alternative levels of investment and alternative net annual returns by level of investment are:

Investment	Annual benefits	Annual O & M cost
$1,000	$160	$10
1,500	265	15
2,000	340	20
2,500	445	25
3,000	535	30
3,500	610	35
4,000	665	40

a   How large an investment should be made?
b   How large would the minimum attractive rate of return of the industry have to be to prevent any of the above investments from being made?
c   What minimum attractive rate of return would lead to a decision to invest $4,000?

2-4   A certain project has a first cost of $100,000 and an annual maintenance cost of $2,500 each year over a 50-year life. Benefits realized increase from $4,000 in the year immediately after construction to $10,000 in the last year of project life.
a   At 4 percent interest, what is the annual project cost?

[1] Problem taken from Eugene L. Grant and Grant Ireson, "Principles of Engineering Economy," 4th ed., rev. ptg. (New York: The Ronald Press Company, 1964), p. 435.

b At 4 percent interest and with a straight-line gradient, what is the annual project benefit?

c What is the benefit-cost ratio?

d What is the annual benefit if benefits increase in an accelerated growth pattern?

e What is the annual benefit if benefits increase in a deferred growth pattern?

f What is the internal rate of return of the project using a straight-line gradient?

2-5 An investor has $20,000 and the four investment opportunities described below:

| | Initial cost | Net cash proceeds in year | | |
		1	2	3
A	$10,000	$10,000	$1,000	$1,000
B	10,000	4,400	4,400	4,400
C	10,000	2,000	3,000	9,000
D	10,000	1,000	2,000	12,000

a In which two projects should a private investor invest his money if he uses the rate-of-return method?

b In which two projects should a public agency invest its money if it uses a social discount rate of 3 percent?

c What should the private investor do if he has no alternative investments this year, but starting next year (year 1), he can invest his money at a guaranteed return of 20 percent?

2-6 The three alternatives described below are available for supplying a community water supply for the next 50 years when all economic lives as well as the period of analysis terminates.

	Project A	Project B	Project C
Construction cost			
Year 0	$20,000,000	$10,000,000	$15,000,000
Year 20	0	10,000,000	12,000,000
Year 35	0	10,000,000	0
O and M cost			
Years 1–20	70,000	40,000	60,000
Years 21–35	80,000	70,000	80,000
Years 36–50	90,000	90,000	90,000

Using a 4.5 percent discount rate where applicable, compare the projects by:

a The present-worth method

b The rate-of-return method

c The benefit-cost ratio method

d The annual-cost method

2-7 A decision must be made between two alternative investments which perform equally well. Investment A has a life of 5 years, first cost of $2,000, annual maintenance cost of $25, and salvage value of $250. Investment B has a life of 10 years, first cost of $4,000, annual maintenance cost of $30, and salvage value of $1,000.

    a Which alternative is to be preferred at a minimum acceptable rate of return of 8 percent?

    b Investment A employs a scarce material which is expected to increase greatly in price during the next 5 years. How much would the cost of replacing A in 5 years have to be in current dollars to make B more economical in the present decision? Assume all other costs are unchanged.

2-8 Already $20,000 has been spent on a $200,000 project when it is learned that a research breakthrough may soon develop a substitute having a cost of $135,000. The substitute has an annual operations and maintenance cost of $4,000 instead of $5,000 with construction in the originally planned manner. Annual benefits are projected to follow an accelerated growth curve from 0 to $50,000 in year 50. The discount rate is 6 percent, and the period of analysis is 50 years.

    a Compute the benefit-cost ratio for the project as initially conceived.

    b Compute the benefit-cost ratio for implementing the substitute project if it could be done immediately.

    c If the breakthrough is delayed 5 years and an interim measure is to be considered, what is the maximum uniform annual cost one could afford to pay to achieve the benefit during the intervening period rather than build the initial project? Neglect the salvage value of the substitute at the end of the period of analysis.

2-9 Two mutually exclusive investment alternatives which provide the identical service may be described as follows:

	First cost	Annual cost	Salvage value	Life
A	$10,000	$2,000	$1,000	10
B	25,000	1,500	5,000	20

Based on a minimum attractive rate of return of 5 percent:

    a Which alternative has the lower annual cost?

    b What is the incremental annual cost of going from the less to the more expensive alternative?

    c Select the optimum alternative by the present-worth method.

    d What is the rate of return on the incremental investment of B?

    e What first cost of replacing A after 10 years would make the two alternatives equivalent, assuming none of the other costs change?

2
MICROECONOMICS AND EFFICIENT RESOURCE ALLOCATION

An economy study assigns a value to each predicted physical consequence of each alternative and proceeds through a series of mathematical operations to condense these values into a scalar index of aggregate worth. A complex set of alternatives is reduced to a group of numbers which can be ranked in order of magnitude for deciding relative merit. The assignment of value is thus the critical step in the procedure. If done improperly, no meaningful conclusion can result from the calculations described in Chap. 2.

Part 2 seeks to provide the framework for evaluating these physical effects. Chapter 3 presents the competitive market under conditions of pure competition as providing the framework for establishing economic value. Chapter 4 shows how values once assigned can be analyzed to indicate an optimum or economically efficient design. Chapter 5 discusses how goals other than economic efficiency can be introduced to achieve desirable social objectives. Chapter 6 presents the implications of these objectives on discount rate selection. Microeconomics provides the tools for designing projects which in the aggregate will allocate to best use the total supply of available resources.

CHAPTER
THREE

PRICE THEORY
AND RESOURCE ALLOCATION

Introduction to Microeconomics

Price exerts a major influence on individual decisions of whether or not to use a particular economic good, and these many little decisions aggregate to allocate resources by use. In an economy based on the private ownership of property, or what may be called *capitalism* or the *free enterprise system*, economic forces interact to determine price. Under ideal conditions (pure competition), economic forces produce a first-order approximation of a normative system. Thus, analysis of these forces can be used to provide the values needed in engineering economy studies (Sec. 2-3). Price theory provides the framework for systematic study of these forces. It provides a foundation for production theory, the study of how a firm should operate to maximize profits. The result is an analogy indicating how a public works project should be designed to maximize benefits. The study of price theory guides the decision on whether a particular market price is a fair measure of true public worth for use in an economy study. It provides the tools needed for generating a shadow price for use where the market price is not fair or where none has been established. Price theory provides the analytic framework for establishing benefits and costs.

3-1 THE MARKET ECONOMY Because price theory analyzes the activities of individual participants in a market economy, it is a microeconomic approach. Study of the cumulative effect of all the many individual decisions on the national economy is a macroeconomic approach. The normative framework traditionally used for establishing value in economy studies is based on the principles of microeconomics under the assumption that water resources projects represent too small a portion of the total national productive capital for individual design decisions to have significant macroeconomic effects. The initial assumption is a macroeconomic setting of a stable economy and full resource employment.

A free enterprise economy reacts to economic decisions of individuals. Within limits, consumers are free to choose from a variety of goods and services, enterprisers are free to produce what they desire, and resource owners are free to sell to whatever buyer may be found. Voluntary exchanges occur in the marketplace whenever it is mutually advantageous to participants. Although profits are made as enterprisers correctly anticipate consumer demands and produce efficiently, losses occur if opposite conditions hold.

The market provides a link between consumers and producers and permits the exchange of goods and services. Some are geographically small; others are worldwide. A market may have few or many buyers and sellers. One product or many products may be offered. Government control may override economic forces in certain instances. In a market system, prices are the basic signals that direct production and distribution. To the degree that the goods exchanged are owned by many individuals free to buy and sell as they wish, prices are determined by impersonal market forces.

Cash flows within a market system can be classified by the use of Fig. 3-1. The owners of productive resources (landowners, laborers, and capitalists) sell them to enterprisers (firms) in the productive resources market. The money the resource owners receive is spent to buy the prod-

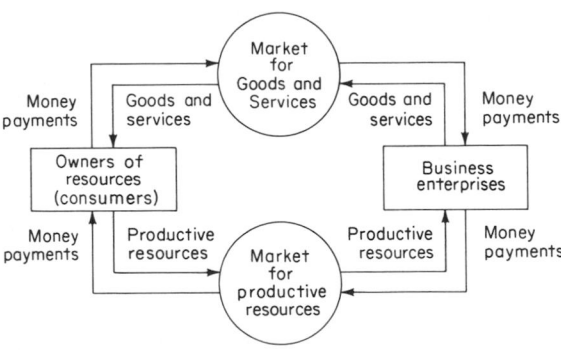

FIGURE 3-1 Model of a free enterprise economy (spending and production).

ucts of the enterprisers in the market for goods and services. In turn, the money that the enterprisers receive from consumers is used to buy additional productive resources. Thus, consumers and enterprisers operate in both the productive resources market and the goods and services market. This simplified model of a free enterprise economy neglects government action, interfirm transactions, and income from gifts or charity. It does not distinguish transactions occurring in the market or private sector of the economy from those occurring in the governmental or public sector.

A free enterprise system determines *what, how,* and *for whom* in the following manner:[1]

1   What is to be produced is determined by the dollar votes of consumers (the demand) cast each day for commodities purchased in the marketplace.
2   How things are to be produced is determined as individual firms are required to adopt the most efficient (least costly) methods of production to stay in business.
3   For whom things are produced is determined by the number of marketplace votes (income) an individual has. Incomes are determined as supply and demand in markets for productive services set wage rates, profits, land rents, and interest payments.

The absence of a costly regulatory structure is one of the greatest strengths of the market system. No central planning authority makes the myriad of economic decisions necessary to supply the goods and services needed for a city such as Chicago. Yet, instead of chaos, an order exists which supplies the variety of food, clothing, sundries, and entertainment that a cosmopolitan city demands. As Samuelson has stated:

> A competitive system is an elaborate mechanism for unconscious coordination through a system of prices and markets, a communication device for pooling the knowledge and actions of millions of diverse individuals. Without a central intelligence, it solves one of the most complex problems imaginable, involving thousands of unknown variables and relations. Nobody designed it, it just evolved, and like human nature, it is changing; but at least it meets the first test of any social organization—it is able to survive.[2]

How does the price system achieve an efficient allocation of productive resources? Allocations must be made at three levels: among industries, among firms in each industry, and within each firm. If an industry's products are in great demand, they can be sold for high prices. The

---

[1]   Much of this paragraph is condensed from Paul A. Samuelson, "Economics: An Introductory Analysis," 5th ed. (New York: McGraw-Hill Book Company, 1962), pp. 41–42.
[2]   *Ibid.,* pp. 38–39.

industry is able to pay high prices for productive resources and bid them away from industries whose products are less highly valued by consumers. Firms within an industry which produce a given output at a lower cost can pay more for productive resources and expand relative to inefficient firms. Lastly, the individual enterpriser strives to produce a given product in the least expensive manner from the cheapest combination of productive resources. According to Stigler:

> A competitive enterprise system allocates resources with maximum efficiency. If resources are used where they obtain the highest rates of renumeration, if they are employed efficiently in these industries, and if they produce the commodities that consumers most desire, output is as large as possible.[1]

Ebenstein says,

> The economy justification of competition is that it keeps everybody— worker, businessman, investor—on his toes, constantly alert to changes in the market, and constantly on the outlook for ways to increase his efficiency and thereby improve his chances in the market. By increasing his own efficiency, the individual worker or entrepreneur proportionately increases the efficiency and productivity of the whole market. Better products, lower prices, better services and ultimately higher living standards for all result from the constant incentive to keep up with, and if possible outdo, one's competitors.[2]

3-2 PURE COMPETITION A market economy will automatically maximize production from a given set of resources and thus be economically efficient under the conditions of pure competition. Competition as defined in economics does not necessarily denote rivalry. In fact, under pure competition, there is no rivalry among individual sellers or buyers. The conditions necessary for pure competition include:[3]

1 Consumers must be consistent and independent. A consistent consumer gets more satisfaction from a larger amount of a given commodity than from a smaller amount. The satisfaction gained by one consumer must be independent of purchases by others.

2 Producers must operate with the goal of profit maximization. The

[1] George J. Stigler, "The Theory of Price" (New York: The Macmillan Company, 1961), p. 9.
[2] William Ebenstein, "Today's Isms," 4th ed. (Englewood Cliffs, N.J.: Prentice-Hall, Inc., 1964), p. 166.
[3] Otto Eckstein, "Water Resource Development: The Economics of Project Evalutaion" (Cambridge, Mass.: Harvard University Press, 1958), pp. 25–30.

production processes of the firms must be independent so that one firm's costs are not borne by others.

3   The transactions by each buyer or seller must be too small in relation to the market to affect prices paid or received.

4   No price regulation or rationing or other artificial constraints by government, labor, business, or other institutions are placed on the demand and supply of goods and resources or on their prices.

5   Goods and services and resources must be mobile. This requires free entry by firms into any industry and goods and labor free to move from one local market to another to seek the best price.

6   Buyers and sellers must be aware of prices throughout the economy. When buyers and sellers receive such information instantaneously, we have what is known as *perfect competition*. The closest approximation to this condition is on the New York Stock Exchange where information on stock prices is transmitted continuously to all parts of the nation.

7   Commodities must be sufficiently divisible so that sellers can withhold all or part of the product from individual buyers who do not pay the market price.

8   The existing income distribution must be considered equitable for the dollar votes of the individual participants to be weighted equally.

9   All resources must be fully employed. When unemployment persists, prices do not reflect opportunity costs or returns from the viewpoint of the nation.

Even though pure competition does not exist in real markets, the model provides an ideal for judging the efficiency of actual markets and guidelines to help develop criteria for establishing value when its conditions are not met.

3-3   MARKET DEMAND   Experience tells us that people will buy less at higher prices provided income, tastes, and prices of substitutes remain constant. Obversely, people buy more at lower prices. The demand for a good is the quantity per unit time that people within a defined area will buy as a function of all possible prices, all other factors remaining constant.

One way to indicate demand is by a demand schedule, a list of the different quantities of a good that people will take within a particular time period at various prices. A hypothetical demand schedule for Idaho potatoes is shown by the first two columns of Table 3-1. A demand curve is the plot of the demand schedule. The vertical axis indicates the price per unit, and the horizontal axis indicates the quantity of the good pur-

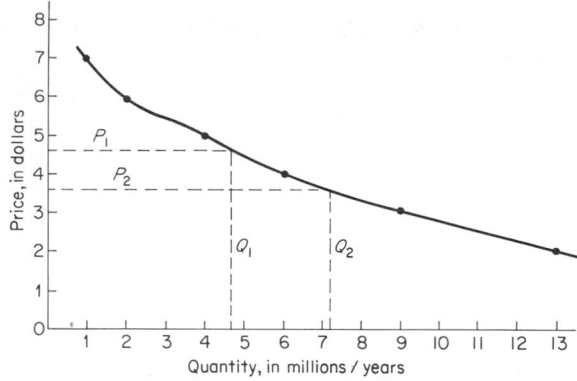

FIGURE 3-2 Hypothetical demand curve for Idaho
potatoes, given for 100-lb sacks.

chased per unit time. Figure 3-2 is a hypothetical demand curve for Idaho
potatoes.

The demand curve slopes downward to the right because lower prices
increase sales, a principle designated as the *law of downward-sloping
demand.* Two reasons for this increase are that (1) lowered prices attract
new buyers and (2) lowered prices induce extra purchases by former users.
Lower water prices would cause some to abandon more expensive alternate
sources of supply and become new buyers. Old buyers would use more.
When water is very expensive, a person only buys enough to drink. As
the price lowers progressively, he buys some for personal cleanliness, then
for household cleaning, and finally for yard watering.

It is important to distinguish between movement along a given

TABLE 3-1 Supply and Demand Schedules for Idaho Potatoes, given for 100-lb sacks

Price, in dollars	Quantity demanded, in millions per year	Quantity supplied, in millions per year	Price tendency	Market conditions
7	1	10	Fall	Surplus
6	2	9	Fall	Surplus
5	4	8	Fall	Surplus
4	6	6	Neutral	Equilibrium
3	9	4	Rise	Shortage
2	13	1	Rise	Shortage

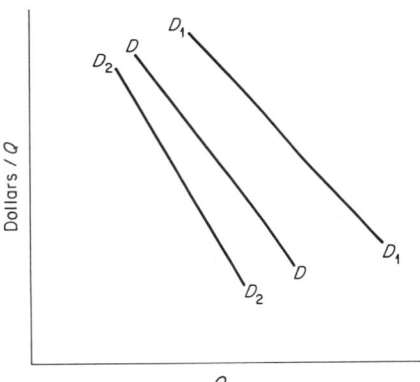

FIGURE 3-3   Shifts in demand curves
(caused by changes in
demand).

demand curve and a shift of the demand curve caused by a change in demand. Movement along a demand curve occurs with a change in the price of the good. Shifting of the demand curve is caused by changes in (1) consumer preferences, (2) the number of consumers, (3) consumer incomes, (4) the prices of related goods, and (5) the range of goods available.[1] When price changes from P_1 to P_2, we should have movement along the demand curve as the quantity of potatoes purchased changed from Q_1 to Q_2 (Fig. 3-2). If there were an increase in consumer preferences for Idaho potatoes, more consumers, greater consumer incomes, higher prices for Maine potatoes, or fewer alternative foods available for purchase, the demand curve would shift from DD to D_1D_1 (Fig. 3-3). Opposite changes would shift the demand curve to D_2D_2.

3-4   PRICE ELASTICITY   One of the most important relationships expressed by a demand curve is the change in sales resulting from a given change in price. This change could be measured by the slope of the demand curve, but the general usefulness of the answer is limited by its units (sacks per dollar in Fig. 3-2). A different slope on a curve plotted in different units (bushels per cent) would indicate the identical relationship between price and demand. Economists avoid this difficulty in units by use of the price elasticity of demand defined as

$$E = \frac{-\Delta Q/Q}{\Delta P/P} \quad \text{or} \quad -\frac{\Delta Q}{\Delta P}\frac{P}{Q} \tag{3-1}$$

The negative sign is introduced because Q increases as P decreases.

[1]   Richard H. Leftwich, "The Price System and Resource Allocation" (New York: Holt, Rinehart and Winston, Inc., 1964), p. 27.

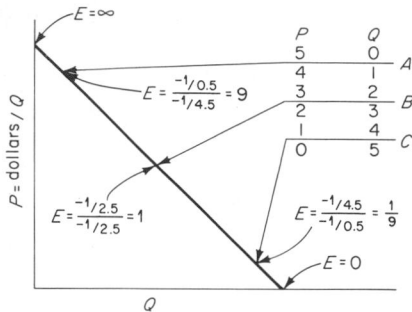

FIGURE 3-4   Price elasticity of demand.

Computation of the price elasticity of demand is illustrated by Fig. 3-4. Applying Eq. (3-1) to points A, B, and C, respectively, gives elasticities of 9, 1, and $\frac{1}{9}$. Even though the demand curve at all three points has the same slope, the price elasticity of demand varies from infinity along the vertical axis to zero along the horizontal axis.

A value of infinity for E indicates a perfectly elastic good which no one at all will buy if the price is raised. It is represented by a horizontal demand curve. Goods become perfectly elastic at the price that they are completely priced out of the market.

As the price is reduced, elasticity drops. Eventually it reaches unity, and the good is no longer said to be elastic. This point would provide the supplier the largest gross revenue; the PQ product is a maximum. Until the elasticity reaches unity, additional sales more than offset lower prices and revenue increases. If the price is reduced past the point of unit elasticity, sales no longer increase fast enough to offset the lowering price and revenue declines. The good is said to be inelastic. A value of zero for E indicates a perfectly inelastic good or one for which price has no effect on demand. It is represented by a vertical demand curve. Goods become perfectly inelastic as the price becomes too low to remain a factor determining the amount purchased. The same good is inelastic at low prices and elastic at high prices.

3-5   MARKET SUPPLY   On the sellers' side of the market, the supply schedule and supply curve indicate the amounts that producers are willing to sell at various prices, other things being equal. The first and third column of Table 3-1 show the supply schedule for Idaho potatoes, and Fig. 3-5 is the corresponding supply curve.

The supply curve slopes upward to the right since old sellers will produce more goods for sale and new sellers will enter the market as the

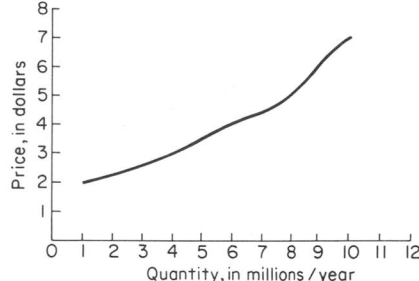

FIGURE 3-5   Hypothetical   supply
curve for Idaho potatoes,
given for 100-lb sacks.

price increases. The supply curve shifts (in contrast with movement along
the curve) with a change in the supply produced when the price remains
unchanged. Shifts to the right may be caused by technological advance,
favorable production conditions, or lower prices for the input factors of
production. Shifts to the left are caused by opposite conditions.

3-6   MARKET PRICE DETERMINATION   The demand curve and
the supply curve combine to establish the equilibrium market price. The
combined demand and supply schedules in Table 3-1 illustrate the tendency
toward an equilibrium price.

If the initial price is above $4 per 100 lb, more will be supplied than
the quantity demanded. Potatoes will be in oversupply, and sellers will
cut prices in order to sell their crops. Also, if the initial price is below
$4 per 100 lb, less will be supplied than the quantity demanded and con-
sumers will bid the price up. Only at the equilibrium price of $4 per 100
lb will the demand equal the supply. Figure 3-6 shows the same result
graphically. This equilibrium price is the minimum under conditions of
pure competition that each individual buyer must pay for each 100 lb
of potatoes purchased and the maximum that each farmer can receive
for each 100 lb of potatoes sold.

3-7   RESULTS OF SHIFTS IN DEMAND AND SUPPLY   If the
demand for potatoes increases while the supply remains fixed, Fig. 3-7
shows how a shift in demand from DD to D_1D_1 causes an increase in price
from P to P_1. This happens because at P there is now a shortage of potatoes,
the price will be bid up, and sellers will be induced to place more on the
market. Just the opposite happens with a decrease in demand: a surplus
creates pressure to lower prices.

When the supply curve shifts and the demand curve is fixed, equilib-

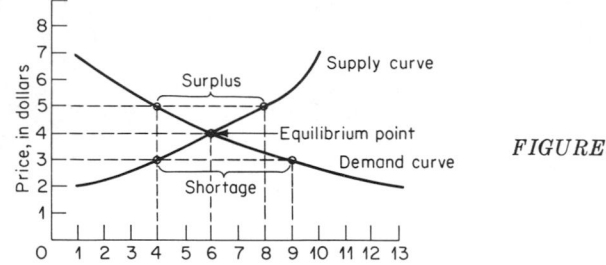

FIGURE 3-6   Hypothetical market demand and supply curves for Idaho potatoes, given for 100-lb sacks.

rium prices and quantities are also affected. Suppose higher labor costs were to increase the cost of growing potatoes. In Fig. 3-8, this would cause a shift from SS to S_1S_1. At the original price P, there would be a shortage and the price would be bid up to P_1. The opposite will happen if lower production costs should shift the supply curve to the right. There will be a surplus and a downward pressure on prices to a new equilibrium point.

3-8   SIGNIFICANCE OF MARKET EQUILIBRIUM   Supply and demand curves provide additional background for understanding the automatic way the market system handles the allocation of goods or answers the basic economic questions of what, how, and for whom. *For whom* is partially determined by individual willingness to pay. If you have the money and wish to eat Idaho potatoes three times a day, you merely pay the market price. On the other hand, you may not like Idaho potatoes

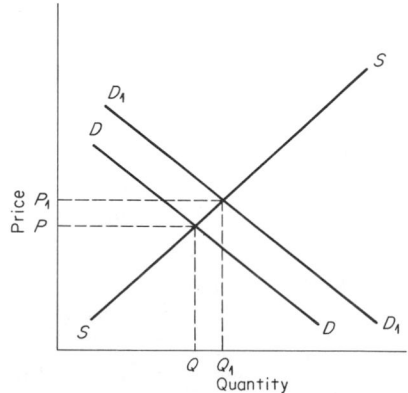

FIGURE 3-7   Shift in demand curve.

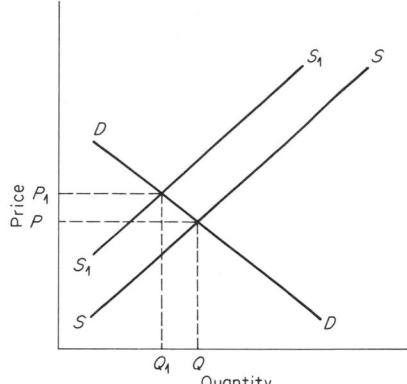

FIGURE 3-8 Shift in supply curve.

and spend your entire income on other goods. *What* is partially determined by the price for potatoes' determining the degree to which farmers shift productive resources from the production of other crops. *How* is also partially answered because the price for potatoes determines the money farmers have to invest in potato processing equipment, sprinkler systems, and fertilizer. A given pair of supply and demand curves only partially answers these questions because events in other food markets and resource markets also affect economic equilibrium. Therefore, the *partial equilibrium* solution for Idaho potatoes plays only a small part in determining the total price structure.

Consumer Demand

The above bird's-eye view of the interaction between supply and demand to achieve equilibrium prices provides the background for a more thorough discussion of the economic principles governing demand. Two approaches have been used to derive a theory of consumer demand. For years, classical economics has used the utility approach based on values assigned in absolute units. More recently, the indifference-curve approach has been developed because it avoids the problem of evaluation in absolute units by using relative values. For brevity, we shall only explain the more recent indifference-curve approach.[1]

---

[1] Leftwich, "The Price System and Resource Allocation," gives both approaches in chaps. 4 and 5.

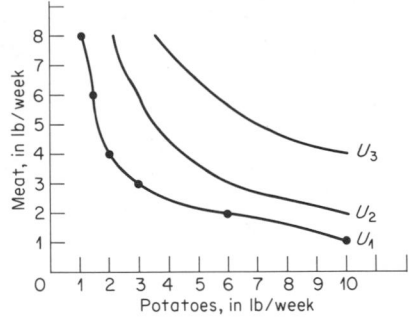

FIGURE 3-9 Indifference curves.

3-9 INDIFFERENCE CURVES An indifference curve (sometimes called the *equal-utility contour*) shows the consumption combinations which give a consumer equal satisfaction. It is called an indifference curve because the consumer is equally satisfied with any of the combinations depicted by the curve. An indifference curve is theoretically obtained by asking a consumer which combinations of goods yield equal satisfaction, and its development assumes he can order his preferences. The indifference curves described below will be two dimensional so they can be graphically presented. However, real consumers must choose in hundreds of dimensions, one for each good consumed. The true indifference curve is a multidimensional indifference surface.

If a consumer buys only two goods with his income, meat and potatoes, the combinations in Table 3-2 might give equal satisfaction. More meat compensates for giving up potatoes and vice versa. The plot of these combinations gives a single indifference curve (Fig. 3-9). Greater

TABLE 3-2 Combinations of Meat and Potatoes Giving Equal Satisfaction

Meat, lb wk⁻¹	Potatoes, lb wk⁻¹
1	10
2	6
3	3
4	2
6	1.5
8	1

quantities of both meat and potatoes will give the consumer with an inadequate diet a greater total value since greater quantities of the goods bring more satisfaction. A second indifference curve can be drawn to indicate the combinations of meat and potatoes that provide this higher level of satisfaction. Thus, there are an infinite number of indifference curves, each one indicating a separate level of satisfaction the consumer may experience. This system of indifference curves is called an *indifference map*. The indifference curves may be viewed as contour lines of increasing elevation as one moves upward to the right.

Some of the properties of indifference curves are:

1 They cannot intersect since it is impossible for a single combination of goods to yield two levels of satisfaction simultaneously.
2 They slope downward to the right. As the amount of one good is increased, the other must decrease if equal satisfaction is to be maintained. The slope of the indifference curve is called the *marginal rate of substitution*.
3 They tend to approach the axes asymptotically because as less and less of a good is consumed, the sacrifice of parting with an additional unit becomes greater. Many more units of the other good must be substituted to bring equal satisfaction.

3-10 MAXIMIZATION OF SATISFACTION A consumer maximizes his satisfaction by picking the highest indifference curve available to him as determined by his income and the prices of the two goods. These two consumer's opportunity factors determine what may be called a *line of attainable combinations*. It intercepts each axis at a value equal to the income divided by the price. For example, one intercept would be the amount of potatoes which could be purchased were the entire income spent for that purpose. The other intercept indicates the amount of meat which could be purchased by the entire income. Points on a straight line between these intercepts indicate the combinations of meat and potatoes open to the consumer. The highest attainable indifference curve is the one tangent to the line of attainable combinations (Fig. 3-10).

The total income I spent on two goods y_a and y_b with respective prices per unit of P_{ya} and P_{yb} equals

$$I = P_{ya}y_a + P_{yb}y_b \qquad (3\text{-}2)$$

The number of units of y_a which can be purchased thus equals

$$X = \frac{-P_{yb}}{P_{ya}}y_b + \frac{I}{P_{ya}} \qquad (3\text{-}3)$$

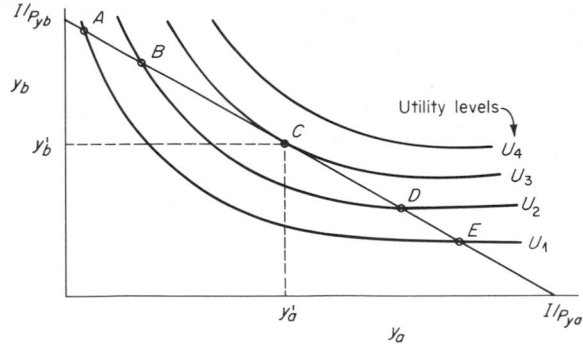

FIGURE 3-10   Income allocation.

This is the equation of a straight line (the line of attainable combinations) with a slope of $-P_{yb}/P_{ya}$.

The consumer is able to attain points A, B, C, D, and E in Fig. 3-10. If he chooses A, he is on U_1, which gives less satisfaction than U_2 or U_3. Point C gives maximum satisfaction. All the other points are on lower indifference curves. The income constraint prevents achievement of U_4. At point C, the slopes of the indifference curves and the line of attainable combinations are equal. The marginal rate of substitution (the slope of the indifference curve) equals the ratio of the prices (the slope of the line of attainable combinations),

$$MRS_{ya,yb} = \frac{P_{yb}}{P_{ya}} \tag{3-4}$$

where $MRS_{ya,yb}$ is read as the marginal rate of substitution of y_a for y_b.

3-11   CONSUMER-DEMAND CURVES   Consumer-demand curves are derived by varying the price of one good, P_{ya}, while keeping constant the income, consumer preferences (position and shape of indifference curves), and the price of the other good, P_{yb}, or in the general case, of all other goods. By changing the price of y_a, the slope of the line of attainable combinations changes to become tangent to a different indifference curve. Suppose the initial line of attainable combinations (AB in Fig. 3-11) is tangent to U_1, which means that for an income of I, an amount of y'_a will be purchased at P'_{y_a}, and an amount y_b at P'_{y_b}. If P_{y_a} increases to P''_{y_a}, the new line of attainable combinations AC will have a steeper slope than AB because fewer units of y_a can be purchased when all of I is spent

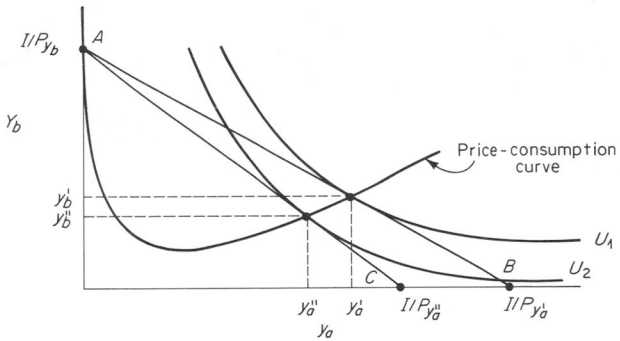

FIGURE 3-11   Derivation of price-consumption curve.

on y_a. The line of attainable combinations pivots about A because I/P_{yb} is constant. The price increase lowers the level of satisfaction the consumer on a fixed income can attain. He moves to a lower indifference curve and now would allocate I so as to purchase y_a'' units of y_a and y_b'' units of y_b. If P_{ya} is assigned a series of values, the line connecting the points of tangency is called the price-consumption curve. The demand curve of a specific individual for y_a can be found by plotting corresponding values of y_a and P_{ya} taken from the price-consumption curve (Fig. 3-12).

3-12   AGGREGATE-DEMAND CURVES   Individual demand curves for Idaho potatoes may be used to develop a combined demand curve (Fig. 3-13). At each price, the demand by each individual may be added

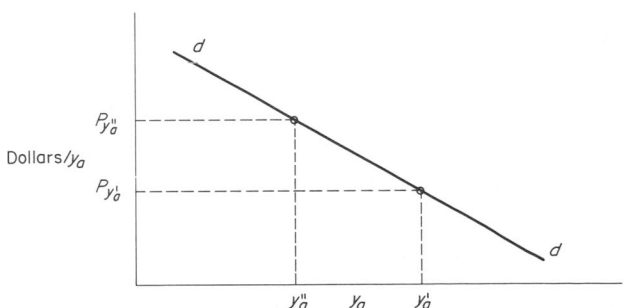

FIGURE 3-12   Consumer-demand curve.

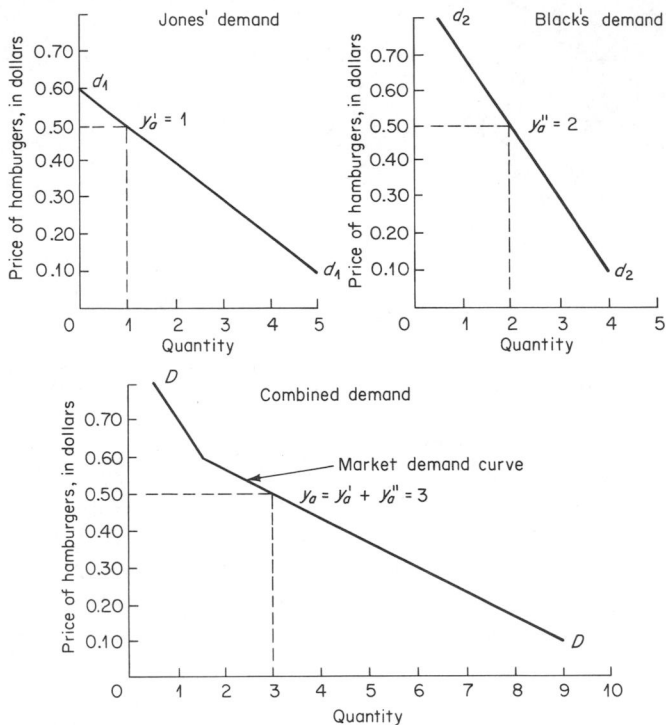

FIGURE 3-13 Summation of consumer demands to obtain market demand curve.

to get the combined demand. This combination occurs automatically in the market because the demand by both individuals must be met from the same supply. Such horizontal addition is thus characteristic of market goods.

Note that each consumer is free to decide his relative preference for different goods according to his own tastes. Since people have different tastes, individual demand curves differ. However, the horizontal addition of the demand integrates different individual tastes into the market demand curve.

SELECTED REFERENCES

Ebenstein, William: "Today's Isms," 4th ed. (Englewood Cliffs, N.J.: Prentice-Hall, Inc., 1964).

Eckstein, Otto: "Water Resource Development: The Economics of Project Evaluation" (Cambridge, Mass.: Harvard University Press, 1958).
Leftwich, Richard H.: "The Price System and Resource Allocation" (New York: Holt, Rinehart and Winston, Inc., 1964).
Samuelson, Paul A.: "Economics: An Introductory Analysis," 5th ed. (New York: McGraw-Hill Book Company, 1962).
Stigler, George J.: "The Theory of Price" (New York: The Macmillan Company, 1961).

PROBLEMS

3-1 The supply and demand schedules for fidwots is:

Price, \$:	1	2	3	4	5	6	7
Demand:	41	30	21	14	9	6	5
Supply:	12	14	18	24	32	42	55

  a Plot the supply and demand curves.
  b What is the equilibrium market price for fidwots?
  c What is the price elasticity of demand at a price of \$2? Of \$6?
  d At what price is there unitary elasticity?
  e What equilibrium price would result from a doubling of demand?

3-2 Lines of consumer indifference between commodities A and B are represented by the indifference map represented by the equation $0.1A^2B = V$, where V is a scalar measure of satisfaction.
  a Construct an indifference map covering the region $A < 10, B < 50$.
  b What level of satisfaction is gained at the point $A = 5, B - 20$? What is the marginal rate of substitution, dA/dB, at this point?
  c A consumer has an income of 20 to spend in a market where $P_A = 2$ and $P_B = 0.5$. Plot the line of attainable combinations. What is the maximum level of satisfaction the consumer can reach? What amounts of A and B does he purchase to obtain this satisfaction?
  d Based on values of $P_B = 1.0, 2.0, 4.0,$ and 10.0, plot the price-consumption curve on the indifference map and then the consumer-demand curve for B.

3-3 A second consumer is in a situation identical with that of the consumer in Prob. 3-2c except his available income is 5.
  a Plot a consumer-demand curve for this second man.
  b Plot a market-demand curve, assuming these are the only two consumers.

CHAPTER
FOUR

CONDITIONS
OF PROJECT OPTIMALITY

Production Theory

Economic forces act within the private sector of the economy to determine the supply curves of individual productive units (firms) and integrate
them into a market-supply curve. Production theory attempts to explain
the operation of these forces in ordering private sector production and
thereby determining:

1 The total expenditure on inputs (raw material, machinery, labor, etc.)
2 The division of this expenditure among individual inputs
3 The way inputs are combined to produce each type of output
4 The amount of each output produced

Water resources development is a production process. In planning a
production process for the public sector, many valuable insights can be
gained from analyzing how economic forces would act to order production
under ideal conditions.

4-1 INPUT AND OUTPUT The basic purpose of production is to
convert material (input) into a more useful form (output). A water
resources project is constructed to produce such desired output as irrigation water, reduced flood damage, a navigable channel, or electric power
from a set of such inputs as earth, concrete, steel, and natural streamflow. As expressions of varied composition, both input and output are
vector quantities. Each coordinate of the vector represents a specific
input or output item.

The input vector consists of the sum of all the individual inputs. Thus,

$$X = x_1 + x_2 + \cdots + x_m \tag{4-1}$$

where X is the total input vector and the x are m individual inputs. The inputs fall by nature into two types. One type is the earth, concrete, and steel which go into a construction project, the required production capital. The other type is the natural streamflow from which the output is produced, the required raw material.

Evaluation of the input vector is complicated by the fact that the timing and magnitude of future streamflows cannot be predicted in advance and vary over wide ranges. Streamflow may be expressed as a continuous hydrograph, a running plot of stream discharge throughout the life of the project, as a probability distribution, or as such distribution moments as the mean and the standard deviation. Furthermore, one must keep in mind that all the other input and output vectors also have probability distributions even though their variance may be much smaller because one cannot predict any future event with absolute certainty.

The concept of the input vector can be simplified by defining its coordinates as the intermediate products of reservoirs, channel improvements, or powerhouses rather than the construction items of earth, concrete, and steel. The optimum combination of construction items in building a given intermediate product (say a dam of specified size) is best found from an engineering economy study seeking to minimize total cost. The first phase or the economy study determines how much earth, concrete, and steel should go into a dam of given size. The second phase or optimality analysis determines how big the dam should be and when and where it should be built.

The output vector consists of the sum of all the individual outputs. Thus,

$$Y = y_a + y_b + \cdots + y_n \tag{4-2}$$

where Y is the total output vector and the y are n individual outputs. Again, each output can only be predicted during planning and has a probability distribution expressing the range of possible values. The individual outputs are distinguished by type (irrigation from flood control) and by location (the area served.)

The composition of both vectors varies with time. Input contains investment in original construction, periodic replacement, and regular operation and maintenance. The output occurs in a time stream lasting the life of the project and varying from year to year but normally increasing with the general growth of the economy.

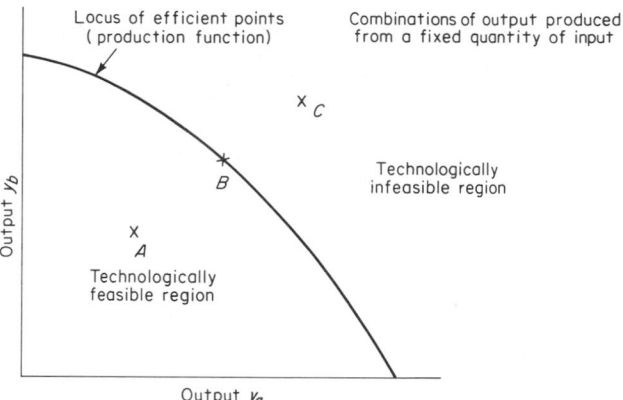

FIGURE 4-1   Production function.

4-2   THE PRODUCTION FUNCTION   Economists have traditionally expressed the ability of a production process to produce an output vector from an input vector by a production function. As a simple illustration, one might have a production process in which two outputs are produced (Fig. 4-1). Engineering analysis may show that the combination of outputs represented by point A could physically be produced and the combination of point C would not be physically possible to produce. Continued analysis of alternative production possibilities will show which output vectors can and which output vectors cannot be produced. All those that can be produced are said to fall in the *technologically feasible region.*

Some points in the technologically feasible region are efficient, while others are inefficient. For example, it would be physically possible to dispose of the input vector without producing anything, but this would be wasteful and inefficient. The production represented by point A is inefficient because with the same input, the output vector could be increased to point B. For an inefficient point, the output vector can be unambiguously increased without increasing the input vector or the same output vector can be produced after an unambiguous decrease in the input vector. An unambiguous increase of a vector means some coordinates are increased without any being decreased. An unambiguous decrease means some coordinates are decreased without any being increased. The locus of efficient points is the outer limit of the technologically feasible region. The production function is the mathematical representation of this line. It is related to the entire input and output vectors and, by putting all the terms on the left-hand side, can be represented by the expression

$$f(X,Y) = 0 \tag{4-3}$$

4-3 THE OBJECTIVE FUNCTION Selection of the best point on the production function requires some criteria for evaluating worth. The criteria must assign a scalar value to each point on the production function. A scalar value is needed because vectors cannot be unambiguously ranked according to magnitude as one may be larger in one coordinate but smaller in the other. The objective function necessarily depends on both the input and output vectors.

$$U = u(X,Y) \tag{4-4}$$

Where n outputs are produced from m inputs,

$$U = \sum_{j=a}^{n} B_j y_j - \sum_{i=1}^{m} C_i x_i \tag{4-5}$$

where the B_i refer to the unit benefits associated with the corresponding coordinates of the output vector, and the C_j refer to the unit costs associated with the corresponding coordinates of the input vector. Conceptually, both benefits and costs may be either measured in monetary units or defined with respect to some broader based social welfare function (Sec. 5-2) without affecting the optimality criteria derived below.

4-4 COST AND BENEFIT CURVES Economic evaluation of production alternatives is based on the variation in total production cost with level of production output (called the *total-cost curve*) and the variation in the resulting benefit with level of production output (called the *total-benefit curve*). The total-cost curve is developed by summing the required input costs for a series of levels of output. The total-benefit curve is developed by summing values received by output users.

The total cost includes fixed cost and variable cost. Fixed costs remain constant regardless of output. They include capital recovery charges on the production facilities and other overhead costs. Variable costs vary with level of output. They include the costs of labor and material which can be added or deleted according to the level of production. Variable costs are marginal costs and are used to determine the optimum level of production according to the incremental-cost principle. Fixed costs are not marginal and thus have no influence on the optimum level of production, but they do influence whether or not total benefits exceed total costs or whether the project should be constructed at all.

Average-cost or -benefit curves are developed from total-cost or

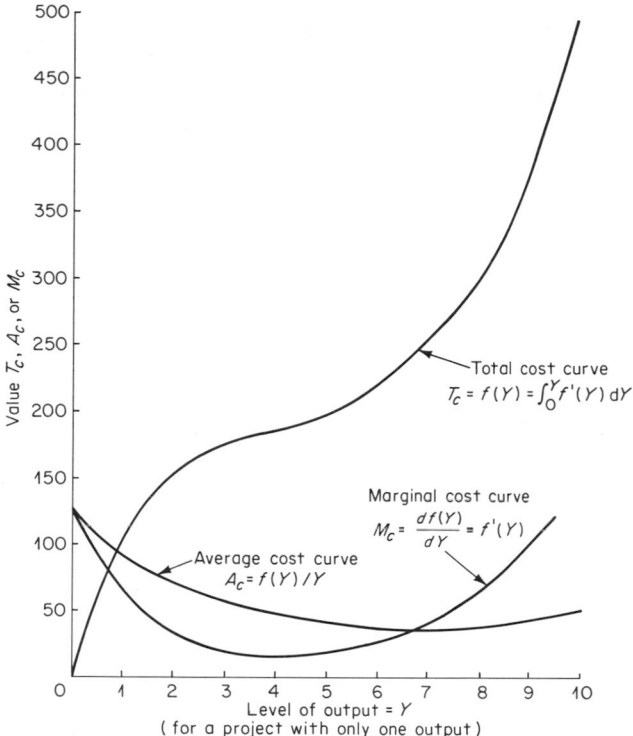

FIGURE 4-2 Representative total-, average-, and marginal-
cost curves.

-benefit curves by dividing the total value by the level of output (Fig.
4-2). Average-cost curves are usually U-shaped. They decrease at first
because of *economies of scale*, savings in production cost per unit stemming
from increases in size of plant and output. Economies of scale result
from (1) specialization of labor and (2) advanced technology. Specialization of labor may be impossible in a small plant because no single task
requires the full-time effort of any individual worker, but as the size of
plant and production increases, assembly line techniques become practical
and reduce unit production costs. Advanced technology may be available,
but its fixed cost may be too large to be warranted for a small plant. However, increased output spreads fixed cost over more units to make advanced
technology economical. In reservoir construction, much of the fixed cost
stems from providing sediment storage space, spillways to pass rare floods,
access roads, and other minimum structural requirements. Average cost

increases again as production becomes very large because of *diseconomies of scale* caused by difficulties in managing, controlling, and coordinating a very large firm or by inducing increases in the price of inputs. In reservoir construction, diseconomies of scale are largely caused by a decreasing yield and increasing dam size per acre-foot of storage as reservoir size gets too large.

Marginal-cost or -benefit curves present the slope of total-cost or -benefit curves. The slope represents the change in total cost or benefit associated with a one-unit change in output. Because a firm will not produce an extra unit unless the price exceeds the marginal cost, the rising limb of the marginal-cost curve is a supply curve. It indicates the price necessary to induce an extra unit of production. Because a buyer will not make a purchase unless it provides a value exceeding the cost, the marginal-benefit curve is a demand curve. It indicates the maximum price that a firm which uses the output produced can afford to spend to acquire an extra unit.

Total values may be established from marginal curves because the area under the marginal curve to the left of an abscissa equals the ordinate of the total curve. The total cost of a group of items equals the sum of their individual costs. At the low point on the average curve, the marginal values equals the average value because, otherwise, adding the marginal increment would change the average. A marginal curve must plot below a falling average curve to cause average values to drop. Obversely, a marginal curve must plot above a rising average curve. Therefore, marginal curves, like average curves, are generally U-shaped, but justified more to the left.

4-5 OPTIMALITY CONDITIONS One approach to determining the optimum production process would be systematic trial-and-error evaluation of the net benefit [Eq. (4-5)] for each point on the production function [Eq. (4-3)], which will lead to the point having maximum value. The search is made easier by being able to recognize the characteristics peculiar to such a point.

A mathematician distinguishes necessary from sufficient conditions when seeking such characteristics. Necessary conditions are characteristics the solution must have, but they do not guarantee that a point having them is the solution. Sufficient conditions guarantee a solution. A simple example applying this distinction to project optimization is found in the production of one output from two inputs. If the two inputs are plotted on a horizontal plane, the maximum output which can be produced from each combination of the two can be plotted vertically to produce what resembles a topographic contour map and is called a *production* or a *response surface*. A necessary condition to show that the maximum output has been produced from these two inputs is that the surface slope downward in all directions. However, this condition is not sufficient because there might be a higher hilltop on the other side of a valley. For greater numbers of inputs the surface is multidimensional, but the principle is the same.

Proof that a given peak is the maximum may follow one of two lines. The height of each peak may be computed to show which is highest. Evidence may be presented to show only one peak exists. A single peak will in fact be the case if all second derivatives of the objective function are continuously negative, a situation occurring under conditions of diminishing marginal utility as supply curves slope continuously upward and demand curves slope continuously downward to the right. The second approach is more frequently used in water resources planning. It needs to be emphasized that the conditions of project optimality to be developed below are necessary but not sufficient conditions. Proof of absolute optimality requires evidence that no higher peak exists.

For a water resources project, the goal is to find an alternative having maximum value of $u(X,Y)$ with the constraint that only alternatives contained on the production function $f(X,Y) = 0$ need be considered. The conditions necessary to having a maximum value may be determined by (1) the geometrical approach or (2) the mathematical approach. The geometrical approach follows immediately, while the mathematical approach is presented later.

Geometric Derivation of Basic Rules

4-6 OPTIMALITY CONDITION 1: COMBINATION OF INPUTS
The optimal production process must use the least costly combination of inputs able to produce any given level of output. For example, the sizes of the two dams to provide flood control must be selected to achieve the desired level of flood reduction at minimum cost. The least-cost combination of inputs can be found geometrically by the use of isoquant lines and isocost lines. If the problem is reduced to two dimensions for practical presentation, isoquant lines (Fig. 4-3) show different combinations of two inputs which can produce equal amounts of a single output.

Isoquants are analogous to indifference curves and have analogous characteristics:

1   Two isoquants cannot intersect. An intersection would require the maximum output which could be produced with the same input to be two different amounts.

2   Isoquants slope downward to the right because increased use of one input reduces the quantity of another required to obtain a given level of output. Channel improvement can be substituted for reservoirs to provide flood control.

3   Isoquants are convex to the origin because of the decreasing ability of one input to be substituted for another to obtain a given level of output. As more channel improvement and less reservoir storage are used to produce a given level of flood control, the larger is the incremental channel improvement required to effect a unit reduction in flood storage. This is called the *principle of diminishing marginal rate of substitution.*

In Fig. 4-3, the isoquant for output y_a shows the possible combinations of x_1 and x_2 which could be used in its production. The most efficient combination depends on the unit prices of the inputs, just as the unit prices of goods guide spending to maximize consumer satisfaction (Sec. 3-10).

Isocost lines (Fig. 4-4) indicate the input combinations that can be purchased by a given production budget and are analogous to the line of attainable combinations–used in demand analysis. If the production budget is T, the price of x_1 is P_{x_1}, and the price of x_2 is P_{x_2};

$$T = P_{x_1}x_1 + P_{x_2}x_2 \tag{4-6}$$

which is the equation of a straight line with a slope of P_{x_1}/P_{x_2}.

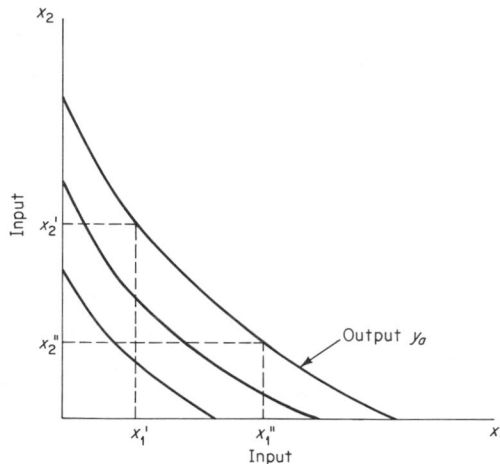

FIGURE 4-3   Isoquants (lines of equal output).

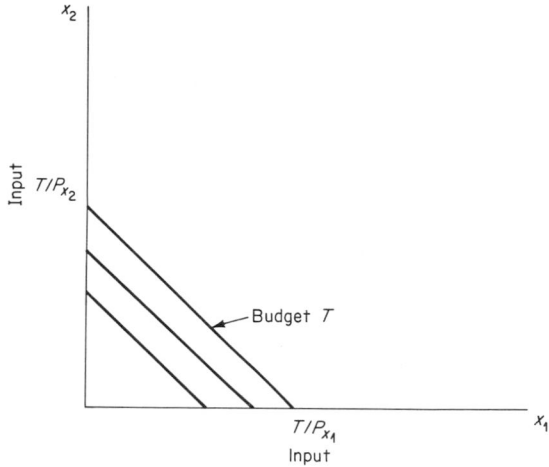

FIGURE 4-4   Isocost lines (lines of equal cost).

Production of a given level of output with the least-cost combination of resources occurs where an isocost line (slope of P_{x_1}/P_{x_2}) is tangent to the isoquant (slope of $MRS_{x_2 x_1}$). Therefore,

$$MRS_{x_2 x_1} = \frac{P_{x_1}}{P_{x_2}} \tag{4-7}$$

Figure 4-5 shows a number of isoquants with tangent isocosts. The line *AB* joining the points of tangency is called the *expansion path* and is the locus of the least-cost combinations of inputs for varying levels of total output.

An example will clarify the procedure for combining inputs. Suppose the axes in Fig. 4-5 represent two single-purpose flood control reservoirs. We can calculate combinations of storage capacity in the two reservoirs providing a fixed level of flood peak reduction (isoquant) and the storage combinations that can be constructed with a fixed budget (isocost). As many isoquants and isocosts as needed may be calculated and drawn. Each point of tangency represents the least-cost combination of reservoirs to provide a given level of flood reduction.

4-7   OPTIMALITY CONDITION 2: COMBINATION OF OUTPUTS
With two outputs, such as municipal water supply and hydropower, total production must be divided between the two to maximize benefits. One may begin the analysis by plotting on coordinate axes representing two

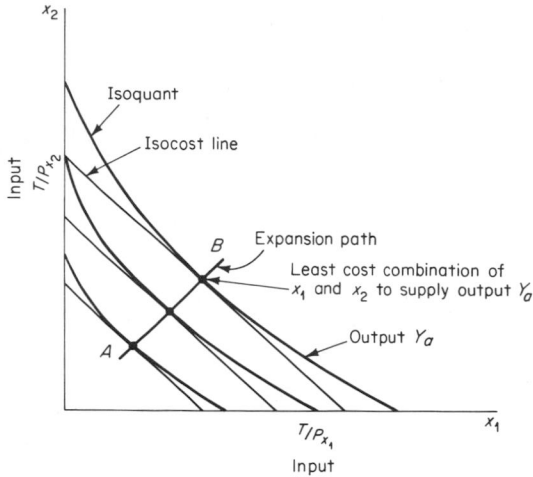

FIGURE 4-5 Determination of least-cost combination of inputs.

outputs y_a and y_b (Fig. 4-6) each of the family of curves showing combinations of outputs that can be produced at a given cost. Each curve indicates all combinations of outputs y_a and y_b that can be produced for the indicated sum and is called a *product-transformation curve* because to move along it, one output must be increased while the other is reduced.

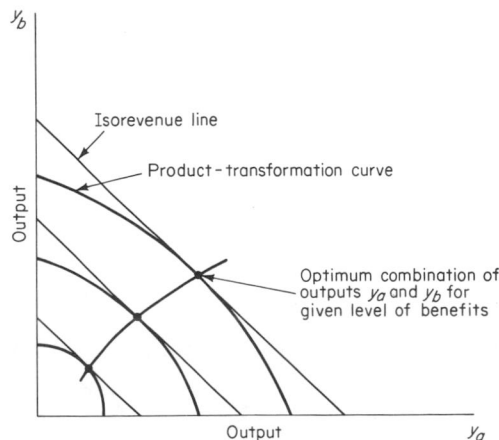

FIGURE 4-6 Optimum combination of outputs.

The slope of the product-transformation curve is called the *marginal rate of transformation*.

A family of parallel lines called *isorevenue lines* may also be drawn in Fig. 4-6. The slopes of these lines are the ratios of the market prices of the two outputs. Each isorevenue line shows the different combinations of outputs that would sell for the same amount of gross revenue or would produce a given benefit.

The optimum mix of outputs achieves a given level of benefits at least cost, or put another way, the maximum level of benefits for a given level of costs. In Fig. 4-6, the optimum combinations are located at the points of tangency of the isorevenue lines (slope of P_{y_a}/P_{y_b}) and product-transformation curves (slope of $MRT_{y_a y_b}$). Therefore,

$$MRT_{y_a y_b} = \frac{P_{y_a}}{P_{y_b}} \tag{4-8}$$

Product-transformation curves are concave to the origin (Fig. 4-6) if the outputs are joint products of the same productive process or if the production of one is facilitated by production of the other. But if the production of one output hinders production of another, the product-transformation curves are convex to the origin. In this case, benefits are maximized by producing only one of the two outputs, a boundary solution for which Eq. (4-8) does not apply (Fig. 4-7). The product-transformation curve reaches the highest isorevenue line on the y_a axis; therefore, only

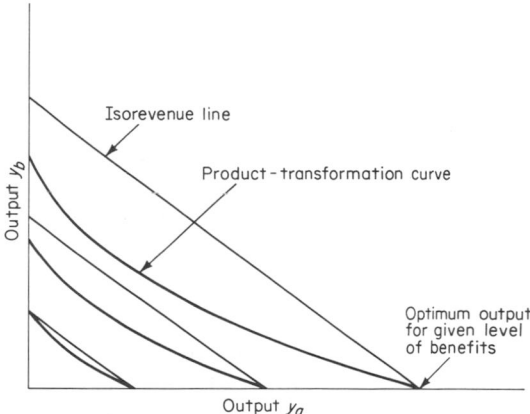

FIGURE 4-7   Optimum output for concave product-transformation curves.

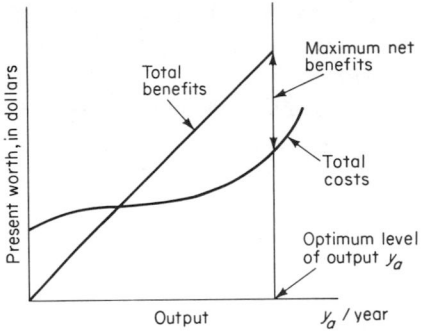

FIGURE 4-8 Determination of optimum level of output.

y_a would be produced. Note the isorevenue line is not tangent to the product-transformation curve at this point.

Optimality condition 2 may be summarized by saying production should be divided between two outputs so that the marginal benefit of any input in the production of one equals the marginal benefit of the input in production of the other. Otherwise production could be shifted between the outputs to increase benefits.

4-8 OPTIMALITY CONDITION 3: LEVEL OF OUTPUT Optimality condition 3 determines the optimum level of output, on the assumption that conditions 1 and 2 have already been met. It states that benefit is maximized if output is increased up to the point where the marginal

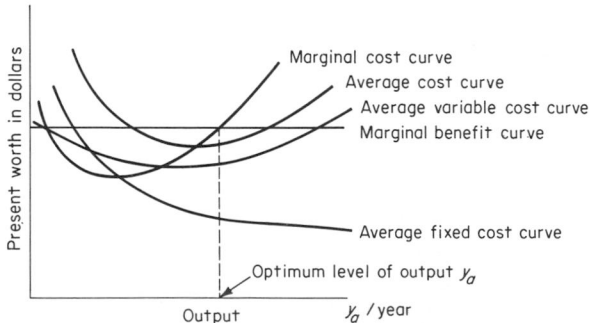

FIGURE 4-9 Optimum level of output by using marginal-cost and marginal-benefit curves.

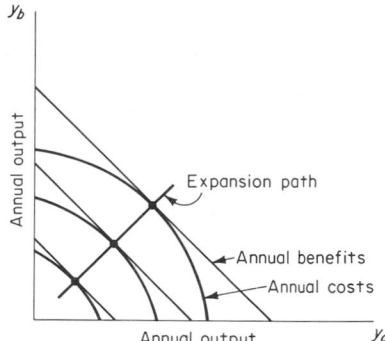

FIGURE 4-10   Optimum   construction costs and combination of outputs.

costs equal the marginal benefits, or in engineering-economy terminology, incremental costs equal incremental benefits. The two marginal values are equal where the slopes of the total-value curves are equal or where the distance between them is maximum (see Fig. 4-11).

For the two-input one-output case, optimality condition 1 provides the basis for calculating the minimum cost of attaining different levels of output. The results may be plotted in a total-cost curve (Fig. 4-8.) The total-benefit curve may be plotted by multiplying the unit price of the output times the quantity of output. Under the conditions of pure competition, the unit price is constant; hence the total-benefit line is straight. For only one output, optimality condition 2 does not apply, and we can

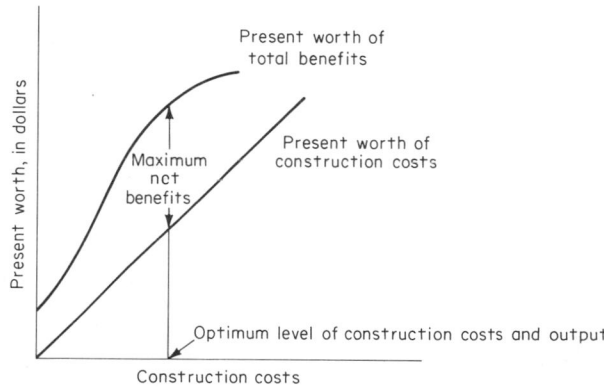

FIGURE 4-11   Determination of optimum level of construction costs and output.

go directly to optimality condition 3. As can be seen from Fig. 4-8, net benefits are maximized where the slopes of the total-benefit and total-cost curves are equal. The same optimum level of output can be expressed on marginal curves as the point where marginal cost equals marginal benefit (supply equals demand) as seen in Fig. 4-9. For the one-input two-output case, only optimality conditions 2 and 3 apply since there is no problem of combining inputs.

The benefits and costs associated with output combinations on the expansion path (Fig. 4-10) may be plotted (Fig. 4-11) to determine the optimal level of construction cost. This cost then is divided between producing outputs y_a and y_b by referring back to the corresponding point on the expansion path. For the multiple-input multiple-output case, total-cost and total-benefit curves must be used as described in the next chapter.

Mathematical Derivation of Basic Rules

The goal of project optimization is to maximize the objective function $u(X,Y)$ by choosing the best alternative on the production function $f(X,Y) = 0$, where X is an m coordinate and Y is an n coordinate vector.

4-9 LAGRANGE MULTIPLIERS Differential calculus can be used to find such a maximum by differentiating the objective function with respect to each of the $(n + m)$ vector components, setting each differential equal to zero, and solving the resulting equations. However, the solution can only be constrained to alternatives contained on the production function by including it in the equations being solved. This introduces one more equation than unknown, and the problem becomes overdetermined. One way out is to introduce an artificial unknown called a *Lagrange multiplier*[1] as a coefficient of the production function and add the product to the objective function. Thus,

$$L = u(X,Y) + \lambda f(X,Y) \tag{4-9}$$

where λ is the Lagrange multiplier and L is the variable to be maximized. Equation (4-9) is based on the principle that if the constraint is satisfied, the production function will equal zero. By differentiating with respect to λ, setting the differential (which will be the production function) equal to

---

[1] Lagrange multipliers are described in much greater detail in William J. Baumol, "Economic Theory and Operations Analysis" (Englewood Cliffs, N.J.: Prentice-Hall, Inc., 1961) pp. 54–59.

zero, and including it in the set of equations to be solved, one incorporates the production function into the solution. The approach is illustrated by Ex. 4-1.

EXAMPLE 4-1

In a constrained maximization problem, the objective function is $Y = 10ab$, and the constraint is $5a + b = 200$. In other words, we are seeking the values for a and b which maximize the first expression without exceeding the upper limit of the second expression. Placed in the format of Eq. (4-9), the constraint expression $5a + b - 200 = 0$ may be added to the objective function without changing its value, to give

$$Y = 10ab + \lambda(5a + b - 200)$$

By partial differentiation with respect to each of the unknowns a, b, and λ and by setting each differential equal to zero,

$$\frac{\partial Y}{\partial a} = 10b + 5\lambda = 0$$

$$\frac{\partial Y}{\partial b} = 10a + \lambda = 0$$

$$\frac{\partial Y}{\partial \lambda} = 5a + b - 200 = 0$$

Solution of the three equations gives $a = 20$, $b = 100$, and $\lambda = -200$. When these values are substituted in the objective function, the maximum value is found to be $Y = 20,000$.

The economic significance of λ is that if the number on the right-hand side of the constraint equation had been 201 instead of 200, the optimum value of Y would have been $20,000 + \lambda$, or $20,200$.

Lagrange multipliers permit constrained maximization by introducing as many artificial unknowns as there are constraints to make the number of unknowns and equations equal. The problem could be solved without using Lagrange multipliers by substituting the constraint expression in the objective function before using the differential calculus approach, but for many expressions the algebra makes this approach difficult if not impossible.

4-10 APPLICATION OF THE LAGRANGE MULTIPLIER In order to find the maximum, Eq. (4-9) must be differentiated individually with respect to each coordinate of the two vectors as well as λ; and each differential must be set equal to zero. Thus,

$$\frac{\partial u(X,Y)}{\partial x_i} = -\lambda \frac{\partial f(X,Y)}{\partial x_i} \qquad i = 1, 2, \ldots, m \tag{4-10}$$

and

$$\frac{\partial u(X,Y)}{\partial y_j} = -\lambda \frac{\partial f(X,Y)}{\partial y_j} \qquad j = a, b, \ldots, n \tag{4-11}$$

and

$$\frac{\partial u(X,Y)}{\partial \lambda} = f(X,Y) \tag{4-12}$$

By dividing Eq. (4-11) into Eq. (4-10) and pairs of Eqs. (4-10) and (4-11) into each other, one obtains

$$\frac{\partial u(X,Y)/\partial x_i}{\partial u(X,Y)/\partial y_j} = \frac{\partial f(X,Y)/\partial x_i}{\partial f(X,Y)/\partial y_j} \tag{4-13}$$

$$\frac{\partial u(X,Y)/\partial x_1}{\partial u(X,Y)/\partial x_2} = \frac{\partial f(X,Y)/\partial x_1}{\partial f(X,Y)/\partial x_2} \tag{4-14}$$

$$\frac{\partial u(X,Y)/\partial y_a}{\partial u(X,Y)/\partial y_b} = \frac{\partial f(X,Y)/\partial y_a}{\partial f(X,Y)/\partial y_b} \tag{4-15}$$

Since $f(X,Y)$ must equal zero, an increase in one element must be offset by a decrease in another. Therefore,

$$\frac{\partial f(X,Y)/\partial x_i}{\partial f(X,Y)/\partial y_j} = -\frac{\partial y_j}{\partial x_i} \tag{4-16}$$

$$\frac{\partial f(X,Y)/\partial x_1}{\partial f(X,Y)/\partial x_2} = -\frac{\partial x_2}{\partial x_1} \tag{4-17}$$

$$\frac{\partial f(X,Y)/\partial y_a}{\partial f(X,Y)/\partial y_b} = -\frac{\partial y_b}{\partial y_a} \tag{4-18}$$

By combining Eqs. (4-13) and (4-16), (4-14) and (4-17), and (4-15) and (4-18), one finally achieves

$$\frac{\partial u(X,Y)/\partial x_i}{\partial u(X,Y)/\partial y_j} = -\frac{\partial y_j}{\partial x_i} \tag{4-19}$$

$$\frac{\partial u(X,Y)/\partial x_1}{\partial u(X,Y)/\partial x_2} = -\frac{\partial x_2}{\partial x_1} \tag{4-20}$$

$$\frac{\partial u(X,Y)/\partial y_a}{\partial u(X,Y)/\partial y_b} = -\frac{\partial y_b}{\partial y_a} \tag{4-21}$$

4-11 THREE BASIC OPTIMALITY CONDITIONS Analysis of the meaning of the terms in Eq. (4-19) reveals $\partial u(X,Y)/\partial x_i$ to equal the marginal cost of input i, or MC_i, and $\partial u(X,Y)/\partial y_j$ to equal the marginal benefit from output j, or MB_j. The term on the right-hand side of the expression, $-\partial y_j/\partial x_i$, is what economists call the *marginal physical product*, or the additional output which can be produced per unit of increase in input. The negative sign results from the opposite nature of inputs and outputs. Thus

$$\frac{MC_i}{MB_j} = MPP_{ij} \qquad\qquad (4\text{-}22)$$

where MPP_{ij} is read as the marginal physical productivity of the ith input when devoted to the jth output.[1] Similar analysis of Eq. (4-20) reveals MC_1 and MC_2. The marginal rate of substitution was defined in Sec. 4-6 as the marginal rate at which quantities of the second input need to be substituted for a unit reduction in the first input while holding the level of production constant, $-\partial x_2/\partial x_1$. Thus

$$\frac{MC_1}{MC_2} = MRS_{21} \qquad\qquad (4\text{-}23)$$

Equation (4-21) contains MB_a, MB_b, and the marginal rate of transformation (Sec. 4-7), or the marginal rate at which production can be shifted from the second output to the first to effect a unit change in the first without changing the input. Thus

$$\frac{MB_a}{MB_b} = MRT_{ba} \qquad\qquad (4\text{-}24)$$

4-12 APPLICATION OF OPTIMALITY CONDITIONS The three equations of the last section may be used to answer the four questions fundamental to structuring production. The application may be illustrated by a water resources project which produces two outputs, flood control y_a and irrigation y_b, from two inputs, reservoir storage x_1 and channel improvement x_2.

The first fundamental question is: How should the inputs be combined to produce a given output? The answer is found in Eq. (4-23). The marginal cost of an input is its unit price. If unit price varies with amount purchased, the marginal price at the input actually used should be applied. Equation (4-23) says the inputs should be combined in such amounts that the ratio of their prices equals the marginal rate at which one input can be substituted for another with all other components of the production function constant. With the other inputs and outputs constant, and based on a typical production function, one may evaluate x_1 as a function of x_2 to obtain the data in Table 4-1 and the curve in Fig. 4-12. The curve is

---

[1] This notation is simplified from that previously used, which would be $MPP_{x_i v_j}$.

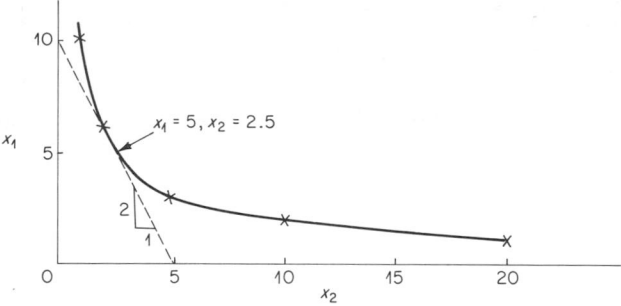

FIGURE 4-12 Optimum combination of inputs.

concave toward the origin because of an increasing inability to substitute a second input for the first as one approaches the point where the first is not used at all. Our rule says to substitute x_2 for x_1 until the marginal rate of substitution MRS of x_2 for x_1 equals the ratio of marginal costs MC. This would give the point $x_1 = 5$, $x_2 = 2.5$. The total-cost TC column in Table 4-1 and the price line in Fig. 4-12 show how this is also the point of minimum total cost.

The second fundamental question is: How should total production be divided among specific outputs? The answer is found in Eq. (4-24). The rule says that the outputs should be produced in such amounts that the ratio of their unit benefits equals the marginal rate at which production can be shifted from one output to another with all other inputs and outputs

TABLE 4-1 Optimum Rate of Substitution

x_1	x_2	MRS	TC	
10	1		60	
		0.25		
6	2		50	
		0.5		
4	3		50	$MC_1 = \$5$
		2		$MC_2 = \$10$
3	5		65	Optimum $MRS_{21} = \frac{5}{10} = 0.5$
		5		
2	10		110	
		10		
1	20		205	

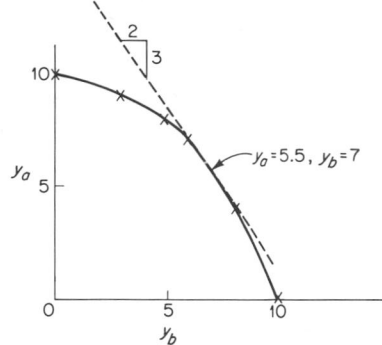

FIGURE 4-13   Optimum division of outputs.

held constant. For this condition, one may evaluate y_a as a function of y_b to obtain the data in Table 4-2 and the curve in Fig. 4-13. The curve is concave away from the origin because the first units of additional output can normally be produced at less marginal cost than later ones. Our rule says to substitute y_b for y_a until the marginal rate of transformation MRT of y_b for y_a equals the ratio of their marginal benefits MB. This corresponds to the point $y_a = 5.5$, $y_b = 7$. The total-benefit TB column in Table 4-2 and the income line in Fig. 4-13 show how this is also the point of maximum total benefit.

The third fundamental question is: How much of a specified input should be devoted to the production of a specified output? The answer is found in Eq. (4-22). The rule says that the input should be utilized in such amount that the ratio of marginal input cost to marginal output

TABLE 4-2   Optimum Rate of Transformation

y_a	y_b	MRT	TB	
10	0		20	
		3		
9	3		27	
		2		
8	5		31	$MB_a = \$2$
		1		$MB_b = \$3$
7	6		32	Optimum $MRT_{ba} = \frac{2}{3} = 0.67$
		0.67		
4	8		32	
		0.50		
0	10		30	

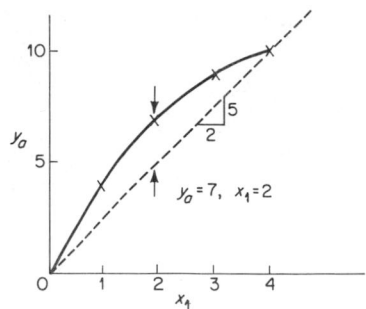

FIGURE 4-14   Optimum input to use in producing a specified output.

benefit equals the ratio of marginal physical output to marginal physical
input. For this condition, one may evaluate y_a as a function of x_1 to obtain
the data in Table 4-3 and the curve in Fig. 4-14. This is only one of four
possible curves of this type for our two-input two-output example, one
for each combination of output and input. Our rule says to increase the
amount of x_1 used in producing y_a until the marginal increase in y_a for
a unit of x_1 equals the ratio of their marginal unit values. This corresponds to the point $y_a = 7$, $x_1 = 2$. The net-benefit $B - C$ column in
Table 4-3 and the distance between the two lines in Fig. 4-14 show this to
be also the point of maximum excess of benefits over costs.

    The fourth fundamental question is: How large should the total
project be? The answer is found by shifting the approach demonstrated
by Fig. 4-14 from coordinate pairs to the total input and output vectors.
However, the analysis requires the selection and evaluation of trial vectors
as no straightforward solution of the type used in answering the first three
questions is possible. A trial output vector is selected. The first rule is

TABLE 4-3   Optimum Physical Product

x_1	y_a	MPP_{1a}	$B - C$
0	0		0
		4	
1	4		3
		3	
2	7		4
		2	
3	9		3
		1	
4	10		0

$MC_1 = 5$
$MB_a = 2$
Optimum $MPP_{1a} = 2.5$

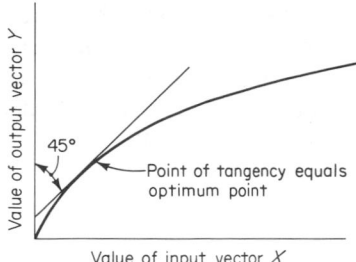

FIGURE 4-15 Selection of the optimum combination of input and output vectors.

applied to determine the optimum input vector for that output vector. The value of the output vector is determined as the sum of the products of the output coordinate magnitudes and the marginal benefits. The value of the input vector is determined as the sum of the products of the input coordinate magnitudes and the marginal costs. Theoretically, an infinite number of trial output vectors would produce points covering the entire area below and to the right of the curve in Fig. 4-15. Because efficient outputs have the maximum value for a given input value, they lie along the locus of points bounding the area on the upper left side. These are also points which meet the conditions of the second and third rules. The optimum input and output vectors are found by the same rule used to determine the optimum level of output in Fig. 4-8.

The complexity of design optimization can be appreciated when one realizes that Eqs. (4-22) to (4-24) only help establish whether a particular project design is in fact optimum. The development of a trial project design requires a long series of economy studies seeking the least-cost means of achieving the desired end, or what economists would call *defining the production function*. Project formulation is a trial-and-error process in which promising designs are tested to determine the resulting net benefits.

While the rules developed in the preceding sections are not even necessary for project optimality if the response surface peaks adjacent to one of the axes (Fig. 4-7) and while they are not in themselves able to guarantee project optimality (Sec. 4-5), neither of these limitations is likely to be encountered in water resources project design. A practical problem of more general consequence is likely to arise in applying optimality criteria where intangible values or outside constraints dictate the project design. Is there any advantage in applying any of the optimality criteria where all of them cannot be satisfied? Is it worthwhile to devote so much effort to optimizing water resources development while optimality criteria are ignored in virtually every other sector of public spending?

Lipsey and Lancaster have developed a "general theory of the second best" showing that improvement in one sector will not invariably produce an overall improvement.[1] Nevertheless, the greater probability is that projects designed more efficiently with respect to as many optimality criteria as can be applied will increase human welfare in the short run. As new techniques are developed and implemented in other kinds of public investment decisions, the chance for improvement is even greater in the long run.

Market Allocation under Pure Competition

The derived optimality conditions would be automatically achieved by a market economy under the ideal conditions of pure competition. This can be shown by analysis of production situations in the very short run, short run, and long run.

4-13 VERY SHORT RUN ANALYSIS In the very short run, the output has already been produced and its amount is fixed. Since no freedom is left to alter design and production decisions, none of the optimality criteria for governing such choices applies. The producer tries to sell at the best price available as long as one can be found in excess of the value of the output as scrap or in excess of the present worth of the net profit expected from storage for later sale. However, a price below the marginal production cost would direct that production be halted as soon as possible.

4-14 SHORT-RUN ANALYSIS In the short run, the firm is free to vary the level of production in response to market conditions. However, an individual firm does not have time to vary the capacity of its production facilities. Industry output can only vary within the capacity of existing firms.

The Firm A firm producing an output in relatively small quantities cannot affect the price by changing the supply and hence faces a horizontal demand curve (Fig. 4-16). The demand curve is the firm's marginal-revenue curve since the incremental revenue from each additional unit of output equals the unit price. Profits are a maximum at the output Y'

---

[1] Richard Lipsey and Kevin Lancaster, The General Theory of the Second Best, *Rev. Econ. Studies*, vol. 24 (December, 1956).

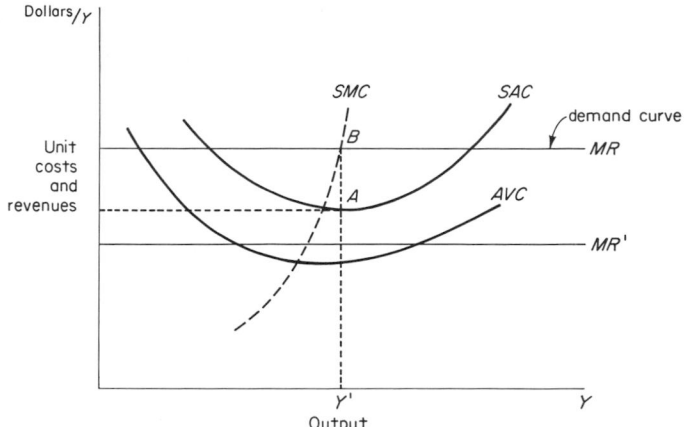

FIGURE 4-16   The firm's short-run unit-revenue and unit-cost curves

where $SMC = MR$. Here SMC is the short-run marginal cost, or the variable cost per marginal unit of production from a fixed plant, and MR is the marginal revenue.

If the market price (MR' in Fig. 4-16) is less than short-run average costs SAC at all possible levels of output, the firm will lose money. However, it should continue to operate at a loss as long as the market price exceeds the average variable costs AVC. This is because revenues exceed the cost of production and can be used to partially defray fixed costs which continue regardless of whether the plant shuts down or not.

The profit-maximizing firm should produce the output for which marginal cost equals market price ($MC = MR$) unless market price falls below the firm's average variable costs. In that event it should shut down. The firm's short-run supply curve is that part of the SMC curve which lies above the AVC curve.

The Industry   The price faced by the firm is determined by the composite supply and demand curves faced by the group of firms comprising the industry. The short-run industry-supply curve is the horizontal summation of the firms' short-run-supply curves as long as production input prices are not affected by the industry. If input prices are affected, firms' unit-cost curves will shift and cause some adjustment in the industry supply curve.

Figure 4-17 shows how prices are signaled by the industry to the

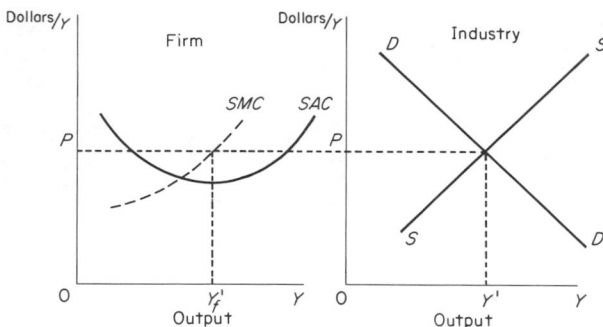

FIGURE 4-17   Short-run equilibrium for single firm and industry

firm. The horizontal axis for the industry is greatly compressed since the output of the firm is very small compared with the output for the industry as a whole. The price axes are the same. Suppose we have the industry demand *DD*, which is the horizontal summation of the consumer-demand curves, and the industry supply *SS*, which is the horizontal summation of the firms' supply curves. The short-run equilibrium market price *P* is established by the interaction of *DD* and *SS*. This price becomes the horizontal demand curve for the firm because it can sell as much as it

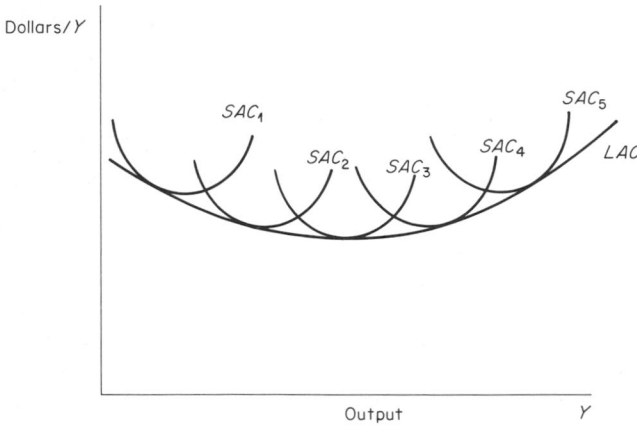

FIGURE 4-18   Long-run average-cost curves.

can make without affecting P. All firms will produce at $SMC = MR = P$, and together their outputs at equilibrium will add up to Y'.

4-15 LONG-RUN ANALYSIS   In the long run, no costs are fixed because the firm can modify its production facilities in whatever way is advantageous. A plant designed to produce any fixed amount of output has a short-run average-cost curve. The long-run average-cost LAC curve is the envelope of the short-run average-cost curves for varying scales of plant (Fig. 4-18).

The optimum scale of plant is the most efficient of all possible plant sizes. It is the one whose SAC curve establishes the minimum-cost point of the LAC curve as shown in Fig. 4-19. The SMC and LMC curves must also pass through this point as they must intersect average-cost curves at their low point. The long-run profit-maximizing rule is for a firm to produce the output for which $LMC = LAC = SAC = SMC$. Each firm must operate an optimum scale of plant at the optimum rate of output. Free entry and exit of firms will restrict production to those firms which have their average-cost curves tangent to the demand line DD. Under pure competition, consumers get products at prices equal to long-run average costs.

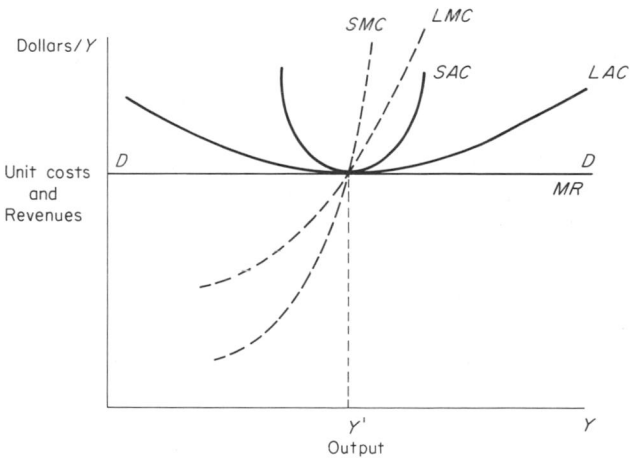

FIGURE 4-19   Long-run cost curves and determination of optimum scale of plant and output.

Applications

4-16 USE OF SUPPLY AND DEMAND CURVES IN PROJECT EVALUATION Application of the principles developed in this chapter to the economic evaluation of engineering projects requires analysis of the demand for project output and of the cost of project production. Long-run values should be used to optimize design in project planning, and short-run values should be used to optimize operation of an existing facility. The demand may be graphically depicted by a marginal-benefit curve, and the supply may be depicted by a marginal-cost curve. Potential-output uses vary greatly in value. Whenever all available output is devoted to the most beneficial use available, marginal benefit monotonically decreases with increasing output. Each increment of output is put to a lower-value use than the previous increment as the higher-value uses are satisfied. Expressed mathematically,

$$MB = f_1(Y) \tag{4-25}$$

or marginal benefit is functionally related to the level of output Y.

The marginal revenue which could be realized from sale of additional output would be less than the marginal benefit. Revenue depends on the sale price, while benefit is received through use and is thus determined by the nature of the use. When production increases, the total benefit is increased by the area added under the marginal-benefit curve. The price is reduced by the larger supply. The lower price inflicts a revenue loss which drops the marginal-revenue curve below the marginal-benefit curve. For example, with an increase in output from di to de (Fig. 4-20), benefits would increase from $adih$ to $adec$, a net gain of $hiec$. Revenues would increase from $gdih$ to $bdec$, an increase of $miec$ partially offset by a decrease of $gbmh$. The gain in revenue is thus less than the gain in benefit.

The functional relationship between the marginal-revenue curve and the marginal-benefit curve may be developed by use of Fig. 4-21. An incremental increase in production would decrease revenue from the items previously produced by area 1, or $Y \Delta Y f_1'(Y)$. The revenue from newly produced items is represented by area 2, or $\Delta Y f_1(Y)$. The total revenue difference resulting from change of output ΔY is the sum of the two areas, or

$$\Delta R = \Delta Y f_1(Y) + Y \Delta Y f_1'(Y) \tag{4-26}$$

Marginal revenue is determined by decreasing ΔY to differential size to get

$$MR = \frac{dR}{dY} = f_1(Y) + Y f_1'(Y) \tag{4-27}$$

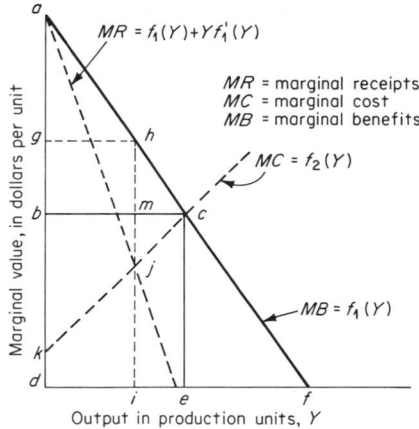

	Private monopoly	Public works projects
Goal	Maximize net receipts	Maximize net benefits
Optimum point	*j*, MR = MC	*c*, MB = MC
At optimum point: gross receipts	*gdih*	*bdec*
Production	*di*	*de*
Price	*hi*	*ce*
Production cost	*kdij*	*kdec*
Net receipts (producer's surplus)	*gkjh* >	*bkc*
Gross benefits	*adih*	*adec*
Net benefits	*akjh* <	*akc*
Consumer's surplus	*agh*	*abc*

FIGURE *4-20*   Definition of terms in benefit computations.

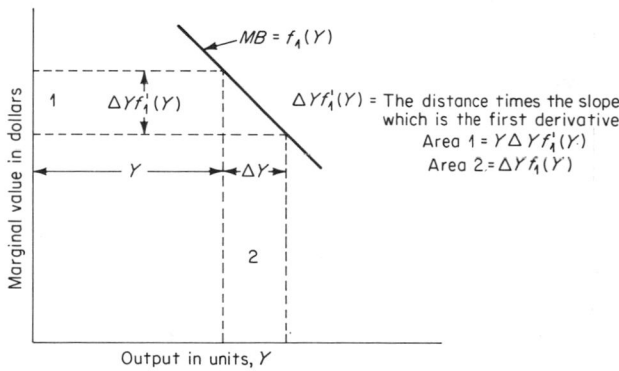

FIGURE *4-21*   Effect of incremental change in output on marginal revenue.

The first term is defined by Eq. (4-25) as the marginal benefit, and the second term is an added quantity. Whenever the demand curve slopes downward to the right, its slope $f'_1(Y)$ and thus the second term are negative. Thus, the marginal-revenue curve plots, beneath the marginal-benefit curve, an amount equal to the product of the output and the slope of the marginal-benefit curve. The marginal cost is also some function of the level of output Y:

$$MC = f_2(Y) \qquad\qquad (4\text{-}28)$$

The balance of the notation in Fig. 4-20 serves to define the benefit and cost terms used in project analysis and to illustrate the difference which would result between planning by a private monopoly seeking to maximize revenues and planning by a public agency seeking to maximize benefits. The optimum project for the monopoly would be a point j where marginal revenue equals marginal cost. The optimum project for the public agency would be at point c where marginal benefit equals marginal cost. At each optimum point, the optimum production, gross receipts, production cost, net receipts, producer's surplus, gross benefits, net benefits, and consumer's surplus are defined as shown.

4-17   MARKET ALLOCATION UNDER PURE MONOPOLY   Pure monopoly is the market situation where a firm produces the entire supply of an output for which there are no good substitutes, a rare situation because most outputs have substitutes. The monopolist has the same cost curves as the firm in pure competition but faces the entire market-demand curve. His actions affect price as well as the economic equilibrium achieved in the short run as well as the long run.

Short Run   The short-run curves are shown in Fig. 4-22. As illustrated by Fig. 4-20, marginal revenue is less than price. The monopolist will produce where $SMC = MR$ to maximize profits. He will be able to sell at a price exceeding his marginal cost. He will produce less than the optimum output for economic efficiency achieved automatically under pure competition.

Long Run   In the long run, the monopolist selects his scale of plant according to the relationship between the market-demand curve and his long-run average-cost curve. The optimum scale of plant (at the minimum of the LAC curve) will be built only if by chance the marginal-revenue curve cuts the minimum of the LAC curve as shown in Fig. 4-23. The monopolist will follow the profit-maximizing rule of $LMC = MR$. Since $SMC = LMC = MR = SAC = LAC$ at output Y', the firm is in both

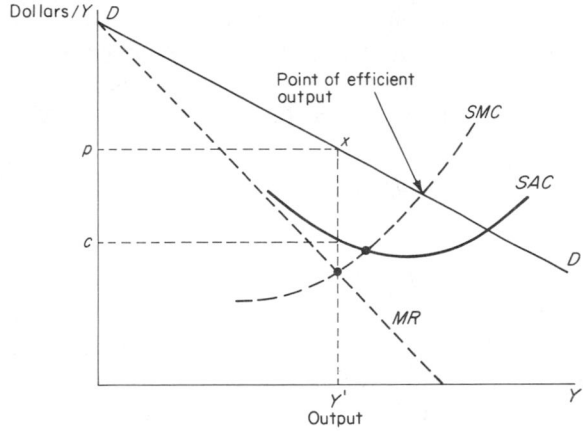

FIGURE 4-22   Unit curves for pure monopoly.

short-run and long-run equilibrium. The monopolist's profit is $(p - c)Y'$. He operates an optimum scale of plant at an optimum rate of output.

However, if the market is so large that the monopolist's marginal-revenue curve cuts the LAC curve to the right of its minimum point, the monopolist will build a larger-than-optimum scale of plant and operate

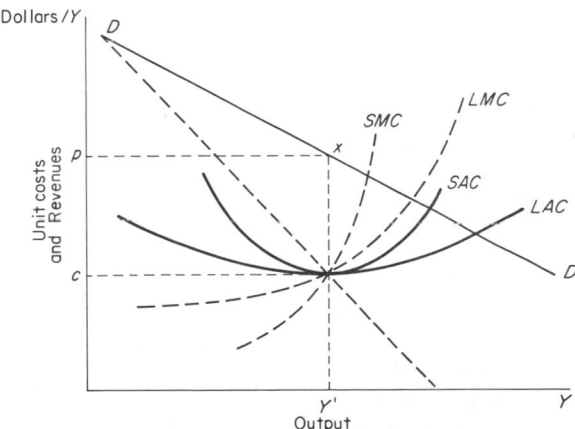

FIGURE 4-23   Monopoly situation for optimum scale of plant.

at a greater-than-optimum rate of output. Obversely, if the market is so small that the marginal-revenue curve cuts the *LAC* curve to the left of its minimum point, the monopolist will build a less-than-optimum scale of plant and operate at a less-than-optimum rate of output.

Effects of Monopoly   As was previously illustrated by Fig. 4-20, a monopoly existing in an industry where pure competition would be possible produces less output at higher prices than would be the case under pure competition. For the purely competitive firm operating in the long run, profits become zero because of free entry of new firms. However, with entry blocked, a monopolist can enjoy long-run profits. Therefore, consumers pay more for the good than is necessary to induce resources to stay in the industry. This means that resources that could be used to expand output of the desired good are being used elsewhere in lower-valued uses.

It is also possible in an industry where the market is limited relative to the optimum scale of plant and rate of output for monopoly to result in lower costs per unit than under pure competition. An example would be a large thermoelectric plant in a small country. The unit cost of electricity produced by a monopoly may be considerably less than that for a number of firms producing with less than optimum scales of plant and rates of output.

Either way, monopoly distorts the efficiency equilibrium achieved automatically under pure competition to the degree the monopolist does not operate an optimum scale of plant at the optimum rate of output. A partial monopoly or oligopoly or any other departure from pure competition will produce some distortion from efficiency conditions. Government market regulation is often theoretically justified with the goal of minimizing these distortions.

REFERENCES

Baumol, William J.: "Economic Theory and Operations Analysis" (Englewood Cliffs, N.J.: Prentice-Hall, Inc., 1961).

———: "Welfare Economics and the Theory of the State," 2d ed. (Cambridge, Mass.: Harvard University Press, 1967).

Krutilla, John V., and Otto Eckstein: "Multiple Purpose River Development: Studies in Applied Economic Analysis" (Baltimore: The Johns Hopkins Press, 1958).

Leftwich, Richard H.: "The Price System and Resource Allocation" (New York: Holt, Rinehart and Winston, Inc., 1962).

Lipsey, Richard, and Kevin Lancaster: The General Theory of the Second Best, *Rev. Econ. Studies*, vol. 24 (December, 1956).

Maass, Arthur, et al.: "Design of Water-resource Systems" (Cambridge, Mass.: Harvard University Press, 1962), pp. 88–117.

Samuelson, Paul A.: "Economics: An Introductory Analysis," 5th ed. (New York: McGraw-Hill Book Company, 1962).

PROBLEMS

4-1 The total cost of producing a given output varies with output in the manner indicated in the following table:

Total cost	Output	Total cost	Output
0	0	385	50
200	10	410	60
300	20	460	70
350	30	560	80
375	40	760	90

a Plot the total-cost curve.

b Plot the average-cost curve.

c Plot the marginal-cost curve.

d If under conditions of pure competition the price of the good is 5, what output will the firm produce in the short run?

e What will be the net profit or loss at this price?

f At what price will the firm just break even?

4-2 For a particular production enterprise, marginal benefits can be related to output by the equation $B + Y = 20$. Marginal costs can be related to output by the equation $C - 2 + 1.5Y$. If the output were produced in a public works project, what would be the:

a Price

b Quantity of output produced

c Gross receipts

d Production cost

e Net receipts (producer's surplus)

f Gross benefits

g Net benefits

h Consumer's surplus

If the output were produced by a private monopoly, what would be the values of each of the above eight items?

4-3 The marginal cost of water supply is expressed by the equation $5P + 5Q = 30$, where P is the cost and Q is the amount produced. The price received for water is expressed by the equation $3P + 6Q = 30$.

a How much water would a private monopoly produce?

b What is the cost of producing the amount of water in part a?

c How much revenue would result from selling this much water?

d How much water would a public works project produce?

e What is the cost of producing the amount of water in part *d*?

f How much revenue would result from selling this much water?

4-4 The demand curve for a particular good is expressed by the equation $2P + 3Y = 15$, where P is the price and Y is the quantity of the good. The curve for another good is expressed by the equation $4P + 3Z = 12$.

a At what price could two units of the first good be sold?

b What is the elasticity of this good at this price?

c At what price is the elasticity of this good equal to 1?

d Plot the aggregate-demand curve for the two goods if they are both market goods.

e Plot the aggregate-demand curve for the two goods if they are both collective goods (Sec. 5-9).

4-5 The demand curve for gadgets is expressed by the equation $2P + 5G = 20$. The number of G available for sale is 1.5.

a What will the price be?

b What will the total revenue be?

c What will the consumer's surplus be?

d What will the aggregate value in use be?

4-6 Use a Lagrange multiplier to find the maximum value of $y = 10xw - 4w^2$ subject to the constraint $x + w = 15$. What would the maximum value be were the constraint $x + w = 16$?

4-7 Gambies are used in the production of whoozits. A factory can sell a whoozit for $10 and buy a gamby for $4. The number of whoozits produced can be increased by using more gambies as follows:

Whoozits:	0	10	20	30	40	50	60	70	80
Gambies:	0	2	4	8	16	32	64	128	256

a What should be the marginal physical product of gambies in producing whoozits? (Fractional answers are legal, and graphical solution is quicker and more accurate for this and the two following problems.)

b How many whoozits should the factory produce?

c How many gambies should be used in their production?

d What will the profit be?

4-8 Xyphos are also used in the production of whoozits. The factory can buy a xypho for $2. The relationship between gambies and xyphos in producing a fixed number of whoozits is as follows:

Xyphos:	15	10	6	3	1
Gambies:	1	3	6	10	15

a What should be the marginal rate of substitution of gambies for xyphos?

b How many gambies should be used?

c How many xyphos should be used?

d What is the total cost of gambies and xyphos used in production?

4-9 Gambies and xyphos can be used to produce whidgits as well as whoozits. Whidgits can be sold for \$6. The relationship between the number of whidgits and the number of whoozits which can be produced from a fixed input is as follows:

Whidgits:	20	19	17	14	10	5	0
Whoozits:	0	5	9	12	14	16	17

a What should be the marginal rate of transformation of whoozits for whidgits?

b How many whoozits should be produced?

c How many whidgits should be produced?

d What is the total revenue from sales of whoozits and whidgits?

4-10 The production function for a two-input two-output process is $Y_a{}^2 + Y_b{}^3 = X_1{}^{1/2} X_2{}^{1/3}$.

a Determine the optimum values for both inputs and both outputs if $MB_a = MB_b = MC_1 = MC_2 = 1$.

b Determine the optimum values for both inputs and both outputs if $MB_a = MB_b = 10$ and $MC_1 = MC_2 = 1$.

CHAPTER FIVE

WELFARE ECONOMICS

Economic Analysis and Social Objectives

5-1   THE ROLE OF WELFARE ECONOMICS   Welfare economics is the science of determining how available resources may be best used to promote human welfare. The study is not entered with bias toward any specific social legislation, proposal for government ownership, or other welfare state program which might be proposed to solve specific social problems. Welfare economics seeks rather to develop better procedures (without prejudice toward either the public or the private sector) for allocating the total resource base (labor, capital, land, etc.) among potential uses and users to meet individual and group needs. Individuals need material resources to improve their economic well-being, a healthy environment to maintain their physical well-being, and psychologically satisfying experiences to maintain their mental well-being. Furthermore, man is a social being. He is affected as he observes the welfare of others. Human needs are met as individuals become better satisfied with their own lives and what they see of the lives of their neighbors.

Welfare economics is *normative* or *prescriptive* in character in the sense that it seeks the resource allocation best achieving consensus values or satisfaction of needs fulfilled. However, it is not prescriptive in the sense of recommending what these values should be. Welfare economics can be contrasted with *positive* or *descriptive* economics, which is concerned with understanding the functioning of economic systems. Descriptive economics provides the tools by which the consequence of alternative courses of action may be predicted. Welfare economics uses these predictions to decide the relative merit of the alternative. It determines and aggregates the values individuals hold, to provide counsel on finding the course of action best promoting overall welfare.

5-2 THE SOCIAL WELFARE FUNCTION Resource development seeks to meet human needs. Some needs are readily met through water resources development. Relief from a periodic flood damage bill frees individuals to concentrate on other economic needs. Waste-water treatment and mosquito control meet man's physical need for improved health. Increased recreation opportunity may provide just the experience required to fulfill the need for mental relaxation. A project may provide jobs for the unemployed and thereby satisfy a group need for a more healthy community. Other kinds of needs cannot be satisfied through water resources development. The satisfactions realized through listening to good music or an inspiring sermon are not achieved through better resources management.

As a planning ideal, water resources development must be evaluated in terms of consequent effects (good and bad) on all human needs. As a practical matter, only certain needs can be satisfied through water-related projects. Other needs might be satisfied through water resources development but can be satisfied at less cost in some other way. Failure to incorporate goals related to either of these two types of needs into water resources planning models is not to say such needs are not worthwhile. The point is that many needs can only or at least can better be met by other means.

The goal of human activity is to meet human needs. Each specific need presents a specific goal. The ideal resource allocation would be achieved by the public policy maximizing a unanimously accepted index of total human welfare. Such an index would be computed by a mathematical formula called a *social welfare function* and incorporating all human goals. For example,

$$I = a_1 G_1 + a_2 G_2 + \cdots + a_n G_n \qquad \sum_{i=1}^{n} a_i = 1.0 \qquad (5\text{-}1)$$

The index I must be a scalar value to rank alternatives unambiguously. The units used to measure progress toward each goal G and the weighting factors a must be defined so that society will become progressively more happy and contented with increasing value of I. Each goal must be defined in units permitting quantitative expression of the degree of fulfillment achieved by alternative proposals. Each weighting factor must indicate the relative influence of the goal in determining human happiness. Construction of a social welfare function requires a series of value judgments. If the result is not unanimously accepted, its application will not settle any controversy among conflicting values.

5-3   FIRST-ORDER (SOCIAL) EFFICIENCY   In applying Eq. (5-1) to select the best alternatives, one would evaluate the contribution of implementing each alternative toward accomplishing each goal and substitute the resulting values in the social welfare function to calculate I. Values of G for a given alternative may be either positive or negative. Project selection may then be based on the procedures developed previously by using I in place of present worth in the present-worth discounting technique (Sec. 2-9) or by using Eq. (5-1) as the objective function in optimality studies (Sec. 4-3).

However, one need only review the social goals related to water resource development listed below and the diversity of opinion on their relative desirability to realize that an ideal social welfare function will never be available to guide planning decisions.

1   *Maximum national income.* People with higher incomes have more resources for providing themselves with a better life. The model of pure competition achieves economic efficiency in that it maximizes national income. However, none can deny that there are many contented poor and miserable rich. Money is far from the total answer to human happiness. What is?

2   *Ideal income distribution.* Collective happiness is not maximized if the maximum national income is achieved by giving the national wealth to an elite group while everyone else lives in abject poverty. A guaranteed equal income for everyone would weaken the incentives of the ambitious. How should income be distributed?

3   *Environmental quality.*[1] Everyone has scenic spots, historical landmarks, and wildlife forms which he would like to see preserved and is disturbed by destructive pollution. Society agrees with respect to Yosemite Valley, Independence Hall, redwood trees, or obnoxious air and water pollution. But all progress would be halted by the preservation of every childhood home that brings back nostalgic memories. Where can the line be drawn?

4   *Institutional stability.* Continuing rapid social change promotes uncertainty and insecurity. A completely static society departs progressively further from achieving social justice with changing times. What is the optimum rate of change?

[1]   Maynard M. Hufschmidt, Environmental Aspects of River Basin Planning, *Proc. ASCE*, vol. 93, no. HY 6 (November, 1967), pp. 323–352.

5   *Public health.* Freedom from disease and accidental injury and the preservation of life involve values that transcend expression in income units. A wealthy man may spend all he has and go into debt to preserve his life or regain his health. Is public health a goal to be preserved at all economic cost? Most would agree that society as a whole is not willing to live in poverty to preserve good health. Accidental death and injury would be substantially reduced by outlawing the automobile, but people would be unwilling to bear the inconvenience. Public health does not completely override all other considerations. How much should be spent to preserve health and life?

6   *Regional development.* A more even geographical distribution of economic development reduces congestion in more highly developed areas, presents the challenge of making wasteland productive, and aids national defense. It improves the income and morale of isolated areas, or even nations, which might otherwise be bypassed by economic growth. Should such areas be developed at a net sacrifice in total income?

If all of the above questions could be resolved, the planner could use the resulting social welfare function to devote available resources to endeavors most efficiently contributing to human welfare. Social, or first-order, efficiency would be achieved. But because no one can precisely measure degrees of accomplishment of all social objectives nor assign relative weights to alternative goals, a universal social welfare function can never be developed for general use. The best that can be hoped for is an approximate, or second-order approach.

5-4   THE QUESTION OF SOVEREIGNTY   The first step in developing an approximate approach must be resolution of the question of sovereignty. Supporters of individual sovereignty say that each man is and should be the best judge of his own best interest. A man should have the right to spend his money, order his activities, and divide his time according to his own desires. The level of human aspiration will increase indefinitely, always remaining just a little higher than the means for fulfillment can provide.[1] No matter what his income, man's wants can never be entirely satisfied, a condition of perpetual scarcity. Certain wants are expressed by the exercise of consumer sovereignty in the marketplace. Others are expressed by the exercise of individual sovereignty in the voting booth. The market and the ballot box aggregate individual wants to determine collective need according to the prevailing values of the community.

[1]   Support for this position is found in Richard S. Weckstein, Welfare Criteria and Changing Tastes, *Am. Econ. Rev.*, vol. 52 (March, 1962).

As long as adequate safeguards are available to make sure that the activities of one man do not infringe on the rights of others, social welfare is maximized by maximizing the sum of the satisfaction brought to each individual.

The second school of thought, which has come to be called *abundancy economics*, attacks the question, "What should man want?" instead of being satisfied with determining prevailing community values.[1] It substitutes value judgments on general welfare by a planning elite for empirical measurement of what the people themselves prefer. It argues that as men become more wealthy, all their reasonable wants are satisfied and they dissipate their excess money. It scorns the idea that a free market dependent on consumer sovereignty can maximize human welfare, with the illustration that $1 million used in cancer research must inherently be more valuable to society than $1 million spent on chewing gum. The rich are spending their money on trivial frivolities while great social needs go begging. It believes market deficiencies to be so vast that no allocation made by the market system can have normative significance. Market theory based on scarcity is not relevant when all reasonable demands for market goods are more than abundantly satisfied. One advocate of this position has stated:

> The assumptions . . . about the efficiency of the private sector achieved through free competition are so removed from reality that I fail completely to understand why they (the advocates of the first position) were led to advance, seriously, criticisms of water-resource development policy built upon such a flimsy foundation.[2]

However, instead of offering a specific social welfare function, this school of thought usually proposes use of political or hierarchical control without defining precise criteria.

Planning and resource allocation through the political process requires people to express their preferences for social action by the ballot box rather than by money votes. The method is based on the assumptions that voting alternatives can be structured in a manner permitting meaningful planning choices, that the voters will make decisions in harmony with a consistent value system, and that voters will base their decisions on overall social welfare rather than their own self-interest. The method is beset with difficulties. Voting motivated by self-interest can produce im-

[1] John Kenneth Galbraith, "The Affluent Society" (Boston: Houghton Mifflin Company, 1958).
[2] Morris E. Garnsey, Welfare Economic and Resource Development, "Western Resource Conference Land and Water Planning for Economic Growth, 1961" (Boulder: University of Colorado Press, 1962), p. 197.

provement only through a more equitable distribution of voting power.[1] Some have hypothesized that voting is based on higher motives than market purchases,[2] but there is no conclusive evidence one way or the other. The voter is faced with broad alternatives, each mixing features which he likes with those he dislikes. The ballot box offers no way to express depth of feeling and thus permits a minority who feel intensely on an issue to be outvoted by a majority who really do not care very much. The outcome of the election can be influenced by the structuring of the alternatives.[3] Political decision making may be used to reach major policy decisions, but is impractical for making the countless little decisions required in resource allocation.

Those who believe man cannot know his own best interest or cannot express it in either the marketplace or the ballot box advocate hierarchal or administrative planning. The leadership should determine the best interest of the people, and experts should organize society in order to achieve that best interest. However, this method has difficulties too. Freedom is lost as leadership decides what is good for the people and molds public opinion to the desired ends. Experts can never be entirely objective or completely free from the same jealousies, ambitions, and desires which influence the thinking of the rest of mankind. The cost of maintaining the organization required to analyze all the available social alternatives and guide the nation in the desired direction is very great. So is the danger of disastrous decisions caused by errors or oversights in using a planning machinery with no self-correcting features. But overwhelming all the other difficulties is the shear impossibility of building the required all-encompassing mathematical model. It is well said:

> Indeed, the best medicine for well meaning central planners is perhaps a stiff dose of down-to-earth operations research on complex problems of the federal government; such an experience would lay bare, more vividly than does meditation alone, the awesome difficulties that would be encountered (and the grim mistakes and concentration of power that would surely occur) in detailed central direction of the economy.[4]

Once the planner overcomes his arrogance enough to realize that the

---

[1] James M. Buchanan, Politics, Policy, and the Pigovian Margins, *Economics*, vol. 29 (February, 1962), p. 17.

[2] Stephen A. Marglin, Economic Factors Affecting System Design, in Arthur Maass et al., "Design of Water-resource Systems" (Cambridge, Mass.: Harvard University Press, 1962), p. 197 ff.
Richard A. Musgrave, "The Theory of Public Finance" (New York: McGraw-Hill Book Company, 1959), p. 87 ff.

[3] Duncan Black, On the Rationale of Group Decision Making, *J. Political Econ.*, vol. 56 (February, 1958), p. 23.

[4] Roland N. McKean, "Efficiency in Government through Systems Analysis" (New York: John Wiley & Sons, Inc., 1958), p. 8.

hierarchical approach to resource allocation is incapable of producing socially acceptable and practically workable results, he has little alternative but to accept individual sovereignty, seek the answer to the question, "What does man want?" and plan to fulfill his desires. The individual may not know his own best interest in an absolute sense, but he probably knows it better than anyone else.

5-5   THE QUESTION OF GOALS   Acceptance of individual sovereignty still leaves the problem of aggregating individual choices into a social welfare function. Market processes provide the most effective mechanism of aggregating the countless individual choices reflecting varying degrees of preference and affecting small groups of people. If the market is perfectly competitive, it will allocate resources so as to maximize national income. Of course, actual markets are not perfect. Market failures require administrative agencies to evaluate their consequences, act to remedy resulting allocation deficiencies, and determine normative shadow prices for use in planning. Specific problems are described in subsequent sections on public wants (Sec. 5-9), external effects (Sec. 5-10), and natural monopoly (Sec. 5-11).

However, optimum resource allocation is influenced as individuals seek goals other than maximization of income. Each alternative needs to be evaluated to determine its consequences for each such goal. The evaluations consider what have traditionally been called intangible values in engineering economy studies (Sec. 1-6). Effects concerning conflicting goals must be tabulated and incorporated into the decision-making process. However, the final resolution should, according to the principle of individual sovereignty, be based on some community consensus and not on the necessarily arbitrary decision of a planning elite. Where market processes cannot work, political choices provide the next best method for defining the relative importance people attach to various goals. For ex-

TABLE 5-1   Comparing Alternatives Achieving Multiple Goals

Alternative goal	Economic benefits	Regional income	Environmental quality*
A	$1,000	$400	50
B	900	400	75
C	900	600	50

* Measured in a unit increasing with a higher-quality environment.

ample, politically determined income tax schedules provide a starting point for establishing the relative importance of income redistribution (Sec. 5-13).

Two approaches are available for mechanically handling multiple goals. One is to predetermine the weighting factors [Eq. (5-1)] and use the resulting social welfare function in systematically comparing alternatives. The second approach is to develop a decision matrix based on alternatives as rows and goals as columns. For example, a particular study may produce the information shown in Table 5-1. With this information at hand, one would have to decide whether an extra 25 units of environmental quality are worth achieving at a sacrifice of $100 in economic benefits. He would have to decide whether $200 of additional benefits to the region were worth a $100 loss in national income. Through answering a series of such questions and trying various design modifications, the planner could eventually produce an optimum or at least an acceptable design. The alternative finally selected from the decision matrix will imply a full set of weighting factors which can be calculated from observed marginal trade-offs.

Several difficulties in designing to achieve multiple objectives are pinpointed by Table 5-1. It is very difficult to express achievement of certain goals (environmental quality, for example) in numerical units. Furthermore, the best project for achieving one goal is seldom the best for achieving other goals. One cannot escape the value judgments required in the trade-offs necessary to resolve conflicting goals. Therefore, an explicit statement of the required value trade-offs so that they can be publicly discussed is one of the major advantages of the matrix approach.

5-6   BASIC OPTIMALITY CRITERIA[1]   The early contributions to welfare economics were based on the premise of individual sovereignty with each individual subjectively evaluating his own goals to maximize his welfare. The first criterion of welfare economics, known as the *Pareto criterion* after the Italian Vilfredo Pareto, who about 1899 first proposed it, is:

> Any change which harms no one and which makes some people better off (in their own estimation) must be considered to be an improvement.[2]

By including the words "in their own estimation," individual sovereignty is explicitly accepted. In order to avoid the severe restriction of being

[1]   For discussion in greater detail, see William J. Baumol, "Economic Theory and Operations Analysis" (Englewood Cliffs, N.J.: Prentice-Hall, Inc., 1961), pp. 262–275.
[2]   As quoted in *ibid.*, p. 267.

unable to make a choice which harms anyone at all, Kaldor proposed the more widely applicable criterion:

> A change is an improvement if those who gain evaluate their gains at a higher figure than the value which the losers set upon their losses.[1]

From the point of view of the general economic welfare, it is irrelevant whether the losers are actually compensated by the gainers. Such an exchange would represent a transfer of money among individuals and not a net increase in national welfare. The exchange represents an income redistribution and must be evaluated with respect to that goal.

5-7   SECOND-ORDER (ECONOMIC) EFFICIENCY   If one uses income as the sole index of individual and social welfare, $I = G$ [Eq. (5-1)], where $G = B - C$. The resulting approximation says social welfare improves as the aggregate national income increases. The optimum project is the one most effective in increasing national income. The criterion for resource allocation is economic efficiency.

The goal of maximizing national income (net benefits) was used in Chap. 4 to derive the conditions characteristic of the optimum production process. Later in the chapter, a review of the pure-competition model showed that an ideal market would automatically achieve these optimum conditions. At this point, we can also show that under the approximation of economic efficiency the same set of rules also satisfies the Kaldor criterion.[2]

RULE 1   *The Optimum Allocation of Goods.* Each consumer maximizes his satisfaction by ordering his consumption so that the marginal rate of substitution between any two goods is equal to the ratio of their prices. Each pair of consumers must have the same marginal rate of substitution or a trade of goods would effect a mutual gain. According to Kaldor's criterion, an improvement would have been registered. An improvement would mean the initial conditions were not optimum in that they did not maximize collective welfare. Pure competition achieves equal marginal rates of substitution by making the price of any good constant throughout the economy and hence making all price ratios uniform.

RULE 2   *The Optimum Degree of Specialization.* Each firm maximizes its profit by making its marginal rate of transformation between any two outputs produced equal to the ratio of their prices. Each firm must have

[1]   As quoted in *ibid.*, p. 269.
[2]   For detailed derivations, see Syed F. Hasan, "Introduction to Welfare Economics" (New York: Asia Publishing House, 1963), chap. 4.

the same marginal rate of transformation to keep a trade of outputs from effecting a mutual gain. Pure competition achieves this goal by making the price ratio between any two outputs constant throughout the economy.

RULE 3   *The Optimum Relationship between Input and Output.* Each firm maximizes its profit by equating the marginal physical product of input in producing output with the ratio of their prices. If this ratio were not constant for any given input-output pair within the economy, a given input shifted to a firm having a higher ratio would achieve a net social gain. The optimal condition of maximum welfare could not have initially existed. Pure competition also satisfies this rule by achieving uniform price ratios.

RULE 4   *The Optimum Allocation of Inputs.* Each firm maximizes its profit by making its marginal rate of substitution between any two inputs used in production equal to the ratio of their prices. Ratio variation among industries would mean trade could improve overall welfare, and pure competition would maintain a uniform ratio.

RULE 5   *The Optimum Direction of Production.* Overall welfare is maximized if the marginal rate of transformation in the production process between any two outputs is the same as the marginal rate of substitution between the same two goods on the part of the consumers. Otherwise, welfare would be increased by shifting production to goods placed in relatively higher value by consumers. The uniform prices of pure competition would also achieve this goal.

RULE 6   *The Optimum Allocation of an Individual's Time.* Optimum welfare also requires that the marginal rate of substitution between leisure and wages for each person must be the same as the marginal physical product between the work done and the resulting output for each firm. An individual maximizes his satisfaction if he equates his marginal rate of substitution between money and leisure with the wage rate he receives for labor. Similarly, a firm maximizes its profits if it equates its marginal physical product between a unit of labor and a unit of output with the ratio of their prices. Under pure competition, all firms sell the identical output for the same price, and all firms must pay the same wage rates for all workers with the same skills.

RULE 7   *The Optimum Allocation of Assets over Time.* An individual maximizes satisfaction by equating his marginal rate of substitution between present consumption and future consumption with the rate of interest he can earn in the market. In the same way a firm equates its marginal rate of substitution between present and future assets with the rate of interest it must pay for borrowed funds. Pure competition equates these two marginal values by making the lending rate equal the borrowing rate.

Conclusions   The achievement of the optimum allocation of goods according to the Kaldor criterion by the purely competitive model means that under ideal conditions the market automatically achieves economic efficiency. Government economic planning could not improve the efficiency of an ideal economy. The ideal market provides the needed community consensus on resolving conflicting economic preference (Sec. 5-5) and thus a basic framework for planning. Project evaluation can begin by determining marketplace values for benefits and costs. However, such values cannot be used indiscriminately. Adjustments are needed for market imperfections. Adjustments are needed to consider other goals. Each is discussed below.

Adjustments Required by Imperfect Markets

A primary role of government in a free economy is to compensate for failures of real markets to organize production as efficiently as the purely competitive model. Such failures are most frequently caused by limitations on the ability of the market to respond to certain types of demand, the effects of market transactions on third parties, and the possibility of creating a natural monopoly by economies of scale.

5-8   ADJUSTMENT PROCEDURE   The complexity of the adjustment analysis required to correct market prices to normative ones for use in project evaluation depends on the degree of market distortion. A partial equilibrium analysis can be used where it is only necessary to adjust a few values inadequately handled by the market. Price corrections and project input and output are assumed to be too small to produce major market disruptions. For example, a typical project would not be large enough to use so much steel as to upset steel prices and thus the production function of other steel users throughout the country. Where major distortions or disruptions exist, a general equilibrium analysis is needed to evaluate the economic ripples. Such an analysis is usually based on an input-output model (Sec. 9-3). It is more likely to be required in a small country or a developing economy.

In conclusion, the following steps can be used to obtain the normative value of an input or output:

1   Determine the market price.
2   Determine whether one of the conditions described below (Secs. 5-9 to 5-11) exists. If so, adjust the price as required.

3 Determine the extent of the effect the project is likely to have on market transactions throughout the economy. If the effect is negligible, adjusted prices can be used directly. If the effect is confined to a few items' changing price, the value for project analysis can be approximated as the mean of the before and after prices as estimated from supply and demand curves. If the project will produce major economic disruptions, general equilibrium analysis is required to estimate subsequent prices.

5-9 PUBLIC WANTS   Public wants comprise human desires which cannot be satisfied or at least cannot be satisfied to an acceptable degree by market processes.[1] Social wants cannot be satisfied at all because they demand goods or services which must be consumed collectively. Clean air must be provided to the entire community if it is provided to anyone. It is not technologically possible to clean only the air breathed by those paying a fee and leave dirty air for those not paying. Such goods or services must be enjoyed by all or none. Other examples are street lighting, national defense, flood protection, and natural environment.

Merit wants can be satisfied to some extent by market processes, but they represent wants where political consensus shows the market provision to be inadequate. The associated goods and services cannot neatly be classed as either a market or a collective good. They lie in the fringe area. For example, public education, health services, outdoor recreation opportunities, and historic landmarks may be provided by private enterprise but not in sufficient quantities because the market can only collect from a small portion of those who benefit. Firearms or liquor may be overprovided by private enterprise because the market cannot register the objections of those who are harmed. The preservation of natural resources represents a special type of merit want where the market is unable to express the wishes of future generations (Sec. 9-5).

Even though the goods and services fulfilling public wants cannot themselves be exchanged in the market, the principles of market analysis can still be applied to establish values. Individual demand curves may be implicitly derived from costs which would occur if the good were not provided (flood control) or from costs borne to obtain the good (recreation). The individual-demand curves are added vertically because each person receives the same level of service and the total value realized by the group is the sum of the values individually realized. This contrasts with the horizontal addition for market goods (Sec. 3-12) where individuals pay the same price but receive different levels of service.

[1]   Richard A. Musgrave, "The Theory of Public Finance" (New York: McGraw-Hill Book Company, 1959), chap. 1.

Aggregate-demand curves for collective goods can be used for project optimization in the same way as aggregate-demand curves for market goods are used (Sec. 4-16). For merit wants, the aggregate-demand curve may be developed by vertically adding appropriate values from derived demand curves representing the social or collective aspects of the demand.

5-10 EXTERNAL EFFECTS

Nature of Effects   External effects may be either external economies or external diseconomies. External economies refer to favorable consequences or benefits which consumption or production by one party has on others. External diseconomies refer to harmful consequences or costs which occur in the same way. An external economy exists when provision of a good or service to one group makes it possible for another group to receive the same or another good or service without paying for the benefit it has received. On the other hand, an external diseconomy exists when provision of a good or service for one group causes increased costs for another group and the second group is not compensated for its loss.

Technological external effects result from physical interaction between the activities of two or more parties. For example, a dam constructed for the purpose of producing hydropower also produces downstream benefits in mitigating both flood and low flows. A private power company will not consider these effects in plant design because it is not reimbursed for them. By the same token, a private firm which discharges untreated wastes directly into a stream causes those downstream to suffer uncompensated loss. The market does not allocate resources efficiently in the presence of external effects because no market transactions are involved. Firms which are not rewarded for their external economies will produce less than is optimum, while those which are not penalized for their external diseconomies will produce more than is optimum. The private power company will normally build a dam that is too small. The firm discharging waste will normally discharge too much.

A separable technological effect influences the variable cost and thus shifts the marginal-cost curves of other production units. A firm benefitting from an external economy will tend to overproduce. A firm subjected to an external diseconomy will tend to underproduce. An inseparable technological effect only influences the fixed cost of other production units. It will not affect the optimum output unless an external economy is large enough to put other firms into business or an external diseconomy is large enough to cause them to withdraw.

Pecuniary external effects result from shifts in the supply and demand curves caused by one firm and altering the production decisions of another. An expanding production unit may bid up prices for the goods and services it uses as inputs (a pecuniary external economy to the supplier of the input and diseconomy to other users), force down the price of substitute products (economy to user and diseconomy to supplier), induce an increase in the price of complementary products (economy to supplier and diseconomy to user), or lower the price of its output (economy to consumer and diseconomy to competitive supplier). Since each pecuniary external effect is a gain to one party offset by a loss to another party, economic efficiency is not affected, but income distribution is. The evaluation of pecuniary external effects is in the scope of first- but not second-order efficiency.

Market external economies are a special type of pecuniary economy which results from the creation of a large new production unit such as a water resources project. They result from the fuller utilization of existing transportation and other public facilities and more efficient operation of processing firms. Many of these economies have come to be known as *secondary benefits.*

Psychological external effects occur when the consumption by one party alters the satisfaction received by other parties. One may not desire a particular type of consumption until he sees another enjoying it, or he may receive satisfaction from seeing others enjoy consumption of a type of which they were previously deprived. Demand analysis assumes the wants of various parties are independent, and economic efficiency criteria can not be used for optimization if this assumption is untenable.

Methods of Dealing with Effects   The technological spillovers should be directly evaluated in project formulation because they physically alter the production functions, and the goal of planning is to pick the optimum production process. This is best done by an analysis of the production function of the second party with and without the external effect caused by the first. Damages from poor water quality can be estimated both with and without the low-flow augmentation provided for navigation. The difference in damage is the value of the technological external economy.

The effect of pecuniary spillovers can best be explained through supply and demand curves. If a commodity characterized by the demand curve of Fig. 5-1 were to reach equilibrium at price P_1 and demand Q_1, it would have an aggregate value in use equal to the sum of areas A, B, and C and a consumer's surplus equal to area A. If the advent of a new low-cost producer (a pecuniary externality) were to cause the price to drop to P_2 and sales to increase to Q_2, the original producers would lose the income represented by area B, but consumers would benefit by an amount represented by the sum of areas B and D. Thus the pecuniary spillover has two

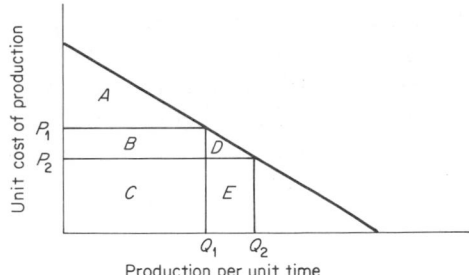

FIGURE 5-1   Effect of pecuniary spillovers.

types of effects. The value of area D is a net gain to consumers. The value of area B is transferred from the producers to the consumers. The transfer has no influence on economic efficiency. It is instead related to income distribution. As a result it does not enter into the economic feasibility of a project, but it is closely tied to the political, social, and institutional factors which help determine whether or not a project is built (Sec. 8-1). Area D is a net benefit when price decreases owing to increased output or reduced demand and a net loss when price increases owing to decreased output or increased demand. In either case, the value of area D should be incorporated into project evaluation just as technological spillovers are.[1]

The water resources planner might deal with external effects in one of a number of ways:

1   He may ignore them. Because the inability of the market to handle external effects efficiently is a major argument for government planning, it is hardly proper for government planners to ignore them. The same results could be achieved by market forces without the planning cost of the government bureaucracy. In fact, this approach is only mentioned because of the number of times it has actually been applied. Irrigation projects have been planned and built while ignoring downstream salinity. Surface-water supplies have been developed with no thought to their influence on ground-water users. Reservoirs have been built with no prior analysis of the effect of reduced sediment flow on downstream channel stability. Planners must do better.

2   The second possibility is to catalogue and evaluate every externality in a truly comprehensive plan. However, the conceptual problems which would be encountered and the magnitude of the task in such a colossal undertaking make the comprehensive approach impractical if not impossible. Even if a good job could be done, the planning cost would quite likely exceed the marginal benefit of the improved results.

[1] Stephen A. Marglin, Objectives of Water-resource Development, in Maass et al., *op. cit.*, pp. 55–58.

3 A variation on comprehensive planning is to internalize the externalities by merging all the parties subject to external effects into a common firm. While this approach may prove valuable for industries with closely linked production functions, it is no answer for water resources planning. The resulting monopoly would negate the normative significance of the market and require its replacement by mathematical planning. All the difficulties of the second approach would have been introduced, and many values once established by the market would be distorted for good measure.

4 A fourth approach is to attempt, by legal means, to prevent externalities from occurring. This may be done either by the passage and enforcement of legislation or by court action. Numerous laws deal with such subjects as land use on flood plains, water pollution control, and channel encroachments. Court decisions have established precedents in cases on water rights, disposition of drainage water, and other external diseconomies where a single individual can be held directly responsible. However, settlements often depend more on political power and legal persuasiveness than on objective analysis. Laymen can hardly be expected to reach a meaningful decision on technical matters without technical advice.

5 One may wonder what course is left if one cannot successfully handle externalities by ignoring them, comprehensively analyzing them, or preventing them. All spillovers can be tabulated qualitatively. The major ones can be selected and evaluated quantitatively so the values can be incorporated into project optimization. Whether or not an effect should be evaluated depends on whether the nature of the optimal project is sensitive to the effect. In accordance with this rule, major technical spillovers require serious analysis; but the consumers-surplus triangle is normally too small to require detailed analysis of pecuniary spillovers.

5-11 NATURAL MONOPOLY Another deviation from the model of pure competition that serves as a justification for government activity is caused by natural monopoly. Monopoly occurs when the optimum plant size (Sec. 4-15) supplies a large enough portion of total market demand to influence market price. Economic efficiency requires that the market price equal marginal cost. However, to any firm finding its price dependent on its output, marginal revenue is less than price; and to maximize profit, the firm will equate marginal revenue with marginal cost. The consumers will be getting less than optimum level of output at a higher price. In addition, the firm will be receiving monopoly profits. To promote efficient resource

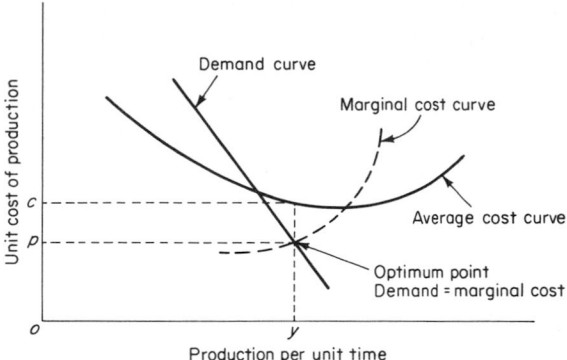

FIGURE 5-2   Decreasing-cost situation.

utilization the monopoly must be regulated or managed by the government so that market price equals marginal cost.

For a natural monopoly, average cost is decreasing at the point of optimal output (i.e., where price equals marginal cost). Where average costs are decreasing because the optimum scale of the plant is large compared with market demand, average costs will always exceed market price. As illustrated by Fig. 5-2, optimum output is y, unit revenue is p, and average unit cost is c. The smallest average cost occurs when the market is cornered by one producer, all other producers are eliminated by the market, and natural monopoly results.

Natural monopoly is characteristic of many utilities as well as water resource development where reservoir sites are limited, large-scale investments are required, and duplicate distribution systems are impractical. A common solution is to allow private enterprise an exclusive market but to regulate charges by the utility to yield only a fair return on its investment. Some utilities may be government owned to serve as a bench mark for regulation of the remaining private utilities. A third possibility is government ownership of the entire utility complex.

Adjustments Required by Multiple Goals

Two steps are required to adjust project planning for economic efficiency to incorporate other social goals. An acceptable measure of progress toward each relevant goal [G in Eq. (5-1)] must be established. The measure must indicate progress toward a more stable economy, desirable income distribution, or satisfying environment. Secondly, an acceptable procedure must be developed for weighing goals. Specific discussion follows for each of the four noneconomic goals generally considered most relevant to water resources planning.

5-12   STABILIZATION OF THE ECONOMY   The national economy is characterized by cyclic fluctuation in employment levels. A market economy periodically fluctuates between expansion and retraction because of the time lag before market equilibrium can be reestablished in response to changing demand or supply. When supply exceeds demand, producers reduce output, workers lose their jobs, and spendable income is reduced. As demand is further reduced, the resulting deflation may bring extensive unemployment before conditions stabilize and recovery begins. The most severe cycles may lead to general economic breakdown or what has been called *general* or *Keynsian unemployment*. Such conditions spread throughout the world in the 1930s. When demand exceeds supply, producers increase output, workers become in short supply and can command higher wages, and spendable income is increased. As more money becomes available, increasing price levels produce an inflationary condition which hurts fixed income groups and discourages long-term investment. Such conditions increased prices in Germany by a factor exceeding 10^{10} in the 1920s.

Government uses fiscal and monetary measures to prevent severe fluctuations. Fiscal measures implement government's taxing and expenditure powers. In principle, if inflation prevails, the government can reduce demand by increasing taxes and reducing its expenditures. If depression threatens, the government can increase demand by reducing taxes and increasing expenditures. Monetary measures adjust the money supply. The Federal Reserve Board can reduce the supply of money in time of inflation and increase it in time of depression. It does this by (1) selling or buying government bonds in the open market—selling bonds will reduce the money supply while buying bonds will increase the money supply—; (2) making or restricting loans to Federal Reserve Banks—making loans increases the reserves of the banks and allows them to increase loans to others—; and (3) changing bank reserve requirements—the higher the reserve requirements, the lower the money supply, and vice versa.[1]

The economic analysis of engineering alternatives normally assumes that government fiscal and monetary policy successfully stabilizes the

[1]   Paul A. Samuelson, "Economics: An Introductory Analysis," 5th ed. (New York: McGraw-Hill Book Company, 1961), chap. 17.

economy at a high level of resource utilization. It would be inconsistent for government agencies planning water resources development to base their decisions on the assumption that policies for economic stabilization will fail. If depression should occur, projects can be reevaluated with lower interest rates to reflect the lower opportunity cost of capital and with lower prices for resources to indicate their lower input cost. Nevertheless, long-term planning should proceed with the assumption of high employment and price stability, especially in view of the fact that the lead time required for project construction exceeds the duration of economic cycles.

General unemployment is not the only type of unemployment which may be reduced to improve economic stability. Structural unemployment involves groups who, because they lack necessary skills, are unable to find work even when the overall economy is booming. Structural unemployment may result when changing demand patterns (horse-drawn carriages to automobiles) or changing production techniques (hand to machine sewing) eliminate the demand for once valuable skills. Others structurally unemployed may have never acquired any productive skill. Water resources projects are generally planned on the assumption that government educational and training programs are more successful in combatting this problem. However, under some conditions, project design or the construction methods should be modified so as to make greater use of the less skilled. The social cost of using unemployed resources is zero, and equating the marginal rates of substitution among project inputs shows the optimum policy is to increase use of unemployed resources until their marginal physical product becomes negative. However, the unskilled become trained in time, and project planning should not be based on a zero resource cost over the entire project life.

Regional unemployment includes groups which are unemployed because they prefer to live in familiar surroundings and remain unemployed than to move to a new location to find a job. Areas whose basic economy is tied to a declining industry present the most critical problem (New England textile mills or Appalachian coal mines). After people are thrown out of work, it takes time for them to move to find a new job. People who value their homes and neighborhood more highly than a steady income may not move at all, and regional adjustment may require two or three generations. While this problem also is not one which water resources development can solve very effectively alone, projects providing electric power, navigation, flood control, or other services may attract new industry to increase regional employment. Such an approach to stablizing a local economy is closely related to the goal of regional development (Sec. 5-14).

Underemployed resources are not used to their full productive capacity. A highly skilled person may take a job requiring little skill when none other is available. Underemployment may be either structural or regional. Underemployment may be handled in project planning in the same manner as unemployment except that the social cost is the value of the resource in its lower-valued use rather than zero.

While water resources development is not a particularly efficient measure for nationwide economic stabilization, projects can be used to reduce the variability of annual regional income. Water development to broaden an agricultural or provide an industrial base can reduce the income fluctuations characteristic of a single-crop economy. Flood control reduces income fluctuations caused by periodic large damages. A project producing benefits which remain fairly constant from year to year or a project reducing damages into a more uniform annual pattern introduces greater economic stability. A useful index for measuring project effect on economic stability is the change in standard deviation of the annual income of the beneficiaries. A sample calculation for flood control is given in Exs. 10-4 and 10-5. The value judgment used to pick V_α for Eq. (8-7) is essentially the selection of an appropriate weighting factor for combining stabilization with economic benefits.

5-13 INCOME REDISTRIBUTION The distribution of income and wealth within a society is determined by the rules governing property ownership and inheritance, market transactions, and taxation and by the distribution among individuals of educational opportunity, ability, and motivation. Individuals view the resultant distribution with varying degrees of satisfaction. Collective dissatisfaction may through the political process promote action to redistribute income to poorer groups. The process has produced progressive income taxes and transfer payments to veterans, the aged, and the unemployed. Minimum wage legislation, tariff protection, farm subsidies, and fair trade legislation are other forms of income redistribution.

Water resource projects have been proposed as an additional method for redistributing income from richer to poorer groups. Several facts need to be kept in mind. Water resource projects are not particularly efficient in redistributing income because the rich always reap part of the benefit and the poor always pay part of the cost. The magnitude of water project expenditure is such a small part of the national income that a major income redistribution is unlikely to be ever achieved. Failure to incorporate income redistribution explicitly as a project objective does not necessarily mean the objective is not considered worthwhile. It only means the redistribution can be accomplished more effectively in some other way.

Explicit analysis of the income redistribution effects of a specific water resources project requires determination of the incidence of project benefit (and cost) among individuals by income category. The value judgment of weighting-factor selection comes in placing a higher value on benefits to those in one income group than in an other. Income redistribution to the poor is encouraged by using weighting factors inversely related to income. An explicit approach is presented in Sec. 8-10.

The redistribution of income is reduced as beneficiaries are required to pay for project output. Income redistribution effects may be even more important as a tool in financial analysis to determine who should pay than they are in economic analysis.

5-14 REGIONAL DEVELOPMENT The geographical distribution of economic growth within a society is determined by the historical response to topography, climate, trade routes, mineral deposits, soil fertility, international disputes, and a host of lesser physical, economic, and social factors. Collective dissatisfaction with the resultant distribution may spring from a number of causes. Settlement of underdeveloped areas may improve military security, lay the groundwork for a future more broadly based economic expansion, and provide new opportunity for the dissatisfied. The ill effects of extreme population congestion may be mitigated. New industry may be brought into rural areas to alleviate urban migration caused by an increasing economic farm size. A thriving rural community can provide better public services to the benefit of long-time residents.

Water resources projects have been proposed as an element of a public program to encourage economic development in lagging regions. The effectiveness of such a program depends on the degree to which an inadequate supply of the kinds of output water resource projects can produce has served as a bottleneck to regional growth. Water resources development can make a major contribution through providing water to a desert, dry land in a swamp, electricity to those still using kerosene, or transportation for exporting a mineral ore. In other situations, economic growth may be restricted in ways which make water resources projects ineffective.

Explicit analysis of the regional development caused by a specific water resources project requires determination of the incidence of project benefit and cost by geographical location. As benefits tend to concentrate in the area near the project location while costs are spread more evenly throughout the country, project construction implies an economic sacrifice on the part of the rest of the country to develop a local area. If development in the local area is judged more important than development elsewhere, a project with a net negative economic benefit can be justified. However, such a decision should reflect a national consenses and not the skill of the few who stand to receive large gains at outmaneuvering the many who have to make a small sacrifice. The legitimate goal of regional development should not be confused with the failure of some project planners to take the national viewpoint. Regional development in the national interest is best encouraged by deriving acceptable weighting factors to apply to cash flows by geographical location.

Project development in a small nation or other limited trade area may find it advantageous to favor locally available to imported inputs. Where the balance of payments requires that imports be limited to what can be financed from exports sold, the available foreign exchange should be used in the manner best promoting national goals. It is seldom possible to import all goods having an economic value exceeding their cost. A shadow price multiplier should be used in project planning to make sure the limited imports are used effectively. The appropriate λ can be estimated by the procedure used in project ranking (Sec. 9-12).

5-15 ENVIRONMENTAL QUALITY Unless explicit safeguards are introduced, planning based on economic criteria may inadvertently destroy the quality of environment required to preserve man's psychological and even long-run physical well-being. Even though individuals differ widely in environmental preference, common consensus is often reached to support unique natural areas and some open countryside and oppose destructive pollution or excessive congestion and resultant blight.

Structural measures for water resources development are widely viewed as having a destructive influence on environmental quality. The conflict can be mitigated by introducing an esthetically more pleasing design or by achieving project objectives through nonstructural measures. Explicit analysis requires both precise definition of what aspect of environmental quality is to be preserved or promoted and development of an index proportional to the quality achieved. Different indices apply in different situations. Sometimes physically measurable quantities such as acres of open land or wildlife populations may be used. Other times more indirect measurement through preference rating based on photographs may be possible. Often environmental quality must itself be handled as a multidimensional goal.

It is very important to remember that planning should seek to maximize the total social welfare function and not just environmental quality alone. The quality of the environment is usually only improved at a sacrifice in national and regional income and employment. A reasonable compromise can only be reached through specific information quantifying the cost of achieving environments of progressively higher quality.

SELECTED REFERENCES

Arrow, Kenneth J.: "Social Choice and Individual Values" (New York: John Wiley & Sons, Inc., 1951).

Baumol, William J.: "Welfare Economics and the Theory of the State," 2d ed. (Cambridge, Mass.: Harvard University Press, 1967).

Bergson, Abram: "Essays in Normative Economics" (Cambridge Mass.: Harvard University Press, 1966).

Buchanan, James W.: Politics, Policy, and the Pigovian Margins, *Economics*, vol. 29 (February, 1962).

Galbraith, John Kenneth: "The Affluent Society" (Boston: Houghton Mifflin Company, 1958).

Garnsey, Morris E.: Welfare Economic and Resource Development, "Western Resource Conference Land and Water Planning for Economic Growth, 1961" (Boulder: University of Colorado Press, 1962).

Hasan, Syed F.: "Introduction to Welfare Economics" (New York: Asia Publishing House, 1963).

Hufschmidt, Maynard M.: Environmental Aspects of River Basin Planning, *Proc. ASCE*, vol. 93, no. HY6 (November, 1967), pp. 323–352.

Pigou, A. C.: "The Economics of Welfare," 4th ed. (London: Macmillan & Company, Ltd., 1932).

Weckstein, Richard S.: Welfare Criteria and Changing Tastes, *Am. Econ. Rev.*, vol. 52 (March, 1962).

PROBLEMS

5-1 Management has three goals which it desires to attain and considers of equal importance. The available alternatives are mutually exclusive and provide degrees of progress toward the goals as summarized in the following matrix:

	G_1	G_2	G_3
A_1	70	12	9
A_2	40	30	33
A_3	25	60	11
A_4	29	37	38
A_5	15	15	65

a Which alternative is to be preferred?

b If goals G_2 and G_3 were equally important, at least what weighting would goal G_1 require to favor alternative A_1? How low would the weighting have to drop to favor alternative A_5?

c For the optimum alternative of part a and assuming equal weighting for the other two goals, for what range in the weighting factor for goal G_1 would the same alternative be selected? What range for goal G_2? What range for goal G_3?

5-2 List as many arguments as you can in support of the *abundancy* approach to planning. List as many arguments as you can supporting the *efficiency* approach. Evaluate the two approaches according to their ability to provide practical guidance to planning decisions. What other considerations are required in choosing between the two approaches?

CHAPTER
SIX

DISCOUNT RATE

6-1 CAPITAL FORMATION A Pacific islander fishing with a spear may obtain enough fish for his daily needs but find himself unable to catch enough extra for a cash income. His entire effort is being spent in producing consumer goods. If he were able at the price of a temporary sacrifice in his diet to forego fishing and spend his time making a fishing lure, he would with the completion of this task be able to catch enough fish for his own use plus extra for sale. By shifting some of his production from consumer to capital goods, he has improved his lot in the long run through a temporary sacrifice.

Basic resources (land, labor, minerals, water, etc.) can be used to produce consumer goods used to satisfy immediate human needs. They can also be used to produce capital goods, the intermediate goods used in the production of more goods. As capital goods are continually produced, the formation of capital provides the production base permitting a long-term improvement in human welfare.

Water resources development is essentially a capital formation process, and two questions must be answered in planning capital formation:

1 How much sacrifice in current consumption should be made to increase production of capital goods?
2 How much of each kind of capital goods should be produced?

The analyses described in the other chapters of this book seek the optimal project design answering the second question. The answer to the first question is the subject at hand.

Clearly, the greater the sacrifice in consumption, the more basic resources can be devoted to producing capital goods and the faster capital will be formed. The rate of economic development is directly tied to a willingness to sacrifice. The discount rate for project planning is essentially a measure of this willingness.

6-2   DISCOUNT RATE VS. INTEREST RATE   While the interest rate may be loosely defined as any expression of the time value of capital, a more precise definition distinguishes between interest rate and discount rate. Interest is the fee one producer pays to use the capital of another. The interest rate is determined by the capital market. It must be considered in financial analysis (Sec. 22-1). An enterprise seeking to improve its own welfare will pay an interest rate determined by the least expensive source of capital and use that rate (unless the intangible determinates of company policy dictate otherwise) to evaluate its investment opportunities, using appropriate discounting techniques. It will make money by investing in projects having a rate of return exceeding its borrowing rate.

The reasoning for investing past earnings follows a slightly different line. These earnings can either be distributed to the owners for their own consumption or outside investment or kept within the enterprise to finance capital expansion. The decision process for allocating earnings between dividends to owners and capital expansion is basically that described in presenting the rate-of-return discounting technique (Sec. 2-10). Management will devote earnings to capital formation starting with the project yielding the highest return but will be careful that funds remaining for distribution to the owners are not reduced to a level that will discourage further investment in the company. Selection of the cutoff point is basically a value judgment by management based on what is good for the company. The cutoff point is in effect the company discount rate.

A discount rate is the expression of the time value of capital used in equivalence calculations comparing alternatives. The rate is essentially a value judgment based on a compromise between present consumption and capital formation from the viewpoint of the decision maker. For public works planning, this means the viewpoint of the people as a whole (Sec. 1-3). The ideal discount rate would achieve a rate of capital formation maximizing total social welfare.

Many viewpoints have been expressed on what is the best discount rate from the public point of view. Some advocate public planning based on a zero discount rate because interest is not directly charged on tax dollars or because of the distrust of usury prevalent in Christian and socialist traditions. However, without discounting, the planner would consider a perpetual income of a penny per year (summing to infinity) preferable to a million dollars tomorrow if both could be obtained through the same investment. Some advocate discounting with the interest rate paid to borrow funds for project financing. However, this approach ignores the opportunity cost of tax funds and makes project merit dependent on the borrowing power of the financing agency. Some advocate discounting with the internal rate of return for the least profitable project which can be financed without exhausting available funds. However, this approach is no help in answering the basic capital formation question of optimum budget size when funds are obtained from tax revenues.

6-3   OPPORTUNITY COST   The fundamental purpose of economic analysis is to determine whether a particular addition to existing investment capital is worthwhile. Capital formation requires two kinds of sacrifice. Some resources will be used which would otherwise have gone into the formation of some other type of productive capital; the opportunity cost of their use equals the productivity they would have had in the investment foregone. Some resources would have otherwise been consumed; their opportunity cost is determined by the value placed by consumers on the required sacrifice.

The value of sacrificed consumption becomes the key to discount rate selection because this sacrifice comes closest to representing the marginal-opportunity cost of additional capital formation. Market analysis may be used to estimate the value of the sacrifice to the individual. Determination of the value to society as a whole is embroiled in assessing collective and external effects of increased production.

6-4   THE CAPITAL MARKET   Just as other markets provide a starting point for evaluating other inputs to public works projects, the interest rate determined by the capital market provides a starting point in discount rate selection. As a factor in production, the price of capital, as is the price of all the other factors, is a market equilibrium position determined by the interaction of supply and demand.

The supply of capital depends on the investment of savings. An individual divides his income between consumption and savings according to his preference as represented by the indifference map of Fig. 6-1. The indifference lines represent combinations of present consumption and uniform annual future income among which the individual has no preference and thus is indifferent. Because uniform annual future income equals the product of the amount invested and the interest rate, CD equals $i(DE)$. The available alternatives range between consuming the entire income at

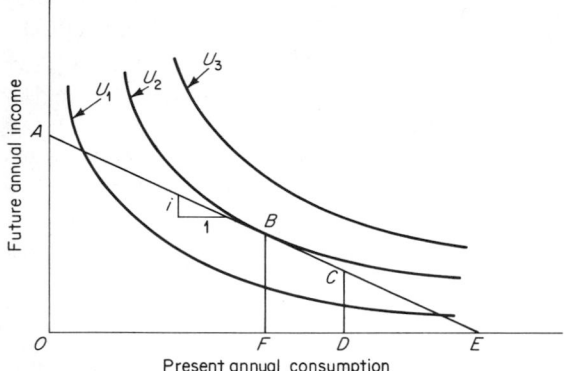

FIGURE 6-1 Representative indifference map between consumption and future income.

point *E* and saving the entire income at point *A*. For the income *OE*, the alternatives fall on the line *ABCE*. The individual whose preferences are represented by Fig. 6-1 and whose income equals *OE* will enjoy the greatest utility from his income at point *B*, for at this point he has reached his highest possible indifference line U_2. He will consume *OF* and save *FE* at interest rate *FB/FE*. At point *B*, his willingness to substitute future interest income for present consumption is exactly equal to the interest rate. In a uniform market, every other individual will have this same marginal rate of substitution between consumption and savings because all will receive the same rate of interest even though people vary widely in the fraction of their income saved because of indifference line differences. Aggregate savings equal the sum of the individual savings. The aggregate marginal rate of substitution is identical with that for each individual.

If the interest rate exceeded *FB/FE*, the line representing available alternatives would be steeper and the higher utility of another indifference curve could be attained. The change in savings by a particular individual would depend on the nature of the individual's indifference map. Those saving toward a fixed objective may prefer extra consumption if a higher interest rate were to allow them to reach their goal by saving a smaller portion of their total income. Nevertheless, for most individuals and certainly for a modern industrial society as a whole, savings increase with interest received. Thus, the investment-capital-supply curve will slope upward to the right as shown on Fig. 6-2.

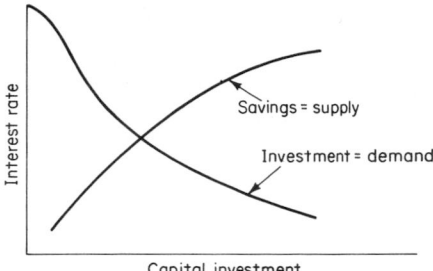

FIGURE 6-2 Supply and demand curves in the capital market.

The demand for capital depends on the available investment opportunities. Each investment opportunity has an internal rate of return. Theoretically, all available investment alternatives could be ranked in order of their internal rate of return. The demand curve would intersect the ordinate of Fig. 6-2 at the internal rate of return of the top project on this list. Other points on the demand curve have an ordinate determined by the rate of return on the marginal project and an abscissa determined by the total investment required to implement all projects having an internal rate of return higher than that indicated. The curve would be unlikely to reach the horizontal axis because any investment providing a perpetual income has a rate of return exceeding zero.

Some have postulated that savings will continue as long as men earn income but that investment opportunities become fewer as the most desirable projects are built. When all investment opportunities have been utilized, economic stagnation will result. However, investment history does not give much substance to this worry as the human capacity to consume and the technical ability to produce seem to expand even faster than general economic growth. Per capita investment in the economically most developed countries far exceeds that in the most primitive. Marginal internal rates of return exceeding 10 percent prevail in American industry. There may be reason to doubt the social desirability of current consumption patterns, but there is little reason to doubt the ability of man's wants and his technical ability to produce to expand into the indefinite future at a rate sufficient to absorb all available savings.

The capital market balances the supply and demand of capital to establish an equilibrium interest rate. An excess of savings reduces interest rates as occurred immediately after World War II. An excess of investment opportunity causes interest rates to rise as has occurred more recently. Either way, the market mechanism allocates the time pattern of consumption by the sacrifice (*FE* in Fig. 6-1) induced to obtain capital for future production. One reaction to this accomplishment of the capital market is that it solves the discount rate problem by providing the discount rate best used to evaluate alternatives. However, the normative significance of the market interest rate hinges on the consequences of market imperfections.

6-5 DEFICIENCIES IN THE CAPITAL MARKET The financial structure of modern government has become so closely entwined with the capital market that government is both the major participant and the regulator charged with keeping the interest rate in line with politically determined economic policy. The first effect has to do with government fiscal policy. A large federal deficit requires heavy borrowing and increases interest rates by increasing the demand for the capital supplied by lenders. The effect is amplified as government spending induces private investment which must also be financed by borrowed money. Spending induces investment by those who sell their goods and services to the government as well as by those who are provided more government produced goods and services. Overall, government participation in the capital market is far too large to maintain the approximation of perfect competition.

In addition, the federal government regulates the supply of money by its monetary policy.[1] By buying and selling federal reserve notes and modifying the rules on borrowing and lending which financial institutions must follow, the government may decrease the supply of money and thus increase rates (a tight money policy) or increase the supply of money and thus reduce interest rates (a loose money policy). Discounting with the market interest rate would cause the desirability of alternative investments to fluctuate with federal monetary policy. Since this policy may be varied by the government at will, the net benefit of alternative investments becomes a manipulated rather than a normative measure of project worth. The arbitrariness is reduced by monetary policy and planning being functions of different government agencies, but the basic argument still holds.

The capital market is also affected by market interest rates having two components: the time value of money and a risk premium. A lender traditionally charges a higher rate of interest to those less likely to repay. The rate of interest charged to a borrower (such as by the United States government) whose ability to repay is in absolutely no doubt may be thought of as risk free or pure interest. It is the market evaluation of the

---

[1] Paul A. Samuelson, "Economics: An Introductory Analysis," 5th ed. (New York: McGraw-Hill Book Company, 1961), pp. 644–662.

time value of money. As the doubt about ability to repay increases, the interest rate will correspondingly increase by a risk premium.

A risk premium may be added to the discount rate to account for risk. Because economic analysis seeks to evaluate the merit of a given project rather than the financial strength of project sponsors, the relevant risk is the probable success of the project. A project should be evaluated on its own merits rather than by the financial strength of those who will pay for it. Some may argue against using a risk premium at all on the grounds that risk is not properly a compounding function of time, but there is little justification for selecting a risk premium on any basis other than the attributes of the investment under consideration.

The capital market is also influenced by the debt aversion of prospective borrowers. People and institutions tend to be more hesitant about spending borrowed than earned capital. A project yielding a low return might be favored over one yielding a higher return if the latter must be financed by borrowing. Debt aversion stems from the threat of extensive borrowing to the solvency of the borrower and the higher interest rate which must be paid on essential subsequent loans. Legal limitations limit borrowing by local government and public utilities. Whether legally or self-imposed, debt aversion distorts the equilibrium point of the capital market.

A difference exists between borrowing and lending rates. An individual pays a higher rate of interest when he borrows than he gets when he lends his money to a bank. Much of the difference can be explained by the difference in risk premium required for the two parties. Institutions which use their money in more productive investments will grow financially stronger and be required to pay a smaller risk premium on borrowed money.

One of the most telling criticisms of the capital market is that it determines how much the present generation wants to save for the future, but it cannot consult the desires of future generations on either the amount or kind of savings. The selection of the proper kind of savings has been a major concern of the conservation movement. The world is changing. Man is replacing an old environment with a new. He must be careful to prevent the economic forces producing the change from sacrificing those noneconomic values of the old environment essential to his well-being.

Many believe planning using a cutoff rate of return equal to the relatively high market interest rate would unduly restrict capital investment.[1] The capital market is the product of many individual investment decisions. They suggest that society may be willing to save more as a group than people will save as individuals. Individuals may be willing to commit

---

[1]   Stephen A. Marglin, Economic Factors Affecting System Design, in Arthur Maass et al., "Design of Water-resource Systems" (Cambridge, Mass.: Harvard University Press, 1962), pp. 194–205.

more of their own income to savings if they could be sure everyone else were also doing so. If a lower social discount rate at which society would be willing to save as a group exists, it is the discount rate which should be used to·evaluate public projects financed from enforced group savings (taxes).[1]

The chief argument against discounting, for selecting public works alternatives with a low group-determined social interest rate, lies in the need to distinguish between two types of capital. Liquid capital is money available for investment. Plant capital is goods used to produce other goods. Theoretically, the decision to use a discount rate for planning in the public sector that is lower than the market rate used in the private sector tends to slow capital formation by diverting capital from the private sector to less productive investment in the public sector. Furthermore, the resultant accumulation of public plant capital may force overall savings from easily convertible liquid capital to a form of plant which may in later years be found to be either incapable of supplying then current needs or technologically obsolete. Unusable savings are as bad as no savings at all.

6-6 BASIC APPROACHES FOR DEALING WITH MARKET DEFICIENCIES Two basic approaches exist on how to deal with capital market deficiencies in developing a discount rate. Some say the defects are too great for the market interest to have any normative significance whatsoever and the discount rate must be selected by some other method. Others recognize the defects in the market but can find no better method. They believe the government should concentrate on formulating policies to correct market defects in order to better coordinate public with private investment rather than pick what must be a somewhat arbitrary rate for its own planning.[2] Financial pressures force the private sector to use the interest rate rather than a normative discount rate. Unless the two rates are identical, project design and justification will depend on who does the planning, a condition reducing economic efficiency.

6-7 SPECIFIC APPROACHES FOR PICKING A DISCOUNT RATE A number of methods for picking a discount rate for use in planning by public agencies have been suggested, and the resulting values vary over a wide range. The first four methods follow a market-based approach. The fifth does not.

[1] Maynard M. Hufschmidt, John V. Krutilla, Julius Margolis, and Stephen A. Marglin, "Standards and Criteria for Formulating and Evaluating Federal Water Resources Developments," Report of Panel of Consultants to the Bureau of the Budget, Washington, 1961, pp. 11–23.
[2] Jack Hirshleifer, James C. DeHaven, and Jerome W. Milliman, "Water Supply: Economics, Technology, and Policy" (Chicago: The University of Chicago Press, 1960), pp. 121–123.

1 One approach is to discount with the market interest rate for risk-free investment. The rate is estimated and adjusted as necessary to correct for known market defects and market allowance for currency inflation. Because government bonds are one of the most risk-free investments available and market interest rate varies with the duration that capital is committed, the interest rate on recently issued government bonds having a maturity period approximately equal to anticipated project life, normally 50 to 100 years, provides a good estimate. The average interest rate on old outstanding government bonds is not particularly relevant to current investment, but all outstanding bonds were considered in selecting the discount rate used by United States government agencies until 1968. In that year, the average discount rate on new government bonds was about 4.625 percent while the average rate on all outstanding bonds was about 3.25 percent.

2 Most rapid capital formation comes by making the most productive investments. If funds were committed to the project yielding the highest return first and then to subsequent projects in order of rate of return, the internal rate of return of the last project selected before funds ran out would be the marginal internal rate of return. The existence of a marginal internal rate of return implies a budgetary constraint or capital rationing because otherwise the funds would not run out. History has shown funds available to public agencies to be chronically less than what could potentially be invested. In order to maximize the rate of capital formation, it is important to recognize that the productivity of capital recovered and reinvested may substantially depart from that of the original investment. Public works projects must consider the reinvestment of those benefits received by the general public, while private industry recovers and reinvests the benefits from its own investment. The overall rate of return is the discount rate equating the present worth of the investment with the present worth of the consumption (by year in which it occurs) plus the present worth of invested and reinvested capital at the end of the period of analysis. The marginal internal rate of return will vary widely among agencies and over time, but a rate which has been suggested for highway planning is 7.0 percent.[1]

3 In order to preserve the merits of a discount rate based on productivity but avoid the weaknesses of one based on a politically controlled budgetary constraint, a third approach is to use the marginal internal rate of return for private companies engaged in comparable activity. The comparable activity requirement limits comparison to investments of

---

[1] Eugene L. Grant, Interest and the Rate of Return on Investments, *Highway Res. Board, Spec. Rept. 56*, 1960.

comparable capital intensity and risk, both factors which have a substantial effect on market interest rate. Efficiency is promoted if all economic planning is based on the same discount rate. If federal monetary control is not used to bring public and private discount rates in line, one approach would be to use the private rate deliberately for public planning. Eugene L. Grant states a common discount rate used by public utilities to be 7.0 percent after income taxes.[1] Hirshleifer has estimated the marginal internal rate of productivity in private companies engaged in water resources type of activity to be about 5.0 percent after income taxes. This is equivalent to about 8.3 percent for tax-free public investment. He rounds this upward to 10.0 percent to include other taxes and because the government usually undertakes the less desirable and hence more risky projects.[2]

4   A fourth approach is to tie the discount rate to the source of funds rather than to productivity. This yields a discount rate equal to the interest paid on borrowed funds for governments using bond financing. For pay-as-you-go financing, tax money has an opportunity cost equaling its productivity had the taxpayer been able to keep it. Rather elaborate statistical studies have been made to estimate tax incidence (who it is who really pays the taxes) and the spending and investment habits of the incident groups in order to determine the social cost of federal financing.[3] Economic efficiency is promoted if the government invests money in projects yielding returns larger than those from taxpayer investment foregone, but tying discount rates to borrowing causes some confusion between financial and economic analysis. Krutilla and Eckstein concluded from their study of federal tax revenue that the social cost of federal financing is about 6.0 percent.

5   A final approach is to pick a social discount rate on the grounds that the capital market is too badly distorted to have any normative significance. It:

assumes the capital market to be imperfect, to be rife with rationing, ignorance, differential tax treatments, reluctance to finance investment from external funds, slow adjustment processes, etc., which destroy the normative significance of actual rates found in the market. . . . Once the interest rates in the markets are denied their normative role, the rate for public decision-making must be derived from other considerations. It can be derived from individual revealed preference, from a planner's preference

[1] *Ibid.*, p. 83.
[2] Hirshleifer, DeHaven, and Milliman, *op. cit.*, pp. 144–148.
[3] John V. Krutilla and Otto Eckstein, "Multiple Purpose River Development" (Baltimore: The John Hopkins Press, 1958), pp. 78–130.

model, or from a vision revealed in a dream, it is a value judgment, pure and simple.[1]

Those who make such a value judgment usually produce a low discount rate with the goal of increasing capital investment for the benefit of future generations.

Whenever market evaluation is discarded, some alternative must be substituted. Some economists have postulated that the political decision-making process both is able to and in fact actually has made meaningful decisions on discount rate selection. Other economists distrust both the market and the political mechanisms and prefer to rely on a value judgment by some decision maker.[2] The discount rate may be selected around a conference table or through the use of a mathematical model designed to achieve a desired rate of economic growth. While advocates of a social discount rate do not agree as to how such a rate should be established, they favor use of a low discount rate to increase savings in the form of more public works projects. A typical value is 2.0 percent.

6-8   *CURRENT DISCOUNTING PRACTICE*   Until 1968, the official policy of the United States government has been:

> The interest rate to be used in plan formulation and evaluation for discounting future benefits and computing costs, or otherwise converting benefits and costs to a common time basis shall be based upon the average rate of interest payable by the Treasury on interest-bearing marketable securities of the United States outstanding at the end of the fiscal year preceding such computation which, upon original issue, had terms to maturity of 15 years or more. Where the average rate so calculated is not a multiple of one-eighth of 1 percent, the rate of interest shall be the multiple of one-eighth of 1 percent, next lower than such average rate.[3]

From 1960 through 1965, this rate rose approximately 0.125 percent per year to 3.25 percent and remained at that value through 1968. "Securities *outstanding* at the end of the fiscal year" have a lower average interest rate than securities *sold within the year* in periods of rising interest rate. In 1968 the Federal Water Resources Council recommended a policy change

---

[1]   Otto Eckstein, A Survey of the Theory of Public Expenditure Criteria, in National Bureau of Economic Research, "Public Finances: Needs, Sources, and Utilization" (Princeton, N.J.: Princeton University Press, 1961), p. 503.

[2]   More discussion is found in Marglin, Economic Factors, *op. cit.*, p. 197.

[3]   The President's Water Resources Council, *Policies, Standards, and Procedures in the Formulation, Evaluation, and Review of Plans for Use and Development of Water and Related Land Resources,* 87th Cong., 2d Sess., Sen. Doc. 97, 1962, p. 12.

to using a rate based on securities sold within the year and rounded to the nearest one-eighth of 1 percent provided that the maximum change in any 1 year shall be limited to one-quarter of 1 percent. When the recommendation was followed in 1969, the rate changed to 4.625 percent.

Federal agencies have used higher rates for discounting benefits and private costs than they have for public costs because private parties must pay higher interest rates for borrowed money, but the practice has been discontinued because of the planning distortions produced by multiple discount rates. The use of a risk-free rate implies adjustment for risk and uncertainty by corrections to the time streams of benefits and costs rather than by adding a risk component to the discount rate. Discounting practice varies among nonfederal planning groups, but most of them use higher rates because of their higher cost of borrowing. Private groups tend to use still higher rates. Thus, diversity in discounting practice still distorts project evaluation among planning groups.

6-9　CONSEQUENCES OF DISCOUNTING AT A LOW RATE　In making the value judgments necessary in discount rate selection, it is necessary to evaluate the consequences of using a low rate.

1　When the private discount rate exceeds the public discount rate, the private sector evaluates the present worth of assets at a higher discount rate and thus gives them a lower present worth. The project analysis evaluates present worth at a low discount rate and thus gives a high value. The value of a project will thus be overstated if its present worth at a low discount rate is compared with the value given other assets in the private sector by a market which implicitly uses a higher discount rate. While economy studies should evaluate all assets on a common basis, the difficulty is especially acute with respect to right-of-way. A major bias in favor of project construction results if the future income on benefitted land is discounted at a low rate, while the future income foregone on land purchased for right-of-way is implicitly discounted at a higher rate by using market prices for land in figuring project cost.[1] The way to achieve consistency is to evaluate right-of-way by a shadow price based on discounting expected income from the land at the lower rate. Such evaluation can readily be made for rural areas where annual farm income is predictable but becomes more complex for urban fringe areas where the predicted time stream of earned income is more uncertain.

2　Planning with a low discount rate increases the optimum project size,

---

[1]　For an example, see Otto Eckstein, "Water Response Development: The Economics of Project Evaluation" (Cambridge, Mass.: Harvard University Press, 1958), pp. 146–148.

favors an earlier time of construction, and is unfavorable to stage construction. The projects selected become bigger and more inflexible to adjustment with changing technoeconomic conditions. A low discount rate increases savings for the future, but it also increases the risk that large amounts of capital will be tied to projects unusable by future generations and, to the extent this happens, defeats the whole purpose of capital formation.

3 Planning with a low discount rate is also highly favorable to project justification. The lower the discount rate and the longer the anticipated project life, the more likely project benefits are to exceed the cost. A low discount rate increases resource allocation to, and the capital intensity of investment within, those sectors in which it is used.

4 Planning with a low discount rate will also normally show many more projects to be economically justified than funds are available to build. A sophisticated method of project ranking (Sec. 9-12) could overcome this difficulty by picking the best of the justified projects, but actual project selection is more likely to be placed on some basis other than economic merit.

Use of a low discount rate is favorable to the construction of public works projects and the interests which profit by project construction, but excessive diversion of resources to the public sector is detrimental to economic and even social efficiency and thus the long-run welfare of the nation. Solutions to pressing current needs may have to be sacrificed for the benefit of those living in the distant future. It is not possible to defend any exact discount rate for use in government planning dogmatically, but too low a rate definitely has serious adverse consequences to national economic growth.

SELECTED REFERENCES

Arrow, Kenneth J.: Discounting and Public Investment Criteria, in Allen V. Kneese and Stephen C. Smith (eds.), "Water Research" (Baltimore: The Johns Hopkins Press, 1966), pp. 13–32.

Baumol, William J.: On the Social Rate of Discount, Am. Econ. Rev., vol. 58 (September, 1968), pp. 788–802.

Grant, Eugene L.: Interest and the Rate of Return on Investments, Highway Res. Board, Spec. Rept. 56, 1960.

Marglin, Stephen A.: The Social Rate of Discount and the Optimal Rate of Investment, Quart. J. Economics, vol. 77 (February, 1963).

Masse, Pierre: "Optimal Investment Decisions" (Englewood Cliffs, N.J.: Prentice-Hall, Inc., 1962).

PROBLEMS

6-1 Assume the lines on the indifference map between consumption C and future income F are represented by $V = C^5(F + 50)$.

    a Derive an expression for C as a function of annual income I and rate of return i on saving S.

    b Derive an expression for the minimum income I_m required for a person to save anything.

    c How much will a person earning \$5,000 annually save if he can obtain a return of 5 percent?

    d How much will his savings increase if his income doubles?

    e If instead, the rate of return doubles, how much will his savings increase?

6-2 Capital investment in a certain water resources development is expected to produce an annual return of 15 percent. Capital formulation may be summarized by the table:

Year	(1) Capital stock	(2) Returns	(3) Investment	(4) Consumption
1	\$1,000	\$150		
2	1,000 + (3) for year 1			

Complete the table for 10 years if no returns are invested to increase capital stock.

6-3 Complete the table of Prob. 2 assuming \$75 is invested annually. What is the average annual growth rate of capital stock? Of consumption?

6-4 Complete the table of Prob. 2 assuming half the returns are invested annually. What is the average annual growth of capital stock? Of consumption?

6-5 Complete the table of Prob. 2 assuming consumption is 100 in the first year and increases at a rate of 4 percent annually thereafter. Also assume capital stock depreciates at a rate of 3 percent annually, $C_t = 0.97C_{t-1} + I_{t-1}$. In which year is capital stock a maximum? In which year does consumption become so large as to prevent further investment?

6-6 Complete the table of Prob. 2 assuming consumption is 80 in the first year and the growth rate of 4 percent and depreciation rate of 3 percent apply. What is the average annual growth rate of investment? of capital stock?

6-7 Compare the solutions of Probs. 5 and 6. What do the results say about the role of "belt-tightening" in economic development? What would be the implications of accepting a lower rate of return on long-term investment vs. continuing short-term investment yielding 15 percent, as far as economic development is concerned?

6-8   A water resources project having a 50-year life has an initial construction cost of $10 million and an annual cost of $250,000. The planning discount rate is 4.5 percent. Right-of-way requirements can be provided by an expenditure of $2 million. The land obtained produces a net annual income of $200,000. Annual project benefits are $1,200,000. What is the project benefit-cost ratio? What rate of return are landowners obtaining? What would the project benefit-cost ratio be if the analysis were based on income lost from the land rather than purchase expenditure?

3
PLANNING
IN A REAL WORLD
SETTING

The purpose of planning is to determine the program of water resources development and management that will contribute most to the welfare of all the people. The methodology of plan formulation should be constantly changing in response to changing social objectives, better and faster techniques of analysis, and an advancing technology for plan implementation. Often, those in the forefront of planning research and those who review current decision making become discouraged or even cynical at the resistance of the established agencies to change. Improved practices meet with inertia: inertia of established agency practice, inertia of political pressure groups seeing a threat to their special interest, and the inertia of existing law.

The acceptance of change depends on the merit of the proposal, but it also depends in part on how existing institutions interpret the proposal in the light of their mission. Therefore, a better theory of project evaluation can only be successfully developed and applied as it takes into account the existing institutional framework. It must consider the nature of the framework, the forces which have shaped its evolution, and the interests of those who will personally feel any suggested change. It must consider the laws as they exist, the forces which shaped them, and the degree to which they constrain planning alternatives. It must consider the practical difficulties of peering into the future where unknown people will react in unknown ways in pursuit of unknown goals and the necessity of maintaining a flexible planning response.

The institutions, the laws on which they are based, and the procedures which they use are also changing. Any detailed description quickly becomes dated. The main thrust of this section will be to present the relationship between the planner and his institutional setting which must be considered if the evolution of more powerful tools for economic analysis is to bear fruit.

CHAPTER SEVEN

THE INSTITUTIONAL FRAMEWORK

Organizational Considerations In Economic Analysis

7-1 THE DIVISION OF RESPONSIBILITY An effective water resources program requires many people to be doing many things in many places. Their efforts must be organized to accomplish program objectives best. Four basic types of organization are possible. Responsibility may be divided according to geography, the area served; function, the service performed; the group of people served; or the skill required. Examples of each type of organization may be found among United States agencies connected with water resources development. The Tennessee Valley Authority provides all types of water resource development in the Tennessee Valley. The Bureau of Reclamation provides irrigation water throughout the arid portion of the country. The Bureau of Indian Affairs helps Indians wherever they are located. The Government Printing Office provides printing skills to all agencies needing them.

Water resource agencies in the United States have traditionally been established in response to specific problems and thus been organized by function in order to coordinate each nationwide program better (flood control, for example). The exception is in the Tennessee Valley where the problem was initially conceived as a need for basin economic development. The practical organization choice is between functional organization with river basin coordination and river basin organization with functional coordination. Functional organization is better able to achieve uniform national standards for program development. Geographical organization is better able to coordinate functional programs in a given area. The choice between the two is governed by a decision on which type of coordination is more important. The trend has been from functional toward geographical coordination as more extensive resource development has increased the conflict among functional programs.

Five federal agencies are charged with the planning and construction of projects for water resources development.

1   The U.S. Army Corps of Engineers of the Department of Defense was established in 1824 to develop and maintain facilities for navigation on inland waterways, the major transportation routes of that time. As the only agency with a nationwide water resources program in 1925, the Corps was charged with making the first attempt at systematic comprehensive river basin planning (the 308 reports). The Flood Control Act of 1936 expanded Corps responsibility to implementing a flood control program. The Corps now plans, designs, builds, and maintains projects whose primary purpose is flood control or navigation and which may have such secondary features as may be required for multipurpose development. Its annual construction budget runs about $900 million.

2   The Bureau of Reclamation of the Department of Interior was established in 1902 to provide irrigation water for the economic development of arid areas. It built a number of smaller projects with mixed success in its early years and completed the first large-scale water project in the country with the construction of Hoover Dam in 1928. Today, the Bureau of Reclamation builds irrigation projects in the 19 states, including Hawaii and Alaska, west of a line from Texas to North Dakota. It also includes other project purposes in multipurpose development. Its annual budget is about $200 million.

3   The Tennessee Valley Authority (the only major agency organized by geography) was established in 1933 to provide flood control, navigation, and hydroelectric power in order to enhance agricultural, industrial, and forestry production and thereby accelerate economic development of the Tennessee Valley. The Tennessee Valley Authority has since constructed water resources development projects for all combinations of purposes throughout the Tennessee Valley. Its annual budget for public works is about $300 million.

4   The Soil Conservation Service of the Department of Agriculture was established in 1936 to combat soil erosion and accelerated runoff caused by improper land use. At first, the Soil Conservation Service specialized on land treatment and improved farming practices, but the Small Watershed Act of 1954 authorized the planning and granting of funds to local agencies to finance projects too large to be installed by individ-

ual land owners and too small to be installed by the Corps or the Bureau. The Soil Conservation Service may spend up to $5 million on projects within watersheds smaller than 250,000 acres. All project purposes may be included, but some, such as power and navigation, seldom apply to small watersheds. The projects are initiated, partially financed, and maintained by local interests. Annual construction grants average about $60 million.

5   The Federal Water Pollution Control Agency of the Department of Interior was organized in 1966 in response to a growing dissatisfaction with deteriorating environmental quality to identify water quality problems and evaluate water quality benefits for use in river basin planning. The agency has authority to install structural measures for water quality control but has not been in operation long enough to develop construction experience. Grants and loans to local groups are approaching $200 million annually.

Many other agencies have responsibilities related in some lesser way to water resources planning. Some provide technical advice or financial assistance to local interests requiring water or sewage systems. Others specialize in fish and wildlife, recreation, land management, or electric power.

Proper water resources planning requires a great deal of data. Data collected and published by federal agencies include the climatological data of the Weather Bureau (Environmental Science Services Administration), the streamflow and water quality records and the topographic and geological mapping of the Geological Survey, the population data of the Census Bureau, and the economic data of the Office of Business Economics. The Area Redevelopment Administration provides data for estimating redevelopment benefits and evaluating the effects of economic dislocations. The Soil Conservation Service publishes soils maps. The Forest Service provides forest-cover maps and advice on fire control and forestation measures. The Agricultural Research Service provides information on the potential of various lands for agricultural development. Land use data may be obtained through the Economic Research Service.[1] The Department of Labor provides information on the regional economy, unemployment, and wage rates.

Groups of states have got together to complete studies (on the Delaware and on the Potomac Rivers, for example) and to expedite development of rivers crossing state lines by defining the rights and responsibilities of each state. An interstate compact is analogous to an international

[1]   Marion Clawson with Charles L. Stewart, "Land Use Information: A Critical Survey of U.S. Statistics Including Possibilities for Greater Uniformity" (Baltimore: The Johns Hopkins Press, 1965).

treaty in that it must be negotiated and approved by the legislature of each state, but it is different in that it must also be approved by the Federal government. Fourteen interstate compacts have been perfected with federal participation as of June, 1965. Two of the best known are the compacts establishing the Ohio River Valley Water Sanitation Compact Commission and the Delaware Basin Commission. Fourteen other interstate compacts do not include federal representation.

The traditional role of the states in water resources development has been to uphold the best interest of the people of the state during the planning of federal projects and to regulate development by local government and private parties so as to prevent the occurrence of major external diseconomies. Water rights are defined and enforced by state law. Most states have water quality standards and dam safety regulations. More recently, many states have established statewide water development plans to improve interproject coordination.

The states also set the operating rules for the various levels of local government including general units such as the counties and cities responsible for many types of local needs and the specialized units such as irrigation or drainage districts responsible for only one or two special problems. A typical state may contain 50 counties, several times that many cities, and a vast number of small and geographically overlapping special districts. The state defines the powers of each local government, prescribes their basic rules of organization and operation, and limits their power to raise money by taxes or bonded indebtedness. Closeness to local needs makes local government ideally suited for the development of projects whose scale and external economies it is capable of handling. An idea of the role of local government in water resources development can be obtained by an estimate that of the $7.5 billion spent for water resources development in California through 1962 only one-third was federal money.[1] As of 1966, the federal budget for water development was about $2 billion annually, while the nonfederal budget was about $10 billion.

Private corporations and individuals also participate in water resources development. Electric utilities have undertaken major hydroelectric projects. Large land companies have installed extensive systems to irrigate their holdings. Most ground water used for irrigation is privately developed. Many cities are served by privately owned water systems. Public projects require private investment before the output can be properly utilized; barges are needed for navigation, land leveling for irrigation, wiring for power, boats and camping equipment for recreation, etc.

The federal construction agencies receive political support from

---

[1] Water and Power Development in California, *Western Water News*, vol. 18 (January, 1966), p. 3.

associations of individuals who endorse their programs. Such booster groups include the National Water Resources Association behind the Bureau of Reclamation, the National Rivers and Harbors Congress behind the Corps of Engineers, and the Soil Conservation Society behind the Soil Conservation Service. Some state and district agencies and certain large projects also have booster organizations. Supporters of public and private hydroelectric development are both organized. Farm organizations uphold agricultural interests in water development. Various conservation groups such as the Isaac Walton League and the Sierra Club vigorously resist the development of wilderness areas.[1] On the whole, the groups gaining from public development of water resources are much better organized than the groups paying the bills.

7-2 INTERAGENCY COORDINATION The many agencies and interests involved in or affected by water resource development makes meaningful coordination imperative. The major construction agencies overlap in both functional and geographic jurisdiction. The Corps and the Bureau of Reclamation have vied for authorization to build particular multipurpose projects in the Western states. Another rivalry has developed between those favoring many small upstream measures for flood control (Soil Conservation Service) and those favoring a few, large, downstream measures (Corps or Bureau of Reclamation). Since the ultimate decisions are made politically, controversy intensifies as rival agencies strive for political advantage. Some interagency competition may motivate increased efficiency, but excessive amounts produce duplication and economic waste.

The need for better coordination is also seen in the interagency diversity in standards for engineering design and economic evaluation. Some diversity is justified by differences in local conditions, project scale, or project purpose. However, unwarranted diversity restricts economic efficiency by making project justification depend on the evaluating agency rather than project merit. If projects found by one agency to have a given benefit-cost ratio are far more worthy than those another agency finds to have the same ratio, decision makers have no way to compare projects planned by different agencies.

For both reasons, a long series of efforts have been made through the years to achieve improved interagency coordination and more uniform design standards and economic evaluation criteria. During the 1930s, a National Resources Planning Board was established to initiate compre-

---

[1] A typical conservationist position is found in David R. Brower, Water and Esthetics in the Lower Colorado River Basin, *Proc. Ann. Am. Water Resources Conf.*, *2d* (Urbana, Ill.: American Water Resources Association, 1966), pages 134–142.

hensive planning for all of the nation's rivers,[1] but the Board had too little authority really to come to grips with the central coordination issue, and it was abolished in 1943. After World War II, separate study commissions for each major river basin were formed by representatives of each of the locally active federal agencies and the state governments. The commissions lacked authority for developing and enforcing the needed coordination and standardization, but they did help promote mutual understanding and provide the basic structure, revitalized by the Water Resources Planning Act of 1965, to coordinate agency efforts at comprehensive river basin planning. Shortly thereafter, the Federal Inter-Agency River Basin Committee was formed from the federal agencies involved in river basin planning to standardize methods for economic evaluation of water resources projects. The result was the first effort to establish consensus methods for handling such items as discount rate, project life, and secondary-benefit evaluation.[2]

However, most of the agencies, because of established policies, legal obligations, and what they felt to be situations peculiar to their own programs, continued to emphasize that their participation did not signify intent to revise established policy.[3]

The Bureau of the Budget is directly responsible to the President and assembles the budget the President submits to Congress. Bureau efforts to budget the best water resource projects have been partly frustrated by agency diversity in project evaluation methods. While the Bureau of the Budget is theoretically in a powerful position to institute reform, its staff is far too small to check individual projects effectively to enforce criteria. However, the Bureau has served as a major force to stimulate better inter-agency coordination.

7-3 SENATE DOCUMENT 97   Finally, in response to pressures for improved coordination and the inability of past efforts to meet this need successfully, Senate Resolution 281, passed in 1956, authorized Senate committee hearings to seek acceptable uniform criteria. In January, 1957, the committee reported, and the proposed standards and criteria were debated and incorporated into Senate Resolution 148. When President Kennedy took office in 1961, he requested the Secretaries of the Army, of the Interior, of Agriculture, and of Health, Education, and Welfare to review existing procedures and recommend a uniform policy. The four

---

[1] National Resources Committee, "Water Planning" (Washington: USGPO, 1938).

[2] United States Inter-Agency Committee on Water Resources, Subcommittee on Evaluation Standards, "Proposed Practices for Economic Analysis of River Basin Projects" (Washington: USGPO, 1958).

[3] *Ibid.*, pp. 53–56.

Secretaries reported in May, 1962. They had agreed upon a common document and expressed intent to implement its provisions. When Senator Clinton Anderson of New Mexico presented the report to the Senate, Senate Resolution 342 was passed to have it printed as the Senate document which has become widely known as Senate Document 97.[1]

Senate Document 97 has been more widely accepted than the previous efforts because of presidential backing and its many provisions favorable to the expansion of the water development agencies. In quest of the glittering goal of the most effective use of water and related land-use resources to promote the well-being of all the people, a framework was provided for evaluating benefits by project purpose. Additional benefits could be added during periods of national unemployment or within chronic unemployment areas. National secondary benefits could be counted if they could be adequately documented, and even regional secondary benefits were allowed in the absence of offsetting adverse consequences to other regions (Sec. 8-8). The economic optimum scale of development was advocated but could be exceeded where justified by intangible benefits. Benefits could be counted for up to 100 years at a relatively low discount rate (Sec. 6-9). The net effect was an increase in the benefits available for use in project justification. The agencies were happy with a document which favored an expanded program of capital intensive, water resource development.[2]

While Senate Document 97 has helped coordinate and standardize federal practice, it has not really come to grips with deciding the optimum allocation of capital between the public and private sectors and among alternative public programs. By advocating a relatively loose test of economic feasibility, it has increased the probability of economic justification of politically favored projects. It has brought benefit figures for water quality control, recreation, and fish and wildlife into the evaluation without adequately laying the theoretical foundation for their estimation. Nevertheless, most of these weaknesses stem from limitations in current economic theory and can be modified as capital formulation processes become better understood. Senate Document 97 must be considered just another step in the evolution of a methodology for project evaluation, a focal point to which specific improvements can be applied.

7-4   THE WATER RESOURCES PLANNING ACT OF 1965   Congress acted in 1965 to implement a number of the suggestions found in

---

[1]   The President's Water Resources Council, *Policies, Standards, and Procedures in the Formulation. Evaluation, and Review of Plans for Use and Development of Water and Related Land Resources,* 87th Cong., 2d Sess., Sen. Doc. 97, 1962.

[2]   Emery N. Castle, et al., Water Resources Development: A Review of the New Federal Evaluation Procedures, *J. Farm Economics* (November, 1963), pp. 693–704.

Senate Document 97. A Water Resources Council composed of the Secretaries of Agriculture; the Army; Health, Education, and Welfare; the Interior; and Transportation and the chairman of the Federal Power Commission was formed to maintain continuing surveillance of national and regional water resources management needs, to appraise and coordinate the current institutional framework, to establish appropriate standards and procedures for use in water resources planning, and to review planned projects. The Council members meet at least quarterly but delegate the detailed responsibilities to their representatives, who meet much more frequently, and to a small technical staff. Financial assistance in the form of matching fund grants is provided to aid the states in developing plans representing the local viewpoint.

The Council has divided the country into 20 regions (Fig. 7-1). Framework studies were initiated on long-run plans for developing water and related land resources. Each study attempts to project economic development, appraise the quantity and quality of water and related land resources, focus on major problem areas, and suggest alternative solutions. Each study requires the cooperation of federal and state forces over a period of several years. Provision has also been made for the establish-

FIGURE 7-1   Water resources regions used in the first national assessment. (*From United States Water Resources Council, "The Nation's Water Resources" Washington: USGPO, 1968, p. 1-23*).

ment of federal-state river basin commissions at the initiative of the states involved to coordinate regional planning and project development. Four commissions were established by the end of 1968.[1]

It is still too soon for a realistic evaluation of these efforts, but they have without a doubt made a significant contribution to better program coordination. Their major weakness seems to be an overemphasis on physical solutions to problems suggested by current price and use patterns and an underemphasis on time changes in economic demand and human ecological needs.

7-5 STEPS IN PROJECT DEVELOPMENT The planning of a water resources project is a complex task which takes a minimum of 3 to 5 years from conception to construction and normally takes several times that long for larger projects. Because most planning agencies have a heavy work load, it is often some time after a project is proposed before a study can be scheduled. The work in gathering all the required data and analyzing countless alternatives in order to come up with a satisfactory plan is extremely time consuming. Most projects have controversial elements involving other agencies, the local people, or some special interest group, and a great deal of time may be spent in working out mutually acceptable compromises. Other delays are often experienced in securing the required local financial support. Once a project is authorized, it may have to wait before it can be worked into the federal budget. The reasons for the time lag in project planning are difficult for the layman to fathom, and the planner often has a major public relations job in explaining the reasons for delay to a public which expects its water problems to be solved immediately.

The steps through which a project proceeds from conception to construction vary among agencies. However, the following steps, which outline the practice of the Corps of Engineers, provide a typical pattern.[2] Most agencies have provisions for short circuiting some of the steps on small projects. Each step depends on the satisfactory completion of those preceding it. A delay in any step will delay the project until the difficulty is overcome. Any unfavorable finding will terminate it.

1   State or local interests inform their congressional delegation of their interest in a water resources project, describe the purposes they believe the project should fulfill, and ask that a study be made.

[1] The status of the Council's activities is described in United States Water Resources Council, "The Nation's Water Resources" (Washington: USGPO, 1968).

[2] U.S. Army Corps of Engineers, Procedures for Conception, Authorization, and Construction of Projects, "Survey Investigations and Reports: General Procedures," *Eng. Manual* EM 1120-2-101 (Washington, October, 1964).

2   The congressman or senator determines whether the problem has been studied previously. If not, he introduces a bill, which is generally combined with all other similar proposals into an omnibus bill, and when it is passed by Congress, he directs that the required study be made. If a previous study has been made, he will request the Committee on Public Works of his house of Congress to review the report. If the committee feels modification or updating of the report would be advisable, it authorizes the required work.

3   When the study has been authorized, the chief of engineers (Department of the Army) assigns it to the appropriate division engineer, who in turn assigns it to the district engineer in whose jurisdiction the study area is located.

4   Upon receiving authorization and funds, the district engineer holds a public hearing to determine the views of the local people on the extent and nature of the problem which can be solved by water resources development.

5   From the data he can obtain and after careful consideration of the local views, the district engineer develops, through field and office studies, the plan of improvement best suited to the project area and determines whether the benefits exceed the costs. The plan is developed in enough detail to establish relatively firm benefits and costs but not in anything like the detail which would be required to contract construction.

6   The financial and other local responsibilities are determined, and the local interests are required to demonstrate the desire and ability to satisfy the requirements. If benefits exceed costs and the local people fulfill their responsibilities, the district engineer reports the project back to the division engineer.

7   The division engineer reviews the report, adds his comments, and sends it to the chief of engineers, who refers it to the appropriate experts on his Washington staff for further review.

8   All interested parties including each affected state and interested federal agency are notified of the contents and findings of the report and given opportunity to present their views.

9   The chief of engineers considers all the comments he receives, makes the revisions he thinks necessary, and transmits the report to the Secretary of the Army.

10   The Secretary of the Army sends the report to the Bureau of the Budget, which reviews the project, incorporates its own comments, and sends the report on to Congress.

11   The Committee on Public Works holds the hearings it feels necessary, assembles the final project document, and if it is favorably inclined,

authorizes the project in an omnibus rivers and harbors bill.[1] Omnibus river and harbor bills are passed every 2 years and contain all projects favorably considered during the preceding period. The major factors influencing congressional authorization are a benefit exceeding project cost, location of the project in an area deserving economic help, and mutual accommodations which have been worked out among congressmen for supporting projects in each other's districts.[2]

12 The Corps requests the Bureau of the Budget to provide funds for the project in the budget. The Bureau of the Budget adjusts the request according to the President's budgetary policy and transmits it to Congress for inclusion in the appropriate appropriations bill.

13 The Committee on Appropriations may hold further hearings and include an appropriation for the project in a civil works appropriation bill. Project funds are usually appropriated in a series of annual allotments according to the time required for project installation.

14 Once funds have been received, the district engineer gathers additional and more detailed information and prepares final plans, specifications, and cost estimates.

15 An invitation to bid is published, various contractors study the project and submit their bids, and the contract is awarded to the low bidder. Portions of large projects may be contracted individually.

16 The contractor performs the required work under the inspection of the district engineer, who accepts the job when it has been satisfactorily completed.

17 The facilities are turned over to the operation and maintenance forces.

Legal Consideration in Economic Analysis

The planner may find he is not free to implement the most economic alternative because of various institutional restraints. Some such restraints are based on policy decisions by agency leadership, but others have been more formally incorporated into law. While in the ideal case, the law should be used to implement rather than impede social welfare, it is only being practical to recognize the legal difficulties inherent in implementing certain water resources development alternatives. For example, a project

---

[1]   A graphic description of committee hearings for some of the more controversial projects is found in John Upton Terrell, "War for the Colorado River," 2 vols. (Glendale, Calif.: The Arthur H. Clark Company, 1965).

[2]   Robert H. Haveman, "Water Resource Investment and the Public Interest" (Nashville, Tenn.: Vanderbilt University Press, 1965), pp. 13–40.

to develop a water supply producing high economic benefit may be legally restrained by prior water rights appropriating the water for a use producing little economic benefit.

Some appreciation of legal restraints to planning is important for two reasons. These restraints must be understood in structuring planning alternatives. They must be understood as a starting point for improvements in the legal system to further social welfare.

7-6 THE LEGAL HIERARCHY Constitutional democracy is based on a hierarchy of laws. At the top is the written constitution, the basic law of the land to which all other laws must conform. It is a relatively short document which outlines the basic organization of the government, the powers the government may exercise, and the fundamental rights of the people.

The second step down the hierarchy is legislation enacted by the official legislative body. It takes precedence over all lower levels in the hierarchy but must conform to the constitution. Legislative law covers, in much more detail than can the constitution, every subject with which the legislature sees fit to deal. Legislation may be subdivided between regulations which the citizens must obey and programs enacted to promote the general welfare.

At the third step is administrative law. When trying to enforce legislative law, the executive branch repeatedly encounters situations not covered in even the most carefully drawn legislation. Within the framework of the legislative and constitutional requirements, administrative decisions produce the procedural details required to implement legislation.

Judicial law is at the fourth and bottom step. Disputes produced by situations not covered by higher law are commonly brought to court for settlement. Each court decision states the facts of the case, outlines the reasoning of the court in reaching its verdict, and sets a precedent for subsequent similar cases. However, courts repeatedly reverse former precedents when they feel change to be in accord with the times.

The volume of law dealing with any subject area is so vast that major legal research is required to compile the applicable laws, administrative regulations, and judicial precedents. Codes are assembled collections of laws on a specific subject. Eminent lawyers and jurists have assembled water codes for a number of states. The code has no legal force but is binding to the degree it accurately records existing laws.

The English common law is the entire body of English law anywhere within the hierarchy. As laws and regulations are constantly being changed, the common law is only defined when specified by date. As new states were organized in the United States, most legislatures recognized that they could not immediately pass all the necessary laws and adopted the then current English common law to apply in the absence of specific legislation.

While the hierarchy of the Anglo-Saxon legal system predominates in English-speaking countries, Roman law, which is based on more formal codes, has had a major influence in Southern Europe and Latin America including Southwestern United States. The five other widely recognized legal systems are Germanic law, Soviet law, Mohammedan law, Hindu law, and Chinese law.[1]

7-7   SURFACE-WATER LAW   The two basic doctrines of surface-water law are the riparian doctrine and the appropriation doctrine. The riparian doctrine originated in the relatively humid climates of France and England where water problems were seldom severe enough to attract the attention of legislative or administrative bodies. When conflicts over water were brought to court, judicial decisions were based on the premise, never applicable to other than humid climates, that a party owning land adjoining a stream is entitled to "the full natural flow of the stream without change in quality or quantity." Literally, this rule would forbid anyone from withdrawing any water from, or placing any foreign substance in, the stream. However, the riparian doctrine has gradually been modified to entitle the user to make beneficial use of the water for any purpose not unduly interfering with the beneficial use of other riparian users. As judicial law, riparian doctrine changes with new court decisions and varies from one judicial jurisdiction to another. Nevertheless, all riparian water rights have certain characteristics:

1   The riparian water right is limited to parcels of land abutting the stream.

2   If a parcel is subdivided into two or more smaller parcels, the smaller parcels not abutting the stream lose their riparian water rights and can never regain them.

3   The riparian owner can use the natural flow of the stream but not store the flows for later use.

4   The riparian right is inherent in the ownership of the land and is transferred with ownership even if not mentioned in the deed and even if no water is used.

5   If water runs short, the right to its use is according to priority, which is normally domestic water, irrigation water, industrial water, and

---

[1]   F. J. Berber, "Rivers in International Law" (Dobbs Ferry, N.Y.: Oceana Publications, Inc., 1959), pp. 135–137.

recreational water. Rights within a priority level are prorated among users according to the ratio of the amount of water the individual can beneficially use to the amount all those within that priority level can beneficially use.

Because riparian doctrine provides no way for supplying water to property not adjacent to a stream and no way to store water for use when low flows occur, economic pressures have from very early days caused civilizations in drier climates to develop another approach to surface-water law. The appropriation doctrine was developed in Southern Europe (Roman law) and adopted by the legislatures of the arid states of the United States as the restriction to economic development imposed by riparian law became evident. The details of the legislation varied by state, but the basic doctrine follows certain rules:

1 A specified quantity of water is appropriated through a procedure prescribed by law and tending to become more formal as water becomes more scarce. The right may stipulate the time of year during which water may be withdrawn.
2 When water runs short, the oldest right is completely satisfied first and then later rights in the chronological order of their appropriation until all the water is used. Because a junior right gets no water until all the older rights are satisfied, it is much less valuable than a senior right.
3 The appropriation right is limited to the amount of water put to bene-ficial use, and the right is lost through disuse.
4 The owner of the right is free to change his point of diversion, type of use, or place of use as long as the change does not harm anyone else.
5 The appropriation right allows for both use and storage.
6 The appropriation right may be sold by a specific deed independently of any sale of land.

States adopting English common law thereby adopted riparian doctrine in the absence of specific legislation establishing appropriation doctrine. Riparian doctrine is practical only in areas having a low demand for a water supply fairly widely distributed over the total area and fairly uniformly distributed over the year. As population grows, so does economic pressure for violating riparian doctrine by transporting water from local rural watersheds to more distant urban centers. In arid areas where dependable flow is found only in larger streams, economic forces require transport of water out of the watershed to supply farms and towns not on a major river. Where runoff is seasonal, economic pressures justify storage during wet periods to prevent hardship during dry periods. These economic pressures forced the driest states to adopt appropriation law from their beginning. Over the years, the doctrine has overcome the resistance of riparian owners who had to surrender unused water and spread to progressively wetter areas. Since 1950, appropriation law elements have begun to appear in the states east of the Mississippi.

While appropriation doctrine provides a mechanism for initially allocating water to those valuing it enough to go to some expense to obtain it, the doctrine does not respond to time changes in relative economic demand for water in alternative uses. As water becomes more scarce, the economic penalty of failing to use it in the applications having the highest physical product (Sec. 4-11) becomes more severe. Unless market transfers of rights from one party to another are permitted, appropriation rights become outdated by economic change. Regions suffering severe water shortage are forced into modifying their legal procedure to allow the transfer of water rights from lower- to higher-value uses. Such transfers must eventually become the chief source of supply for new high-value uses in water-short areas. The most promising means for accomplishing this task would be through a market mechanism with legal safeguards to protect the interests of third parties.[1]

For international water-right disputes, two basic rights of sovereign nations conflict. By virtue of territorial sovereignty, a nation may dispose of waters flowing through its territory without obligation to the interest of those downstream. By virtue of territorial integrity, a nation may demand continuation of the natural quantity and quality of waters entering its borders from upstream nations.[2] Because of the absence of an effective judicial system for dealing with international disputes and because of the rigidity of judicial decisions which inherently make them unsuitable for apportioning water under changing conditions,[3] international water rights are characteristically defined by treaties established by the mutual consent of all parties.

7-8 GROUND-WATER LAW   According to English common law, a landowner has the right to pump ground water at any point on his property as long as he does not waste or sell the water and does not act maliciously. When the supply runs short, pumping rights are generally taken to court. Typically the resulting judgment specifies maximum pumping rates in a formula based on the reasonable use by each party and possibly the character of the use and the date pumping began. While the typical apportionment formula favors uses producing greater economic benefit, the common

---

[1]   Jack Hirshleifer, James C. DeHaven, and Jerome W. Milliman, "Water Supply: Economics, Technology, and Policy" (Chicago: The University of Chicago Press, 1960), pp. 222–254.

[2]   Berber, *op. cit.*, pp. 11–14.

[3]   *Nebraska v. Wyoming*, 325 U.S. 589, 65 Sup. Ct. Rept. 1332 (1945).

law restriction against sale prevents possible use of the water, for greater benefit, by those other than the landowner. This fact has caused the more arid states to apply appropriation doctrine to ground water. The value of water is too great to confine its use legally to agriculture on what may be poor-quality overlying land. Under appropriation doctrine, permission to drill a new well is granted by an administrative agency, provided sufficient water is available and no serious detrimental effect will result to older wells. During water shortages, the oldest wells are first in right.

While the large volumes of ground water under many arid areas has caused the pressures to shift from lower- to higher-value use to be slower than for surface water, both water sources are physically interrelated. In the long run, any legal distinction between surface- and ground-water rights makes little hydrologic or economic sense. Legal procedures for dynamic adjustment of combined surface- and ground-water rights will eventually be required.

7-9 LAW ON DIFFUSE SURFACE WATERS English common law applies a principle called the *common-enemy rule* to deal with flow not occurring in any recognized water course and thus likely to cause flood damage. Any downstream owner is allowed to construct dikes or other works to prevent water from flowing onto his property. Any upstream landowner must secure an easement to change the location or timing of discharges onto downstream property.

Roman civil law entitles an upstream owner to discharge his excess water through natural depressions without obstruction by those downstream. He may accelerate the flow to provide better drainage for his land, but he may not flood his neighbor with water transferred across drainage boundaries nor relocate his drainage outlet without first obtaining a drainage easement.

Under both legal systems, a party disrupting the drainage pattern is liable for damages. Economic analysis would find the disruption worthwhile if benefits exceeded damages. Both legal approaches would be more likely to encourage economic efficiency by reducing external diseconomies if they were enforced by requiring payment of realistically appraised damages rather than by prohibiting damage-producing acts.

7-10 OTHER MISCELLANEOUS LAWS The formulation of engineering alternatives must recognize a number of other laws designed to protect the public safety or promote the general welfare. Laws govern the design and construction of dams to ensure their safety against failure. Channel restrictions are controlled to prevent induced flooding and maintain navigation channels. Placing trash or debris within streams is prohibited because it restricts channel capacity and washes onto downstream property. Water quality control legislation limits stream pollution. Each such law has economic implications. The cost of compliance needs to be weighed against the social objectives accomplished.

7-11   THE FEDERAL GOVERNMENT AND WATER LAW   Many potential conflicts exist between federal water projects and state law. Congress recognized state appropriation rights in the Desert Land Act of 1877; however, the supremacy of state water law has been challenged by court rulings in more recent years. The Federal Power Commission was allowed to license a power plant for which license was denied by Oregon because of harm to fish (The Pelton Dam Case).[1] The Navy was not required to comply with Nevada law in developing new wells (The Fallon Case). However, after 14 years of litigation on an earlier ruling that a federal military installation did not have to follow the appropriation procedure required by California law, the United States Court of Appeals in May, 1965, ruled that the federal water right was limited by state law.

Bills have been periodically introduced in Congress to better define the respective rights of the Federal and the state governments. The Federal government's attitude as stated by the Attorney General in his analysis of one of these bills is:

> The United States . . . can utilize these waters without paying any compensation for the impairment of alleged water rights recognized under state law.[2]

Most legal authorities and most of those connected with state and local government advocate requiring the United States to pay for the water it takes from others. The external diseconomies created when water is expropriated without compensation reinforce this position.

7-12   CONSTITUTIONAL BASIS FOR FEDERAL PROJECT DEVELOPMENT   The basic authority for federal water resources development comes from five clauses in the United States Constitution. The commerce clause, found in Article I, Section 8, states:

> The Congress shall have power . . . to regulate commerce with foreign nations, and among the several states and with the Indian Tribes

[1] *Federal Power Commission v. Oregon*, 349 U.S. 435, 75 Sup. Ct. Rept. 832 (1955).
[2] Harvey O. Banks, Federal versus State Interests in Water Development, *Proc. ASCE*, vol. 91, no. IR 1 (March, 1965), p. 34.

and implies control of navigation and navigable waterways and also of implementing structural changes benefitting navigation. This would naturally include all streams and rivers capable in their natural state of being used for commerce. Even rivers entirely located in one state may be used to transport goods eventually winding up in another state. Because regulation of upstream flows affects downstream navigability, the Supreme Court first extended the power to the upper reaches of rivers navigable further downstream[1] and later to all tributaries of a navigable river.[2] The definition of navigability also gradually changed with time to include all streams which might possibly be used for navigation during high water or through channel improvement. Federal water development based on the commerce clause has thus extended to every stream in the country except small creeks discharging directly into the ocean or a closed drainage basin. Furthermore, the Supreme Court also ruled Congress to be the final judge in deciding if a particular water resources project actually benefits navigation.[3] Congress had expressed improved navigation as a purpose in building Hoover Dam, and the Court ruled that all the other features of the project could be justified constitutionally as part of a navigation improvement project even though navigation on the Colorado River was insignificant. A later ruling constitutionally justified flood control on minor tributaries by beneficial effects on navigation on the lower Mississippi River.[4] The commerce clause has also been used to justify Federal Power Commission regulation of hydroelectric plant construction to produce electric power for interstate sale.[5]

The treaty-making power, found in Article II, Section 2, states:

(The President) shall have power, by and with the advice and consent of the Senate, to make treaties, provided two-thirds of the Senators present concur . . .

and Article VI, Section 2, states:

This Constitution, and the laws of the United States which shall be made in pursuance thereof; and all treaties made, or which shall be made, under the authority of the United States, shall be the supreme law of the land; and the judges in every State shall be bound thereby, anything in the Constitution or laws of any State to the contrary not withstanding.

Theoretically, the President and two-thirds of the Senate have power to

[1] *United States v. Rio Grande Dam Co.*, 174 U.S. 690, 19 Sup. Ct. Rept. 770 (1899).
[2] *Oklahoma v. Atkinson*, 313 U.S. 508, 61 Sup. Ct. Rept. 1050 (1941).
[3] *Arizona v. California*, 283 U.S. 423, 51 Sup. Ct. Rept. 522 (1931).
[4] *Oklahoma v. Atkinson*, 313 U.S., 508, 61 Sup. Ct. Rept. 1050 (1941).
[5] *First Iowa Co. v. Federal Power Commission*, 328 U.S. 152, 66 Sup. Ct. Rept. 906 (1946).

build any desired project if a relevant treaty can be made with a foreign power. The scarcity of major rivers crossing international boundaries limits the applicability of this power to water resources development, but treaties do apply to the Colorado, Rio Grande, Columbia, and St. Lawrence River systems. A treaty with Canada has been used to limit diversions by Chicago from Lake Michigan into the Illinois River. Projects affecting migratory birds are also controlled by international treaty.

The proprietary power, found in Article IV, Section 3, states:

> The Congress shall have power to dispose of and make all needful rules and regulations respecting the territory or other property belonging to the United States.

Historically, most of the land in the country has been owned by the United States except for the 19 non-public-land states (the 13 colonies, Maine, Vermont, West Virginia, Kentucky, Hawaii, and Texas) which were settled prior to their coming into the United States. The Federal government has also purchased large acreages in all states for building, park, military or other uses. The proprietary clause gives the United States power to develop the water resources located on its own property and to govern the use of public land by others for building a water resources project. The Reclamation Act of 1902 was judged constitutional as a measure for improving public lands for easier sale.[1] The Supreme Court has also ruled that hydroelectric power generated in federal water projects is the property of the United States and may be disposed of in any way the government sees fit.[2]

The war power, found in Article I, Section 8, gives the government authority to "provide for the common defense." The output from water resources projects may become essential to the common defense during times of war, and the clause was used to constitutionally justify Wilson Dam, in the Tennessee Valley, to generate power for use in the manufacture of nitrates to be used in munitions for World War I.

The general welfare clause, found in Article I, Section 8, states:

> The Congress shall have power to . . . provide for the . . . general welfare of the United States. . . .

For many years, the Supreme Court consistently ruled this phrase to be merely a summary of the preceding list of more specific powers, but in 1936 it was ruled to be a separate power.[3] The next year the Supreme

---

[1]   *United States v. Hanson*, 167 F. 881 (1909).
[2]   *Ashwander v. Tennessee Valley Authority*, 297 U.S. 288, 56 Sup. Ct. Rept. 466 (1936).
[3]   *United States v. Butler*, 297 U.S. 1, 56 Sup. Ct. Rept. 312 (1936).

Court stated that the Congress has the discretion to use this power to promote the public interest when none of the other specific powers apply.[1] Since 1937, the trend has been to justify water projects as promoting the general welfare rather than on a strained interpretation of one of the other clauses. The change provides a much more solid and logical constitutional basis for federal involvement in water resources development. It brings the test of constitutionality close to the test of first-order efficiency (Sec. 5-3).

7-13 GOVERNMENT LIABILITY   According to English common law, the king could not be sued for the actions of his men in executing his orders. Those upholding community safety and welfare must be free to act without worrying about liability for incidental injury to third parties. The resulting doctrine of sovereign immunity prevents the government from being sued no matter how negligent the actions of its employees. However, reasoning that the government is much more able than the individual to withstand the financial burden resulting from the negligence of public officials, Congress has passed the Federal Tort Claims Act[2] accepting specific types of liability. Other levels of government have accepted varying degrees of liability.

Government liability becomes an issue whenever individuals are harmed as a consequence of water resources development. While damages are rarely paid to property owners subject to residual flooding when properly designed facilities are overtopped, the government definitely is liable for property which would not otherwise be flooded if it is inundated in the course of project construction or operation. It may also be liable for damages resulting from neglecting to follow good engineering practice or failure to foresee probable adverse effects in project design, construction, or operation.[3]

The practice in the United States is for no compensation to be paid those who are deprived of the full use of their land by regulation or zoning measures. The practice may be justified as a means of controlling the external diseconomies of obnoxious land use, but it is less equitable when uncompensated regulation is used to confer a benefit on the general public (preserving reservoir sites or eliminating the expense of building structural measures for flood control). The land owner is required to bear a cost, which the government is better able to bear than he. Most British Commonwealth countries require the state to compensate when it restricts the

---

[1] *Helvering v. Davis*, 301 U.S. 619, 57 Sup. Ct. Rept. 904 (1937).

[2] U.S. Code, Title 28, secs. 2671 et seq. (Washington: USGPO).

[3] A discussion of government liability by a deputy attorney general of California is found in John R. Burton, "Is the Government Liable When Levees Fail during a Flood?" Paper submitted to the *Hydraulics Div. Conf., ASCE, Davis, Calif.*, August, 1962.

privileges of private ownership in order to achieve a public benefit. Many American legal decisions follow the same reasoning, but following the hierarchy of law, the courts have often deferred to contrary legislative judgment.[1]

The trend toward more liberal interpretation of government liability means that potential damages must be considered with increasing care in the planning of water resource projects. Since all adverse consequences should be evaluated in project planning whether the government pays for them or not, the degree of liability does not affect the economic feasibility of a project. However, the additional funds required to pay for the damages may have a substantial effect on financial feasibility. The assumption of liability by government merely shifts the cost bearing from individuals damaged to the agency responsible for the project. While government liability would not theoretically affect economic feasibility, the increased financial responsibility of development agencies may spark increased care in project economic evaluation.

SELECTED REFERENCES

Castle, Emery, et al.: Water Resources Development: A Review of the New Federal Evaluation Procedures, *J. Farm Economics*, vol. 45 (November, 1963), pp. 693–704.

Ellis, Willis H.: Water Transfer Problems: Law, in Allen V. Kneese and Stephen C. Smith (eds.), "Water Research" (Baltimore: The Johns Hopkins Press, 1966), pp. 233–248.

Hirshleifer, Jack, James C. DeHaven, and Jerome W. Milliman: "Water Supply: Economics, Technology, and Policy" (Chicago: The University of Chicago Press, 1960).

Milliman, Jerome W.: Water Law and Private Decision-making: A Critique, *J. Law and Economics*, vol. 2 (October, 1959), pp. 41–63.

Pealy, Robert H: "Comprehensive River Basin Planning: The Arkansas-White-Red Basins Interagency Committee Experience" (Ann Arbor: The University of Michigan Press, Institute of Public Administration, 1959).

Sax, Joseph L.: "Water Law: Cases and Commentary" (Boulder, Colo.: Pruett Press, 1965).

Trelease, Frank J.: Policies for Water Law: Property Rights, Economic Forces, and Public Regulation, *Nat. Resources J.*, vol. 1 (May, 1965).

Water Resources Council: "The Nation's Water Resources" (Washington: USGPO, 1968).

---

[1] Allison Dunham, City Planning: An Analysis of the Content of the Master Plan, *J. Law and Economics*, vol. 1 (October, 1958), pp. 170–186.

PROBLEMS

7-1 Several federal agencies perform economic analyses of water resources development alternatives. However, they differ in procedures and standards used for evaluating benefits and costs.

    a What difficulties does this situation cause in achieving economic efficiency?

    b What does past experience in trying to develop a uniform approach tell about the kind of uniform approach the agencies are more likely to accept?

    c In what ways may the best interest of the agencies conflict with overall public welfare?

7-2 Select a water resources project currently being discussed for an area with which you are familiar. From your knowledge of the situation and the mission of the various groups, which agencies would be involved in any way with the project? What would their concern be? Consider federal, state, local, private, and organized-group interests. Are these interests likely to prejudice project feasibility studies in any way? How?

7-3 List the characteristics a doctrine of surface-water law should have to encourage economic efficiency best.

7-4 The Congress of the United States passed a law, duly signed by the President, directing the Army Corps of Engineers to build a dam on a nonnavigable stream lying wholly within the limits of one state, for the purpose of storing water to be used solely for generating electricity to be sold to five cities and towns all in the same state as the stream, these cities and towns having municipal electric distribution systems. Under what, if any, provisions of the United States Constitution can this statute be upheld?

7-5 A project is economically feasible if benefits to whomsoever they may accrue exceed the costs. A project is financially feasible if sufficient money can be raised to pay all bills which result from its construction.

    a Evaluate the paragraph below.

    b Does government liability affect economic feasibility?

    c Does government liability affect financial feasibility?

> We will not know the outcome of the Feather River suits for several years. But, important from your present standpoint is that the possibility of governmental liability must now be taken into account as a real factor in planning these projects. Such potential damage liability can be of significance in determining the economics of a

project. The economic feasibility of a project may be greatly reduced if, in addition to the huge expenditures of money that may be required for construction, you must also take into account the possibility of extensive call upon the government treasuries for damages at a future date. I do not mean to suggest that construction of levee projects will cease. Obviously it won't. But, some projects may not be constructed that otherwise would be. Without doubt, if a legislative body during some years must provide sums in the millions of dollars for damages from a levee break, funds for new construction during that year are likely to be considerably reduced. The new construction will be foregone or delayed.[1]

7-6   The following statement was made by James K. Carr, undersecretary of the interior, to the Joint Meeting of the Missouri Basin Inter-Agency Commission and the Columbia Basin Inter-Agency Commission at Jackson Lake Lodge, Wyoming, June 19, 1963:

Opponents said that Grand Coulee Dam would be a "white elephant"—the jackrabbits in the sagebrush would be the only power and water customers.

The Missouri River basin plan was attacked as mainly one to aggrandize the dam builders of the Federal government.

You know the record. This nation will forever be indebted to the men who had the courage and forsight to see the opportunity for national expansion through these projects and stand by their guns under fire. And an additional dividend was the American lives saved because Grand Coulee and Bonneville power was available to turn ships off the ways and produce the weapons that shortened World War II. The enhanced economic strength in both basins resulting from water and power projects are bastions of national strength in these uneasy times.

When short-sighted, self-styled experts criticized Grand Coulee, they were wrong. Had we known then what we know now, we would have long ago built more dams, more power plants at greater capacities and the people of this country would have been billions of dollars ahead for it.

Let's take a backsight on Grand Coulee and Columbia Basin development and get an accurate bearing on the direction we now need to travel. We cannot afford to let any part of America lie fallow.

Specifically, it is time we build structures such as Knowles Dam, decide on a plan for the Upper Missouri, and move forward with ready projects and plans for further development, in every other river basin in the United States. The need for greater water conservation is growing critical. The savings to the taxpayers will belie every criticism of your dedicated and enthusiastic public service.

[1]   John R. Burton, *op. cit.*, pp. 16–17.

    a To what type of audience does a statement of this type appeal?

    b What reasoning can you give to support Carr's argument?

    c What objections to it can you list?

    d How does the statement relate to the economic problem of selecting the optimum construction schedule?

CHAPTER
EIGHT

BENEFIT-COST
ANALYSIS

Project Evaluation

8-1 FEASIBILITY TESTS Project planners must select from a myriad of proposed projects. Each proposal must pass five feasibility tests. The test of engineering feasibility is passed if the proposed project is physically capable of performing its intended function. The point is not that almost any desired water resources project could be built if expense were no object. A specific proposal consists of a specific physical system which may not work satisfactorily. Engineering design must be confined to the technologically feasible region (Fig. 4-1).

The test of economic feasibility is passed if the total benefits that result from the project exceed those which would accrue without the project by an amount in excess of the project cost. It is important that the comparison be *with* and *without* rather than *before* and *after* because many of the after affects may even occur without the project and can thus not properly be used in project justification. Economic feasibility is contingent on engineering feasibility because a project incapable of producing the desired output is not going to produce the benefits needed for its justification.

The test of financial feasibility is passed if sufficient funds can be raised to pay for project installation and operation. While financial feasibility should always be contingent on engineering feasibility, projects have been constructed which simply do not work. A project may be economically feasible but financially infeasible because the benefits are insufficiently concrete for the beneficiaries to appreciate their true value or are distributed among too many people for payment to be practical. A project may be economically infeasible but financially feasible because someone is willing to pay for the fulfillment of noneconomic goals. One goal of economic evaluation in the United States is to make federal financial participation and hence, to a large extent, financial feasibility contingent on economic feasibility. Financial feasibility also depends on local interests believing estimated economic benefit to the degree that they are willing to raise their portion of the required funds.

The test of political feasibility is passed if the required political approval can be secured. Ordinarily political support follows proof of economic and engineering feasibility. Political pressure for project construction may even be quite strong despite proof of economic infeasibility. On the other hand, groups which feel they are adversely affected often oppose project installation. For example, a humid region may oppose water export to an arid region. Almost every project harms someone, and if enough people are harmed or if those who are harmed are sufficiently vocal, they may be able to use political processes to prevent project construction.

The test of social feasibility is passed if the potential users will respond favorably to project construction. Project success depends on the users of project output being motivated to shift to irrigated agriculture, to utilize electrical equipment, or to do whatever else is needed to realize potential project benefits. The more drastic the changes are that the project requires in the lives of the beneficiaries, the greater is the inertia that can be expected from those slow to change their way of living. The infusion of productive capital will not automatically transform a tradition-bound society. Some projects, such as recirculation of municipal waste water after treatment, may encounter increased inertia because of psychological connotations or cultural unacceptability.

Engineering feasibility is ascertained through design analysis as described in standard engineering texts.[1] Financial feasibility is determined by examining potential sources of available funds (Sec. 22-1). Political feasibility is determined by analysis of how key decision makers assess the favorable and adverse effects of the project, the intensity of popular feelings, and the project potential for obtaining widespread public support. Social feasibility is determined by assessing the change the project can be expected to impart to the daily lives of the beneficiaries and evaluating the willingness of those affected to adapt.

---

[1] Ray K. Linsley and Joseph B. Franzini, "Water Resources Engineering" (New York: McGraw-Hill Book Company, 1964); Edward Kuiper, "Water Resources Development: Planning, Engineering and Economics" London: Butterworth & Co. (Publishers), Ltd., 1965).

8-2   THE NEED FOR TESTING ECONOMIC FEASIBILITY   The
government has taken over water resources planning because collective
action has been needed to overcome allocation deficiencies in a market
economy, to coordinate multiproject systems effectively, and to provide
the extensive financial resources required. It may exercise taxing authority
or regulatory action to incorporate external effects into the decision-
making process or control the adverse effects of natural monopoly. It may
build projects to provide public wants or achieve the broad-based objectives of a social welfare function.

In the private sector, firms are motivated to innovate and cut costs
by "the love of profits and the threat of bankruptcy."[1] If they do not produce efficiently, private firms will not survive. However, in government,
"there are no forces which operate to reveal the cheapest methods of performing public functions and to induce or compel the government to
adopt such methods."[2] As a result of the lack of market incentives in the
public sector, allocations of public funds are often made by the path of mo-
mentary least political resistance rather than by objective evaluation.
Projects are built which are economically infeasible because so many
politicians regard the budget for water resources development as a pork
barrel from which.they can withdraw funds to further their own political
interests.[3] The objective of benefit-cost analysis is to force the decision
maker into an objective evaluation of the merits of each proposed project
and thereby encourage an improved allocation of public funds.

One of the major accomplishments of the federal program for water
resources development has been the introduction of economic criteria into
government decision making. Investment alternatives are evaluated by the
consequences of project installation with the required expenditure. The
Bureau of Reclamation has been concerned with the economic justification
of its projects since the advent of its program in 1902, even though in the
early years financial analysis was given greater emphasis. However, the
classic legislative description of benefit-cost analysis is in the Flood Control Act of 1936,[4] which started the Corps of Engineers on its modern
flood control program. Since that date, the method has been extended to
every water resource development purpose.

8-3   DEFINING BENEFITS AND COSTS   Benefits and costs can
only be measured with respect to a goal. Each alternative course of action

---

[1]   Roland N. McKean, "Efficiency in Government through Systems Analysis" (New York: John
Wiley & Sons, Inc., 1958), p. 10.

[2]   *Ibid.*, p. 11.

[3]   See Keith Wheeler et al., Now—See the Innards of a Fat Pig, *Life* (Aug. 16, 1963), pp. 21-26, 55-61
for one account of the abuses that can result.

[4]   U.S. Code (Washington: USGPO 1940), p. 2964.

requires the commitment of resources. Benefits measure the effectiveness of the action in achieving the goal. The resources once committed cannot be used elsewhere. Their commitment has the opportunity cost of other uses sacrificed. Costs measure the effectiveness of the sacrificed action in achieving the goal.

Theoretically, benefits and costs may be based on any desired goal. Ideally, the goal would be an unambiguous and unanimously accepted social welfare function. Practically, the goal becomes the second-order efficiency objective of economic efficiency or maximum national income (Sec. 5-7). However, numerical estimates of benefits and costs with respect to other goals are sometimes also included. Strictly speaking, such effects cannot be measured in the same units as efficiency benefits or efficiency costs. Combining the two requires a value judgment on the relative merits of the goals (Sec. 5-3).

The effectiveness of alternative courses of action in reaching the efficiency goal is measured with reference to the pure-competition model. Even though planning from the public viewpoint is based on a market model, the analysis differs from that which would be made by a private firm. The primary differences are:

1 The public viewpoint incorporates all costs and all benefits to whomsoever they may accrue. External economies and diseconomies need to be evaluated (Sec. 5-10).

2 The discount rate may be lower than that used by private firms because of the substitution of collective time preference for the financial cost of borrowed money (Sec. 6-7).

3 When market prices lose their normative significance because of deviation from the pure-competition model (Sec. 3-2), the government planner, rather than continue to use them as does the private planner, should attempt to evaluate the true economic worth of each input and output (Sec. 5-8).

4 When analyzing projects producing products or outputs which are not marketable (Sec. 5-9), the government planner must derive an equivalent market value through demand analysis.

8-4 BENEFIT-COST CATEGORIES Because benefits and costs stem from so many kinds of effects, a systematic procedure is required to make sure each effect is considered and evaluated. Unfortunately water resource planners and government agencies have not used consistent terminology to describe the individual effects. The result is:

. . . a jungle of . . . categories: pecuniary and nonpecuniary, internal and external, private and social, nontransfer and transfer, on-site and off-site, direct and indirect, market and extra-market, economic and noneconomic, measurable, monetary and nonmonetary, tangible and intangible, direct and spillover, individual and collective, primary and secondary.[1]

Even though the distinctions among these categories vary among practicing economists and are often arbitrary, systematic classification is essential to orderly economic analysis. The reader should concentrate his attention on the concept behind each benefit and cost rather than the name given it.

All agencies express the results of their economic analysis as a single ratio with gross benefits in the numerator and costs in the denominator and consider the project justified if this ratio exceeds 1 (Sec. 2-11). Net benefit is the numerator less the denominator. The project is justified if the net benefit is positive. Economic justification is not influenced by whether a cost item is added to the denominator or subtracted from the numerator (a negative benefit) as it requires only that benefits exceed costs or that the ratio exceed 1. However, the practice has been to place in the denominator all public financial costs no matter whether they were borne by federal, state, or local agencies or whether they were for initial construction or subsequent upkeep. The numerator contains the algebraic sum of the values of beneficial and adverse project consequences to private parties. Project consequences fall into four main classes:

1 Tangible (market) benefits result from the consequences to private parties which can be assigned a monetary value. Many consequences are evaluated in the market place, but consequences are still considered tangible even though they must be established by a more elaborate deductive process. The decision of how abstract a consequence must be before it can no longer be assigned a meaningful monetary value is essentially a value judgment, and hence some agencies set numerical values on consequences which other agencies consider intangibles. Benefit as used in the following discussion is a net value incorporating both adverse and favorable consequences and may on occasion be negative.

   a Primary benefits denote the value obtained from project-produced goods and services. The benefits accrue from physical effects of the project on the user as contrasted with effects transmitted through market transactions.

   i Direct benefits accrue to those who put project output to its intended use. By project purpose, they may consist of a reduction in physical damage to items coming in contact with floodwater, increases in farm income resulting from application of irrigation water, the value the consumer received from the use

---

[1] Tillo Kuhn, "Public Enterprise Economics and Transport Problems" (Berkeley: University of California Press, 1962), p. 7. Reprinted by permission of the Regents of the University of California.

of electric power, the savings in transportation cost for goods moved by navigation, or the satisfaction the recreationist derives from his experience.

ii Indirect benefits result as individuals realize the economic consequences of technological external effects. The effects may result either from the production of project output or from its use by others. Output intended for one purpose (low-flow augmentation for water quality control) may also achieve other beneficial effects (navigation). Flood control projects may benefit users of transportation and communication systems by reducing interruptions and reduce the wages lost by workers or crop losses by farmers when industrial or food-processing plants are closed by flooding. Irrigation may reduce dust storms.

iii Land-enhancement benefits result when a more productive land use is made possible by the project and are distinguished from direct benefits to the land use which would prevail without the project. For example, a flood control project may enable farmers to shift from a lower- to a higher-value crop by reducing flooding. Land-enhancement benefits equal the net crop income from the higher-value crop with flood protection less the net crop income from the lower-value crop with flood protection. The direct benefits are the net gain in crop income from the lower-value crop which results because of the prevention of flood losses. Sometimes flood protection causes agriculture to be replaced by urban development, and the increase in land productivity is considered a land-enhancement benefit. Agricultural land-enhancement benefit is not distinguished from other primary benefits in irrigation projects where the crop pattern radically changes with the arrival of irrigation water. However, the enhancement of land value within urban areas surrounded by newly irrigated land is a benefit which may be properly attributed to project construction.

b Secondary benefits denote value added to activities influenced by the project through economic rather than technological linkages. They result from pecuniary external effects.

i Secondary benefits ("stemming-from" benefits) may result from forward production linkages that increase the net income of those who process project output. Cotton produced by an irrigation project must be processed a number of times before it is sold as clothing, and each intermediate processor may profit from the increased business. The net stemming-from benefit is the income from processing project output net of the sum of the income which would be obtained from processing output displaced by the project and output which would result were the money spent on the project devoted to an alternative investment.

ii Secondary benefits ("induced-by" benefits) may result from backward production linkages which increase the net income of those who provide goods and services to the project area. Cotton produced by an irrigation project will require the purchase of farm machinery, fertilizer, and other materials and thus initiate a chain reaction profiting all these businesses and all those who in turn supply them. Again, the net induced-by benefit would be the increased income of those serving the project area less the loss in income of those who would otherwise provide input for the alternate and the displaced investments.

c Employment benefits denote the economic value gained from the increased employment opportunity from new jobs created to construct, maintain, or operate the project. All agencies have placed greater emphasis on these effects since the passage of the Area Redevelopment Act of 1961. A related effect is the increased employment opportunity induced by production of project output. Irrigation projects attract those living elsewhere on a marginal income to a new productive rural enterprise. Project output may also stimulate investment opportunity on the farms and within the communities where it is used.

d Public benefits are realized in achievement of goals other than economic efficiency and thus can be evaluated in efficiency dollars only by means of a value judgment on the relative desirability of the second goal. Specific recognition is most often given economic stabilization (Sec. 5-12), income redistribution (Sec. 5-13), regional development (Sec. 5-14), and environmental quality (Sec. 5-15).

2 Intangible (extramarket) benefits describe consequences which cannot be assigned a monetary value but which should be considered when deciding whether or not to build a project. Examples are the saving of life or improvement of health, improved environmental esthetics, and the preservation of areas of unique natural beauty and scenic, historical, or scientific interest.

3 Project construction requires private parties to bear costs as well as realize benefits. These costs are subtracted from the benefits to calculate a net benefit realized.

a Associated costs include private investment to produce or utilize project output. An example is the farm costs required to prepare the land for irrigation, convert to a new cropping pattern, and purchase the machinery required by the new crops. Whenever secondary benefits are counted for project justification their associated costs should also be counted. Sometimes nonsponsoring public agencies may be required to pay the cost of such items as schools and better roads to serve the more intensive land use.

b Induced costs evaluate adverse consequences of project construction and should be evaluated whether or not the sponsoring agency has a legal financial obligation to pay damages. Examples are the cost of downstream flood control measures necessitated by upstream land drainage, the increased cost of transportation around reservoir sites, and the cost of a drainage system to remove excess irrigation water.

4 The cost of project installation is placed in the denominator of the benefit-cost ratio. The initial cost includes construction cost, engineering and administration cost, right-of-way cost, the cost of relocating facilities, and other minor costs. Construction cost is the amount paid to the contractor for completing the work outlined in the plans and specifications. Engineering and administration cost is the expense of preparing the necessary plans and specifications, inspecting construction work, providing technical review of engineering details, conducting special investigations such as hydraulic-model studies or geologic exploration, and completing the incidental administrative paper work. Right-of-way cost is the opportunity cost of using the land required for project installation and maintenance. Lands which may still be used by the original owner such as lands along a reservoir periphery, inundated only during exceedingly rare floods, or lands under overhead powerlines or over underground pipelines may be secured by easements. The cost of relocating facilities is the amount required to move or modify bridges, roads, railroads, pipelines, and powerlines located on the project right-of-way. Other costs include state dam filing fees or payments for water-rights acquisition.

After installation, the project has continuing costs of operation, maintenance, and replacement. Operation includes the opening and closing of gates, overseeing hydroelectric plants, purchasing power for pumping, and other activities required to produce project output on a continuing basis. Maintenance includes preventive maintenance to reduce anticipated breakdowns and repairs to the project production mechanism. Weeds must be cleaned out of channels and erosion damage repaired. Machinery must be serviced. Recreational areas must be kept clean and attractive. Trash blocking flow through culverts must be removed. Major repairs may be needed after large floods. Replacement includes installing at periodic intervals new pumps, well casings, or machinery whose useful life is less than that of the project as a whole.

Benefit-Cost Measurement

Project evaluation requires a comparison between the events predicted to occur if the project is built and those predicted to occur if the project is not built. This is called the *with-and-without principle*. It differs from the before-and-after principle because conditions will change even without project construction. Application of the with-and-without principle requires prediction of the changes which will occur if the project is not built as well as those which will occur if the project is built.

8-5   DIRECT PRIMARY BENEFITS   The two most widely used approaches to estimating direct primary benefits are through the market value of output produced and through the cost of producing the same output in some alternative manner. The market-value approach is easier to apply and more reliable if a market exists for project output or if project output can be tied to specific market commodities. Alternative cost provides a second-order approximation where market value cannot be approximated.

The gross benefit resulting from output marketable under conditions of pure competition would equal market price times output quantity. However, prevailing market conditions may rob market price of its normative significance through external effects (Sec. 5-10), natural monopoly (Sec. 5-11), outside intervention (price regulation, for example), export-import restrictions, etc. In such cases, shadow prices may be estimated by employing an economic model (Sec. 9-3). If price or unit value received varies with the level of project output, the demand curve must be derived (Secs. 12-17 and 16-15), and benefits will equal aggregate value in use (Sec. 4-16). If no direct market exists for project output, benefits may be imputed from demand curves developed through analysis of output-related market gains and losses such as is normally done for irrigation water or flood control. A more detailed analysis of problems of benefit analysis by project purpose is found in Chaps. 10 to 17.

Benefits most often appear as changes in the income of the beneficiaries, but they may appear, particularly in agricultural areas or underdeveloped cultures, as changes in consumption. Sometimes attempts are made to evaluate benefits from changing land values. The market value of land is the discounted present worth of the income (or consumption) the owner expects to derive. Thus, one should estimate benefits either directly from changes in income from the land or indirectly from changes in land value and not double count by combining estimates from the two methods. Income analysis is a better tool for evaluating market goods produced by the project. Land value analysis is a promising tool for goods or services not generally exchanged in the marketplace. Sometimes, benefits may be estimated both ways as a check.

Where derivation of a meaningful demand curve is difficult, costly, or time consuming (a common circumstance for hydroelectric power, navigation, or municipal water supply projects), benefits have often been taken as the cost of the least costly alternative project. The reasoning is that if a demand for an output is sufficiently strong that it would be satisfied in the second least costly manner even if the least costly alternative were not built, the gross benefit equals the value of the stream of resources released by not constructing the second-best alternative. For example, if a project can supply water at $50 an acre-foot which would otherwise be supplied at $70 an acre-foot from the second-best alternative, the gross benefit is $70 an acre-foot and the net benefit is $20 an acre-foot.

The alternative-cost approach is subject to severe abuse in the absence of proof that the second-best alternative would be built if the best were not. It is always possible to find a more expensive way of building any project. At the other extreme, the net benefit may be made as small as one might like by comparing the project with an alternative that differs from it by only a very slight modification. This possibility should be avoided by not using alternatives with common elements. The only case where alternative cost can be directly taken as benefit is where a project having exactly the same effects will definitely be built by someone else if the project in question is not built. If the effects are almost the same, the alternative cost may be taken as the benefit after adjusting for differences.

The alternative-cost method inherently assumes some project to be justified from the beginning because the second-best alternative will always cost more than the best. Use of the requirements approach or the assumption that specific levels of goods or services are essential voids much of the value of economic analysis. McKean has suggested that consumers might all "need Cadillacs" if costs were not a factor.[1] Most of us buy cheaper transportation and use the savings for other purposes. However, many projected future water requirements have been made without reference to cost. One suspects, for example, that the requirements for water on certain arid lands would diminish considerably were the users required to repay the full cost (Sec. 12-20). The requirement of removing all pollution from the streams and rivers of the country would be significantly modified were the full increase in the economic cost of waste disposal explicitly paid by the beneficiaries.

[1]   McKean, *op. cit.*, p. 12.

8-6 INDIRECT PRIMARY BENEFITS Indirect benefits are best evaluated by developing a check list of potential project technological external effects (Sec. 5-10) and methodically assessing each one. The check list for a flood control project would include the amount of use and the duration of interruption of transportation and communication facilities, the number of workers and farmers depending on closed plants, and the amount of business lost by flooded merchants. The magnitude of each effect may be estimated by interviewing those affected during recent floods, and unit economic values may be assigned by market analysis. Finally, the results may be summed for a total benefit. The same detailed evaluation of potential technological external effects based on known local conditions and consequences of similar projects can be applied to other project purposes.

The complexity of the above evaluation process has lead the agencies to estimate indirect benefits from direct benefits based on percentages originally derived from case studies. The SCS uses percentages ranging from 5.0 to 20.0 depending on the type of direct benefit for flood control.[1] However, it is very poor practice to apply such fixed percentages without first carefully documenting the relative magnitude of indirect benefits for probable project conditions.

8-7 LAND–ENHANCEMENT BENEFITS Land-enhancement benefits may be used for project justification after developing substantial evidence that land use will change as the direct result of the project. From the national point of view, the change should not be a mere shift in location from one spot to another. Agricultural land-enhancement benefit equals the increase in net income resulting from shifting from a lower- to a higher-valued crop. It is estimated from cropping patterns with and without the project and from crop income figures estimated by farm budgets. Urban land-enhancement benefit equals the net project-effected change in the value of urban land. A project may divert urban development into an area of project benefit. The loss in land value at the alternative site should be deducted from the gain within the area of benefit.

8-8 SECONDARY BENEFITS Senate Document 97 requires the agencies when evaluating secondary benefits for project formulation and justification to indicate:

---

[1] U.S. Soil Conservation Service, "Economics Guide for Watershed Protection and Flood Prevention" (Washington, 1964), chap. 3, pp. 31–32.

a The amount of secondary benefits considered attributable to the project from a national viewpoint. Such benefits, combined with primary benefits, shall be included in the computation of a benefit-cost ratio.

b Secondary benefits attributable to the project from a regional, state, or local viewpoint. Such benefits shall also be evaluated, when this procedure is considered pertinent, and an additional benefit-cost ratio computed.

c Presentations in planning reports shall include an explanation of the nature of each type of secondary benefit taken into account from either viewpoint and the methods used in the computation of each of their values. The implications, from the national viewpoint, of considering secondary benefits of the project from a regional, state, or local viewpoint shall be set forth.[1]

The evaluation of secondary benefits thus includes estimation of their total magnitude, their division between those national and those local in character, and analysis of the implications of local secondary benefits toward achieving national goals other than economic efficiency.

The Bureau of Reclamation (USBR) has estimated the secondary benefits associated with the production of agricultural crops as a percentage of direct benefits. Typical percentages used for stemming-from benefits are summarized in Table 8-1.[2] A uniform percentage of 18 is recommended for induced-by benefits.[3] Marts has developed a methodology for estimating local secondary benefits which gives values ranging from 112 to 174 percent of direct benefits.[4]

While secondary benefits from the local point of view are quite large as shown by the magnitude of these estimates, secondary benefits from the national point of view are much smaller. Eckstein concluded that they are

[1] The President's Water Resources Council, *Policies, Standards, and Procedures in the Formulation, Evaluation, and Review of Plans for Use and Development of Water and Related Land Resources,* 87th Cong., 2d Sess., Sen. Doc. 97, 1962, pp. 6–7.

[2] McKean, *op. cit.*, pp. 154–157.

[3] *Ibid.*

[4] M. E. Marts, Use of Indirect Benefit Analysis in Establishing Repayment Responsibility for Irrigation Projects, *Econ. Geography* (April, 1956), pp. 132–138.

TABLE 8-1   USBR Stemming-from Benefits by Crop

Cotton	88	Dry beans	28
Wool	83	Rice	18
Grain (wheat, oats, corn, barley)	53	Livestock (meat)	16
Oil crops (flax, cotton seed, soy beans)	35	Seed crops	15
Sugar beets	31	Dairy products	12
Fruits and vegetables	29	Poultry products	11

essentially zero from the national viewpoint in times of full employment.[1] Failure to build a project releases resources to be spent in some other manner producing another set of effects through economic linkages. The secondary benefit from the national point of view equals the net difference between the economic value of the secondary consequences of water resources projects and the displaced investment. The Soil Conservation Service arbitrarily estimates this value as 10.0 percent of the direct benefits (assuming water projects have more economic linkage effects than other investment), but no one has conclusively proved a net benefit actually to exist. More empirical research on the nature of the displaced investment and on the study of economic linkages through input-output models (Sec. 9-3) is needed to improve secondary-benefit estimation.

The implications of local secondary benefits from the national viewpoint depend on the effectiveness of local economic development in achieving national noneconomic goals. Income redistribution toward low-income areas, improved economic stability by building a broader economic base, and effects on the quality of the local environment particularly need to be considered. Water resources projects can be used as a tool for controlling the diseconomies inherent in the excessive congestion associated with large metropolitan complexes as well as a tool for accelerating economic growth in lagging areas. The secondary effects of new development in congested areas are likely to be of negative value.

8-9   EMPLOYMENT BENEFITS   The economic benefit of using unemployed resources in project construction, operation, or maintenance is evaluated as the wages paid to those who would otherwise be unemployed or the increase in wages paid to those who would otherwise be underemployed. Use of the benefit for project justification must be substantiated by evidence that alternative local employment opportunity in the affected skills is lacking and that the labor force is immobile. High levels of local unemployment do not automatically ensure that an increased-employment-opportunity benefit will be achieved unless the unemployment involves skills able to be used in project construction or operation. Furthermore, it is unreasonable to assume that the unemployment will continue throughout the life of the project. The Soil Conservation Service assumes that full employment will be reached within a maximum of 20 years, and thus it does not count benefits after that date. Theoretically, use of unemployed resources could be reckoned by a deduction from project cost, but adding to project benefit is more widely used.

---

[1]   Otto Eckstein, "Water Resource Development: The Economics of Project Evaluation" (Cambridge, Mass.: Harvard University Press, 1958), p. 212.

The Bureau of Reclamation has added benefits for increased employment (settlement) opportunity by assigning an arbitrary value (about $1,000) per family. A more refined analysis would consider the increase in income resulting to those whom the project attracted to move into the area, over what they earned in their previous occupation. New investment opportunity is evaluated as the interest income resulting from returns on the associated costs of project installation less the interest income that would otherwise be received from the next best investment. Unless a better alternate investment opportunity can be demonstrated, government bonds are used. However, these effects are largely included in the direct primary benefits as part of the value of the output to those who use it, and additional benefits should not be added unless significant changes in market structure can be demonstrated by general equilibrium analysis.

The increased employment opportunity directly and indirectly induced by project construction may be estimated by input-output analysis (Sec. 9-3).[1] Project expenditures can be divided among wages, interest, profit, capital consumption, rent, and taxes, which can be traced through the model to specific production increases by specific industries and related through labor-response functions to increased employment requirements. The labor-response functions would need to portray the relationship between production by industry and labor requirements by occupation and should reflect the ability of industry to draw laborers from the unemployed. The increased employment opportunity from water resources development should be compared with that generated by alternative types of public investment.

8-10 INCOME-REDISTRIBUTION BENEFITS   The magnitude of a project-produced income redistribution is determined by using empirical data to establish the incidence, by income tax bracket, of the cost of the project among those providing the funds to pay for it, of the money spent on project installation, and of the tangible efficiency benefits. If project beneficiaries must pay for the project in proportion to the benefit they receive, the incidence of the cost and benefits would cancel, and only the effect of spending would be left.

The income-redistribution effect of project funding (cost) is determined by establishing the magnitude of the subsidy of federal, state, and local funds as well as the year the funds are required. The federal subsidy will, at least in the long run, add to the tax burden. Taxes may be divided into the three broad classes of consumer taxes, individual income taxes,

[1]   Robert H. Haveman and John Krutilla, Unemployment, Excess Capacity, and Benefit-Cost Investment Criteria, *Rev. Economics and Statistics* (August, 1967), pp. 382–392.

and corporate taxes. Because individual income taxes lie between the other two in the level of income of those most affected and are generally the most sensitive to marginal changes in tax revenue requirements, a reasonable first approximation of subsidy incidence by income bracket is the incidence of federal individual income taxes during the corresponding year, as published periodically.[1] The incidence of state or local subsidies may be estimated from similiar data on their respective tax structures.

The income-redistribution effect of project spending is determined from the income distribution of those receiving employment benefits (Sec. 8-9). Project spending to hire those who would be employed anyway would not significantly affect their income. The income bracket of the hired unemployed may be determined from the mean of their annual incomes with and without the employment. Normally such incomes will be well below average. The income-redistribution effect of project benefit is determined from the income distribution of those receiving tangible efficiency benefits. Empirical studies are available for aid in estimating the incidence by income bracket of direct benefits from flood control, irrigation, and recreation projects.[2]

The time lag between project expenditure and economic benefit realization also affects income-redistribution benefits. Income levels increase with time. Incomes will be generally higher when benefits are realized than when funds are raised and expenditures made. The reduction in income-redistribution benefit can be handled in project planning by basing the evaluation of benefit incidence by tax bracket on conditions projected for the year when half the present worth of the benefits have been realized.

Various proposals have been made for weighing the value of an achieved income redistribution.[3] While such weighting is essentially a value judgment of the planner's, the proposed method coming closest to being based on some type of group consensus is that initially suggested by Eckstein[4] and later developed by Haveman[5] based on marginal income tax rates. The marginal tax rates are calculated by dividing the change in average income tax paid per return between consecutive tax brackets by the change in average adjusted gross income per return. By dividing the

[1]   U.S. Treasury Department, "Statistics of Income, 1960" (Washington: USGPO, 1962), for example.
[2]   L. Douglas James, A Case Study in Income Redistribution from Reservoir Construction, *Water Resources Res.*, vol. 4 (June, 1968), pp. 499–506; A. Myrick Freeman, Six Federal Reclamation Projects and the Distribution of Income, *Water Resources Res.*, vol. 3 (2d Quarter, 1967), pp. 319–332.
[3]   Myrick Freeman, Income Distribution and Planning for Public Investment, *Am. Econ. Rev.*, vol. 57 (1967), pp. 495–508.
[4]   Otto Eckstein, A Survey of the Theory of Public Expenditure Criteria, in National Bureau of Economic Research, "Public Finances: Needs, Sources, and Utilization" (Princeton, N.J.: Princeton University Press, 1961), pp. 447–448 and 503.
[5]   Robert H. Haveman, "Water Resources Investment and the Public Interest" (Nashville, Tenn.: Vanderbilt University Press, 1965).

marginal tax rate for the bracket into the marginal tax rate for the bracket containing the overall average income, income-weighting factors may be calculated for each tax bracket. The weighting factors vary with changing incomes and tax laws, and Table 8-2 provides values for four recent years.

A desirable income redistribution results when income is transferred from a higher- to a lower-income group. The tabulated weighting factors are used to estimate the income-redistribution benefit to beneficiaries and recipients of project expenditures by multiplying the factor minus 1 times the efficiency benefit or payment respectively. The income-redistribution benefit resulting from taxes paid to finance the project is estimated by multiplying 1 minus the factor times the taxes paid. The total income-redistribution benefit is found by summing the three values in the manner illustrated by Ex. 8-1.

EXAMPLE 8-1

A flood control project will be subsidized by $1 million in federal funds. It is to be built in an area with large-scale local unemployment where $200,000 will be spent employing otherwise unemployed labor. Capitalized flood control benefits, net of beneficiary-financed operation and maintenance, equal $1,500,000. All values are in current dollars. The subsidy is allocated among federal income taxpayers in proportion to 1960 statistics.

TABLE 8-2 Weighting Factors by Income Class by Year

WELFARE EQUIVALENT WEIGHTS

Gross income range	1950	1958	1962	1964
0–1,000	2.28	2.65	2.68	3.05
1,000–2,000	1.50	1.71	1.79	1.63
2,000–3,000	1.30	1.34	1.24	1.36
3,000–4,000	0.99	1.07	1.12	1.13
4,000–5,000	0.75	1.03	1.02	1.05
5,000–6,000	0.59	0.94	1.00	1.01
6,000–7,000	0.59	0.80	0.91	0.99
7,000–8,000	0.59	0.73	0.80	0.89
8,000–9,000	0.59	0.69	0.73	0.78
9,000–10,000	0.59	0.65	0.72	0.73
10,000–15,000	0.46	0.61	0.62	0.66
15,000–20,000	0.41	0.52	0.58	0.61
20,000–25,000	0.34	0.33	0.48	0.59

SOURCE: L. Douglas James, A Case Study in Income Redistribution from Reservoir Construction, *Water Resources Res.*, vol. 4 (June, 1968), p. 504.

Employment benefits are allocated by a survey of local incomes. Project benefits are allocated proportional to the findings of a published survey.[1] The result is:

Bracket $/year	Cost $	Employment benefit, $	Flood control benefit, $
0–3,000	40,000	175,000	121,000
3,000–5,000	117,000	25,000	421,000
5,000–7,000	176,000	0	400,000
7,000–10,000	215,000	0	272,000
Over 10,000	452,000	0	286,000
Total	1,000,000	200,000	1,500,000

For a discount rate of 4.5 percent and a life of 50 years, half of the present worth of the benefits accrues during the first 13 years (P/A,4.5%, 13) = 0.5 (P/A,4.5%,50). Assuming average incomes in constant dollars are increasing 2 percent annually would indicate an increase by a factor of 1.294 over 13 years. Weighting factors for 1964 are used in the following table.

Bracket, mean	Weighting factor f	$C(1-f)$	$EB(f-1)$	1.294 Bracket, mean	Factor f'	$FCB(f'-1)$	Total
1,500	1.63	−25,000	110,000	1,900	1.52	63,000	148,000
4,000	1.09	−10,000	2,000	5,200	1.02	8,000	0
6,000	1.00	0	0	7,800	0.86	−56,000	−56,000
8,500	0.78	47,000	0	11,000	0.69	−115,000	−68,000
17,500	0.61	176,000	0	22,700	0.59	−117,000	59,000
Total		188,000	112,000			−217,000	83,000

The capitalized income-redistribution benefit equals $83,000. It would be negative were it not for employment benefits.

Additional problems arise in predicting the present worth of income-redistribution benefits over the project life. As income is distributed to the poor, they will become relatively richer over time (as distinguished from the population as a whole becoming richer, which has already been considered) so that income-redistribution benefits can be expected to decline. One way to handle this problem is by counting income-redistribution benefits over a shorter time horizon than other benefits are counted. An alternate procedure would be to discount at a higher rate. Theoretically each project objective incorporated in a weighted-objective function has a different discount rate.[2]

[1] James, *op. cit.*, p. 503.
[2] Stephen A. Marglin, "Public Investment Criteria" (Cambridge, Mass.: The M.I.T. Press, 1966), p. 47ff.

8-11   OTHER PUBLIC BENEFITS   Evaluation of the benefit from stabilization of a local economy (Sec. 5-12) is best done through estimates of the standard deviation of annual income with and without the project. The stabilization benefit could then be evaluated from the reduction in uncertainty in annual income pattern. The concept is used in estimating the stabilization benefits from flood control in Ex. 10-4.

An estimate of the value of improved community facilities and services may be made from the increase in real and personal property taxes paid by preproject residents, on the theory that the benefits from the improved facilities approximately equal their cost. The evaluation of other regional development (Sec. 5-14) and environmental quality (Sec. 5-15) benefits is less refined.

8-12   INTANGIBLE BENEFITS   While it is not possible to assign intangible benefits a monetary value, each effect should be described as precisely as possible (Sec. 1-6). Major intangibles may be considered by use of a decision matrix (Sec. 5-5). Senate Document 97 presents the recommended approach as:[1]

> When there are major differences among technically possible plans conceived as desirable on the basis of consideration of intangible benefits and costs, in comparison with optimum plans based on tangible benefits and costs, alternative combinations of projects within a river basin or alternative projects, giving expression to these major differences, shall be planned. Comparison of their economic and financial costs shall be set forth in reports to provide a basis for selection among the alternatives by reviewing authorities in the executive branch and by the Congress. Minor differences, with regard to intangible considerations, shall be handled, to the extent practicable and economically feasible, by adjustments in plans. Planning reports shall clearly indicate alternatives, their consequences, and adjustments made to take account of these minor differences.

8-13   ASSOCIATED AND INDUCED COSTS   Agricultural associated costs are evaluated from an analysis of the farm investment necessary to utilize project output. Analogous analyses are required for estimating associated costs for other types of activities. Quantity and unit cost estimates may be used where a particular facility, such as a drainage ditch, must be built. Induced costs are evaluated from an analysis of the nature and severity of the particular adverse consequences. They should be evaluated as the smaller of the value of the inflicted damage or the cost of damage prevention measures.

[1]   The President's Water Resources Council, *op. cit.*, pp. 6–7.

8-14 PROJECT INSTALLATION COST Construction cost is estimated by determining the quantity of each pay item required to complete the project and multiplying the quantity by a unit cost determined from contract bid prices for that item in previous construction projects. A pay item represents a practical division of the construction work according to standard construction practice. The unit cost should be modified where required to account for abnormal working conditions. In isolated areas or in developing countries, additional cost allowances may be necessary for transporting materials, moving in skilled labor, use of limited foreign exchange, and import taxes. A contingency estimate of about 15 percent of the sum of the item costs is normally added to the total to allow for situations which may develop during construction that were not foreseen in planning. The contingency allowance should be larger for preliminary planning estimates where the analysis has been less thorough.

Engineering and administration cost is estimated as a fixed percentage of construction cost as determined by past agency experience. Extra costs may be added when unusual design or construction problems are to be encountered. Precise costs are difficult to obtain because of cost accounting problems in dividing engineering effort among projects.

The price paid to purchase right-of-way or its financial cost is estimated as the amount a willing buyer would pay a willing seller as estimated by the best judgment of professional appraisers from their experience with the real estate market. However, two adjustments to this financial cost are needed to estimate the economic cost of real property. First, the market value of the real property is based on an implicit capitalization of expected future income at a discount rate well in excess of that used in project planning.[1] Because the use of two discount rates severely distorts project evaluation, market value M_v should be adjusted to economic value E_v by using

$$E_v = \frac{iM_v}{d} \tag{8-1}$$

where d is the planning discount rate and i is the implicit market discount rate. Equation (8-1) uses the discount rate in place of the capital-recovery factor by assuming an indefinitely long life. The Corps of Engineers recommends 5.0 percent for i,[2] but a more realistic value would probably be about 7.0 to 8.0 percent. Second, an unwilling seller places value on real property in excess of the market price between a willing buyer and a willing seller. He derives a personal value from his property based on

[1] Eckstein, "Water Resource Development," pp. 146–148.
[2] U.S. Army Corps of Engineers, "Survey Investigations and Reports," *Eng. Manuals* EM 1120-2-104, par. 9*b*, and EM 1120-2-111.

sentimental attachment, effect on his way of life, and established relationships with others in his community. Resistance to selling depends on the
degree of threatened change in his life and has a real economic value for
which the seller would be "willing to pay." The economic value is difficult
to quantify, but one estimate gives the additional value as 0.86 of market
value for a location where most sellers lost their homes, 0.66 were farmland but few homes were affected, and 0.39 for investment property in the
urban fringe.[1] This second adjustment is partially handled by including
the cost of moving and resettling those who lose their homes.

Easement costs are taken as a percentage of purchase cost determined by the degree the easement restricts private land use, but easements are not too popular because their cost is usually close to full land
value. Severance damages must be paid when the right-of-way separates
parcels under common ownership or interferes with land use or access.
The payment should equal the capitalized value of the extra expense to
the landowner. When access roads are less expensive, they may be built
as an alternative to paying severance damages. Mineral rights are acquired
only where their development would interfere with project operation. The
acquisition cost, legal fees, and administrative expenses averages about 15
percent of market value but is best estimated as a fixed sum for each parcel
which must be purchased.

The policy of the major federal agencies since 1960 has been to
acquire in fee at reservoir sites all lands:

a Necessary for construction of the dam and all other permanent structures,
  often including source locations for construction materials or waste locations for spoil materials.
b Up to an elevation providing a reasonable freeboard allowance above the
  maximum flood storage pool elevation or within 300 feet horizontally of
  the maximum flood storage pool line.
c Necessary to provide public access to the reservoir for development of
  fish and wildlife and outdoor recreation.
d Needed to complete purchase parcels so as to avoid excessive severance
  damages or excessive costs of replacing access.[2]

Land acquisition policy when reservoirs are not involved follows
similar rules.

The cost of relocations is summed from individual estimates for each
facility which must be relocated. The cost of building a new facility
equivalent to the old one displaced is estimated from unit costs and con-

---

[1] L. Douglas James, The Economic Value of Real Estate Acquired for Right-of-Way, *Land Economics*, vol. 44 (August, 1968), pp. 363–370.
[2] U.S. Federal Register, Joint Policies of the Departments of the Interior and the Army Relative to Reservoir Project Lands, vol. 27 (Feb. 22, 1962), p. 1734.

struction quantities plus allowances for contingencies and engineering. Lump sum estimates may be made for minor items. Only replacement by an equivalent facility can be justified as a project cost, and any improvement in the new over the old facility must be justified by benefits to those whom the facility serves.

The other, minor installation costs are estimated from established fees or a study of the circumstances.

8-15   OPERATION,   MAINTENANCE,   AND   REPLACEMENT COSTS   Operation costs are estimated from the expected salaries, fringe benefits, and overhead costs of hiring the required operating personnel, providing them with the required equipment and supplies, and the market cost of electricity or fuel for pumping or other uses. The number and type of operational personnel, supplies, and equipment required can be estimated from experience in operating similar projects. The annual cost of project administration should also be included.

Annual maintenance cost may be estimated as a percentage of construction cost for each group of construction items. For example, typical percentages are 3.0 for earth channels, 0.5 for earth dams, and 0.1 for concrete structures. An alternative method is to estimate maintenance cost from a maintenance program in which the required quantity of personnel, equipment, and supplies is estimated, and its cost is determined from prevailing prices.

Replacement costs are developed from the estimated dates and costs of replacing assets whose lives are shorter than that of the project. Annual replacement cost over the project life is determined as

$$A_c = (P - L)\left[\left(\frac{A}{P}, i\%, L_a\right) - \left(\frac{A}{P}, i\%, L_p\right)\right] \tag{8-2}$$

where P is the cost of new asset, L is the salvage value of the old, L_p is the project life, and L_a is the asset life.

Benefit-Cost Variation

8-16   THE PROBABILISTIC APPROACH   Benefit and cost estimates are projected future events. They can never be forecast with certainty. If the potential values can be represented by probability distributions which can be theoretically or experimentally determined, the risk inherent in specific projects can be calculated and considered in planning.

As probability distributions become harder to estimate, the analysis approaches conditions of pure uncertainty.

The calculation of probabilities requires data on the magnitudes of past events, and their usefulness in economy studies depends on future events following the past pattern. The probability that an event will occur can be defined as:

> . . . the ratio of the number of occurrences of the event to the number of opportunities or trials for the event to occur as the number of opportunities or trials is indefinitely increased.[1]

The probability of an event's taking a value within a specific range is the ratio of the number of occurrences within that range to the total number of occurrences as the number of trials is indefinitely increased. A large number of trials reduces the possibility of encountering a string of unrepresentative occurrences. The probability distribution is a plot of the probability of events falling within specific size ranges vs. mean size-range magnitude as the included size-range limits are indefinitely decreased to develop a smoother curve. If events follow some well-known distribution such as the binomial, Poisson, or normal distribution,[2] event probabilities may be evaluated from available tables. Otherwise, numerical procedures are required.

As an example, data on average, historical, wheat yields in a certain area might reveal the distribution of Table 8-3. The distribution may be

[1] Norman H. Barish, "Economic Analysis for Engineering and Managerial Decision Making" (New York: McGraw-Hill Book Company, 1962).
[2] For a text on probability theory, see E. Parzen, "Modern Probability and Its Applications" (New York: John Wiley & Sons, Inc., 1954).

TABLE 8-3 Hypothetical Distribution of Wheat Yield

Yield interval, bu/acre	Annual yield events	Probability	Gross income*	Expected value
14–16	2	0.04	$30	$1.20
16–18	9	0.18	34	6.12
18–20	19	0.38	38	14.44
20–22	14	0.28	42	11.76
22–24	5	0.10	46	4.60
24–26	1	0.02	50	1.00
Total	50	1.00	. . .	$39.12

* Estimated at a $2.00 per bushel price.

used for decision making as tabulated or may be approximated by a normal distribution having a mean of 19.56 and a standard deviation of 2.118 as calculated by Eqs. (8-3) and (8-5) below. The expected value is estimated as

$$\mu = \sum_{i=1}^{n} P_i x_i \qquad (8\text{-}3)$$

where P is the probability of the variable falling in the interval of representative value x. Where all values are equally probable, the equation reduces to an estimation of the mean value as

$$\mu = \frac{\sum_{i=1}^{n} x_i}{n} \qquad (8\text{-}4)$$

The standard deviation is estimated as

$$\sigma = \left[\sum_{i=1}^{n} P_i (x_i - \mu)^2 \right]^{0.5} \qquad (8\text{-}5)$$

Where all values are equally probable, the equation reduces to

$$\sigma = \left[\frac{\sum_{i=1}^{n} (x_i - \mu)^2}{(n-1)} \right]^{0.5} \qquad (8\text{-}6)$$

One is subtracted from n for statistical reasons.

The use of Eq. (8-3) to estimate the expected value per acre of the annual wheat crop is illustrated in Table 8-3. A graphical application to calculate expected flood control benefits is illustrated by Ex. 8-2.

EXAMPLE 8-2

Historical streamflow records for a certain stream were evaluated to determine the probability of flood peaks of selected magnitude's being equaled or exceeded during a given year. The economic development in the area inundated by each flood peak was then used to estimate the flood damage which would result from each peak. The results were:

Probability:	0.005	0.01	0.04	0.15	0.433
Damage:	$881,500	$867,500	$495,500	$329,500	$57,400

The average annual expected damage may then be estimated as the area under a damage-frequency curve and is shown to be $120,000 in Fig. 8-1.

However, one alternative may not always be preferred above another just because it has a higher expected value. The spread of possible out-

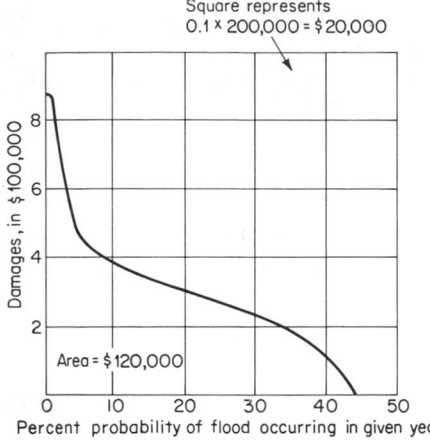

FIGURE 8-1   Flood-damage-proba-
bility distribution.

comes around the expected value as indexed by the standard deviation of the probability is also important. If two distributions have equal expected values but different standard deviations, the one with the smaller standard deviation is usually preferred. The recipients of benefits following distribution a (Fig. 8-2) are in a preferable position to recipients of benefits following distribution b because the realized benefit remains more consistent from year to year instead of varying between very high values some years and very low values other years. Most individuals prefer a consistent to an irregular income of the same average value.

Thomas has suggested using an insurance approach to evaluate the gain in expected value caused by a decrease in standard deviation.[1] If the

[1]   Arthur Maass et al., "Design of Water-resource Systems" (Cambridge, Mass.: Harvard University Press, 1962).

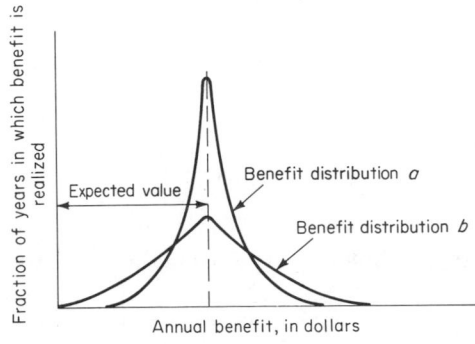

FIGURE 8-2   Comparison of benefit patterns.

benefits actually realized were accumulated in a fund as they occurred, a constant value could be withdrawn annually. The constant withdrawal would have to be less than the expected benefit by an amount dependent on the risk α which can be taken of the fund's becoming exhausted by a sequence of low benefits. The amount less is

$$e = \frac{r V_\alpha \sigma}{\sqrt{2r}} \tag{8-7}$$

where V_α is the normal deviate with probability α of being exceeded as determined from any normal distribution table, σ is the standard deviation of the annual benefits, and r is the interest rate earned by the fund. The difference in the value of e produced by a reduction in value of σ is the estimated acceptable gain in expected value.

Water resources planners must recognize the tendency of economic consequences to vary from year to year as shown in Fig. 8-2, but they must also realize mean values cannot be predicted with certainty. Some projects may turn out to be much more effective than originally anticipated, while others may prove to have been justified by overly optimistic forecasts. Experience based on a large number of projects will show expenditures to be distributed around planning estimates. The nature of the distribution can be evaluated by comparing values after construction is completed. Project benefits will also be distributed around planning estimates, but postaudit comparison is more difficult (Sec. 8-19). By basing the distribution of costs around planning estimates on Bureau of Reclamation records and the benefit distribution on the scatter of materialized population growth in small areas around past projections, Altouney was able, by assuming complete independence between the two distributions, to develop an expression for determining the probability that realized benefits will exceed required expenditure.[1] The probability, as calculated from the expression, varies with project life, the projected growth rate, the planning discount rate, and the predicted benefit-cost ratio in the manner shown in Table 8-4. The tabulated figures assume that benefits per unit of project output can be estimated perfectly and only the quantity of output which will be required is in question. From 1950 to 1967 in the United States, the average rate of economic growth in constant dollars was just over 4 percent, while the average rate of population growth was about 1.5 percent. While the numbers in Table 8-4 should not be regarded as the last word on the reliability of estimated benefits and costs, they should instill a healthy appreciation for the inherent uncertainty in projecting future economic effects.

---

[1]   Edward G. Altouney, "The Role of Uncertainties in the Economic Evaluation of Water Resources Projects" (Stanford, Calif.: Stanford University, Institute in Engineering Economic Systems, EEP-7, 1963), p. 68.

8-17 SENSITIVITY ANALYSIS   A very practical approach to the treatment of uncertainty is to test the sensitivity of the outcome of project evaluation to variation in the magnitude of key parameters. In order to be meaningful, it is best to use optimistic and pessimistic values which differ from expected values by an amount proportional to the degree of uncertainty present. If the project is feasible even when pessimistic values are used, it should be rejected.

A shift in project feasibility as one goes from optimistic to pessimistic projections implies existence of a break-even point between the two extremes. The value of the parameter at the point where the project becomes feasible may be determined either explicitly or by trial and error according to the complexity of the relationship. If the probability distribution of parameter values can be determined, it provides the probability of the parameter's falling on the feasible side of its breakeven value. The decision maker must decide whether this probability is acceptably large. If the complete probability distribution cannot be determined, one must make a more approximate or, if needs be, a subjective evaluation of the chances of the parameter value's lying in the acceptable range.

TABLE 8-4   Probabilities of Realized Benefit-Cost Ratio Exceeding Unity

Predicted B/C	DISCOUNT RATE LESS PROJECTED GROWTH RATE					
	−0.04	−0.02	0.00	0.02	0.04	0.06
Project life, 50 years						
0.5	0.009	0.008	0.006	0.000	0.000	0.000
1.0	0.131	0.134	0.143	0.155	0.162	0.172
1.5	0.318	0.335	0.358	0.382	0.404	0.422
2.0	0.486	0.515	0.550	0.583	0.611	0.631
3.0	0.714	0.757	0.795	0.822	0.841	0.854
4.0	0.834	0.871	0.906	0.925	0.936	0.943
5.0	0.900	0.931	0.952	0.966	0.974	0.977
Project life, 100 years						
0.5	0.011	0.009	0.006	0.000	0.000	0.000
1.0	0.080	0.075	0.086	0.113	0.143	0.164
1.5	0.183	0.191	0.233	0.305	0.369	0.409
2.0	0.277	0.302	0.378	0.487	0.572	0.615
3.0	0.421	0.480	0.603	0.742	0.814	0.845
4.0	0.512	0.598	0.738	0.869	0.921	0.938
5.0	0.574	0.669	0.823	0.928	0.965	0.975

The Value of Benefit-Cost Analysis

8-18 PROJECT FORMULATION   Much of the value to be gained from economic analysis is not realized unless estimated benefits and costs are actively used to select the best design according to the rules of engineering economy (Chap. 2) and project optimality (Chap. 4). Senate Document 97 specifies the standards for formulating plans as:[1]

1   All plans shall be formulated with due regard to all pertinent benefits and costs, both tangible and intangible. Benefits and costs shall be expressed in comparable quantitative economic terms to the fullest extent possible.

2   Comprehensive plans shall be formulated initially to include all units and purposes which satisfy these criteria in quantitative economic terms:
   a Tangible benefits exceed project economic costs.
   b Each separable unit or purpose provides benefits at least equal to its costs.
   c The scope of development is such as to provide the maximum net benefits.
   d There is no more economical means, evaluated on a comparable basis, of accomplishing the same purpose or purposes which would be precluded from development if the plan were undertaken. This limitation refers only to those alternative possibilities that would be physically displaced or economically precluded from development if the project is undertaken.

3   Net benefits are maximized when the scope of development is extended to the point where the benefits added by the last increment of scale (i.e., an increment of size of a unit, an individual purpose in a multiple-purpose plan or a unit in a comprehensive plan) are equal to the costs of adding that increment of scale. The increments to be considered in this way are the smallest increments on which there is a practical choice of omission from the plan.

4   Reports or plans shall indicate the scale of development that would result from application of the foregoing criteria considering tangible benefits and project economic costs expressed in comparable terms. This will provide a baseline from which the effect of considering intangibles can be judged.

5   Reports and plans shall also indicate the extent to which departures from that scale of development are proposed in order to take into account intangibles or other considerations warranting a modification in scale not reflected in the tangible benefits and project economic costs.

[1] The President's Water Resources Council, *op. cit.*, pp. 7–8.

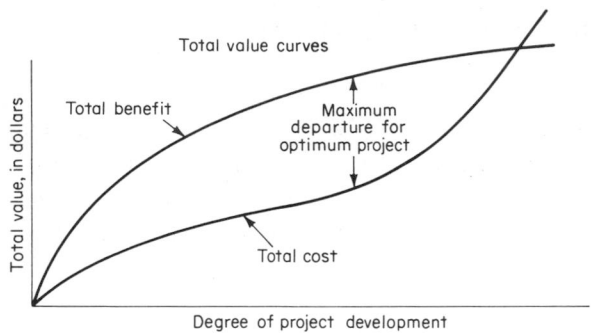

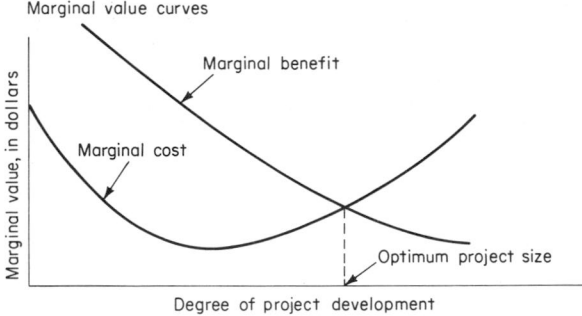

Definition of degree of project development

Project Purpose	Yard Stick	Units
Flood control	Design flood return period	Return period, in years
Land drainage	Design depth to water	Feet
Navigation	Waterway capacity	Tons per year
Hydroelectric power	Installed capacity	Kilowatts
Water supply	Water delivered	Acre-ft per year
Recreation	Installed capacity	Visitor days
Water quality control	Pollution reduction	Parts per million

FIGURE 8-3 Representative value curve.

The formulation process (Sec. 4-12) may be condensed into the form outlined in Fig. 8-3. A suitable yardstick indexing project size or the degree of project development must be selected, with some which might be used by project purpose being suggested at the bottom of the figure. Total benefits and total costs for various yardstick values are estimated by determining the minimum cost combination of measures providing the required output. The procedures used depend on the project purpose and are described in detail in Chaps. 10 to 17. Marginal-value curves are then plotted from the slope of the total-value curves (Sec. 4-4), and the optimum project size is selected. It is important to emphasize that the optimization is a two-phase process. Each point on the curve represents an optimum design for a given output as determined by an engineering economy study. The optimum scale of development is determined from the curves.

8-19   ADEQUACY OF MEASUREMENT   The value of benefit-cost analysis as a decision-making tool depends on the reliability of estimated benefits and costs. The adequacy of the benefit and cost estimates as they were developed for planning a particular project can be checked against expenditures incurred during and economic consequences realized after project construction. Comparison on the cost side is relatively less complicated. The agencies have had extensive experience in estimating construction quantities and unit costs for all but the most unusual design circumstances. The time lag from planning estimate to construction completion is short enough for feedback adjustment of estimating procedures. However, a comparison of the Bureau of Reclamation planning estimates for 103 projects with adjusted final project cost has found the probability is 77 percent that project cost will exceed the planning estimate.[1] The median planning underestimate was 30 percent. The average underestimate was 78 percent. These figures were calculated after adjustments for changes in construction cost levels between planning and construction dates, for changes in the structural features of the project plan, and for the extra cost of emergency work which had to be done without adequate planning.

Comparison of planning with realized benefits is made relatively more complicated by the difficulty in separating project-caused benefits from those which would have occurred anyway and the much longer waiting period from planning to the time when many benefits are realized. By the time benefits have materialized sufficiently to be measured, the benefit evaluation methodology is likely to have changed to the point where it is necessary to redo the planning estimates with the use of the new methods to get comparable figures. Generally speaking, greater uncertainty and longer time lags cause benefits to depart from planning estimates more than costs.

Inadequate benefit and cost estimates for project evaluation may be caused by a failure to use the best available estimating procedures. Among the more common deviations from best practice are failure to recognize the probabilistic nature of benefit and cost estimates (Sec. 8-16), incorrect application of the alternative-cost approach to benefit evaluation (Sec.

---

[1]   Altouney, *op. cit.*, pp. 45–61.

8-5), use of local secondary benefits for economic justification from the national viewpoint (Sec. 8-8), overlooking of major induced costs (Sec. 8-13), and overstatement of project effectiveness at area redevelopment (Sec. 8-9). Other inconsistencies are caused by variations in policy with respect to such debatable value judgments as discount rate selection (Sec. 6-7) and weighting of multiple goals (Sec. 5-5).

Variation between planning and realized benefits and costs may for individual projects be explained by the probabilistic nature of forecasts. A future value (of projected traffic on a navigable waterway, for example) could potentially be anywhere within a range. Planning based on the expected or most probable value within the range should in the aggregate produce estimates in which deviations one way cancel those the other way. However, an individual project may have a substantial deviation. Extreme care should be exercised to determine whether standard values (of percentages for use in estimating indirect benefits, for example) apply to a given project. The tendency for agency planners is to be optimistic and thus overestimate benefits and underestimate costs.

When outputs are not marketable, benefit measurement becomes very difficult. Kneese and Nobe subdivide nonmarketable water resource project outputs into three classes.[1] Project output in the first class is consumed individually, but the cost of collecting a fee from those desiring consumption is prohibitive. An example might be a recreational lake. A private owner will not develop the property if it is too costly to deny access to those not paying the entrance fee even if the demand justifies public development. Project output in the second class is "public," but failure to provide it results in easily measured market consequences. For example, flood control cannot be exchanged directly in the market, but flood control benefits can be estimated by assuming they are equivalent to flood damages prevented. Project output in the third class can neither be exchanged in the marketplace itself nor does it substitute for another good or service which can be. An example is water quality control to maintain the aesthetic value of the riverfront or to preserve public health. Specific approaches to measuring specific benefits are discussed in more detail in connection with the individual project purposes.

The economic evaluation of many project effects is hampered by difficulties in handling the macroeconomic effects of water resources development. The planner may worry about how best to correct market price to normative value, or he may encounter difficulty in defining the role of projects in capital formation or economic development, in pinpointing secondary benefits from the national and local viewpoints, or in evaluating

---

[1]   Allen V. Kneese and Kenneth C. Nobe, The Role of Economic Evaluation in Planning for Water Resource Development, *Nat. Resources J.*, vol. 2 (December, 1962), pp. 456–457.

the opportunity cost of tax funds taken from the private sector or other public budgets. He customarily deals with each such situation by building an economic model (Sec. 9-3). Such models use a sequence of assumptions and empirically measured properties of market interactions to produce exact-looking numerical answers. The analyst should not lose sight of the difficulty in developing a set of mathematical equations adequately portraying market processes and the probabilistic nature of the market properties and the assumed values. Unless each step is explicitly derived and documented, the results have little normative value for decision making. A complicated economic model does not necessarily produce valid results.

The contribution of water resources projects to economic development stems in part from effects on the production function of those using project output. The project may reduce the cost or increase the supply of water, power, transportation, etc. The key phase of project evaluation is determining precisely how these effects on the production function will influence new industry to enter an area. So many factors influence industrial location decisions that it is very difficult to predict the influence of a single production factor, water. Even proof that a particular site provides the greatest potential economic advantage to industry is insufficient to guarantee development, because management may be operating under limited knowledge or in response to extraeconomic goals. The contribution of a water resources project to economic development may be more through demonstrated community initiative than through the project itself. Industries for which water is a minor production factor may locate near a new reservoir because the local resources consumed in its installation indicate a willingness of the community to accept change, work toward self improvement, and thus create a favorable climate for economic expansion.

8-20 A CRITIQUE OF BENEFIT-COST ANALYSIS Benefit-cost analysis can be and has been corrupted.[1] Many feel the requirement that benefits exceed costs unduly restricts worthy water resources development. Others believe the government inflates benefits and ignores costs in order to justify projects and thereby perpetuate agency growth or appease special interest groups. The skeptics wonder whether a calculated net benefit is really a proof of merit or merely a number concocted to gain more widespread acceptance of a decision already made on some other basis.

[1] Fred A. Clarenback, Reliability of Estimates of Agricultural Damages from Floods, in U.S. Commission on Organization of the Executive Branch of the Government, "Task Force Report on Water Resources and Power" (Washington: USGPO, 1955), vol. 3. See also Luna B. Leopold and Thomas Maddock, Jr., "The Flood Control Controversy" (New York: The Ronald Press Company, 1954).

Those who object to specific findings consistently stress the value of social goals other than economic efficiency.

Efficiency benefits and other benefits measure progress toward different goals. When comparing a group of alternative expenditures similar enough in character for the ratio of the nonefficiency benefits to the efficiency benefits to be of the same order of magnitude, efficiency benefits are a reliable guide. However, this is not the case when comparing water resources development with expenditures whose primary purpose is to achieve other social goals. The comparison of efficiency benefits with efficiency costs is thus not a practical method for setting the federal water resources budget by dividing total expenditure among water resources, national defense, and medical care. Benefit-cost analysis provides a valuable tool for aiding the political selection of the best water resource projects.

Ciriacy-Wantrup lists other reasons for using benefit-cost analysis:[1]

1 It restrains the abuse of economic arguments·in the political process. Federal water agencies often compete for funds and scrutinize carefully each other's figures.
2 The attempt at quantification of benefits and costs has promoted scientific understanding of physical and social problems in water resource development.
3 It helps (1) broaden the repayment base by identifying project beneficiaries, (2) obtain dependable repayment contracts and (3) make public districts and special taxes more acceptable.

Benefit-cost analysis is a worthwhile endeavor in spite of abuses that may occur. There really is no substitute for explicit procedures which force the analysis of the complex relationships among and the implications of decision or alternatives and thereby bring into working contact a host of specialists with widely varying skills. However, none should imagine:

. . . evaluations in economic analyses are the voice of the absolute speaking through its mortal mouth pieces, that they are the gospel to be ignored at perils or that government decision makers are going to stand in awe before the revelatory brillance of their pronouncements.[2]

SELECTED REFERENCES
Ciriacy-Wantrup, S. V.: Benefit-Cost Analysis and Public Resource Development, in Stephen C. Smith and Emery N. Castle (eds.),

[1] S. V. Ciriacy-Wantrup, Benefit-Cost Analysis and Public Resource Development, in Stephen C. Smith and Emery N. Castle (eds.), "Economics and Public Policy in Water Resource Development" (Ames: Iowa State University Press, 1964), pp. 19–21. © 1964 by the Iowa State University Press.
[2] M. M. Kelso, Economic Analysis in the Allocation of the Federal Budget to Resource Development, in Smith and Castle (eds.), *op. cit.*, p. 59. © 1964 by the Iowa State University Press.

"Economics and Public Policy in Water Resource Development" (Ames: Iowa State University Press, 1964).

Eckstein, Otto: "Water Resource Development: The Economics of Project Evaluation" (Cambridge, Mass.: Harvard University Press, 1958).

Haveman, Robert H.: "Water Resources Investment and the Public Interest" (Nashville, Tenn.: Vanderbilt University Press, 1965).

Hirshleifer, Jack, James C. DeHaven, and Jerome W. Milliman: "Water Supply: Economics, Technology, and Policy" (Chicago: The University of Chicago Press, 1960).

Kneese, Allen V., and Kenneth C. Nobe: The Role of Economic Evaluation in Planning for Water Resource Development, *Nat. Resources J.*, vol. 2 (December, 1962), pp. 456–457.

Krutilla, John V., and Otto Eckstein: "Multiple Purpose River Development" (Baltimore: The Johns Hopkins Press, 1958).

Maass, Arthur, et al.: "Design of Water-resource Systems" (Cambridge, Mass.: Harvard University Press, 1962).

McKean, Roland N.: "Efficiency in Government through Systems Analysis" (New York: John Wiley & Sons, Inc., 1958).

Marglin, Stephen A.: "Public Investment Criteria" (Cambridge, Mass.: The M.I.T. Press, 1966).

Steiner, Peter O.: The Role of Alternative Cost in Project Design and Selection, in Allen V. Kneese and Stephen C. Smith (eds.), "Water Research" (Baltimore: The Johns Hopkins Press, 1966).

PROBLEMS

8-1 A river flows through a farming valley. The land is divided into small plots, each of which has been farmed by the same family for generations. The valley is located in an arid climate where irrigation is essential to agriculture, and the river serves as the sole source of water. An urban area in a different watershed has been growing rapidly in recent years and needs a new source of water supply. A project to dam and divert the river and thereby eliminate irrigated farming in the valley has been proposed.

   a What information would you obtain and what type of analysis would you perform to determine whether the project is engineeringly feasible?

   b Economically feasible?

   c Financially feasible?

   d Socially feasible?

   e Politically feasible?

8-2 A proposed project will provide irrigation water to 10,000 acres which are presently used to grow grain and for grazing. After irrigation, all the acreage will be used to grow fruit and vegetable crops so that net annual farm income per acre will increase from $5 to $100 and gross income from $50 to $500. Farm families will increase from 8 to 80.

   a What would you estimate the direct benefits to be?

   b What additional information would you like to have to make a more thorough analysis of:

     i Indirect benefits?

     ii Land enhancement benefits?

     iii Secondary benefits?

     iv Public benefits?

     v Intangible benefits?

     vi Associated costs?

     vii Induced costs?

   c What would you expect the approximate magnitude of each of the seven items in part *b* to be?

8-3 Discuss and evaluate the wisdom of using the following procedures in project evaluation:

   a A single-purpose flood control reservoir produces benefits of 8 and cost of 9. Maintaining a small permanent pool produces benefits of 3 and cost of 1 for recreation. The multipurpose project is justified with a benefit-cost ratio of 1.1.

   b Local economic development consequential to a water supply project is expected to provide enough tax revenue for a community to be able to afford a new school. The cost of the new school is taken as a benefit for project justification.

   c Construction of a reservoir provides a water transportation route which makes possible a new coal mining development. The value of the mine is taken as a project benefit.

8-4 A flood control project is being planned to protect 300 acres of bottomland along Jake Creek near Johnsville. The bottomland is now subject to such severe flooding that it cannot be put to any economic use. If protected, the land will increase in market value to $800 per acre and urban development will completely occupy the land over the next 15 years. If the bottomland is not protected, urban development over the same period will move onto 300 acres of hillside land currently producing a net annual crop income of $25 per acre. This land now sells for $300 per acre, but its price would increase to $600 per acre if the project were built and the resultant development took place anyway. The capitalized cost to the city of providing urban facilities to the hillside land is $600,000 higher than for the bottomland nearer the city. The project is to be evaluated for a 50-year life and 5 percent discount rate.

a Estimate the annual benefit of protecting the bottom land.

b Estimate the annual benefit if, with the project, the new development takes place on the hillsides anyway and the bottomland is farmed to produce a net annual crop income of $100 per acre.

c Qualitatively evaluate the secondary benefits of possibilities a and b.

8-5 The annual flood peaks recorded for the Kentucky River at Frankfort, Kentucky, have been (measured in cfs):

1933	57,800	1944	55,400	1955	84,000
1934	65,400	1945	78,400	1956	75,000
1935	79,700	1946	73,200	1957	84,200
1936	65,900	1947	48,100	1958	60,800
1937	115,000	1948	88,700	1959	42,600
1938	41,000	1949	62,500	1960	48,900
1939	88,800	1950	87,000	1961	58,100
1940	45,700	1951	70,900	1962	95,700
1941	25,600	1952	76,400	1963	62,100
1942	43,200	1953	49,100	1964	81,300
1943	81,500	1954	19,800	1965	59,400

a What is the probability of an annual flood between 70,000 and 80,000 cfs?

b Plot a probability distribution for the above events.

c What is the expected annual flood peak?

8-6 If the data in Prob. 8-5 were taken as flood damages in dollars:

a What is the expected value of the damages?

b What is the adjusted value of the damages based on a discount rate of 4 percent and an exhaustion probability of 1 percent?

8-7 Consider the costs and revenues of Prob. 1-1.

a Which project level should be selected if each revenue had been underestimated by 20 percent?

b Which project level should be selected if each revenue had been overestimated by 20 percent?

c If X is the probability of revenues' being overestimated by 20 percent and $1 - X$ is the probability of their being estimated correctly, what value of X would be required to favor an investment of 39.

CHAPTER
NINE

THE DYNAMICS
OF PROJECT ANALYSIS

Economic merit is judged by comparing projected benefits with projected costs. The benefits and costs resulting from any project will vary with changing project environment. Changing benefits and costs cause changes in the nature of the optimum project. The best project for tomorrow will differ from the best for today. The planner cannot select the best project and then forget about it. He must continually study and evaluate project response to a changing environment and suggest modifications to increase project effectiveness. Project analysis is a dynamic process.

9-1 THE ROLE OF PROJECTIONS The planner must choose from alternative present courses of action. The merit of each alternative is determined from its projected effect on future events. Three properties of each effect are relevant.

1 The magnitude of the associated cash flow
2 The date
3 The certainty that it will take place

The possible magnitudes of a projected cash flow may be represented by a probability distribution (Sec. 8-16). The chance of a value occurring along the abscissa is indicated by the ordinate. The most likely value is approximately the mean. The degree of uncertainty is represented by the standard deviation of the distribution. The possible dates of the cash flow follow an analogous probability distribution. Uncertainty may exist on whether events will occur at all as well as together, on magnitude, and on timing.

An economy study requires projections describing supply, demand,

and resulting price. The demand for project output depends on the magnitude of the future population and the consumer preferences within that population. The consumer preference is the demand per unit population for project output and changes with time along with income levels, exposure to new ideas, and technological advance. On the supply side, projections need to recognize changes in the availability of the raw materials required in production and possibilities of technological improvement increasing future productivity or developing improved substitute outputs. The interaction between demand and supply will determine future price levels and differential inflation patterns.

Every unit cost, every construction quantity, and every other numerical value used in economic analysis is a prediction of what will occur during project life (Sec. 8-16). Each projection should be derived as explicitly as possible. A common failing in planning is to document the basis for projected events improperly and thereby introduce implicit assumptions which become so hidden within the bulk of the analysis that they are not noticed during review. Projects whose feasibility depends on untenable assumptions may inadvertently be accepted. It is far better to state the assumptions and outline the reasoning behind them. Explicit assumptions can be evaluated when the plan is being reviewed, force more systematic analysis, and reduce error resulting from hasty work. Without the discipline of a well-organized analysis, too much planning time is often spent on detail having little effect on either benefits or costs, and too little time is spent in analyzing the critical assumptions which govern feasibility.

Each number introduced into a feasibility study should be properly referenced. The reason each referenced value is believed applicable should be stated. The factors affecting time variation of the variable must be explored to determine whether its value will remain constant over the period of analysis or vary with time. If project feasibility is affected by variation of the value within the range of probable values, the range of values for which the project is feasible and the probability of the number falling within that range should be determined. For example, the feasibility of improving a navigable waterway depends on the projected vessel traffic. A particular waterway improvement may be feasible if used by more than 10,000 vessels per year. Demand analysis may indicate a 60 percent chance that at least this level of traffic will occur.

9-2 POPULATION PROJECTION Demand is partially determined by the population of the area served by the project. For output which has appreciable transportation cost, such as water supply, or which cannot be moved, such as flood control, the area is relatively small. It is much larger for more easily transported output such as electric power.

Four basic methods are available for projecting populations for a limited area.[1] The simplest and most widely used method is by graphic or mathematical extrapolation of a time series of historical values. Alternate relationships among the historical values which might be used include a uniform growth expressed in people per period, a uniform growth rate expressed in percent of the population per period, a decreasing percentage growth rate in which the percentage growth in each period is smaller than that during the preceding period, a graphic extension of the historical curve, and an extension by least squares or some other curve-fitting procedure.[2] A variation on the extrapolation of past trends is to apply the "law of growth in a limited area," expounded by P. F. Verhulst in 1838, to historic growth patterns to predict future populations. Verhulst postulated that the population within a limited area varies from zero to a saturation value ranging from 30 to 200 people per acre according to the type of dwellings and that the time pattern of growth follows an S curve, having the fastest growth when population is half saturation. Projection based on historical trends are relatively simple to make but give little recognition to causal economic forces.

The second or demographic method is to estimate population from rates of births, deaths, and in and out migration. The total existing population is classified by age and sex. Current birth and death rates are determined for each class and extrapolated into the future. Migration rates are based on historical and projected future trends in the vitality of the local economy. The population change during a time period equals the algebraic sum of the products of classification rates and populations. Each population classification can then be reckoned one time period older and the recursion repeated as far into the future as desired. Demographic projections are more reliable for large than for small areas because the migration rates, which are more difficult to predict, are relatively less significant.

The third projection method is to estimate population as a percentage of the population projected for a larger area within which the smaller area is contained. When using this method, total population for the large area is usually obtained from published projections based on some other method. The small-area population is taken as a percentage forecast from trends in past percentages in any of the ways suggested by the first projection method, but consideration should be given to probable local economic conditions.

The fourth or economic method is to estimate population from the

---

[1] Edward G. Altouney, "The Role of Uncertainties in the Economic Evaluation of Water-resources Projects" (Stanford, Calif.: Stanford University, Institute in Engineering Economic Systems, EEP-7, 1964), pp. 10–33.

[2] Ray K. Linsley and Joseph B. Franzini, "Water-resources Engineering" (New York: McGraw-Hill Book Company, 1964), pp. 410–412.

employment required to satisfy the demand for local production. The basic tool is the input-output model, a method developed by W. W. Leontief to study general equilibrium phenomena by analyzing the economic inter-relationships among production centers.[1] The analysis begins with an economic base study to determine the primary activities providing local employment and income and so to establish the initial conditions for economic growth of the local economy. Study methodology has been developed by, and may be obtained through, the Department of Labor in the United States and corresponding agencies in many other countries.[2]

9-3 INPUT-OUTPUT ANALYSIS Every industry utilizes its own output and output produced by other industries as input to produce a new output which will in turn be used by itself and others in other production processes. An increase in demand will trigger an increase in production by a primary supplying industry. The increased production will increase demand for inputs, and the resulting effects will ripple through the economy. Input-output analysis develops a mathematical model of the interactions among major industries as a tool for predicting the accumulative effect of potential changes. Each industry requires supporting activities to provide input materials, transport and market finished goods, and supply the needs of the labor force. Output in turn is used as input to that or other activities, is consumed by the workers, or is exported. In a typical study, 30 to 70 industries are used. The accuracy increases with the number of industries, but the computational complexity increases geometrically. The statistical research and analysis to complete the needed matrix of production coefficients may require several man-years.[3] Fortunately, the coeffi-

---

[1] William J. Baumol, "Economic Theory and Operations Analysis" (Englewood Cliffs, N.J.: Prentice-Hall, Inc., 1961), pp. 299–310.
[2] "Manpower Report of the President," U.S. Dept. of Labor, (March 1963), p. 129.
[3] William H. Miernyk, "The Elements of Input-Output Analysis" (New York: Random House, Inc., 1966).

TABLE 9-1   Illustrative Input-Output Matrix

Producer of input	USER OF OUTPUT			External demand
	Industry	Agriculture	Water	
Industry	0.40	0.20	0.60	20
Agriculture	0.10	0.10	0.10	200
Water	0.10	0.30	0.20	20
Labor	0.40	0.40	0.10	

cients from an increasing number of completed models may be found in the literature.

The concept of the approach may be explained by using the overly simplified example of an economy represented by three producers: industry, agriculture, and water.[1] The required coefficients fill the matrix of Table 9-1. The first column of coefficients signifies that the production of $1 worth of industrial output requires 40 cents worth of industrial output as input, 10 cents worth of agricultural output, 10 cents worth of water, and 40 cents worth of labor. The first row of coefficients means that sufficient industrial output (cement, for example) is required so that 40 percent of it can be used as input for more industrial production, a quantity of industrial output (gasoline) worth 20 percent of the value of the agricultural output can be used for agricultural production, and a quantity of industrial output (electricity for pumping) worth 60 percent of the value of the water produced can be used to produce water. In addition, sufficient industrial output must be produced to supply external demand estimated by analysis of the export market to be $20,000 worth. If, I, A, and W denote the values of industrial, agricultural, and water production respectively, the rows in Table 9-1 state that

$$I = 0.4I + 0.2A + 0.6W + 20 \tag{9-1a}$$
$$A = 0.1I + 0.1A + 0.1W + 200 \tag{9-1b}$$
$$W = 0.1I + 0.3A + 0.2W + 20 \tag{9-1c}$$

The three equations when solved for the three unknowns yield values of 288 for I, 272 for A, and 163 for W.

Table 9-1 also shows that the wages labor requires are

$$L = 0.4I + 0.4A + 0.1W \tag{9-2}$$

or, for the above example, $L = 240$. If the mean wage were 8 ($8,000), the total number of workers required would be 30. If the ratio of total population (including children, retired, unemployed, housewives, etc.) to workers were 2.5, this simplified model would give a population of 75. The predicted export demand at any desired future date can be entered in the matrix to estimate the population required to produce the revised output.

The model as described above is called an *open model* because it considers only the production and not the consumption of goods. A *closed model* would include a second matrix containing consumption coefficients expressing imports from external sources and the amount of goods that various groups within the population could be expected to consume. Because, in the long run, production must equal consumption, the closed model provides a check against a serious imbalance between production

[1] Baumol, *loc. cit.*

and consumption totals. Another check is to compare the population predicted by the input-output model with that predicted by a demographic model.[1] A greater population predicted by the input-output model than by the demographic model would indicate a labor shortage, while the reverse would indicate unemployment.

The open and closed models described above are both *static models*. They consider output used to provide for consumption and output used in production, but they ignore output used to increase capital (provide new machinery) for future production. A *dynamic model* would add three capital stock equations to the three production equations (9-1), add three more unknowns which might be denoted K_I, K_A, and K_W, and solve for six values. K_I would signify the value of industrial output required in capital equipment and would be evaluated by an equation of the form

$$K_I = 4.2I + 2.7A + 3.6W \tag{9-3}$$

The coefficients denote that capital equipment containing $4.20 worth of industrial output (factories, for example) must be available for each dollar's worth of industrial output produced, capital equipment containing $2.70 worth of industrial output (tractors) must be available for each dollar's worth of agricultural output produced, and capital equipment containing $3.60 worth of industrial output (dams) must be available for each dollar's worth of water produced. The capital coefficients are normally larger than the production coefficients in a capital intensive economy where modern production methods require more capital than labor or raw materials.

In order to complete the dynamic model, it is necessary to subscript each variable by year and convert the equations to inequalities to allow for unused capital and overproduction. The resulting set of equations for industrial production would then be

$$I_{69} \geq 0.4I_{69} + 0.2A_{69} + 0.6W_{69} + D_{I69} + K_{I70} - K_{I69}$$
$$K_{I69} \geq 4.2I_{69} + 2.7A_{69} + 3.6W_{69} \tag{9-4}$$

where the subscripted number refers to the year, and D_I refers to the external demand. Corresponding pairs of equations would be introduced for agriculture and water. The external demand for each year could either be forecast independently and applied to an open model or be mathematically related to consumption within a closed model. The three initial capital availabilities (K_{I69}, K_{A69}, and K_{W69}) must be determined. Equation (9-4) says that industrial production must equal or exceed the sum of the amount used in current production, the external demand, and the amount needed to expand capital as required by the next year's production. A similar set

[1] Arthur D. Little, Inc., Projective Economic Study of the Ohio River Basin, "Ohio River Basin Comprehensive Survey" (Washington: USGPO, 1964), app. B.

of six equations is written for the succeeding year, and production unknowns subscripted 70 and capital unknowns subscripted 71 are introduced. By continuing the iteration from year to year, the equations may be extended to any desired future date, and the complete set involving six times as many unknowns as years may be solved simultaneously. The resulting time series of production outputs may then be converted to employment opportunities or population.

Both production and capital coefficients are statistical averages for existing production processes and are subject to change with time; they do not necessarily indicate optimum conditions. The optimum production process in an area having abundant labor and raw materials would have higher production coefficients and lower capital coefficients than that in an area having abundant capital. However, econometric models have not yet been developed to the point where they can successfully select the optimum production process.

Input-output models fulfill many functions in water resources planning besides serving as a projection tool. For example, a shortage in the available water supply might limit the maximum value of W in Eq. (9-1) to 100. The export could be cut from 20 to 0, but reducing W below 143 requires a cutback in industrial and agricultural production. Substituting 100 for W in Eq. (9-1) and converting to inequalities to denote the required cutback gives

$$0.6I - 0.2A \leq 80$$
$$-0.1I + 0.9A \leq 210 \tag{9-5}$$
$$0.1I + 0.3A \leq 80$$

Since the system of equations is overdetermined, one must select from among many possible solutions. By using the goal of maximizing the value of industrial and agricultural production as the objective function for a linear programming model (Sec. 19-2), the problem formulation becomes

$$
\begin{aligned}
R - I - \quad A \qquad\qquad\qquad &= 0 \\
0.6I - 0.2A + \quad a \qquad\qquad &= 80 \\
-0.1I + 0.9A \qquad\quad + b \qquad &= 210 \\
0.1I + 0.3A \qquad\qquad\quad + \quad c &= 80
\end{aligned}
\tag{9-6}
$$

for which the solution maximizing R (the value of the objective function) is

$$
\begin{aligned}
R \qquad\qquad + \quad a \quad + \quad 4c &= 400 \\
I \qquad + 1.5a \quad + \quad c &= 200 \\
0.6a + b - 2.6c &= 50 \\
A - 0.5a \qquad + \quad 3c &= 200
\end{aligned}
\tag{9-7}
$$

The optimum production is seen to be 200 from industry, 200 from agriculture (for the total R of 400), and 100 from water. With this production, \$50,000 ($b = 50$) of demand for agricultural production cannot be satisfied. The coefficient of 4 for c in the top row of Eq. (9-7) implies a marginal benefit-cost ratio of 4 for additional water development.

The model can also be used to evaluate secondary and employment benefits. If the available water supply were increased from 100 to 110, the model of Eq. (9-5) could be adjusted to determine the resulting increase in production by the other industries. The industries could be located geographically to distinguish local from national secondary benefits. The increased production by industry could be used to estimate employment benefits. The lifting of other constraints could be tried to see if investment in other forms of capital expansion would produce greater secondary benefits. The largest coefficients of the slack variables in the first row of the solution equations suggest the industries where capital expansion would be most profitable.

The secondary effects of water resources development as evaluated by an input-output model can be visualized by considering the effect on the economy of Table 9-1 of increasing the external demand for water by 20 to 40. The extra demand cannot simply be satisfied by increasing production by 20 to 183. From Eq. (9-1c), an external demand of 40, without changing I and A, gives $W = 188$ ($+25$). From Eq. (9-1a), I must be increased to 312 ($+24$) to provide the extra W. From Eq. (9-1b), A must be increased to 278 ($+6$) to provide for the extra W and I. After changing A and I to their new values, W [Eq. (9-1c)] becomes 193 ($+5$ more). After continuing around the cycle a number of times, the results will stablize at the solution of the three simultaneous equations of $I = 324$, $A = 280$, and $W = 196$. After accounting for interactions in the production process, increasing the external demand for W by 20 is seen to increase W by 33, I by 36, and A by 8.

Still additional information can be obtained by inverting the input-output matrix.[1] Each element of the inverse matrix signifies the amount of the specified input necessary to produce a unit of output. The elements will be in dollars, but unit values can be used to convert each element to such physical units as tons of steel, million gallons of water, etc.

9-4 CONSUMER PREFERENCE PROJECTION   While future demand depends as much on consumer preference (or individual unit consumption) as it does on population, much less attention has been given

---

[1]   Everard M. Lofting and H. Craig Davis, The Interindustry Water Content Matrix: Applications on a Multiregional Basis, *Water Resources Res.*, vol. 4 (April, 1968), pp. 689–695.

consumer preference projection. Existing consumer preference can be determined by analysis of market purchases and varies from place to place with cultural, environmental, and other factors. Regression techniques can be used to relate consumer preference to specific independent variables. Future preference trends will result from interaction between the introduction of new goods and services and the changes in means to purchase and time to enjoy them. In reality, consumer preference can only be projected by regression equations in the most general terms. Imagine the difficulty of predicting in 1920 the use individuals in 1970 would make of electric power or outdoor recreation facilities, and yet project planning requires predictions extending at least 50 years into the future.

9-5 CONSERVATION DYNAMICS AND SUPPLY PROJECTIONS

Projections on the supply side estimate the availability of raw materials and the extent of productivity and technological improvements. Extensive controversy has existed between those fearing natural resources will gradually be depleted until mankind will seriously suffer and those believing technological advances will continuously provide new production methods that will more than compensate for raw materials depletion.

Conservationists claim "how we treat our natural resources will determine the future of mankind."[1] Many ecologists even reject the goal of maximizing human welfare in favor of maximizing aggregate welfare for all species,[2] an objective giving very high priority to preservation of the existing natural environment. However, even without adopting such a value system, a strong case exists for protecting the ecological environment required for the spiritual well-being of mankind. Kuiper presents the essence of the argument with the paragraph:

We must face up to the problem of choosing the sort of environment that we want our children and their children to live in. Do we want them to live in material abundance with the probable loss of the things of the mind? Or do we want it the other way round? Are we going to advocate the most rapid depletion of our nonrenewable natural resources? Or do we have some obligation towards future generations that would caution us to use no more of these resources than is required for our basic needs? Are we going to continue building asphalt, concrete, smog, billboards and traffic lights? Or do we want to live and work in an environment where space, beauty, and quietude prevail? It is easy to ask these questions. It is not so easy to find the answers, but unless we face up to this challenge, we will never be able to

---

[1] Raymond F. Dasmann, "Environmental Conservation" (New York: John Wiley & Sons, Inc., 1959), p. 2.

[2] Kenneth E. Boulding, Economics and Ecology, in F. Fraser Darling and John P. Milton (eds.), "Future Environments of North America" (Garden City, N.Y.: Natural History Press, 1966), p. 230

clearly define the ends that will make the creation of our engineering projects a desirable objective.[1]

In what may seem to be a direct contradiction, Herfindahl states:

> Thus the countries which have been and are chewing up high grade mineral deposits have purchased an easy conscience. They have done this by advancing knowledge to the point where future generations will not have to worry about "running out." Surely the greatest contribution we can make to their material welfare is by continuing to advance and extend this knowledge rather than by attempting to restrict the rate at which high grade mineral deposits are being consumed.[2]

Perhaps the situation has been best summarized in a report to the National Academy of Sciences by its Committee on Water in the words:

> The change in concept of the natural environment from that of a workshop to that of a Temple and the conflicting existence of both concepts presents the resource planner with his most sensitive task: drawing a line between workshop and Temple, or attempting to merge them.[3]

The true conservationist must distinguish between economic and environmental resources.[4] Economic resources are used in the production of output to supply man's needs. The resources may be renewable naturally or replenished as in the case of water and timber or nonrenewable as in the case of iron ore. Environmental resources supply man's need for pleasing surroundings.

Technology rather than natural resources is the bottleneck that restricts economic growth in modern society. "The economic role of natural resources diminishes as the economy grows."[5] It is not rational for the present to deprive itself of economic resources for a future that will be wealthier, have more advanced technology, and to whom the resources may have less value. Mineral ores for which economic substitutes can be developed should be extracted at a rate which maximizes the present worth of their value in use. Underuse may inflict even a more severe hardship to the present than overuse does to the future.

---

[1] Edward Kuiper, "Water Resources Development: Planning, Engineering and Economics" (London: Butterworth & Co. (Publishers), Ltd., 1965), p. 4.

[2] Orris C. Herfindahl, Goals and Standards of Performance for the Conservation of Minerals, "Western Resources Papers" (Golden, Colo.: Colorado School of Mines, 1962).

[3] Alternatives in Water Management, *Natl. Acad. Sci.-Natl. Res. Council Publ. 1408* (1966), p. 26.

[4] John V. Krutilla, Conservation Reconsidered, *Am. Econ. Rev.*, vol. 57 (September, 1967), pp. 777–786.

[5] Morris Miller, The Scope and Content of Resource Policy in Relation to Economic Development, *Land Economics*, vol. 37 (November, 1961), p. 330.

However, this argument with respect to economic resources does not necessarily apply to environmental resources' meeting psychological needs. Economic resources are technologically substitutable, but the environmental resources of the seashore, the open countryside, virgin forests, or historical or cultural monuments may not have a substitute of equal psychological value. While the existence of substitutes for such experiences is plausible, our present understanding of the environmental contribution to man's psychological well-being does not allow us to assume their existence. On the other hand, if environmental resources are essential to man's well-being, larger future populations crowded into a limited area may environmentally be substantially poorer than the present.

Future production will find a balance between an increasing shortage of raw materials and an improving technology that will provide substitute synthetic materials and increased productivity from consumed raw materials. The consumption of raw materials (especially nonrenewable ones) promotes supply shortages. A developing technology promotes supply surplus. A reasonable goal in supply projection is an analysis of the relative import of the two effects.

9-6   PRICE INDICES   Price changes may be divided into two components. The value of money may decrease (inflation) or increase (deflation) with time. An economy study must use commensurable value units and hence constant dollars. This requirement is met if all values are expressed in dollars current to the year the study is made. Secondly, changes with time in the supply and demand relationships for specific commodities may cause their value to change relative to overall price levels. Commodities for which demand increases faster than supply or for which the input required in production becomes restricted will increase in value in constant dollars. A faster increase in supply, often caused by improved production technology, will decrease relative value with time.

Price indices are used to evaluate changes in both general and commodity price levels. General indices such as the Consumer's Price Index and the Wholesale Price Index[1] may be used for estimating time changes in the value of money and thus for converting costs at different dates to constant dollars defined by some preselected date. Specialized price indices may be used to indicate relative price changes within particular cost classes.

A price index is the cost of a preselected group of items called a *bundle of goods* expressed as a percentage of the cost of the same items at some base date. One of the most widely used specialized price indices is

[1] U.S. Department of Commerce, "Statistical Abstract of the United States—1962" (Washington: USGPO, 1963), pp. 231, 348–358.

the Engineering News Record (ENR) Construction Cost Index. The base date for the index is 1913. The bundle of goods is selected to represent the cost of heavy construction and consists of fixed quantities of common labor, cement, steel, and lumber. The index is computed from the average cost of the bundle in 20 cities in the United States. It equaled 474 in 1949 and 1,097 in September, 1967. The ENR Building Cost Index is intended to indicate the relative cost of constructing large buildings. The bundle of goods includes materials used in building construction and skilled labor. The base year is also 1913. The index equaled 352 in 1949 and 686 in September, 1967. The Bureau of Reclamation uses a bundle of 36 contract bid items to compute an index intended to indicate the relative cost of water resources project construction. The base year is 1949. The July, 1967, value was 146. Many other price indices are also available.[1]

Use of an index assumes cost to vary with time in the same manner as the value of the bundle of goods on which the selected index is based. If a dam was constructed for $1 million in 1949 and the Bureau of Reclamation Cost Index applies, an estimate of the 1967 cost of constructing a similar dam would be $1,460,000.

Use of cost indices has three major difficulties. The bundle of goods may become out of date. The design and expected performance of engineering structures changes with time. The changes may result either from changes in taste or change in income levels. The U.S. Department of Commerce periodically with changing buying habits shifts the bundle of goods it uses to compute the Consumer's Price Index.

Secondly, construction practice changes. No construction project would be built with the same proportions of labor and materials today as it would have been in 1913. The ENR indices overstate the time increase in construction cost because of their failure to incorporate the increased productivity of labor as more highly skilled workers use improved mechanical equipment and higher-quality materials. The Bureau of Public Roads found the average manhours of labor per million dollars of highway construction to have decreased from 163,800 in 1950 to 87,400 in 1964. This agency computes a Highway Bid Price Index which at least partially overcomes this difficulty by using contract bid prices. Contractors reduce bids as increased labor productivity and material quality allow less expensive construction. The Bureau of Public Roads Index was 120 in 1965 based on 100 in 1950. The overstatement of inflation by the ENR indices is seen from their increase by an average factor of 1.94 between 1949 and 1965, while the Bureau of Public Roads and Bureau of Reclamation indices were increasing by an average factor of 1.28.

[1] Current values for most cost indices associated with major construction projects are published four times a year in the Quarterly Cost Roundup of the *Engineering News Record*.

The third major difficulty stems from variation between items considered in the price index and items composing the project one wants to evaluate. Even though the specialized cost indices indicate differential inflation among broad groups of cost items, the composition of input to any given construction project will never exactly duplicate the index bundle of goods. Price indices should only be used after comparing the cost items one is studying with the cost items within the index bundle of goods to determine whether their respective patterns of cost change are similar.

Price indices have a number of uses in project planning. General price indices are used in converting cash flows at different dates to constant dollars while reviewing past economic effects. Specific price indices may be compared with general indices to determine whether particular prices are changing faster or slower than the value of money. Specific price indices are also required for predicting short-term changes in construction cost for financial analysis.

9-7 NORMALIZED PRICES   Strikes, adverse weather, crop failures, or other factors may cause certain prices to deviate temporarily from their value under more normal conditions. In estimating future cash flows for economy studies, prices under normal or average conditions should be used. Otherwise, project feasibility will depend on short-term market abnormalities. The normalized price, which should be used, is the price in constant dollars averaged over a number of recent years.

9-8 INFLATION   The goal of an economy study is to compare relative values by expressing consequences in commensurable units. The most satisfactory value unit is money expressed in constant dollars specified by date.[1] Dollars spent at one date may be transformed to constant dollars specified by another date by use of a general price index (Sec. 9-6). Trends in general price level should never be incorporated into economic analysis.[2]

Only when dealing with goods or services whose price is expected to change relative to the general price level, differential inflation, does the current normalized price in constant dollars need adjustment. This is done by reckoning the value of the transaction as the product of the expected future cost and the ratio of the present to the future value of money. If the value of money changes from 100 to 150 (determined by a general price index) while the value of an item changes from 100 to 200 (determined by a

[1] Jack Hirshleifer, James C. DeHaven, and Jerome W. Milliman, "Water Supply: Economics, Technology, and Policy" (Chicago: The University of Chicago Press, 1960), pp. 142–143.

[2] Panel of Consultants to the Bureau of the Budget, "Standards and Criteria for Formulating and Evaluating Federal Water Resources Development" (Washington: USGPO, 1961), p. 39.

specific cost index), the future cost in present dollars will be $200(^{100}\!/_{150})$, or \$133. Uncertainty in predicting future differential inflation precludes extending this adjustment more than about 10 years into the future.[1]

Just as for economic analysis, trends in general price levels have little place in financial analysis except for short-term changes between the appropriation and expenditure of funds. Sufficient funds must be obtained to pay rising construction costs. Federal monetary and fiscal policy has the control of inflation as a prime objective. Altering investment planning to take advantage of monetary inflation would mean the Federal government was predicting in advance that its inflation control policies would fail. State and local water planners would find it advantageous to borrow money and then pay back their obligations in inflated dollars. However, lenders will require higher interest rates if they anticipate general inflation. The borrower can take advantage of inflation only by outguessing lenders to get money from them at too low an interest rate. Practically, nonfederal analysts must treat inflation in the same manner as federal analysts do.

9-9 STAGES OF PROJECT LIFE   The potential benefits of project construction may be defined as the maximum benefit which can be realized by using project output in the highest available economic use. As time goes by, economic development creates new higher-valued economic uses, and potential benefits increase. Potential benefits vary with calendar time as they depend on general economic conditions. However, potential benefit cannot be realized until the output is actually produced. Realized benefits vary with project time.

The relationship between potential and realized benefit may be illustrated by dividing project life into four stages (Fig. 9-1). The first stage is construction. A single-unit project will not provide any benefit until construction is completed. A multiunit project will provide benefits as soon as the first unit begins to function. Economic evaluation of a project constructed over 2 or more years should discount construction expen-

[1] *Ibid.*

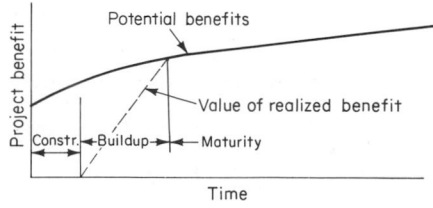

Time   *FIGURE 9-1* Stages of project life.

ditures. If the project is analyzed as of the date construction begins, construction expenditures in later years should be discounted back to that date. If the project is analyzed as of the date construction ends, construction expenditures in former years should be increased by interest during construction. Interest during construction is a financial obligation of those agencies which borrow money to build a project.

The second stage is buildup. It lasts from the production of initial project output until full potential benefits are realized. Most projects require expenditure to provide the associated facilities required to utilize project output. For example, a project producing irrigation water cannot properly function without expenditure to develop on-farm irrigation systems. During buildup, construction is completed and the associated facilities are installed. In planning, the time lag in private investment is usually assumed to extend buildup to 5 to 10 years after construction is completed.

The third stage is maturity. During this time full economic use is made of project output, so full potential benefits can be realized. However, benefits realized may still continue to increase as higher-valued economic uses develop. Strictly speaking, full economic utilization of project output is never realized but is prevented by time delays in economic adjustment, the seeking of extraeconomic goals, hindrance of associated investment by financial limitations, and a number of other reasons. Practical maturity is reached when realized benefit has stabilized at a large fraction of potential benefit.

The final stage is decline. The time comes when realized net benefit begins to decrease. The annual upkeep costs may increase with project time until it becomes less expensive to discard the old project and build a new one. This is what happens to the family car or to a reservoir filled with silt. A shift in technology may reduce or eliminate the demand for the output. This is what happened to manufacturers of horse-drawn carriages and to navigation canals in the nineteenth century. A shift in technology might also outdate the production process as has happened to the hand reaping of grain and may happen to imported water supply with the advent of salt water conversion or to hydroelectric power with the advent of atomic power. The timing of project decline is very difficult to anticipate during planning, but economic justification should be based on benefits which can reasonably be expected before decline begins.

9-10 OPTIMUM CONSTRUCTION DATE As potential benefits increase with calendar time, they eventually become large enough to justify project construction. The optimum time to build may be derived from

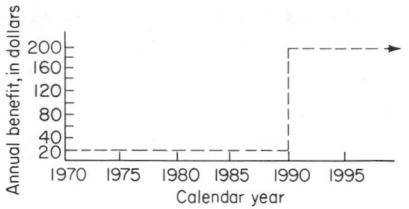

FIGURE 9-2   Potential benefits from a hypothetical project.

the optimality objective of maximizing the present worth of net benefits (benefits minus costs, Sec. 4-16).

The principle may be illustrated by a project whose potential benefits vary with time as shown in Fig. 9-2 and which has a 1-year construction period with instantaneous buildup and indefinite life.[1] If the project had an installation cost of \$2,000 and no operation and maintenance cost, the present worth of the cost would be

$$C = 2,000 \left(\frac{P}{F}, i\%, N \right) \tag{9-8}$$

where N is the number of years until the date the project is to be installed. The value of N is to be varied to find the optimum construction date. The present worth of the benefit would be

$$B = 20 \left(\frac{P}{F}, i\%, N \right) \left(\frac{P}{A}, i\%, 20 - N \right) + 200 \left(\frac{P}{F}, i\%, 20 \right) \left(\frac{P}{A}, i\%, \infty \right) \tag{9-9}$$

unless N exceeds 20, in which case the first term would drop out and 20 would be replaced by N in the second term. The net benefit equals Eq. (9-9) less Eq. (9-8). The present worths of the net benefits based on a 5 percent discount rate are tabulated in Table 9-2 for a series of construction dates. Even though the project could be economically justified anytime after 1973, the optimum construction date does not come until 1990. In 1973, the excess of benefits over costs after 1990 will be realized soon enough to have greater present worth than the excess of costs over benefits before that date, but construction should not begin until the year is reached when benefits actually begin to exceed-cost.

The optimum construction date has already passed and consequently installation should begin as soon as practical if the present worth of all project benefits exceeds the present worth of all project costs and current

---

[1]   For further discussion, see Stephen A. Marglin, Economic Factors Affecting System Design, in Arthur Maass et al., "Design of Water-resource Systems" (Cambridge, Mass.: Harvard University Press, 1962), pp. 179–192.

annual potential benefits exceed discounted average annual cost. In other words, a project with instantaneous buildup should be built in the year for which potential benefits first exceed average annual cost, provided benefits continue to exceed cost in years thereafter. However, the basic rule of maximizing net benefit has to be used to evaluate the effect of the buildup period or to handle unusual time streams of benefits or costs.

If construction is delayed, the benefits which the project would have realized during the intervening period are lost. In addition, construction cost may change. If the change is caused entirely by the changing value of money, it should not influence project timing. If the cost of construction is expected to decrease with respect to general price levels, project construction should begin earlier because the first date for which benefits exceed costs will come sooner. The optimum date may be estimated by obtaining the present worth of the construction cost with the use of the discount rate plus the net excess of the general inflation rate over the construction cost inflation rate. If, as has happened in the past, construction cost is expected to inflate more rapidly than the general economy, project construction should be further delayed. The optimum date may be estimated by determining the present worth of the construction cost through adjustment of the discount rate downward according to the net excess of the construction cost over the general inflation rate. In the special case where the excess of the construction cost over the general inflation rate exceeds the discount rate, justified projects should be constructed as soon as possible purely to minimize cost.

Furthermore, construction costs change with calendar time for reasons other than inflation. The cost increases as urban expansion changes construction-site environment. Land prices and the value of improvements multiply rapidly. More transverse utility and transportation lines

TABLE 9-2   Optimum Construction
Date Computations

Construction date	Cost, Eq. (9-8)	Benefit Eq. (9-9)	Net benefit
1970	2,000	1,757	−243
1975	1,567	1,671	104
1980	1,228	1,603	375
1985	962	1,550	588
1990	754	1,508	754
1995	591	1,181	590
2000	463	926	463

must be relocated and maintained during construction. The confining effect of an urban environment reduces contractor efficiency and may require more expensive construction methods. Agitation over the disruptive influence of construction on community life multiplies, and special problems result when large numbers of people must be relocated. Extra expenses may be required to develop an esthetically pleasing design for the community environment. These changes in construction environment influence construction cost, are not incorporated into price indices, and should be considered in project timing.

One approach to project timing is to delay project construction but to purchase the required right-of-way immediately. This alternative is especially attractive when land prices including the cost of buildings and other improvements are expected to escalate quite rapidly. The problem is most acute when dealing with the large areas required by major reservoirs. However, the planner should remember that the economic value of right-of-way is not necessarily the market value of the land but rather an expression of the present worth of its future productivity (Sec. 8-14). The productivity of the land in nonproject uses usually terminates at the date of its purchase for use as right-of-way. Early purchase may cause the land to sit idle until construction begins, and the earlier the purchase, the greater the loss. The financial savings in installation cost may eliminate the opportunity for investment which would be profitable even during the interim period. The land may be leased until needed, but the lessee may find it difficult to realize the full productivity of odd-shaped parcels. The planner must also face uncertainty in predicting the boundaries of the right-of-way required for future projects.

The government may preserve right-of-way by means other than early purchase. It may purchase *development rights*, leaving the owner free to continue to use the land but not to convert it to urban or some other more intensive use. The value of such rights should approximately equal the present worth of the anticipated increase in income from the land from more intensified future use. It may discourage development of the land by not providing access and other service facilities. It may reduce property taxes for those agreeing to preserve their land in agricultural use. It may instigate zoning restrictions on new development. Each method has been used, and each has a cost which must be borne by either the land owner or the government. The social cost depends principally on the area, degree, and duration of growth restriction and only slightly on the method used. Any method of land use control which does not involve compensation requires property owners to confer a benefit on the public without recoupment of the cost. The true social value of right-of-way may be hard to establish, but it is hardly reasonable to justify public planning by the failure of private parties to consider external effects and then proceed to evaluate the cost-of-way or land use regulation as only the financial obligation incurred by a governmental agency.

9-11   STAGE CONSTRUCTION   The calculations in Table 9-2 for determining the optimum construction date assumed the project to be one indivisible unit. Even greater net benefit may be realized if the project is divided into construction units and the optimum construction date is individually determined for each unit. It is not even necessary for all the construction within a unit to take place at one time. The facilities may be originally built to meet current needs and later enlarged when more project output is required.

One need not initially plan the optimum stage construction schedule into the indefinite future. One need only determine what portions of the project should be built now and what portions should wait. After a period of time, the situation can be reviewed to see what portions should then be constructed. Periodic review and revision are more efficient than constructing now and foregoing the possibility of modification if original growth projections turn out to be in error. The major advantage of stage construction is that it greatly increases flexibility for coping with unforeseen events.

While stage construction maintains greater flexibility for future selection of alternative courses of action and reduces the commitment of large amounts of capital at an early date, the savings have offsetting costs. Many economies of scale are lost when the work is done in smaller increments. The site must be prepared, construction forces must be moved in and out, and the local community is disrupted more often. The difference between the cost of constructing all the facilities at one time and the present worth of the stage construction costs must be considered in the economic analysis.

While stage construction may produce substantial economic savings, the planner must not retreat to a series of day-by-day decisions that ignore ultimate consequences. Long-term goals must be kept in mind, or time will foreclose major planning choices. Planning by crises or creeping expediency may overemphasize short-term goals which can be achieved with little investment. Practices established to achieve short-term goals may become institutionally, or even legally, frozen and be very difficult to alter when long-term needs become better known. This is what has happened to water rights. Human inertia is one of the greatest obstacles to flexible planning.

*9-12 PROJECT FORMULATION AND RANKING UNDER CAP-
ITAL RATIONING*   The investment planner has a budget which can
be spent and a group of projects which might be built. The total cost of
the potential projects normally exceeds the available budget so that only
a portion of the projects can be funded. Economic efficiency requires the
better projects to be selected. A ranking of the potential projects from best
to worst permits identification of the best projects for budgets of various
sizes.

As an ideal, the planner would like every potential project in all
sectors of the economy to be ranked. The capital budget could then be
divided among the best projects independently of whether they happened
to be steel mills, hospitals, or flood control reservoirs. As a result, the
marginal productivity of capital would be identical in all spending sectors.
The marginal public works project would be of value equivalent to that of
the marginal project in private business. As a practical matter, the ideal
cannot be achieved because of the impossibility of developing acceptable
trade-offs among the realization of diverse goals. A ton of steel cannot be
evaluated in units commensurable with those used in evaluating health
standards. However, even though intersector ranking is impractical, ranking within a sector can still achieve more efficient expenditure of the sector
budget (Sec. 4-12).

According to economic efficiency, all projects whose benefits exceed
their costs, whose internal rate of return exceeds the normative discount
rate, should be built. Those failing to pass this test should not be built.
The need for ranking comes when financial rather than economic limitations control project investment. If there is not enough money available
to build all projects whose benefits exceed their cost, some method must be
found to determine which of the economically feasible projects should be
built. If the budget which must be spent exceeds the installation cost of
the projects which are economically feasible, the best of those which are
not economically feasible must also be selected.

If the budgeted amount were known prior to the ranking and each
independent project an indivisable unit, one could rank each project by
its internal rate of return, then start at the top of the list and authorize
each project proceeding down the list until the sum of the required investments equalled the total budget. Incremental adjustments might be
required at the margins where capital rationing could cause projects to
become mutually exclusive (Sec. 2-1). The first problem with this
approach is that investment alternatives do not come in indivisable units.
Alternatives may be mutually exclusive. All alternative scales of project
development fall in this class. Each project will have marginal elements
whose inclusion depends on the cutoff internal rate of return. Alternatives

of structural location, materials of construction, and construction timing also depend on the cutoff point. Project divisability may be overcome in project ranking by the following trial and error procedure.

1 Pick a cutoff discount rate based on judgment gained from past experience.
2 Design all potential projects by using this discount rate in all the incidental engineering economy studies required in project formulation.
3 Estimate the total cost required to install all the project elements economically justified when this discount rate is used and compare this amount with the allotted budget.
4 Adjust the discount rate upward if the total cost exceeds the allotted budget and downward if it does not, and repeat the procedure until the budget and the required expenditure are approximately equal.

More often, the budget is unknown when the ranking must be made. Since project design is affected by discount rate and marginal discount rate is affected by the budget, there is no way to design, let alone rank, projects correctly if the budget is unknown. The best that can be done is to develop an approximation based on a budget estimated from past experience. The trial-and-error analysis can then be completed based on an estimated rather than a firm budget figure.

The above procedure of project formulation and ranking requires explicit description of the budget to which the financial constraint applies. Seldom do all the funds for a water resource project come from a common source. Some will come from the Federal government, and these may be split among agencies and legislative authorizations, or in some other way. Other funds will come from state and local sources. For example, for flood control in California, project construction is financed by the Federal government, right-of-way costs are borne by the state government, and operation and maintenance is a local cost. In determining the optimum allocation of funds in a constrained budget, the costs paid from that budget must be specified. In case more than one budget is constrained, one can proceed with the trial-and-error procedure until the first budgetary restriction controls and then make such adjustments as may be possible by shifting design to use more funds from other budgets and less from the constrained budget with the goal of increasing net benefit. However, such an effort leads to a different cutoff discount rate for each budget and to a much more complicated trial-and-error procedure.

An alternative to a marginal discount rate cutoff is a marginal benefit-cost ratio cutoff. The first step in this approach is the selection of a normative discount rate. The most common practice is to use a risk-free rate based on the selling price of government bonds, a rate substantially lower than the marginal internal rate of return. A cutoff benefit-cost ratio is next selected. The amount by which the cutoff benefit-cost ratio exceeds unity is called λ. The trial-and-error process of optimizing project design is repeated until a λ is found which equates total expenditures and the available budget. It is still necessary to define the constrained budget explicitly. Only cash flows from the constrained budget should be placed in the denominator of the benefit-cost ratio.[1] Costs from all other funds should be included as negative benefits in the numerator. Multiple budgetary constraints will again complicate the calculations and lead to distinct λ's for each constraint. Both the λ and the discount rate method are illustrated in Ex. 9-1.

EXAMPLE 9-1

A decision maker has a budget of $25 million to spend in the installation of water resource projects. The annual budget for operation and maintenance is not constrained. He must divide the expenditure among three projects. The first project yields a benefit of $1 million each of the 50 years of project life. Alternate project designs for achieving this benefit are available. Some have high installation cost and low annual cost, while others have low installation cost and high annual cost. Analysis of alternate designs reveals the relationship between the two costs to be as shown in Fig. 9-3. The second project yields benefits which increase at a uniform

---

[1]   Otto Eckstein, "Water Resource Development: The Economics of Project Evaluation" (Cambridge, Mass.: Harvard University Press, 1958), pp. 55–65.

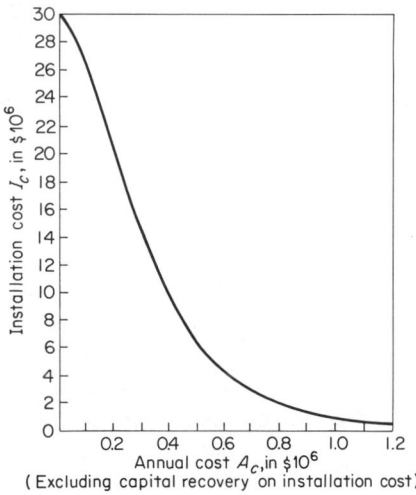

FIGURE 9-3 Relationship between installation cost and annual cost for Ex. 9-1.

annual rate from \$500,000 in the first year of project life to \$2,500,000 in the fiftieth year. The third project yields benefits which decrease at a uniform annual rate from \$2,500,000 in the first year of project life to \$500,000 in the fiftieth year. Figure 9-3 also applies to these other two projects.

1 Divide the budget among the three projects by the cutoff discount rate method. What is the cutoff discount rate?
2 Divide the budget among the three projects by the λ method, using a social discount rate of 3 percent. What is the cutoff λ?
3 What are the differences between the results of the two methods?

SOLUTION
1 Cutoff discount rate method
   a Try 10 percent.
      Project 1:

      Annual benefit $=$ (inst. cost) $\left(\dfrac{A}{P}, 10\%, 50\right)$ + annual cost

      $A_b = I_c(0.10086) + A_c$ (a)

      An examination of alternative designs reveals this equality to hold for two of the designs represented by Fig. 9-3. However, as one should continue investing capital until the marginal rate of return drops below the cutoff discount rate, the one of the two points representing the higher installation cost should be used. Using $A_b = 1.0^*$ in Eq. (a) gives the design represented by the point

      $I_c = 3.97$ $A_c = 0.60$ (optimum design for $i = 10$ percent)

      Project 2:

      Gradient $= \dfrac{2.5 - 0.5}{50} = 0.04$

      $A_b = 0.46 + 0.04 \left(\dfrac{P}{G}, 10\%, 50\right)\left(\dfrac{A}{P}, 10\%, 50\right)$

         $= 0.46 + 0.04(104.80)(0.1009) = 0.46 + 0.04(10.57)$

         $= 0.88$ (equivalent annual benefit at $i = 10$ percent)

      From Eq. (a) and Fig. 9-3,

      $I_c = 0.00$ $A_c = 0.00$

                (no design available yields a return as high as 10 percent)

      Project 3:

      $A_b = 2.54 - 0.04(10.57) = 2.12$

* All values are expressed in millions of dollars.

From Eq. (a) and Fig. 9-3,

$I_c = 18.84 \qquad A_c = 0.22 \qquad$ (optimum design for $i = 10$ percent)

Total expenditure

$3.97 + 0.00 + 18.84 = 22.81$

(not all money spent; $\therefore$ must try lower i)

b Try 8 percent.

Project 1:

$A_b = 1.0 + I_c(0.08174) + A_c$

$I_c = 5.75 \qquad A_c = 0.53$

Project 2:

$A_b = 0.46 + 0.04(12.41) = 0.96$

$I_c = 4.77 \qquad A_c = 0.57$

Project 3:

$A_b = 2.54 - 0.04(12.41) = 2.04$

$I_c = 23.12 \qquad A_c = 0.15$

Total expenditure

$5.75 + 4.77 + 23.12 = 33.64$

$c \quad \therefore$ Too much, and so interpolate.

$$i = 8 + \frac{33.64 - 25.00}{33.64 - 22.81} 2 = 9.60 \text{ percent}$$

Project 2: Not feasible at this rate; $\therefore$ divide between 1 and 3.

Project 1:

$I_c = 4.62 \qquad A_c = 0.57$

Project 3:

$I_c = 20.38 \qquad A_c = 0.19$

$2 \quad \lambda$ method:

a Try $\lambda = 1.0$ (cutoff $B/C = 2.0$).

Project 1:

$$\frac{B}{C} = \frac{A_b - A_c}{I_c(A/P,3\%,50)} = \frac{1.0 - A_c}{0.03887I_c} = 2.0$$

(A_c is considered a negative benefit because it is not within

the constrained budget.)

$A_b = 1.0 = 0.07774I_c + A_c$

From Fig. 9-3,

$I_c = 6.43 \qquad A_c = 0.50$

Project 2:

$$A_b = 0.46 + 0.04 \left(\frac{P}{G}, 3\%, 50 \right) \left(\frac{A}{P}, 3\%, 50 \right)$$

$$= 0.46 + 0.04(503.21)(0.0389)$$

$$= 1.24$$

$1.24 = 0.07774 I_c + A_c$

From Fig. 9-3,

$I_c = 11.19 \qquad A_c = 0.37$

Project 3:

$A_b = 2.54 - 0.04(19.56) = 1.76$

$1.76 = 0.07774 I_c + A_c$

From Fig. 9-3,

$I_c = 20.07 \qquad A_c = 0.20$

Total expenditure

$6.43 + 11.19 + 20.07 = 37.69$

(too much expenditure; $\therefore$ increase λ`

b Try $\lambda = 1.5$ (cutoff $B/C = 2.5$).

Project 1:

$1.0 = 0.09718 I_2 + A_c$

From Fig. 9-3,

$I_c = 4.32 \qquad A_c = 0.58$

Project 2:

$1.24 = 0.09718 I_c + A_c$

From Fig. 9-3,

$I_c = 8.23 \qquad A_c = 0.44$

Project 3:

$1.76 = 0.09718 I_c + A_c$

From Fig. 9-3,

$I_c = 15.23 \qquad A_c = 0.28$

Total expenditure

$4.32 + 8.23 + 15.23 = 27.78$

 c Try $\lambda = 1.75$ (cutoff $B/C = 2.75$).

  Project 1:

  $1.10 = 1.069 I_c + A_c$

  From Fig. 9-3,

  $I_c = 3.27$ $A_c = 0.65$

  Project 2:

  $1.24 = 1.069 I_c + A_c$

  From Fig. 9-3,

  $I_c = 7.11$ $A_c = 0.48$

  Project 3:

  $1.76 = 1.069 I_c + A_c$

  From Fig. 9-3,

  $I_c = 13.47$ $A_c = 0.32$

  Total expenditure

  $3.27 + 7.11 + 13.47 = 23.85$

 d Interpolate between $\lambda = 1.50$ and $\lambda = 1.75$

$$\lambda = 1.5 + \frac{27.78 - 25.00}{27.78 - 23.85} \, 0.25 = 1.68$$

  Optimum values for each project:

  Project 1:

  $I_c = 3.57$ $A_c = 0.63$

  Project 2:

  $I_c = 7.44$ $A_c = 0.47$

  Project 3:

  $I_c = 13.99$ $A_c = 0.31$

3 The λ method resulted in larger expenditure for projects with more distant benefits (Project 2) and less expenditure for projects with immediate benefits (Project 3). This is what advocates of a social interest rate wish to accomplish.

 Inspection of the results of Ex. 9-1 reveals an increasing project capital intensity with increasing benefits. Two projects might produce identical output from identical input. The output from one project may be put to a higher-value use than that from the other. Should the two projects be designed differently? The above analysis says that they should. A less-capital-intensive design for the project with less benefits allows greater flexibility if benefits do not materialize as forecast.

The use of a normative discount rate lower than the marginal internal rate of return will cause the λ method to select a more capital-intensive project mix than the discount rate method. If the marginal internal rate of return were to remain above the planning discount rate, the long-run effect would be a lower rate of economic growth (Sec. 6-1). However, the use of a marginal λ has its advantages. If one were to match investment with the budget each year by varying the discount rate, one would end up with a marginal discount rate that varied from year to year. The capital intensity as a function of discount rate would vary from year to year. This difficulty can be avoided by basing all economy studies on a long-term average discount rate and then varying λ in the year-to-year project ranking. While justification for using the λ method of ranking with the social discount rate must be on grounds outside economic efficiency, the λ method with an average marginal internal rate of return does serve to standardize project design.

SELECTED REFERENCES

Arthur D. Little, Inc.: Projective Economic Study of the Ohio River Basin, "Ohio River Basin Comprehensive Survey" (Washington: USGPO, 1964), app. B.

Baumol, William J.: "Economic Theory and Operations Analysis" (Englewood Cliffs, N.J.: Prentice-Hall, Inc., 1961).

Ciriacy-Wantrup, S. V.: "Resource Conservation Economics and Policies," Rev. ed. (Berkeley: University of California Press, 1963).

Dasmann, Raymond F.: "Environmental Conservation" (New York: John Wiley & Sons, Inc., 1959).

Lofting, Everard M., and H. Craig Davis: The Interindustry Water Content Matrix: Applications on a Multiregional Basis, *Water Resources Res.*, vol. 4 (August, 1968), pp. 689–695.

Marglin, Stephen A.: Economic Factors Affecting System Design, in Arthur Maass et al., "Design of Water-resource Systems" (Cambridge, Mass.: Harvard University Press, 1962), pp. 179–192.

Miernyk, William H.: "The Elements of Input-Output Analysis," (New York: Random House, Inc., 1966).

PROBLEMS

9-1 From the simplified input-output example presented in this chapter, what population would have been predicted had the required external demands been 200 for industrial output, 40 for agricultural output, and zero for water.

9-2   A water resources project requires 5 years to construct and has a 10-year buildup period at a uniform annual rate. It will last indefinitely once constructed and is to be analyzed at 4 percent interest. Total construction cost is $3,000. One-fifth of the construction will be completed each year. Potential benefits for a mature project are $50 in year 1; $45 + 5t$ in each subsequent year, where t is the year number, until the annual benefit reaches $200; and constant at the last figure thereafter. Annual operation, maintenance and replacement costs are constant at $20 each year after the project is completed.

 If project construction were begun at the beginning of year 1, what would be the present worth of the cost, the present worth of the benefit, and benefit-cost ratio for the project?

 Calculate the same three values ("present" is the beginning of year 1) for a project with construction commencing at the start of year 11.

 In which year should construction begin to maximize the present worth of the resulting net benefit?

9-3   A certain project has a marginal-cost curve for water supply which is U-shaped and defined by the equations $P + Q = 60$ on the left side, $P = 10$ on the bottom, and $Q = P + 70$ on the right side. P is the marginal cost of producing the water in dollars per acre-foot, and Q is the design capacity of the facilities in 100 acre-ft. The marginal-benefit curve is defined by the equation $P + 2Q = 60(1.05)^n$, where $n = 0$ during the current year and increases by 1 at the start of each subsequent year.

 a What is the annual cost of providing 15,000 acre-ft of water per year?

 b If a single project must be built to supply the demand for water for the next 50 years, what is the economically optimum design capacity for the facilities if the project is to be evaluated at a discount rate of 3 percent?

 c What are the annual benefits, annual cost, net annual benefits, and benefit-cost ratio for the optimum project in b?

 d If instead it would be possible to build now a project only large enough to meet the demand for the next 10 years, then enlarge it to meet the demand for the subsequent 10 years, etc., what would be the optimum size of the project to build now? By how much should the size be enlarged at the end of 10 years? At the end of 20 years? 30 years? 40 years?

e What is the average cost per acre-foot of water supply, and what percent of the required cost could be raised by marginal-cost pricing during each 10-year period? What are the implications of your answer?

f Plot the average annual benefits and the average annual costs during each 10-year period, and determine the average annual benefits and average annual costs over the 50-year period.

g How do the net annual benefits for stage construction compare with those for present construction?

h Can you think of any assumptions included in the above computations which might invalidate the above advantage for stage construction?

9-4 A certain investment which will instantaneously after construction reap full current potential benefits is to be considered for a situation where potential benefits amount to $1 in year 1, $2 in year 2, $3 in year 3, and continue on the same uniform-gradient-growth pattern indefinitely into the future. Construction costs $1,000 and requires no continuing annual maintenance cost. The minimum acceptable rate of return is 4 percent.

a What is the present worth of the potential benefits? Specify any base year you find convenient.

b What rate of return would be realized from construction in the base year you specified?

c What is the optimum year for construction at the 4 percent rate of return?

9-5 Over the last 10 years the general price index has gone from 175 to 211, while the special price index applicable to the investment in Prob. 9-4 has gone from 611 to 914. Assume the special price index considers changes in the productivity of labor.

a In which direction would this information influence the optimum year for construction? Explain your reasoning.

b Make and state whatever assumptions you feel necessary, and estimate the optimum year of construction under these conditions.

9-6 A small community has a limited water supply and an economy based on raising sheep and processing wool. The input-output coefficients representing the economy are:

USER OF OUTPUT

	Input	Sheep	Wool processing	Water
Producer of Input	Sheep	0.2	0.3	0.0
	Wool processing	0.5	0.2	0.4
	Water	0.1	0.3	0.1
	Labor	0.2	0.2	0.5

a If the potential demand for sheep is 150 and for wool is 450 but the existing water supply is limited to 100, what is the total quantity of sheep and wool which can be produced by the economy? What quantity of sheep and wool is available for export? How many workers can be hired at a wage rate of 6?

b A water supply project is to be built to provide all the water needed to meet the external demand for sheep and wool and to export 300 units of water. How much water must the project supply? How much of the total is used by each industry? What will be the resulting increase in employment? What are the secondary benefits computed as the increase in value of total production by the economy net of the value of the water?

9-7 Work Ex. 9-1 for a decision maker who has a budget of $40 million.

9-8 If alternative project designs are represented by Fig. 9-3, what design could potentially yield the maximum rate of return? What is the maximum possible rate of return?

4
ECONOMIC PLANNING
BY PROJECT PURPOSE

Benefits from a multipurpose project are determined by summing benefits achieved by accomplishing individual project purposes. Even though the sharing of fixed costs usually makes a single multipurpose water resources development project more economical than a group of single-purpose projects to achieve the same ends, benefits are realized through the collective solution of individual problems. The background in economic evaluation techniques provided by the foregoing chapters is necessary but hardly sufficient for handling the complex problems involved in selecting the optimum group of measures to achieve such specific objectives as flood control or recreation. This section contains the additional information needed to apply the optimality conditions of Chap. 4 and the benefit-cost analysis of Chap. 8 to multipurpose planning as presented in Part 5.

Economic planning is the ordering of production facilities. Water resources development for each of the several purposes produces a distinct group of goods and services. The best projects can only be determined by those able to list viable alternatives, quantify the economic value of specific outputs, and relate output amount to degree of project development. The following chapters introduce the alternatives and outline the steps in economic analysis.

While it is necessary to go into some detail to introduce the alternatives, the emphasis is on economic implications rather than the design details found in engineering literature. Historical background is given to bring out the institutional factors affecting project benefit. However, the reader knowledgeable in the nature of the planning alternatives may pass quickly through these introductory sections to get to the main purpose of each of the following chapters: a step-by-step development of the project-supply curve, the project-demand curve, and the combination of the two curves in project optimization.

The goal is not to present stereotype procedures which are easy to execute but, likely as not, depart drastically from stating true economic benefit. It is rather to develop a framework for realistic economic appraisal of water resources planning alternatives. As such, the methods presented in the following pages should not be regarded as cookbook approaches to be followed in minute detail. It is hoped they will stimulate the student and the experienced water resources planner alike to a more diligent search for improved methods of economic analysis.

As benefit evaluation for many project purposes is still in the developmental stage, many of the techniques described are subject to radical change with continued research and application. Many points will be controversial. However, if the issues raised contribute to better water resources planning, the intent will be achieved.

CHAPTER
TEN

FLOOD CONTROL

The Planning Context

10-1 DEFINITION A flood is "an overflow of lands which, although they are adjacent to water, are not normally covered by it, and hence are used (or usable) in the same way that other lands are used."[1] Such overflows cause economic losses, or flood damages. Flood control measures strive to reduce the frequency and the magnitude of flood damages, but cannot eliminate the residual hazard from rare events.

Since United States practice provides federal financing to pay nearly the full cost of flood control projects, the government has had to set arbitrary limits to what it will consider flood control. Smaller projects are considered drainage, and local government or individuals pay most costs. Federally financed projects should benefit at least seven people, and every project component should benefit at least two. A minimum project cost of about $100,000 is required to justify the overhead cost of federal project planning. The flooding must result from overflow caused by abnormal precipitation or snowmelt,[2] so as to be distinguished from land drainage. The flooding must not be caused by runoff from small urban areas, so as to be distinguished from storm drainage. However, the arbitrary boundary between drainage and flood control does not represent a fundamental difference in the nature of the problem.

10-2 HISTORICAL DEVELOPMENT Flood-plain land alongside rivers and streams has always offered advantages to the potential

---

[1] U.S. Code (Washington: USGPO 1940), p. 2964.
[2] Soil Conservation Service, "Watershed Protection Handbook," Sec. 105.00.

developer. Rivers provide a transportation artery, recreational advantage, industrial power, water supply, and waste removal. Flood-plain fertility encourages agriculture, and flatness encourages urban development and railroad and highway construction. However, nature does not provide these advantages without exacting a price from those who benefit. The rivers and streams which attract settlement periodically leave their banks to reap a toll in lives and property.

Men may develop the flood plain as if the threat did not exist and suffer periodic damage, develop the flood plain in a manner less susceptible to damage, locate their development instead at otherwise less advantageous locations outside the flood plain, or install structural measures to confine the flooding. Each of the four alternatives has been used in varying degrees. Individuals have always selected among the first three alternatives. As towns developed, group action became possible and flood-susceptible communities built levees and other protective devices. The first flood control project in the United States was built by plantation owners along the Mississippi River near New Orleans in 1717. As still larger measures were required to protect expanding urban areas, flood-plain inhabitants, for example, the conservancy districts in Ohio, joined forces to install flood control reservoirs and levees. In 1879, the United States Congress created the Mississippi River Commission, assumed some responsibility for flood control, and in 1917 initiated programs of levee construction along the Mississippi and Sacramento Rivers. After a disastrous series of floods, Congress passed the Flood Control Act of 1936 by which the government assumed responsibility for flood control and initiated a nationwide program of constructing structural measures. From 1936 through 1966, the Corps of Engineers, the principal federal flood control agency, spent about $7 billion,[1] and spending by others brings the total to over $10 billion.[2]

These structural measures have shifted the bulk of the damage from great disasters along major rivers to relatively small-scale inundation along lesser tributaries. The expectation of publicly financed flood control measures may also be in part responsible for the fact that average annual flood damage has continued to rise as more urban development moves into flood plains. Economic forces have been distorted by over-emphasis on a limited range of measures. In the 1960s, the pendulum has been swinging back toward nonstructural measures. However,

[1]   *Communications from the President of the United States Transmitting a Report by the Task Force on Federal Flood Control Policy: A Unified National Program for Managing Flood Losses*, 89th Congress, 2d Sess., H.R. Doc. 465, 1966, p. 3.
[2]   This figure is updated by the recent annual rate of expenditure from Gilbert F. White et al., "Changes in Urban Occupance of Flood Plains in the United States" (Chicago: The University of Chicago Press, Department of Geography Res. Paper 57, 1958), p. 2.

economic evaluation procedures capable of selecting the optimum from the full range of alternatives are just beginning to be applied.

10-3 FLOOD HYDROLOGY   In order to quantify flood threat, it is necessary to determine the frequency of occurrence of flood peaks of various magnitudes. One might find, for example, that the *5 percent flood* peak equals 5,000 cfs. The same flood may be described interchangeably by the reciprocal of probability, the return period, as a *20-year flood.* This means that a flood peak of 5,000 cfs or more has a 5 percent chance of occurring during any given year or, over a very long period, would occur on the average of once in 20 years. It does not imply that the flood will occur at regular 20-year intervals but only that over a period of 1,000 years it could be expected to occur in 5 percent of the years, or 50 times. It would be possible to have occurrences in successive years or periods of 100 years or more during which the flow was not exceeded.

When available, a long streamflow record can be analyzed to relate flood magnitude to frequency. The maximum flows recorded in each year are arranged in descending order, starting with the largest flood of record. Each annual flood is assigned a frequency with the most widely used formula[1] being

$$f = \frac{m}{n + 1} \tag{10-1}$$

where f is the frequency of the annual flood ranked m in a total of n years of record.

The frequency of flood peaks small enough to have occurred several times during the historical record can be assigned quite accurately by Eq. (10-1). However, structural measures for flood control in urban areas are customarily designed to contain a flood having a return period that is much longer than the historical record. The peak for such rare events is estimated by assuming the statistical distribution applicable to annual flood events. As flood records are too short to pick a best distribution conclusively, several have been widely used.[2] However, for greater consistency in project formulation, the Water Resources Council has recommended use of the log–Pearson type III distribution.[3]

---

[1] Further discussion is found in Ray K. Linsley, Jr., Max A. Kohler, and Joseph L. H. Paulhus, "Applied Hydrology" (New York: McGraw-Hill Book Company, 1949), pp. 546–551.

[2] A number are presented in R. W. Cruff and S. E. Rantz, "A Comparison of Methods Used in Flood-frequency Studies for Coastal Basins in California," *U.S. Geol. Survey, Water Supply Papers,* 1580-E (1965).

[3] "A Uniform Technique for Determining Flood Flow Frequencies," Hydrology Committee, Water Resources Council, Bull. 15 (1967).

The basic equation for relating flood peak x to return period is

$$x = \bar{x} + K\sigma \qquad (10\text{-}2)$$

where $\bar{x}$ is the mean, σ is the standard deviation of the recorded annual flood peaks, and K is the frequency factor which increases with return period with the functional relationship dependent on the assumed

TABLE 10-1   K Values for Pearson Type III Distribution*

RETURN PERIOD, YEARS

G	2	5	10	25	50	100	200
3.0	−0.396	0.420	1.180	2.278	3.152	4.051	4.970
2.8	−0.384	0.460	1.210	2.275	3.114	3.973	4.847
2.6	−0.368	0.499	1.238	2.267	3.071	3.889	4.718
2.4	−0.351	0.537	1.262	2.256	3.023	3.800	4.584
2.2	−0.330	0.574	1.284	2.240	2.970	3.705	4.444
2.0	−0.307	0.609	1.302	2.219	2.912	3.605	4.298
1.8	−0.282	0.643	1.318	2.193	2.848	3.499	4.147
1.6	−0.254	0.675	1.329	2.163	2.780	3.388	3.990
1.4	−0.225	0.705	1.337	2.128	2.706	3.271	3.828
1.2	−0.195	0.732	1.340	2.087	2.626	3.149	3.661
1.0	−0.164	0.758	1.340	2.043	2.542	3.022	3.489
0.8	−0.132	0.780	1.336	1.993	2.453	2.891	3.312
0.6	−0.099	0.800	1.328	1.939	2.359	2.755	3.132
0.4	−0.066	0.816	1.317	1.880	2.261	2.615	2.949
0.2	−0.033	0.830	1.301	1.818	2.159	2.472	2.763
0.0	0.000	0.842	1.282	1.751	2.054	2.326	2.576
−0.2	0.033	0.850	1.258	1.680	1.945	2.178	2.388
−0.4	0.066	0.855	1.231	1.606	1.834	2.029	2.201
−0.6	0.099	0.857	1.200	1.528	1.720	1.880	2.016
−0.8	0.132	0.856	1.166	1.448	1.606	1.733	1.837
−1.0	0.164	0.852	1.128	1.366	1.492	1.588	1.664
−1.2	0.195	0.844	1.086	1.282	1.379	1.449	1.501
−1.4	0.225	0.832	1.041	1.198	1.270	1.318	1.351
−1.6	0.254	0.817	0.994	1.116	1.166	1.197	1.216
−1.8	0.282	0.799	0.945	1.035	1.069	1.087	1.097
−2.0	0.307	0.777	0.895	0.959	0.980	0.990	0.995
−2.2	0.330	0.752	0.844	0.888	0.900	0.905	0.907
−2.4	0.351	0.725	0.795	0.823	0.830	0.832	0.833
−2.6	0.368	0.696	0.747	0.764	0.768	0.769	0.769
−2.8	0.384	0.666	0.702	0.712	0.714	0.714	0.714
−3.0	0.396	0.636	0.660	0.666	0.666	0.667	0.667

* Values calculated by Central Technical Unit, Soil Conservation Service, "New Tables of Percentage Points of the Pearson Type III Distribution" (January, 1968).

distribution. For the Pearson type III distribution, the relationship depends on the skewness of the annual flood peaks with specific factors as shown in Table 10-1. The log–Pearson type III analysis is illustrated in Ex. 10-1.

EXAMPLE 10-1
Annual flood peaks as recorded on Mill Creek at Reading, Ohio, from 1941 through 1960:

1941	730	1951	2,700
1942	2,240	1952	3,310
1943	4,200	1953	4,530
1944	2,080	1954	2,040
1945	5,780	1955	2,330
1946	2,200	1956	3,330
1947	3,680	1957	3,530
1948	3,520	1958	3,940
1949	3,260	1959	5,640
1950	2,520	1960	2,130

The 100-year flood peak is estimated by arranging the 20 floods in descending order and proceeding as follows:

CALCULATIONS WITH LOGARITHMS TO BASE 10

m	Peak	$Q = log\ peak$	$Q - \bar{Q}$	$(Q - \bar{Q})^2$	$(Q - \bar{Q})^3$
1	5,780	3.7619	0.2961	0.08768	0.02596
2	5,640	3.7513	0.2855	0.08151	0.02327
3	4,530	3.6561	0.1903	0.03621	0.00689
4	4,200	3.6233	0.1575	0.02481	0.00391
5	3,940	3.5955	0.1297	0.01682	0.00218
6	3,680	3.5659	0.1001	0.01002	0.00100
7	3,530	3.5478	0.0820	0.00672	0.00055
8	3,520	3.5465	0.0807	0.00651	0.00053
9	3,330	3.5224	0.0566	0.00320	0.00018
10	3,310	3.5198	0.0540	0.00292	0.00016
11	3,260	3.5132	0.0474	0.00225	0.00011
12	2,700	3.4314	−0.0344	0.00118	−0.00004
13	2,520	3.4014	−0.0644	0.00414	−0.00027
14	2,330	3.3674	−0.0984	0.00968	−0.00095
15	2,240	3.3503	−0.1155	0.01334	−0.00154
16	2,200	3.3424	−0.1234	0.01523	−0.00188
17	2,130	3.3284	−0.1374	0.01888	−0.00259
18	2,080	3.3181	−0.1477	0.02182	−0.00322
19	2,040	3.3096	−0.1562	0.02440	−0.00381
20	730	2.8633	−0.6025	0.36301	−0.21871
		69.3160		0.75033	−0.16827

$$\bar{Q} = \frac{69.316}{20} = 3.4658 \tag{8-3}$$

$$\sigma = \left(\frac{0.75033}{19}\right)^{0.5} = 0.1987 \tag{8-5}$$

$$G = \frac{n}{(n-1)(n-2)} \frac{\Sigma(Q - \bar{Q})^3}{\sigma^3} = \frac{20}{19 \times 18} \frac{-0.16827}{0.1987^3} = -1.254$$

$K = 1.413$ (Table 10-1)

$\log Q = 3.4658 + 1.413(0.1987) = 3.7465 \tag{10-2}$

$Q = 5580$ cfs

No frequency analysis can compensate for historical data collected during a period not representative of the long-term flood frequency relationship. Flood-frequency estimates become less reliable with shorter records, particularly in areas of arid climate with highly variable streamflow.

If a long-term runoff record is unavailable, the planner may synthesize flows from other data:[1]

1   For smaller drainage basins, a unit hydrograph may be derived and then applied to rainfall excess estimated for the major storms of each year to determine each annual flood for the frequency analysis.[2]

2   Direct application of the unit hydrograph gives unsatisfactory results for large heterogeneous drainage basins (over 3,000 sq. miles). Individual unit hydrographs must be developed for each small, homogeneous component basin from which the flood hydrographs may be routed and combined to find the flood peak.

3   Flood hydrograph peaks do not really vary linearly with storm-runoff volume as is assumed by the unit hydrograph. More refined methods of hydrograph reconstruction use digital computer models with moisture balance accounting. The Stanford watershed model synthesizes the entire annual hydrograph from hourly rainfall records and watershed parameters developed from 3 or 4 years of stream records.[3]

4   An alternative method is to develop long-term flow sequences having statistical parameters derived from the historical record but not representing historical flow sequences (Sec. 20-11).

Because of the uncertainty inherent in estimating the frequency of rare floods from a short record and a desire to avoid misplaced public

---

[1]   Additional discussion is found in J. Amorocho and W. E. Hart, A Critique of Current Methods in Hydrologic Systems Investigation, *Trans. Am. Geophys. Union*, vol. 45 (June, 1964), pp. 309–321.

[2]   Linsley, Kohler, and Paulhus, *op. cit.*, pp. 194–208.

[3]   N. H. Crawford and Ray K. Linsley, "Digital Simulation in Hydrology: Stanford Watershed Model IV" [Stanford, Calif.: Stanford University, Department of Civil Engineering (Tech. Rept. 39), 1966].

overconfidence in constructed measures, flood control agencies seldom specify design floods by frequency. The Corps of Engineers uses a *standard project flood* based on "the most severe combination of meteorological and hydrological conditions that are considered reasonably characteristic of the geographic region involved, excluding extraordinarily rare combinations."[1] The Tennessee Valley Authority uses a *regional flood* based on the maximum historical flood recorded on any stream within the hydrologic area. While both agencies may use lesser floods for the design of structural measures, standard practice is to protect urban areas against a flood in excess of the maximum of record. Despite the hesitancy to base structural measure design on frequency, economic analysis requires an evaluation of the frequency of damages prevented. A publicized design frequency calls attention to the risk of residual flood damage.

Flood control planning is complicated by both the peak and the shape of the flood hydrograph's being functionally related to land use and structural measures installed. Flood routing is used to determine the effects of detention storage and channel improvement. Significant hydrologic changes follow land treatment and forest fire prevention measures, but the effect becomes progressively smaller for increasingly rarer floods. Where changing land use is expected to alter design flood peaks, it is necessary to predict flood hazard as a function of calendar time.

Rigorous analysis of the downstream movement of a flood wave is complicated by variations of flow rate with time, channel hydraulic properties with distance, and lateral inflow. However, the change to a flood hydrograph as it passes through a channel reach or reservoir can be made by applying a series of difference equations based on the principle of continuity.[2]

Developing the Supply

10-4 STRUCTURAL MEASURES Structural measures is a collective term for those efforts that reduce flood damage by restricting movement of flood water into the flood plain. Reservoirs and retarding structures store peak flows. Channel improvements increase flood-

---

[1] U.S. Army Corps of Engineers, "Survey Investigations and Reports: General Procedures," *Eng. Manual* EM 1120-2-101 (Washington, May, 1961), p. 49.

[2] Linsley, Kohler, and Paulhus, *op. cit.*, pp. 220–229.

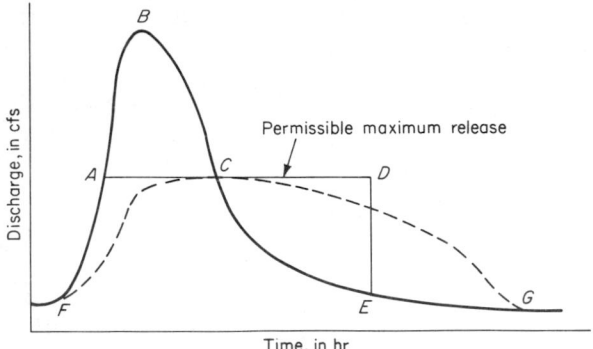

FIGURE 10-1 Flood control operating plans.

carrying capacity. Levees keep the water away from highly developed areas. Bypasses and floodways divert flood flows from the main channel and carry them around large cities built up along the river.

Storage reservoirs are regulated by gates and valves operated according to rules designed to minimize downstream flood damage. If the flows represented by the hydrograph illustrated in Fig. 10-1 were to enter a reservoir, an ideal operating procedure would use a reservoir of capacity ABC to reduce the flood peak from B to line ACD. Flows would pass directly through the reservoir unchanged until point A; they would then be stored until point C when the reservoir would be exactly full; finally, the reservoir would be emptied as fast as possible without exceeding flow level AC, to provide storage for a possible second flood. At point D ($ABC = CDE$) the reservoir would be empty, and flows would once again pass through the reservoir unchanged.

The ideal operating procedure requires perfect foreknowledge of hydrograph shape. Otherwise, the operator would not know when to begin storing flood water in order to equate ABC with reservoir capacity. No matter which way he misses, peak outflow will exceed ACD. If he starts restricting outflow too soon, the reservoir will fill before inflow has receded to point C. If he waits too long, outflow will pass point A and the reservoir never will fill. Furthermore, gates cannot be operated to produce outflow hydrograph $FACDE$. Storage will begin to fill as soon as the inflow begins to increase, and outflow cannot be maintained at the peak rate until the reservoir is empty. The outflow hydrograph shape which can practically be achieved is FCG ($FBC = CGE$). Thus, the reservoir capacity required to cut the flood peak from B to C is $FABC$. If $ABC/FABC$ is defined as reservoir efficiency, Rutter has found

TVA reservoir operation to be only about 50 percent efficient.[1] In other words, perfect flood forecasting could cut required reservoir storage by up to 50 percent. The possible trade-off between construction and forecasting cost should be evaluated in project planning.

A reservoir might be operated to reduce every flood peak by the maximum possible amount, or it might be operated by ignoring smaller flood flows in order to reserve storage for possible larger ones. Nothing is gained by operating the reservoir to reduce peaks which are already below channel capacity. The ideal operating procedure reduces to less than channel capacity every flood peak between that causing incipient damage and the reservoir-design flood and reduces larger peaks as much as possible. The reservoir release causing incipient damage equals downstream channel capacity less local inflow between the reservoir and the flood plain.

Flood damage can be further reduced by operating a group of storage reservoirs as a system. If a reservoir is built on a tributary, the outflow hydrograph peak might coincide with peak flows on the main river. Thus, reservoir outflow timing must be coordinated with the timing of flood peaks on both controlled and uncontrolled downstream watersheds. Devising an operating procedure for timing releases is a trial-and-error process of selecting plausible operating schemes and routing floods through the reservoirs and channels to compute peaks at specified points.

Retarding structures are ungated storage reservoirs. The cost of gated reservoir operation amounts to the costs of the gating system, of keeping an operator permanently at the site, and of making streamflow forecasts and informing the operator of them; the cost is justified by savings in required storage through more efficient operation. For small flood control structures, cost of the additional storage is too small to justify the large fixed cost of operation. Furthermore, difficulty in flood forecasting for the quickly rising hydrographs on smaller streams reduces the reservoir efficiency to be gained by gated operation on small watersheds. A compromise design is to increase reservoir efficiency by using gates automatically regulated by reservoir water-surface elevation.

Channel improvements increase the capacity of the waterway. Increased capacity wrought by cleaning snags, trash, and weeds from the channel has a relatively low first cost but a high maintenance cost because it must be periodically repeated. A more permanent improvement is replacing the natural channel with a larger prismatic channel on straighter alignment. Setback levees may be placed on either side of the

[1]   E. J. Rutter, Flood-control Operations of Tennessee Valley Authority Reservoirs, *Trans. ASCE*, vol. 116 (1951), pp. 671–707.

main channel of larger rivers to achieve a straighter alignment for flood flows and yet avoid costly underwater construction. Channel erosion may be reduced by using drop structures to decrease the hydraulic gradient. Channel lining reduces maintenance cost and right-of-way requirement. Thin, lightly reinforced concrete, grout, or asphalt lining doubles the capacity of a trapezoidal cross section. The right-of-way required for a given channel capacity can be further reduced at a higher construction cost by a thicker and more heavily reinforced rectangular concrete cross section. Covered channels may be used in the most congested urban areas. Trapezoidal lined sections may be justified either by soil instability or high right-of-way values. Rectangular sections may be justified either by wave control for supercritical flow on a circuitous alignment or by very high right-of-way values. Perimeter channels may be used to carry flood flows around densely developed urban areas and thus preserve high-valued land for other uses.

Unless the design flow line is too high, an improved channel will reduce upstream flooding by alleviating backwater. However, it will probably increase downstream flood peaks by reducing the natural reservoir action as floodwater spreads freely over the flood plain. Both effects should be evaluated in project formulation. If channel improvement significantly increases downstream flood damage and there is no compensating upstream storage, the increased damage should be considered a negative benefit.

10-5   LAND TREATMENT   Land-treatment measures attempt to decrease runoff by increasing infiltration. Typical measures include contour plowing, land leveling, and crop residue use on crop land; brush control, range seeding, and farm ponds on pasture land; and tree management and fire control on forest land. Minor channel improvements or grade stabilization structures are installed on small watercourses. Actually, the agricultural and forestry benefits of land treatment govern the selection and provide the primary justification of the measures.[1] Nevertheless, it is necessary to estimate the effectiveness of the installed land-treatment measures in reducing flood damages in order not to double-count their benefits in justifying other project measures. In addition to reducing flood peaks, land treatment reduces flood damage by reducing the sediment content of the water.

Quantitative evaluation of the effectiveness of land-treatment measures in reducing flood peaks requires development of flood-frequency

[1]   "Relative Profitability and Order of Adoption of Soil Conservation Practices" (Madison: The University of Wisconsin Press, Department of Agricultural Economics Res. Bull. 237, 1962).

curves with and without the measures. Land treatment functions by increasing soil moisture-storage capacity and delaying overland flow to reduce direct runoff while increasing interflow and base flow. Several methods have been proposed for estimating the effect on flood peaks,[1] but digital computer models of the runoff cycle offer a promising evaluation tool. Since land treatment tends to reduce storm runoff by a fixed amount, the percentage reduction for rare floods is much smaller than for smaller floods. Where structural measures are designed to contain rare floods, land treatment has only a minor effect on the design flood or residual damages. However, the lower sediment load will reduce channel maintenance cost and prolong the life of retarding basins.

10-6 FLOOD PROOFING   Flood proofing may be defined to include all actions by individuals or small groups within the flood plain to reduce flood damage to their property. Emergency measures may be taken. Immediately prior to the flood, people and property may be evacuated. During the flood, sand bags or temporary levees may be used to restrict the area inundated. After the flood, rapid cleanup and rehabilitation will reduce damages substantially. Most emergency measures require prediction of a coming flood by meteorological and hydrological analysis,[2] rapid warning of flood-plain inhabitants, and advance preparation within the flood plain. Evacuation may require a program of police protection to prevent looting. Advance preparation involves provision of flood-fighting materials and a prepared plan of action for intense activity immediately prior, during, or immediately following flooding. Economic analysis of emergency measures is complicated by the tendency of individuals not to act in a uniform, predictable manner during crises and for them to become progressively less prepared for emergency action through long flood-free periods. The effectiveness of emergency action increases as the local residents become more familiar with the techniques and is thus greater in areas of regular flooding. The same course of action will not be followed from place to place within the flood plain nor at a particular spot from flood to flood. Because emergency measures other than cleanup and rehabilitation require advance warning, their effectiveness declines as watershed size and hence time of concentration decrease. While emergency action is both necessary and evident during and after flood events, the variability of its effectiveness makes it difficult to

[1]   H. C. Storey, R. L. Hobba, and J. M. Rosa, Hydrology of Forest Lands and Rangelands, in Ven Te Chow (ed.), "Handbook of Applied Hydrology," (New York: McGraw-Hill Book Company, 1964).
[2]   P. Davidson and R. A. Hargreaves, River Flood Warning Systems, in R. B. Thorn (ed.), "River Engineering and Water Conservation Works" [London: Butterworth & Co. (Publishers) Ltd., 1966].

quantify the cost and the effect on flood damage, particularly in small watersheds subject to infrequent flooding.

Flood proofing also includes building with materials or methods of construction which are less susceptible to flood damage. For example, houses with slab floors suffer less damage than those with hardwood floors. Floor plans placing more damageable contents at higher elevations reduce damage. Assuming two or more alternative materials or floor plans provide equal utility, the economic choice would have the least sum of first cost, maintenance cost, and expected value of flood damage. Reasonable estimates may be made of the first two costs, but further research will be required to evaluate the resistance of various building materials to flood damage. Because special flood-resistant building designs may create a psychological disadvantage by advertising flood hazard, it may be difficult to secure their public acceptance.

A third type of flood proofing is to prevent water from entering buildings. Methods used include sealing walls to control seepage, permanent closure of unnecessary openings, removable bulkheads for necessary openings, higher structural elevation, proper anchorage to prevent buoyant forces from lifting buildings off their foundations, and local levees to restrict and direct flood waters.[1] Public acceptance has been limited, and the United States Task Force on Federal Flood Control Policy recently recommended that a better understanding of the value of this alternative should be sought by dissemination of information throughout the flood plain.[2] The information should tell owners and prospective purchasers of flood-plain land the extent of the flood threat and the risk of damage and show them how to save money by flood proofing. Legal implementation through building codes, subdivision regulation, and maintenance inspection is conceivable. Flood proofing has been implemented in several cities and combined with structural measures in a joint flood control program of Bristol, Tennessee, and Bristol, Virginia.[3]

10-7   LAND USE ADJUSTMENT   In order to prevent uneconomic flood-plain development from forcing installation of structural measures, the Corps of Engineers, as a result of Executive Order 11296, now requires investigation of land-use control as an alternative to constructing structural measures and is increasing pressure on local government to design

[1]   John R. Sheaffer, "Flood Proofing: An Element in a Flood Damage Reduction Program" (Chicago: The University of Chicago Press, Department of Geography Res. Paper 65, 1960).
[2]   *Communication from the President of the United States Transmitting a Report by the Task Force on Federal Flood Control Policy: A Unified National Program for Managing Flood Losses*, 89th Cong., 2d Sess., H.R. Doc. 465, 1966, p. 35.
[3]   John W. Weathers, Comprehensive Flood Damage Prevention, *Proc. ASCE*, vol. 91, no. HY 1 (January, 1965), pp. 17–27.

zoning laws to regulate flood-plain land use. A number of local governments have zoning laws, and the Corps of Engineers, the Geological Survey, and the Tennessee Valley Authority make hazard surveys to provide communities with quantitative flood-risk data.

Land developers have always tended to locate the more intense development in areas of lower hazard. Some make a strong case for relying solely on the land market to effect the economic flood-plain land use.[1] Others emphasize that spillover effects and the public policy of providing free protection may invalidate land market operation. Individual land development may increase the flood damage suffered by others by changing flood patterns. Indirect and secondary damages are excluded from the private calculus. Public help to flood victims cushions their personal loss and encourages increased flood-plain development. It is difficult to convey the concept of flood risk as understood by engineers to laymen meaningfully enough to influence occupancy decisions. Only in frequently inundated areas do individuals become sufficiently aware of the flood damage potential for flood-plain land use to adjust to an economic equilibrium. Speculative land development may take place with the intention of selling to the unaware.

While ample legal authority exists for public control of flood-plain development,[2] public action has practical problems. Regulations are determined through the political process, and there is little reason to believe that political action can in the long run overcome the economic pressures for development which emerge with time. An individual community which regulates flood-plain development may cause industry to locate instead in another community. The community loses the industry and accomplishes no useful purpose if the industry locates in another flood plain. The regulation of flood-plain development has a cost just as real as structural measures have. Part of the total cost is the legal and administrative cost of enacting and enforcing the regulation. The major economic cost is the advantage lost by those kept from locating in the flood plain. Furthermore, many development decisions are influenced by cultural, social, or esthetic rather than economic goals. Many conflicting goals may have to be compromised in determining the best land-use plan (Sec. 5-5). Location theory and urban development models are only beginning to find order in the complex factors which influence alternative urban development patterns.[3]

[1]   Robert C. Lind, Flood Control Alternatives and the Economics of Flood Protection, *Water Resources Res.*, vol. 3, no. 2 (2d Quarter, 1967), pp. 345–357.
[2]   Allison Dunham, Flood Control via the Police Power, *Univ. Penn. Law Rev.*, vol. 107 (June, 1959), p. 1098.
[3]   The principles and techniques used in these models are found in Walter Isard, "Methods of Regional Analysis: An Introduction to Regional Science" (New York: John Wiley & Sons, Inc., 1960).

Three methods of land-use regulation have been proposed. The most effective, public purchase, imposes the largest financial obligation.[1] Public purchase of flood-plain land has an additional economic cost to the degree it prevents land uses compatible with the flood risk. The second method is to reduce the financial outlay by only purchasing the right to develop the property.[2] The third and most common method is to restrict the development of private property by zoning. The alternatives differ in who bears the cost, but the financial cost of flood-plain purchase approximately equals the loss to the economy when zoning laws prevent individuals from taking advantage of their flood-plain location through development commensurate with the risk.

10-8 FLOOD INSURANCE Flood insurance does not reduce the physical damages caused by a given flood event, but it does convert the highly irregular flood loss pattern into a uniform annual series of payments. Use of accumulated payments to reimburse those suffering flood damage would reduce the financial uncertainty associated with possible catastrophic flood losses (Sec. 8-16). By requiring a certain annual payment proportional to flood hazard, insurance might also be used to discourage uneconomic flood-plain development.[3] The premium would become a means of implementing the optimum land use by being made an integral part of land-use decisions in the private economy.

A number of practical problems would be encountered in implementing a flood insurance program.[4] The amount of flood damage suffered by a given property during a given flood depends on a large number of factors. Standard procedures for estimating flood damage use only a very few of these. Consequently flood damage estimates based on so few factors display considerable scatter when compared on a property-by-property basis with damages actually suffered during a flood. An estimate of average damage is sufficient for establishing total benefits to justify structural measures but not for establishing a property-by-property flood insurance premium. Excessive development will be encouraged on properties for which the premium is too low, and economic development will be

---

[1] Giving the Corps of Engineers authority to purchase flood-plain land to reduce flood damage is recommended in *Communication from the President of the United States Transmitting a Report by the Task Force on Federal Flood Control Policy: A Unified National Program for Managing Flood Losses*, 89th Congr., 2d Sess., H.R. Doc. 465, 1966.

[2] Jan Kransnowiecki and Ann Louise Strong, Compensible Regulations for Open Space, *J. Am. Inst. Planners*, vol. 29 (May, 1963).

[3] John V. Krutilla, An Economic Approach to Coping with Flood Damage, *Water Resources Res.*, vol. 2 (Spring, 1966), pp. 183–190.

[4] For further discussion on the feasibility of flood insurance from the viewpoints of engineers and insurance companies, see in the *Proc. ASCE, J. Hydraulics Div.*: H. A. Foster, Technical Problems of Flood Insurance (February, 1957); A. A. Koch, Some Physical Problems Related to Flood Insurance (February, 1957); and J. F. Neville, Is the Writing of Flood Insurance Feasible? (April, 1957).

discouraged on properties for which the premium is too high. A more exact estimate of flood damage will be required, and development and application of more refined procedures will add to the administrative cost of implementing the insurance program. Raising premiums to a value high enough to cover this cost may in itself discourage economic flood-plain development. It is also important to recognize that substantial flood damages are indirect (Sec. 8-6) or associated with long-term effects (unseen damages to foundations) which are difficult to recompense through normal insurance procedures. Another important factor is the psychological effect of insurance on effort expended on flood proofing and on repairing minor flood damage. Many damages would cost more to repair than the harmful effects of going without repair warrant.

10-9   THE SUPPLY CURVE   Marginal values for economic analysis of flood control projects (Fig. 8-3) are normally expressed as functions of the frequency of the design flood. Each marginal benefit or cost should reflect the combination of structural and nonstructural measures and residual damages having the least total cost for the indicated level of protection (Sec. 8-18).

An equal degree of flood protection may be provided by various combinations of detention storage and channel improvement. One might build a large detention reservoir with little channel improvement or install major channel improvement without any detention storage. The channel capacity required to confine the flood peak's residual to a given detention storage is determined by routing the design flood through the reservoir and down the channel. The cost of both the reservoir and the channel improvement may be estimated from their required capacities. By repeating the process over a range of detention storage values, the optimum combination is determined (Fig. 10-2). The optimum combination of channel improvement and detention storage differs with design flood frequency and must be determined individually for each design frequency in order to determine the cost of the optimum combination of detention storage and channel improvement as a function of design frequency.

The cost of flood proofing is the cost of installing the least-expensive combination of external flood-proofing measures able to prevent the design flood from entering buildings (or the cost of the least-expensive combination of emergency measures or building-material measures able to achieve a specified damage-reduction objective). In the final analysis, the cost should be determined from estimates based on alternative designs as is done for structural measures. However, for planning purposes a reasonable estimate of the total cost of flood proofing all structures in the

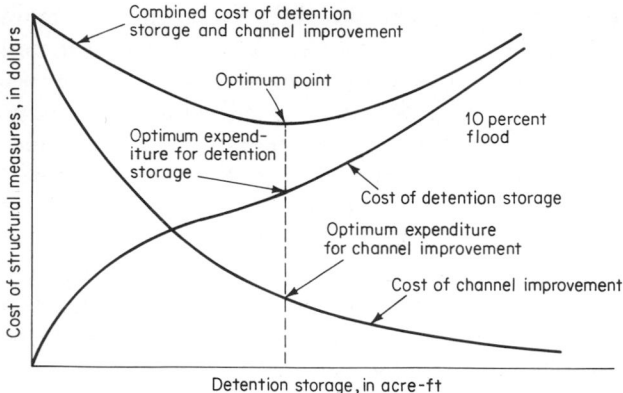

FIGURE 10-2   Combining detention storage and channel improvement.

flood plain may be obtained from a formula of the form

$$C_p = C_d C_2 (CRF_p + M_p) M_s h A \qquad (10\text{-}3)$$

where each term may be evaluated as follows:

C_p — The average annual cost of flood proofing determined from Eq. (10-3).

C_d — A factor to account for contingencies and the cost of designing flood-proofing measures and administering a flood-proofing program. A reasonable estimate is 1.30.

C_2 — The initial cost in dollars of flood proofing per foot of flood depth per dollar of market value of the flood-proofed structure. An analysis of flood-proofing costs for Bristol, Tennessee and Virginia, produced a value of 0.035.[1]

CRF_p — A capital-recovery factor (A/P) based on the appropriate discount rate and flood-proofing-measure life.

M_p — The annual maintenance cost of flood-proofing measures including the operation cost during floods, expressed as a fraction of total installation cost.

M_s — The market value of all structures to be flood proofed, in dollars per acre. It may be estimated from assessment records.

h — The average depth of flooding in feet.

A — The area flooded, in acres.

[1] L. Douglas James, "A Time-dependent Planning Process for Combining Structural Measures, Land Use, and Flood Proofing to Minimize the Economic Cost of Floods" (Stanford, Calif.: Stanford University, Institute in Engineering Economic Systems, EEP-12, 1964).

Equation (10-3) assumes flood-proofing cost increases linearly with depth of flooding and development is scattered over the flood plain in a reasonably uniform pattern. If the first assumption does not hold, C_2 may be expressed as the appropriate function of depth. If the second assumption does not hold, the flood plain may be subdivided and Eq. (10-3) evaluated independently for each section.

The cost of controlling flood-plain land use equals the sum of the cost of enacting and enforcing the regulation and the net economic loss produced by the forced rearrangement of the pattern of community development. A properly functioning land market would automatically alter the development pattern as individuals were forced by flood damages into otherwise less desirable locations. When the planner substitutes his calculations for an improperly functioning land market, he must analyze the land whose use is altered by regulation for differences in:

1 Agricultural productivity as determined by differences in soil fertility, microclimate, or subsurface drainage
2 The cost of constructing urban improvements as determined by differences in ground slope, foundation conditions, or prior site use
3 The cost of roads, utilities, and other public services as determined by the compactness of the service network, foundation conditions, and the pattern of the existing facilities
4 The private cost of occupying a site such as transportation and damage from storms, wind, erosion, or landslides
5 Amenities produced by use of open flood-plain land for various recreational, institutional, or historical purposes or as a green belt structurally differentiating communities

Because of the difficulty in predicting land-use patterns with and without flood-plain regulation and in evaluating these differences even after developing two patterns for comparison, a more practical approach is to use the land market for an estimate of the value of flood-plain land and then to correct this estimate to reflect values not reflected in the market. The market evaluation of land is

$$M_0 = \sum_{n=0}^{\infty} \left(\frac{P}{F}, j\%, n \right) I_n \tag{10-4}$$

where P/F, j percent, n expresses the value of a dollar in year n to a landowner now at his rate of time preference, j (Sec. 8-14), and I_n is the expected income from the land in year n. If M_t is the market value of the land in year t, one may terminate the series and solve for I to get

$$I = \left(\frac{A}{P}, i\%, t \right) \left[M_0 - \left(\frac{P}{F}, j\%, t \right) M_t \right] \tag{10-5}$$

where I is the discounted average annual income expected by the owner over the next t years. The value selected for t should reflect long-term trends rather than short-term price cycles without disguising major alterations in relative location advantage. Ten years is a reasonable compromise. Substitution of a planning discount rate, i, for the expected private rate of return, j, is necessary to put cost evaluation on a commensurate basis with benefit evaluation.

The economic loss caused by an outside force (such as flood-plain zoning) preventing the realization of the full potential income from the land would equal the difference between the potential and the actual income. While many kinds and degrees of restriction are possible, the normal restriction is to prevent urban development of the flood plain and thereby confine it to agricultural use. If Eq. (10-5) is applied to comparable flood-free land, I will equal the income expected from the most profitable combination of agricultural and urban land use. From farm income analysis, I_a may be estimated as the income expected from agricultural use. If I_p corrects for extramarket values, the net value nonowners realize from agricultural use over that realized from urban use, the economic loss is

$$C_L = I - I_a - I_p \tag{10-6}$$

The public income I_p should increase with urbanization as vacant land becomes scarcer. The agricultural income I_a may be determined from crop patterns and crop income. The total location cost may be estimated by multiplying C_L (dollars per acre) by the acreage flooded by the design flood. A flood plain should be developed if C_L exceeds the expected annual flood damages. Since C_L is estimated from values based on comparable flood-free land, the kinds of flood-plain development which produce a net positive payoff after considering flood damage should be permitted.

The computation of location cost as a function of land value may be justified by the fact that failure to develop the flood plain will change many location decisions within the urban development pattern. At the margin, some will move to fringe areas which would otherwise have no urban development and hence produce no urban income. Thus Eq. (10-6) compares two location values, but one is zero. A time lag in location adjustment or institutional restrictions may increase the value of C_L if urban development of marginal land is delayed or prevented.

Where land-use adjustment is conceived as relocating existing facilities away from hazard areas, it is necessary to include the cost of moving plus the net cost of developing the new site above the salvage value of the old. This correction should be made to the value of C_L in Eq. (10-6). Normally this added cost is too large for relocation of existing urban develop ment to be an economical flood damage reduction method, but it should not be automatically eliminated from consideration.

Projected values of M_t for Eq. (10-5) can be based on population projections. The magnitude and distribution of the existing population is determined from census data and land-use maps. Existing land values are determined from assessment data for comparable flood-free land. Land values can then be correlated with the distribution of land use, population, and the other factors causing land value differences. If the correlation is based on a fairly large area, any distortions caused by differential market failures will be dampened. Projected populations (Sec. 9-2) may be used to project land-use distribution and then be converted into land values through the correlation.

For the optimum combination of inputs (measures) to produce a single output (flood control), the marginal rates of substitution among inputs must be equal (Sec. 4-6). The marginal equality holds true where the sum of the flood-control-measure costs and the flood damage costs is a minimum. Cost estimates for various combinations of measures must be made in order to find the optimum mix for a design flood specified by frequency. The total-cost curve is the locus of minimum cost points for a range of design flood magnitudes plotted against frequency. Marginal analysis should be applied individually to each portion of the flood plain for which flood protection can be independently provided. The procedure is illustrated by Ex. 10-2.

EXAMPLE 10-2

The following steps are taken in computing a supply curve for flood control measures consisting of channel improvement, flood proofing, and location adjustment:

1 Hydraulic analysis indicates a channel capacity of 310 cfs. A hydrologic study (Sec. 10-3) reveals:

Freq., %:	43	20	10	4	1	0.5
Peak, cfs:	570	850	1,090	1,380	1,830	2,040

Flooding begins with the 67 percent event ($Q = 310$ cfs).

2 From the above design flows, the cost of channel improvement is estimated as

Freq., %:	43	20	10	4	1	0.5
Cost, \$/year:	6,230	7,590	8,480	9,750	11,500	12,360

3 The following values are determined for use in Eq. (10-3) to estimate the cost of flood proofing:

$$C_d = 1.30 \quad C_2 = 0.035 \quad CRF_p = 0.117 \quad M_p = 0.05 \quad M_s = 1,035$$

Thus

$$C_p = (1.30)(0.035)(0.167)1,035hA = 7.85hA$$

Areas flooded, average flood depths, and annual flood-proofing costs are estimated by frequency as follows:

Freq., %:	43	20	10	4	1	0.5
Area, acres:	290	360	396	450	510	532
Depth, ft:	1.01	1.25	1.41	1.56	1.77	1.85
Cost, $/year:	2,300	3,540	4,500	5,510	7,090	7,720

4   More values are determined to find the cost of restricting flood-plain land use.

From a land value projection,

$$M_0 = \$990 \text{ per acre} \qquad M_{10} = \$1,600 \text{ per acre} \qquad j = 8 \text{ percent}$$
$$i = 3 \text{ percent} \qquad t = 10 \text{ years} \qquad I_p = 0$$

$$I = 0.1172[990 - 0.463(1,600)] = \$29.20 \text{ per acre per year} \qquad (10\text{-}5)$$

From analysis of crop pattern and crop income,

$$I_a = \$15.20 \text{ per acre per year}$$
$$C_L = 29.20 - 15.20 - 0.00 = \$14.00 \text{ per acre per year} \qquad (10\text{-}6)$$

This value of C_L times the areas of step 3 gives:

Freq., %:	43	20	10	4	1	0.5
Cost, $/year:	4,060	5,040	5,540	6,300	7,140	7,450

5   The optimum combination of flood proofing and location restriction is found by noting that from Eqs. (10-3) and (10-6), $C_L = C_p$ if 14.00 =

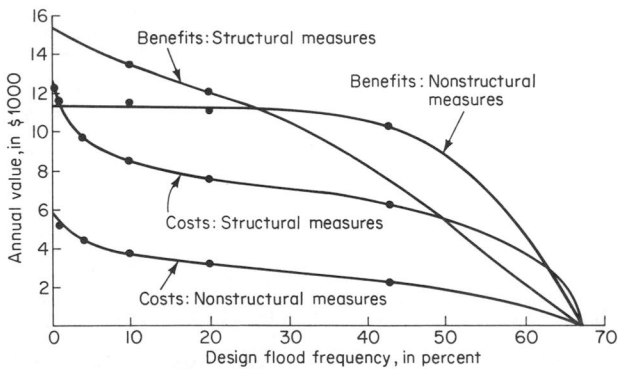

FIGURE 10-3   Total-value   curves   for   flood   control
                        examples.

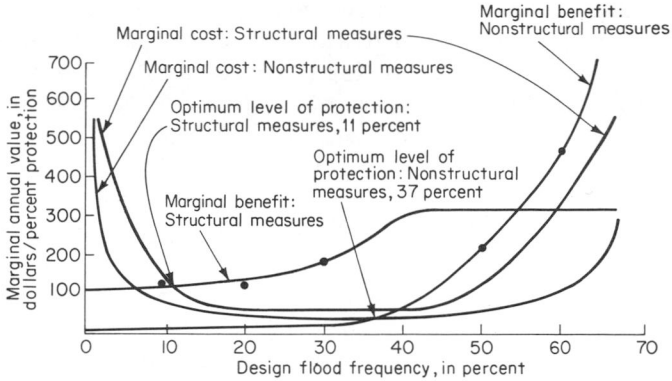

FIGURE 10-4   Marginal-value curves for flood control examples.

7.85h or when $h = 1.78$ ft. Thus, the least-cost combination of the two measures is to flood-proof areas inundated to depths less than 1.78 ft and restrict development from areas inundated to greater depths. From data on area flooded by depth it is found:

Design Freq., %:	43	20	10	4	1	0.5
Area $h > 1.78$ ft, acres:	34	104	150	194	254	276
C_L, \$/year:	480	1,460	2,100	2,720	3,560	3,860
Area $h < 1.78$ ft, acres:	256	256	256	256	256	256
Av depth, ft:	0.89	0.89	0.89	0.89	0.89	0.89
C_p, \$/year:	1,790	1,790	1,790	1,790	1,790	1,790
$C_L + C_p$, \$/year:	2,270	3,250	3,890	4,510	5,350	5,650

6 By comparing steps 2 and 5, it is evident that no combination including structural measures could cost less than the values found in step 5.

7 Total costs from step 5 are plotted in Fig. 10-3. The slope of the total-cost curve is used to develop the marginal-cost curve in Fig. 10-4. Total- and marginal-cost curves for structural measures are similarly developed.

Estimating the Demand

Because flood control cannot be independently provided for selected individuals, it is a collective rather than a market good. Thus, flood control benefits cannot be evaluated directly from market demand. They are evaluated indirectly by reasoning that an individual would be willing to pay up to the value he places on his loss to prevent the damage from taking place. The economic demand for flood control is thus determined by the difference between the expected flood damages before and those after mitigation measures are installed.

10-10 FLOOD SEVERITY   The first step in estimating flood damage is to estimate the severity of the flooding produced by a given flood hydrograph. The primary measure of spot flood severity is depth of flooding. The total severity of a flood event depends on the areal extent of flooding to each depth. This information may be summarized on a map showing lines of equal depth of flooding. If the flood flows remain hydraulically connected to the watercourse even though outside its normal banks, the depth and area inundated are governed by the flood peak. In the flood flows separate from the watercourse and flow overland, the flood severity is primarily governed by the volume of flood water leaving the channel and the length of the flow path. The best estimates of flood severity come from historical flood data. Where historical records are unavailable, one must resort to backwater calculations[1] or to flood severity data for similar basins.

For the purpose of establishing a continuous relationship between flood peak and flood severity for marginal economic analysis, it is convenient to correlate the area inundated A with the flood peak less the channel capacity Q_x by using the relationship

$$A = KQ_x{}^a \tag{10-7}$$

In a corresponding fashion for the average depth of flooding (h),

$$h = CQ_x{}^b \tag{10-8}$$

K, a, C, and b are parameters of the flood plain evaluated from the area flooded, average depth of flooding, and flood peak for two or more historical floods. For wide flood plains, a and b usually equal about 0.375.

Other important factors determining flood severity are the duration of flooding, flow velocity, sediment content, and season of occurrence. Data on each of these factors should be collected by observing or analyzing flood events.

10-11 FLOOD DAMAGES   The amount of flood damage is determined by the severity of the flood. Direct damages are losses caused by physical contact with the flood and are generally evaluated as the cost of replacing,

---

[1] Ven Te Chow, "Open-channel Hydraulics" (New York: McGraw-Hill Book Company, 1959), chap. 10.

repairing, or rehabilitating the affected property in the case of urban damages and as the net effect on farm income in the case of crop damages. They may be estimated by a thorough examination of the flood plain immediately after the water recedes. If such estimates were available for every flood over a period of many years, a damage-frequency curve could be made from the same type of analysis used to develop a flood-frequency curve (Sec. 10-3). An alternative method is to determine the damage caused by three or four recent floods whose hydrologic frequency can be determined and plot a smooth damage-frequency curve through these points.

For most flood plains, changes in land use with calendar time prevent direct use of a damage-frequency relationship from historical damages. Kates has postulated as included in an ideal process for synthesizing damages in a flood plain of time-variant damage potential:[1]

1 Use a regional economic model to project regional urban growth throughout the period of analysis.
2 Outline the flood-plain boundaries by hydrologic analysis and allocate a portion of the urban growth to it.
3 Specify each structure in the flood plain by location, size, contents, and economic value, all as functions of time.
4 Develop appropriate curves relating flood severity to damage for each structure as a function of time.
5 Aggregate the individual flood-severity-damage curves to provide a series of curves for the entire flood plain reflecting changes with time.

The distribution of flood damage potential within the flood plain may be summarized by a series of land-use maps each indicating the location of various development classes (agriculture, residential, etc.) for a given date. A second series of maps, each indicating for a given frequency the severity of flooding throughout the flood plain, may also be prepared. By superimposing the series of flood-severity maps by one frequency at a time over the land-use map for a specific date, flood damage as a function of frequency may be determined throughout the flood plain. Repeating the process with land-use maps for later dates will give flood damage as a function of time.

If the flooding is shallow, flood damage to yards, buildings, and contents increases approximately linearly with depth.

$$C_d = K_d M_s d \tag{10-9}$$

where C_d is the direct flood damage in dollars, M_s is the market value of the inundated structures in dollars and may be estimated from assessment

---

[1] Robert W. Kates, "Industrial Flood Losses: Damage Estimation in the Lehigh Valley" (Chicago: The University of Chicago Press, Department of Geography Res. Paper 98, 1965), p. 37.

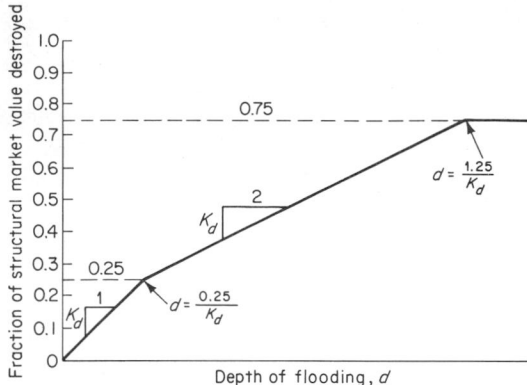

FIGURE 10-5 Flood-damage-depth curve for urban property.

records, d is depth of flooding in feet, and K_d is a factor determined by analysis of the direct damage caused to like property by historical floods. Values for K_d average about 0.044.[1] The scatter of values for K_d among buildings of a given kind (say, service stations) is so great that separate values of K_d by building type have little statistical significance, and the extra work required to use them is not warranted. If the floodwater has a high sediment content or a high velocity, a higher value of K_d should be used. For deeper flooding, marginal flood damage per unit of depth can be expected to decline approximately as shown in Fig. 10-5. At very large depths, marginal flood damage drops to zero. Total building damage is determined by summing the damages to all the buildings.

Flood damages to farm crops are estimated from farm budgets.[2] A farm budget itemizes the costs of the farm operations and materials required to grow a particular crop, the costs being obtained from the products of the amount of labor and material required and appropriate unit costs. Budgets are developed for the major crops in a given area by local farm advisors, but their unit prices represent costs to the individual farmer, which should be checked against the value and opportunity cost concepts more appropriate to economic analysis. The crop budget pro-

[1] James, *op. cit.*, pp. 85–87.

[2] R. A. Freund and G. S. Tolley, Operational Procedures for Evaluating Flood Protection Benefits, in Stephen C. Smith and Emory N. Castle (eds.), "Economics and Public Policy in Water Resource Development" (Ames: Iowa State University Press, 1964).

See also examples in Leroy F. Rogers and William V. Neely, "Costs and Returns from Crops and Livestock in the Upland Desert Valleys of Nevada" (Reno: University of Nevada, Desert Research Institute, 1966).

vides a cost which may be subtracted from the product of gross yield and unit price to estimate expected crop income per acre, I_a, based on average soil and growing conditions and no flooding. When flooding occurs, additional farm operations and materials may be required (cleanup, releveling, replanting, extra fertilizer, etc.), and crop yield may be reduced. The changes are incorporated into the crop budget and a revised income I_f is estimated. Separate values of I_f should be estimated by season or by month of flooding because of seasonal differences in flood effects. The seasonal distribution of the flood threat may be estimated from the time of year of historical flood events. The damage to a given crop is the difference between I_f and I_a. The average damage to a given crop when flooded is the sum of the products of seasonal crop damage and seasonal flood probability (Ex. 10-3).

EXAMPLE 10-3

Cropland within a certain flood plain is planted 40 percent to corn, 50 percent to oats, and 10 percent to tomatoes. Hydrologic analysis reveals that 50 percent of the historical floods have occurred in the spring, 25 percent in the summer, 10 percent in the fall, and 15 percent in the winter. Crop income without flooding and with flooding by season, in dollars per acre per year, is as follows:

		I_f			
Crop	*I_a*	*Spring*	*Summer*	*Fall*	*Winter*
Corn	120	70	30	30	110
Oats	65	15	45	55	40
Tomatoes	200	100	30	50	180

What is the expected damage per acre to this cropland when it is flooded?

SOLUTION

Average damage to corn when flooded:

$$0.50(120 - 70) + 0.25(120 - 30) + 0.10(120 - 30) + 0.15(120 - 110)$$
$$= 25.00 + 22.50 + 9.00 + 1.50 = \$58.00 \text{ per acre}$$

Average damage to oats when flooded:

$$0.50(65 - 15) + 0.25(65 - 45) + 0.10(65 - 55) + 0.15(65 - 40)$$
$$= 25.00 + 5.00 + 1.00 + 3.75 = \$34.75 \text{ per acre}$$

Average damage to tomatoes when flooded:

$$0.50(200 - 100) + 0.25(200 - 30) + 0.10(200 - 50) + 0.15(200 - 180)$$
$$= 50.00 + 42.50 + 15.00 + 3.00 = \$110.50 \text{ per acre}$$

Average damage per flooded crop acre F_a:

$$0.40(58.00) + 0.50(34.75) + 0.10(110.50)$$
$$= 23.20 + 17.38 + 11.05 = \$51.63$$

The average damage per flooded crop acre F_a is the sum of the products of the damage to the crops when flooded and the fraction of the flood-plain cropland devoted to that crop. Total direct flood damage is the sum of the building and the crop flood damages plus damages to transportation and utility facilities. The last must largely be determined by analysis of historical damage patterns.

Indirect damages (Sec. 8-6) include the travel cost of detouring around the flooded area, losses stemming from flood-induced interruptions in utility service, and the "net loss of normal profit and earnings to capital, management, and labor in the readily identifiable zone of flood influence."[1] Net costs incremental for the flood of forecasting and warning, evacuating and reoccupying flood-threatened areas, flood fighting, and temporary living in flood-free areas are also included.[2] Because business losses tend to be offset by business gains, indirect losses are much lower from the national than from a local viewpoint.[2] In practice, indirect damages are usually taken as a fixed percentage of the direct damages because the time required for detailed analysis of indirect damages is too great to be justified for each flood study. Kates analyzed a number of studies by the Corps of Engineers to find values of 15 percent for residential damage, 37 percent for commercial, 45 percent for industrial, 10 percent for utilities, 34 percent for public property, 10 percent for agriculture, 25 percent for highway, and 23 percent for railroads.[3]

Intangible damages (Sec. 8-12) include loss of life, impairment to public health by well contamination or insect breeding, and adverse effect on national defense of temporary closure of major transportation arteries. The intangible effect most strongly emphasized in flood control planning is the sense of security which comes when floods no longer occur so regularly. Most agencies use rare design floods because:

> If the degree of protection originally provided is too low, a false sense of security is induced, unwarranted development is encouraged, and when the great flood comes inevitably the stage will be set for a disaster.[4]

The insecurity brought on by uncertainty of when major floods

---

[1]   U.S. Army Corps of Engineers, "Survey Investigations and Reports: General Procedures," *Eng. Manual* EM 1120-2-101 (Washington, April, 1958), p. 50a.

[2]   A detailed method for evaluating these losses is described in Kates, *op. cit.*, pp. 47–57.

[3]   *Idem.*, p. 17.

[4]   *Water Resources Activities in the United States: Floods and Flood Control*, 86th Cong., 2d Sess., Sen. Comm. on Natl. Water Resources, Print 15, 1960, p. 10.

will occur may be considered to create a cost above the expected damages. The uncertainty cost [e in Eq. (8-7)] is the amount in excess of the expected value of the damages that individuals are willing to pay to avoid a flood loss pattern that is highly variable from year to year and occasionally reaches catastrophic proportions.[1] One must select the chance of the uncertainty fund's running dry, α, which he is willing to accept. The higher the value selected, the greater the uncertainty cost and the higher the optimum level of protection will be. Planning agencies currently increase the level of protection to standardized levels rather than specifically evaluate α (Sec. 10-3).

The average annual flood damages are determined by summing the direct damages for floods of a number of different frequencies, applying an indirect damage factor, and plotting a curve of damage vs. frequency. The area under the curve is the expected annual damage (Ex. 8-2). An uncertainty cost may be added by selecting a value of α, determining the standard deviation of the damage values, and applying Eq. (8-7). The procedure is demonstrated in Ex. 10-4.

EXAMPLE 10-4

The following steps are taken in computing the average annual flood damages before any measures are installed for the watershed of Ex. 10-2:

1 Estimating building damages:

M_s = \$870 per acre

(averaged from county assessment records for flood plain)

Urban flood damage = $K_d M_s h A$ K_d = 0.044

Freq., %:	43	20	10	4	1	0.5
h, ft:	1.01	1.25	1.41	1.56	1.77	1.85
a, acre:	290	360	396	450	510	532
Damage, \$:	11,200	17,300	22,000	26,900	34,600	37,700

2 Estimating crop damage:

From crop budgets,

F_a = \$9.18 per acre

From land-use maps,

f_a = 0.977   (fraction of area in crops)

Crop flood damage = $F_a f_a A$

Damage, \$:	2,600	3,200	3,600	4,000	4,600	4,800

[1] Viraf A. Bhavnagri and George Bugliarello, Mathematical Representation of an Urban Flood Plain, *Proc. ASCE*, vol. 91, no. HY 2 (March, 1965), p. 158.

3   Estimating indirect damage:

Use 10 percent of crop plus 15 percent of urban direct damages.

Damage, $:   1,900   2,900   3,700   4,400   5,700   6,000

4   Total damages:

Damage, $:   15,700   23,400   29,300   35,300   44,900   48,500

These values are plotted in Fig. 10-6.

5   Means and standard deviations of flood damage might be estimated graphically (Fig. 8-1) or numerically as below:

Frequency, %	Damage, $	$D - \bar{D}$	$(D - \bar{D})^2$
97.5	0	−13.0	169
92.5	0	−13.0	169
87.5	0	−13.0	169
82.5	0	−13.0	169
77.5	0	−13.0	169
72.5	0	−13.0	169
67.5	0	−13.0	169
62.5	6.5	−6.5	42
57.5	10.0	−3.0	9
52.5	12.5	−0.5	0
47.5	14.0	1.0	1
42.5	16.0	3.0	9
37.5	17.0	4.0	16
32.5	18.5	5.5	30
27.5	20.5	7.5	56
22.5	22.5	9.5	90
17.5	24.5	11.5	107
12.5	27.5	14.5	210
7.5	31.0	18.0	324
2.5	39.0	26.0	676
Totals	259.5		2753

$$\bar{D} = \frac{259.5}{20} = \$12,980$$

$$\sigma = \sqrt{\frac{2,753}{19}} = \$12,050$$

6   Annual uncertainty damage:

$i = 3$ percent $\alpha = 0.05$ $V_\alpha = 1.645$

$$U = \frac{0.03(1.645)12,050}{\sqrt{0.06}} = \$2,420 \tag{8-7}$$

7   Total annual flood damage:

$12,980 + 2,420 = \$15,400$

10-12 FLOOD PROTECTION BENEFITS Flood control benefits equal the expected damage without a measure less the expected damage with it. Application of the with-and-without principle requires care in handling the effect of flood control measures on flood-plain land use. On a before-and-after basis, benefits as related to flood-plain land use may be classified into three groups.

1 Reduction in expected damage to development which occurs in the flood plain after the measure is applied but would have occurred there even without the measure is a benefit.
2 A portion of the reduction in damage to development which could not economically locate in the flood plain without the measure, but can and does with it, should be counted. The portion equals the further damage reduction beyond the reduction that is just sufficient to entice development into the flood plain. It is approximately one-half the reduction for a mixture of many types of development: some on the verge of entering the flood plain without any measures at all and some barely enticed even after the measures are installed.
3 None of the reduction in damage to development that is lulled into the flood plain by a false sense of security stemming from overconfidence in project effectiveness should be counted.

While additional empirical research is needed to define flood-plain

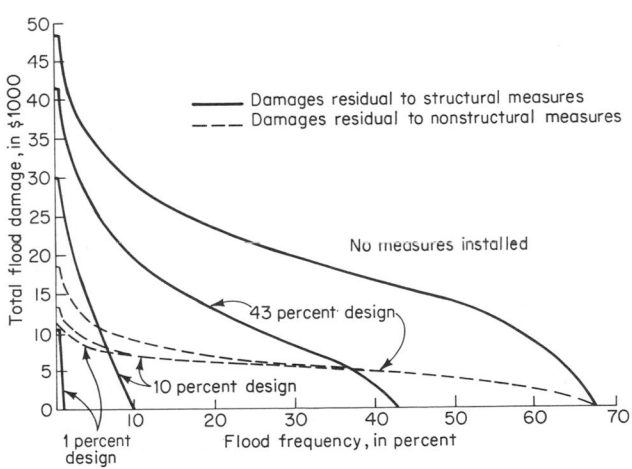

FIGURE 10-6 Flood damage by frequency for flood control examples.

land use better as a function of protection, the inclusion of land use as a decision alternative in measure optimization (as is done in Ex. 10-5) limits the benefits to those that are ligitimately counted.

Structural measures eliminate all damages from floods smaller than the design flood. However, crops cannot be flood-proofed, and flood-plain regulation increases total crop damage to the degree it shifts land use from urban development to crops. Flood proofing does not reduce many indirect damages stemming from inconvenience to those living outside the flood plain or direct damages to yards and other outside property in urban areas. Location restrictions ordinarily do not prevent damage to urban property located in the flood plain prior to implementation of the restriction. The net result is that nonstructural measures must be primarily justified by reduction in direct urban damages, while structural measures gain economic advantage through reducing all kinds of damages. Figure 10-6 illustrates representative residual-damage patterns for the two types of measures.

Project Feasibility

10-13   ECONOMIC   FEASIBILITY   Residual   damage   differences between structural and nonstructural measures require two steps in flood control project optimization (Ex. 10-5).

EXAMPLE 10-5
The optimum flood control project for the flood plain analyzed in Exs.10-2 and 10-4 is determined in the following steps.
1   Analysis of damages residual to various levels of protection with the use of nonstructural measures selected in Ex. 10-2. Residual areas and depths are determined from Eqs. (10-7) and (10-8). The term Q_x equals flood peak for frequency less design flood peak. Urban damages are determined after the manner of Ex. 10-4, step 1. Total damages include full-crop and indirect damages. In this example, the acreage shifted to crops by land-use restriction is not large enough to affect crop damage materially.

   a 43 percent design flood frequency:

Freq., %:	43	20	10	4	1	0.5
h, ft:	0	0.24	0.40	0.55	0.76	0.84
A, acre:	0	70	106	160	220	242
Urban damage, $:	0	600	1,600	3,400	6,400	7,800
Total damage, $:	4,500	6,700	8,900	11,800	16,700	18,600

b **10 percent design flood frequency:**

h, ft:	0	0	0	0.15	0.36	0.44
A, acre:	0	0	0	54	114	136
Urban damage, $:	0	0	0	300	1,600	2,300
Total damage, $:	4,500	6,100	7,300	8,700	11,900	13,100

c **1 percent design flood frequency:**

h, ft:	0	0	0	0	0	0.08
A, acre:	0	0	0	0	0	22
Urban damage, $:	0	0	0	0	0	100
Total damage, $:	4,500	6,100	7,300	8,400	10,300	10,900

d Residual damages for each design are plotted in Fig. 10-6, and the mean and standard deviation of the damages are figured (Ex. 10-4, step 5. Residual U is estimated from Eq. (8-7). Gross benefit from each design is determined as 15,400 less residual damages.

Design freq., %:	43	10	1
Residual $\bar{D}$, $/year:	3,960	3,420	3,370
Residual U, $/year:	810	620	590
Residual damages, $/year:	4,770	4,040	3,960
Gross benefit, $/year:	10,630	11,360	11,440
Cost, $/year:	2,270	3,890	5,350
Net benefit, $/year:	8,360	7,470	6,090

2 Analysis of damages residual to providing the various levels of protection with structural measures. Values of A and h differ from those in step 1 because the unprotected area flooded is adjacent to the channel rather than on the flood-plain fringes.

a **43 percent design flood frequency:**

Freq., %:	43	20	10	4	1	0.5
h, ft:	0	0.91	1.15	1.36	1.60	1.70
A, acre:	0	263	330	391	461	489
Urban damage $:	0	9,200	14,500	20,400	28,300	31,800
Agr. damage $:	0	2,400	3,000	3,500	4,100	4,400
Indirect damage $:	0	1,600	2,500	3,400	4,700	5,200
Total damage $:	0	13,200	20,000	27,300	37,100	41,400

b **10 percent design flood frequency:**

h, ft:	0	0	0	0.92	1.30	1.44
A, acre:	0	0	0	266	375	414
Urban damage, $:	0	0	0	9,400	18,700	22,800
Agr. damage, $:	0	0	0	2,400	3,400	3,700
Indirect damage, $:	0	0	0	1,700	3,100	3,800
Total damage, $:	0	0	0	13,500	25,200	30,300

c 1 percent design flood frequency:

The only damage is caused by the 0.5 percent flood for which $h = 0.81$ ft, $A = 234$ acres, and total damage $= 7,300 + 2,100 + 1,300 = \$10,700$.

d Residual damages are plotted in Fig. 10-6, and mean damage, the standard deviation, and U are determined.

e Net benefits from each design are determined:

Design freq., %:	43	10	1
Residual $\bar{D}$, \$/year:	6,000	1,130	80
Residual U, \$/year:	1,830	840	170
Residual damages, \$/year:	7,830	1,970	250
Gross benefit, \$/year:	7,570	13,430	15,150
Cost, \$/year:	6,230	8,480	11,500
Net benefit, \$/year:	1,340	4,950	3,650

3   Comparison of steps 1 and 2 reveals nonstructural measures produce the greater net benefit for each design frequency. Thus, the demand curve should be based on the gross benefit of step 1, part d. Demand curves are determined from the slope of the total-benefit curves (Fig. 10-3) for structural and nonstructural measures.

4   The four marginal curves are plotted (Fig. 10-4). The optimum project is found to be one designed to use nonstructural measures to protect against a 37 percent flood. For this project, annual benefits equal \$11,000 (Fig. 10-3), annual costs equal \$2,500 (Fig. 10-3), net annual benefits equal \$8,500, and the benefit-cost ratio equals 4.4.

5   If only structural measures were to be considered, the optimum project would be designed to provide protection against an 11 percent flood. For this project, annual benefits equal \$13,300 (Fig. 10-3), annual costs equal \$8,300 (Fig. 10-3), net annual benefits equal \$5,000, and the benefit-cost ratio equals 1.6.

A project using the least-cost combination of all measures must be optimized first. Next, a project using only structural measures must be optimized. The better of the two is the one with the greatest net benefit. If the least-cost combination of measures turns out to include only structural measures, the two alternatives turn out to be identical. The tedium of the required calculations is greatly reduced by the use of available digital computer programs.[1]

Because nonstructural measures produce a substantially different residual-damage pattern than do structural measures, uncertainty

[1] L. Douglas James, "Economic Analysis of Alternative Flood Control Measures" (Lexington: University of Kentucky, Water Resources Institute Res. Rept. 16, 1968).

damages residual to structural measures exceed those residual to non-structural measures unless a high level of protection is provided. Also, the optimum level of protection is substantially higher for structural than for nonstructural measures (Fig. 10-4). Inclusion of uncertainty damages increases the optimum level of protection with the increase becoming progressively larger as smaller values of α [Eq. (8-7)] are selected.

10-14   EVALUATION OF ALTERNATIVE MEASURES   The optimum flood control policy is determined by the flood-plain characteristics.[1] Where both agricultural and urban damages are small, the optimum policy is to suffer whatever flood damages occur. Structural measures provide the only means for protecting cropland, but their economic justification requires good cropland or frequent flooding. Widely scattered buildings can best be protected by flood proofing. Economies of scale determine a building density where structural measures become less costly than flood proofing. Impending scattered urban development favors land-use regulation. As development pressure increases, a point in time is finally reached when it is less costly to protect the land by structural measures. In a dynamic context, location restrictions may be considered as a means of delaying premature construction of structural measures and adding flexibility to the damage reduction program. In summary, nonstructural measures are most applicable for protecting areas where urban development is widely scattered, where additional planning flexibility is desired, where channel improvement severely increases downstream flooding, where channel construction is relatively costly, or where the money cannot be raised to pay for structural measures.

10-15   OPTIMUM LEVEL OF PROTECTION   The point where the supply and demand curves for flood control cross reveals the optimum level of protection. However, flood control agencies customarily use a higher level of protection than can be justified by marginal economic analysis unless a very low value for α is selected when calculating uncertainty damages. Three arguments have been used to justify this policy. A project providing a low level of protection may induce uneconomic flood-plain settlement by a public which underestimates the threat of residual flood damages. Intangible damages may warrant increased protection. Flood-plain occupants may desire to avoid risk. This last argument does not apply if uncertainty cost is used in optimizing the level of protection.

[1]   L. Douglas James, Economic Analysis of Alternative Flood Control Measures, *Water Resources Res.*, vol. 3, no. 2 (2d Quarter, 1967), pp. 333-343.

After analyzing patterns of flood-plain development, Roder concluded, "in an established community the public promise of protection is not directly linked with further invasion of the flood plain."[1] Kates found the "common advice" estimate of the flood problem to overestimate the actual flood hazard severely.[2] One might conclude that public underestimation of residual flood hazard would be at a maximum immediately after project construction and would diminish to a negligible or negative quantity in the long run. Induced uneconomic growth is a transient condition lasting from the time of project completion to the first damage-producing flood. Eckstein has concluded that "intangibles can be no more than a minor part of the justification of flood control expenditures."[3] In conclusion, if a normative value of α can be selected, it is difficult to justify further increase in the level of protection. In fact, benefit maximization to determine the level of protection is the expressed policy of the Corps of Engineers.[4]

10-16   FINANCIAL FEASIBILITY   Since passage of the Flood Control Act of 1936, federal funds have financed most measures for flood control in the United States. The exceptions consist of projects to alleviate local flooding in urban areas, projects using nonstructural measures, and a portion of the cost of levees, channel improvements, and small reservoirs. The government assumes full cost of the design and construction of structural measures. The costs of rights-of-way, roadway or utility relocation, and bridges as well as the responsibility for administration of contracts and operation and maintenance have been left to local interests.[5] However, some states have assumed many local costs to increase their share of total federal expenditures, and loans at low interest rates are often available to local agencies. Individual landowners pay for installation of land-treatment measures, but the Federal government offers free technical assistance and low-interest loans. Costs of alterations in land-use

[1]   Wolf Roder, Attitudes and Knowledge on the Topeka Flood Plain, in Gilbert F. White (ed.), "Papers on Flood Problems" (Chicago: The University of Chicago Press, Department of Geography Res. Paper 70, 1961), p. 83.

[2]   Robert W. Kates, "Hazard and Choice Perception in Flood Plain Management" (Chicago: The University of Chicago Press, Department of Geography Res. Paper 78, 1962), pp. 57–66. On page 59, Kates defines *common advice* as "the impression of flood frequency that a . . . citizen might glean from published sources and conversations with interested officials."

[3]   Otto Eckstein, "Water Resource Development: The Economics of Project Evaluation" (Cambridge, Mass.: Harvard University Press, 1958), p. 144.

[4]   U.S. Army Corps of Engineers, "Survey Investigations and Reports: General Procedures," *Eng. Manual* EM 1120-2-101 (Washington, May, 1961), pp. 54–54a.

[5]   This division applies specifically to the Public Law 566 program of the Department of Agriculture. The Corps of Engineers has the authority to buy right-of-way and maintain flood control projects, but it may require some local financial contribution depending on the geographical distribution of project benefits.

patterns or flood proofing are borne privately. Federal and state funds provide for flood forecasting, warning, and fighting.

The prevailing institutional arrangement for financing has been frequently criticized because the very small share of the total financial responsibility assigned to the beneficiaries results in political pressure for flood control measures which cannot be economically justified and because it encourages use of structural measures for which the government bears the cost instead of nonstructural measures for which the cost is borne locally. The overdevelopment of flood plains is encouraged as individuals reap the benefits from flood-plain location and are reimbursed for, or protected from, their losses. Redefining financial responsibility to increase local contributions would be one way to offset this effect. Eckstein suggests three factors to consider in determining the local contribution. They are the degree to which flood control is a primary project purpose, the proportion of direct to total benefit, and the frequency of flooding.[1] The United States Task Force on Federal Flood Control Policy proposed a nonfederal contribution of 25 percent of the cost of measures protecting existing development and 50 percent of the cost of measures protecting future development.[2]

SELECTED REFERENCES

Benson, Manuel A.: "Evolution of Methods for Evaluating the Occurrence of Floods," *U.S. Geol. Survey, Water Supply Papers*, 1580-A (1962).

Beuchert, Edward W.: "A Legal View of the Flood Plain" (Cambridge, Mass.: Harvard Law School, 1961).

Dunham, Allison: Flood Control via the Police Power, *Univ. Penn. Law Rev.*, vol. 107 (June, 1959), p. 1098.

Eckstein, Otto: "Water Resource Development: The Economics of Project Evaluation" (Cambridge, Mass.: Harvard University Press, 1958).

James, L. Douglas: "A Time-dependent Planning Process for Combining Structural Measures, Land Use, and Flood Proofing to Minimize the Economic Cost of Floods" (Stanford, Calif.: Stanford University, Institute in Engineering Economic Systems, EEP-12, 1964).

Kates, Robert W: "Hazard and Choice Perception in Flood Plain Management" (Chicago: The University of Chicago Press, Department of Geography Res. Paper 78, 1962).

Murphy, Francis C.: "Regulating Flood-plain Development" (Chicago:

---

[1] Eckstein, *op. cit.*, pp. 155–9.

[2] *Communication from the President of the United States transmitting a Report by the Task Force on Federal Flood Control Policy, A Unified National Program for Managing Flood Losses*, 89th Cong., 2d Sess., H.R. Doc. 465, 1966, p. 42.

The University of Chicago Press, Department of Geography Res. Paper 56, 1958).

Sheaffer, John R.: "Flood Proofing: An Element in a Flood Damage Reduction Program" (Chicago: The University of Chicago Press, Department of Geography Res. Paper 65, 1960).

White, Gilbert F.: "Choice of Adjustments to Floods" (Chicago: The University of Chicago Press, Department of Geography Res. Paper 93, 1964).

PROBLEMS

10-1 On a given flood plain, a study was made to determine the relationships between flood frequency and flood damage and between flood frequency and the cost of measures designed to control a flood of that frequency. Costs were calculated on an annual basis, including operation and maintenance.

Frequency, %:	60	50	40	30	20	15	10	6	2	0.5
Damage, $1,000:	0	20	30	40	90	145	215	310	435	500
Cost, $1000:	0	10	15	18	20	21	23	28	40	80

Assume the structural measures prevent all damages from smaller than design floods and have no effect on damages from larger than design floods.

a Plot the damage-frequency curve.

b A project to protect against a 6 percent flood is being considered.

   i What is the annual cost of the project?

   ii What are the annual benefits from the project?

   iii What is the benefit-cost ratio? The net benefits?

c Plot a curve of total benefits vs. design frequency.

d Plot a curve of marginal benefits vs. design frequency.

e Plot a curve of marginal cost vs. design frequency.

f Find the design frequency of the optimum project.

   i What is the annual cost of this project?

   ii What are the annual benefits from this project?

   iii What is the benefit-cost ratio? The net benefits?

10-2 You have been given the responsibility of analyzing the flooding situation within the Jones Creek watershed and recommending a plan of action. An analysis of streamflows in order to determine annual flood peak by frequency and an analysis of the annual cost of building a channel to contain each flood revealed the following information.

Frequency, %:	43	20	10	4	1	0.5
Flood peak, cfs:	210	320	380	480	620	690
Channel cost, $/year:	8,560	10,370	11,100	12,100	13,580	14,220

The existing channel has a capacity of 100 cfs, is 1.8 miles long, and has a slope of 0.0009. The flood-plain slopes toward the channel at 15 ft/mile in both directions and has a Manning roughness of 0.040. The market value of structures within the flood-plain averages $100,000 per acre of urban land, forecast to increase from 2 to 5 percent of the total area, and the market value of land is expected to increase from $4,950 to $8,760 per acre over the next 10 years. From the 75 percent of the flood plain which is farmed, farm income averages $30 per acre from land when it is flooded and $80 per acre when it is not.

What flood control program would you recommend? Document your recommendation with supporting calculation. Assume the values for any constants not given in the above problem are identical with those in the text.

CHAPTER
ELEVEN

DRAINAGE

The Planning Context

11-1 DEFINITION Both drainage and flood control deal with excess water, but drainage is concerned with moisture accumulations which because of their long duration, small volume, or frequent occurrence cannot be considered floods. The differentiation between the two has been defined for institutional and financial purposes and does not represent a clear physical distinction (Sec. 10-1).

Drainage may be subdivided into three classes. Storm drainage collects runoff from very small drainage basins, usually within urban areas, to prevent water from ponding on the surface. Highway drainage includes surface drainage to remove storm water from the traveled way, cross drainage when the highway crosses natural watercourses, and subsurface drainage to remove excess soil water to increase subgrade and slope stability. Land drainage consists of measures designed to remove excess water from land which would otherwise be too wet for normal agricultural production. The nutrients available to the plants decrease as the zone of unsaturated soil becomes thinner, and the limited oxygen content of waterlogged soils may produce harmful anaerobic decomposition.

Land drainage removes water ponded on the soil surface and from enough of the root zone to permit crop growth. In arid climates, land drainage is required by every irrigation project to prevent excessive soil-moisture buildup and salt accumulation. All irrigation water contains salt (inorganic compounds other than acids or bases), and unless the amount carried away by drainage water equals that brought in by the irrigation water, the salt content of the soil will eventually increase until crops can no longer be grown. Drainage facilities should keep the water table low enough so that the water will not rise to the soil surface, evaporate, and leave a salt residue. In humid climates, drainage facilities remove excess precipitation that would otherwise accumulate within the soil. Drainage facilities may also be required to prevent accumulation of water in areas where natural-gravity drainage patterns have been upset by mining-caused land subsidence.[1] The importance of land drainage in the United States is seen in the figures of 20 million acres of cropland irrigated and 90 million acres of cropland drained. About 40 percent of the cultivatable soils east of the Mississippi have a dominant wetness hazard.

11-2 HISTORICAL DEVELOPMENT   The oldest cities contained facilities to dispose of excess storm water. The oldest roadways passed over cross-drainage facilities. The earliest farmers drained swamps and planted crops. Over the years, more water resources projects have been built for drainage than for all the other purposes put together. However, most drainage projects are too small to be spectacular and too inexpensive to produce the agitation needed to obtain large amounts of federal funds. Individual cities, highway agencies, railroads, and farms have installed and paid for the measures they required. The basic reason for the small scale of drainage projects is that they cause few spillover effects and contain few economies of scale.

Developing the Supply

11-3 STORM DRAINAGE   Structural measures for storm drainage are basically the same as those for flood control. Small open ditches or underground sewers transport storm water from low-lying areas to a nearby major water course. Storm drainage may be combined with urban waste-water disposal. This increases the load on waste-water-treatment plants but reduces contamination from waste material picked up by the storm runoff. The system for the collection and disposal of storm water includes gutters, inlets, manholes, and outlet works.[2] Pumping plants

---

[1] D. L. Hocklin, Mining Subsidence and Land Drainage Remedial Measures, in R. B. Thorn (ed.), "River Engineering and Water Conservation Works" (London: Butterworth & Co. (Publishers), Ltd., 1966).

[2] Ray K. Linsley, Jr., and Joseph B. Franzini, *Water-resources Engineering* (New York: McGraw-Hill Book Company, 1964), pp. 493–506.

and gates to prevent backflow are required in low areas where storm runoff may coincide with high water levels in rivers and estuaries.

Hydrographs from small urban watersheds tend to have very sharp peaks. Because small amounts of storage can substantially reduce flow peaks, storm-sewer cost (including required pumping cost) can be substantially reduced by detention storage in small sumps. The relationship between sump capacity and storm-sewer capacity for a given storm frequency may be approximated from an accumulated runoff diagram (Ex. 11-1).

EXAMPLE 11-1

A sump is to be designed to store runoff from 300 acres based on a 48-hr detention period and a 2 percent design storm. A study of local rainfall records is completed to determine expected rainfall as a function of duration by frequency. A rainfall-runoff correlation is used to convert rainfalls to runoffs, and the results are plotted in an accumulated runoff diagram (Fig. 11-1). The required sump release is the slope of the line from the origin to the accumulated runoff after 48 hr. Since 1 cfs = 1 acre-in./hr, 300(0.175) = 52.5 cfs. If a sump were not used, the peak runoff would be 300(1.10) = 330.0 cfs. The required sump capacity is the maximum departure between the accumulated runoff and the sump-release curves or (2.90/12)(300) = 72.5 acre-ft.

Sump storage is made expensive by the high cost of right-of-way in urban areas, but the portion of the cost allocated to drainage may be

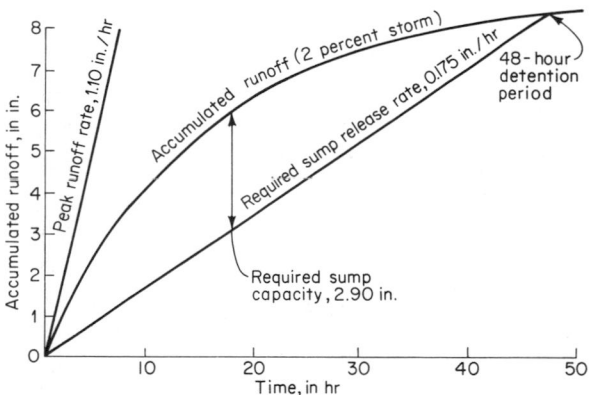

FIGURE 11-1 Accumulative-runoff diagram for storm-sump design.

substantially reduced by also using the area for recreation and esthetic purposes.

Overall system cost is largely governed by population density and design standards.[1] The supply curve for storm drainage is developed in the same way as that for structural measures for flood control (Fig. 10-3). The nonstructural measures used for flood control are unlikely to be economical where the storm water rises very quickly, is shallow, and seldom enters buildings. The least-cost combination of sump storage and sewer capacity for each of a series of selected design frequencies defines a total-cost curve. The marginal-cost or -supply curve is the slope of the total-cost curve.

11-4 HIGHWAY DRAINAGE Cross drainage is carried under highways through culvert or bridge openings. Historically, openings were sized by use of empirical formulas,[2] but a far better approach is to develop culvert design hydrographs by frequency from rainfall-runoff relationships and channel routing. The culvert size required to pass the flood flow may then be determined by hydraulic analysis.[3]

The culvert opening should only be made large enough to pass the flood peak when that can be shown to be more economical than making it smaller and allowing the water to back up for short periods during floods. Maintenance cost is relatively independent of culvert size except for a higher cost for smaller sizes caused by difficulty in removing debris. While selection of the economic culvert size requires analysis of alternative combinations of backwater storage and culvert capacity,[4] storage cost equals damage caused by backed up floodwater and is best analyzed as part of demand rather than supply. The total-cost curve is thus a plot of the sum of the installation cost and the capitalized maintenance cost of the culvert or bridge required to provide a given flow capacity vs. the frequency of the flood peak that is equal to the capacity.

Surface drainage is provided by a system of gutters, drainage inlets, culverts, and downdrains designed to carry away the water falling on the highway surface. Design methods of, and the procedure for, developing the supply curve are analogous to those used for storm drainage. Highway subsurface-drainage design is analogous to land drainage design except

---

[1] Colby V. Ardis, Kenneth J. Dueker, and Arno T. Lenz, Storm Drainage Practices of 32 Cities, *Proc. ASCE*, vol. 35, no. HY 1 (January, 1969), pp. 383–408.

[2] R. Robinson Rowe, Philosophy of Culvert Design, *Proc. ASCE*, vol. 92, no. HW 1 (March, 1966).

[3] Ven Te Chow, "Open-channel Hydraulics" (New York: McGraw-Hill Book Company, 1959), pp. 493–506.
    Linsley and Franzini, *op. cit.*, pp. 518–530.

[4] Harold D. Pritchett, *Application of the Principles of Engineering Economy to the Selection of Highway Culverts* (Stanford, Calif.: Stanford University, Institute on Engineering Economic Systems EEP-13, 1964).

that the benefits accrue from a reduction in highway maintenance and replacement cost rather than an increase in farm income.

11-5 LAND DRAINAGE The sizing of channels to carry away accumulated moisture from the soil surface depends on the permissible duration of surface ponding. In areas of high winter rainfall, the design may be planned to remove the water in time for spring planting. Allowable ponding duration during the growing season depends on tolerance to inundation. Accumulated-runoff diagrams are used to relate drain capacity to ponding duration. The same channels may also be used to remove subsurface and surface drainage water.

Where low-lying areas are inundated by waters from nearby lakes, rivers, or tidal estuaries, land drainage may be provided by surrounding the area with levees. Such facilities are widespread in tidal flats and in the deltas of major rivers. Drainage ditches just inside the levee intercept seepage. Subsurface drainage facilities lower the water table within the island. If gravity drainage is prevented by long periods of high water outside the levees or by the low elevation of the island interior, pumping is required.[1] The combination of pumping, gravity drainage, and storage having minimum cost should be selected.[2] The construction of leveed islands is justified within the area where the value in use of the reclaimed land exceeds the cost of reclamation.

A subsurface drainage system consists of an outlet, a collector system to carry the water from the fields to the outlet, and field drains to remove the water from the soil.[3] Unless the drainage water is of poor quality, the outlet should discharge into the nearest stream having sufficient capacity to handle the flow quantities. If an area could be drained to one of two or more outlets, it should be drained in the direction of least cost. If the drainage water substantially alters the low-flow regime in the receiving channel, it is necessary to consider for project evaluation whether the added water will induce weed growth, affect channel stability, or require replacement of fords with farm bridges. If the drainage water is of poor quality, the outlet may be moved downstream until the incremental cost of extending the drain farther equals the incremental savings in water quality damages along the intermediate stream reach. An alternate solution to compare on a least-cost basis is terminal storage of drainage water until floodwater is available for dilution. The economic

---

[1] H. W. Adams, Pumping Requirements for Leveed Agriculture Areas, *Proc. ASCE*, vol. 83, no. IR 1 (May, 1957).

[2] G. McLeod, Land Drainage Pumping Stations, in Thorn (ed.), *op. cit.*

[3] Linsley and Franzini, *op. cit.*, pp. 506–516.

James N. Luthin (ed.), "Drainage of Agricultural Lands" (Madison, Wis.: American Society of Agronomy, 1957).

feasibility of the drainage project depends on its benefits' exceeding the sum of the cost of the entire system including outlet extension and the net increase in water quality damages downstream from the outlet.

Collector drains may be either open ditches or pipes with the choice based on least cost; however, open ditches are not desirable in densely populated areas for esthetic and safety reasons. The collector-drain flow line must be low enough to intercept all the field drains. Pumping is required to maintain the water table at an elevation lower than the outlet. Where pumping is required anyway, cost savings may sometimes be realized by using several smaller upstream pumps and a shallower collection system.

The best method for determining drain design flows is to analyze flow records from nearby drains to develop a curve of flow rate vs. drainage area applicable to local conditions. The relationship between drainage flow and the area drained takes the form

$$Q = aA^b \tag{11-1}$$

where a and b are parameters of the local area and b is less than 1, Q is the design flow in cubic feet per second, and A is the area in square miles. The flow increases with the diameter and depth of the drain pipe. Hurley has developed a method for predicting return flows by routing irrigation and excess precipitation water through soil moisture storage.[1] When a new drain is installed, flow rates will be initially high as the water table is dropping and will gradually decrease until drainage equilibrium is reached over a drawdown period which may last several years with a tight soil. Where leaching is required, increased capacity must be provided for the leaching water. Where drainage facilities are part of an irrigation project, the cost of drainage-water collection and irrigation water may both be reduced by discharging drainage water into the irrigation system as long as irrigation water quality is not significantly impaired.

Field drains, like the collectors, may be either open or closed. Drainage ditches are favored by low land values, wide drain spacing, and shallow water-table depths. The extra cost of farm operations caused by fields' being dissected by ditches becomes prohibitive if large farm machinery is used. Closed underdrains are most often 4- or 6-in.-diameter clay or concrete pipe, though recent experiments have been made with plastic pipe as small as 1.5 in. Filter material is placed around the pipe to prevent fine-grained material from entering and clogging the drainage

[1] Patrick A. Hurley, Predicting Return Flows from Irrigation, *ASCE Environ. Eng. Conf., Dallas, Tex., February, 1967*, Conf. Preprint 432.

system. Field drains must be placed closer together with low soil permeability, shallow impervious layers, or large volumes of drainage water.[1] The close tile spacing required to drain soils of low permeability means that drainage may not be economical or even practical for tight soils. Field drains are often first installed at a rather wide spacing with the idea that additional drains may be installed in between later if the initial spacing is not adequate.

A drainage system may be laid out in a number of different patterns. Where the excess soil moisture concentrates in specific areas, only a few pipes serving the critical points may be necessary. Where the excess moisture enters the problem area from an outside source, a single interceptor drain may prove satisfactory. Where the water comes from local sources, field drains must be spaced throughout the area.

If the soils are extremely pervious and the drainage problem is caused by a perched water table, drainage holes may be drilled through the underlying impervious layer to allow the water to penetrate. Where deeper layers are saturated or impervious or the water can be put to beneficial use, the water may be pumped to the surface in drainage wells.

The ratio of maintenance cost to first cost is normally much greater for land drainage than for other water resource projects because continuous wetness promotes weed growth and bank sloughing in drainage ditches, and drainage pipes are easily clogged by roots and sediment. The continuous implementation of a good maintenance plan is imperative for the project to function.

The total cost of land drainage sums the cost of the on-farm, collection, and disposal systems. A series of engineering designs may be used to estimate the sum of these costs for several depths to water table. As depth is increased, the cost will be increased by the additional expense of laying deeper lines, the requirement of closer field drain spacing, and the need to provide drainage to additional areas where the without-project depth to water is within the increment interval. Individual points are plotted on a curve of total cost vs. depth. The marginal-cost curve is then developed from the slope of the total-cost curve.

Economic optimization of a drainage project requires separate marginal-cost curves for each homogeneous segment of the total area studied. Each major soil type should be evaluated independently as soil may vary widely in tile-drain-spacing requirements and in cropping patterns. For combined irrigation-drainage projects, combined analysis is required (Sec. 12-8).

---

[1] Linsley and Franzini, *op. cit.*, pp. 509–512.

Estimating the Demand

11-6 STORM DRAINAGE   The benefits from storm drainage measures result from the reduction in damages caused by ponded storm water. However, damages estimated by the procedure used for flood control (Sec. 10-11) are seldom sufficient to justify the level of protection for which storm drainage measures are customarily designed. Increased protection implicitly places a high nuisance value on ponded storm water.

While the expense borne by individuals to drain storm water from private land indicates a nuisance damage of significant magnitude, difficulty in its direct quantification has caused alternate approaches to be used for selecting the optimum level of protection. They include:

1   To install storm drains on a trial-and-error basis with additional facilities provided when public pressure develops.
2   To regard nuisance damage as an intangible and to allow the planner to use his judgment in selecting design frequency with economic analysis' being used only to determine the least-cost design for accomplishing the objective.
3   To postulate a function relating nuisance damage to the depth and duration of ponding and combine benefits from reduced damage nuisance with flood damage for economic justification of the measure.
4   To survey storm drainage practice to derive an implicit nuisance damage function for use in studying new measures. One would expect the parameters of the derived nuisance damage function to relate to local land use.

The first two methods have been widely practiced, but experience has shown them to result in a wide variation of drainage design among spots with identical drainage problems. Such design diversity is not an economically efficient resource allocation. While the third method relies on an arbitrarily selected nuisance damage function, it ensures consistent evaluation of equivalent situations. Resources would be efficiently allocated among drainage projects, but no demonstration of economic feasibility is provided. The fourth method offers promising research possibilities as private investment in drainage may offer the key to evaluating nuisance damage. Once a method for evaluating nuisance damages has been selected, the demand curve is the customary plot of marginal benefits vs. design storm frequency (Fig. 10-4).

11-7 HIGHWAY DRAINAGE   When a flood peak exceeds the culvert capacity, water will be backed onto upstream land and, if it gets deep enough, may flow over the road. The upstream damage depends on the land use and can be determined by the techniques used to evaluate other flood damages (Sec. 10-11). Overtopping will damage the highway and interrupt traffic. Damage to the highway equals the cost required to restore the highway to its condition before the flood. Damage caused by traffic interruptions depends on whether the traffic will still be able to use the road. If traffic can get through, the traffic damage equals the sum of the cost to the vehicles of slowing down and then speeding up again,[1] the cost of warning signs and flagmen, and the cost of increased accident probability. If traffic cannot get through because the floodwater is too deep or the road is washed out, the damage may be taken as

$$T_d = \Delta D \ \bar{V} V_m \tag{11-2}$$

where ΔD is the incremental additional travel distance along an alternate route, $\bar{V}$ is the average of the number of vehicles which would have used the road had it not been flooded and the number which take the detour, and V_m is the economic cost of traveling a vehicle mile. If the road does not wash out when overtopped, $\bar{V}$ includes all vehicles which wanted to use the road during the flood peak. If it is washed out, vehicles must be summed from the time the road is overtopped until the time it is repaired. Intangible damages may include closure of national defense routes, interruptions of police and fire protection, or isolation from medical care. If significant volumes of water are backed up by the culvert, downstream floodpeaks will be reduced. The reduction in downstream flood damages should be included as a negative cost in total damage evaluation.

The marginal-benefit or demand curve for selecting optimum culvert size may be developed through the following steps (Fig. 11-2):

1 A trial culvert size is selected.
2 The culvert capacity is hydraulically determined as the flow through the culvert during the greatest headwater which can occur without causing any damages.
3 The frequency of the flood having a peak equal to the culvert capacity is determined from a hydrologic analysis of the contributing watershed. This is the frequency of zero damages, curve *A*.
4 A larger flood is selected by frequency.
5 The upstream area flooded by the larger flood is estimated from the head required to provide the peak discharge or, with greater accuracy, by routing the flood through detention storage with the culvert at its

[1] Clarkson H. Oglesby and Laurence I. Hewes, "Highway Engineering" (New York: John Wiley & Sons, Inc., 1963).

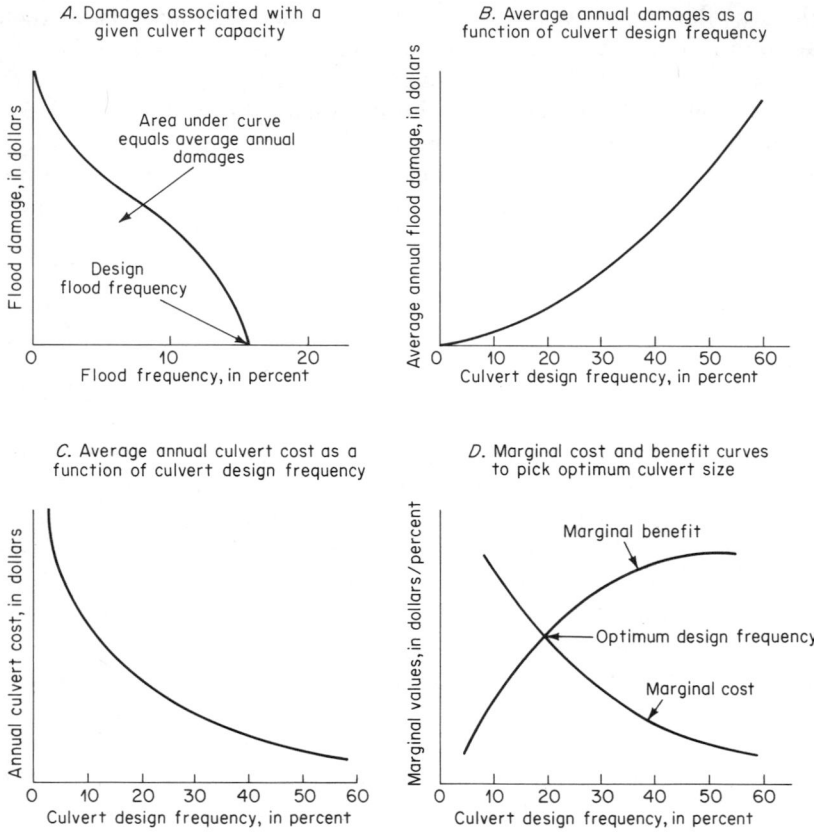

FIGURE 11-2   Economic optimization of culvert design.

outlet. If routing shows the highway will be overtopped; the maximum depth and duration of the overtopping flow is estimated.

6   The resulting damages are estimated from the sum of flooding damages and highway overtopping damages. A second point is now established on curve A.

7   Steps 4 through 6 are repeated until enough points are established to define the balance of curve A.

8   The annual damages are evaluated from curve A (Ex. 10-4). This damage when plotted against the frequency of step 3 gives one point on curve B.

9   Another culvert size is selected, and steps 1 through 8 are repeated until enough points are established to define the entire curve B.

10   A cost estimate for installing each culvert used in defining curve *B* is made and used to define curve *C*.

11   A marginal-benefit curve is developed from the slope of curve *B*. A marginal-cost curve is developed from the slope of curve *C*. The optimum culvert size is the one for the design frequency where the two marginal-cost curves cross.

By repeating the process for a series of culverts in diverse locations, a correlation between site characteristics and design frequency could be developed and used to select the design frequency for additional locations. Culvert design capacities must be selected so frequently that economic analysis of each site is not warranted. However, the designer should consider the economic factors peculiar to the specific site rather than factors representing average conditions over a large area.

Selecting culvert design capacity by economic efficiency ignores the income redistribution effects of the cost bearing (Sec. 8-10). The costs of installing the culvert and repairing damage to the highway are borne by the highway agency. Damages from backwater flooding initially afflict adjacent property owners. Since highway construction causes the backwater damage, equity would require the highway agency to compensate upstream property owners who are flooded and to collect from downstream owners for the benefits they receive from culvert-dampened flood peaks. If the culvert design is based on economic efficiency, the agency would pay out less than the cost of enlarging the culvert. Damages from traffic interruption are distributed among a large group of motorists. Since the highway provides a net benefit to motorists despite the interruption, there is no obligation (it would be impractical anyway) to track them down and pay damages.

The benefits from highway surface drainage accrue to motorists. Puddles on the highway surface may slow traffic, cause cars to stall, or increase hydroplaning accidents. Wet pavement is known to be a major factor contributing to automobile accidents. The economic cost of poor surface drainage can only be estimated through the statistical evaluation of measured effects of ponded surface water on traffic. A nuisance damage may be added and benefits determined from changes in the duration and frequency of water ponded on the roadway by following the same basic methodology used for storm drainage (Sec. 11-6).

11-8   LAND DRAINAGE   Land drainage benefits equal the increased income made possible by the project. If the land is to be drained for urban use, the benefits may be estimated from the net increase in total land value with the postproject value based on regional values for similar land.

Drainage to remove soil water from agricultural land produces benefits determined by the relationship between net farm income (estimated from farm budgets) and depth to water.[1] As the depth to water is increased, farm income will be increased by increases in crop yield, shifts in cropping pattern to higher-income crops, and reductions in production expenses induced by excess soil water. The evaluation of drainage benefits may proceed in the following manner:

1 Estimate net farm income without the drainage project:
    a Estimate the cropping pattern which would be followed in the absence of drainage facilities by using income potential under expected wetness conditions. The results can be best expressed in a table showing the percentage of the land within each soil class devoted to each crop. The analysis may be substantially simplified with little loss of accuracy by ignoring crops that produce a relatively minor portion of total farm income.
    b Consult with the local farm advisors to develop farm budgets for each crop included in the cropping pattern.
    c Estimate the yield and then the net farm income per acre for each crop. The best data relating crop yield to depth to water come from information gleaned from regional crop experience. Budgets and yield depend on the soil in which a crop is grown; therefore, incomes per acre by soil type should be developed.
    d Determine total farm income within the study area by multiplying the crop income per acre by crop acreage and summing all the values. Total crop income divided by total acreage provides the income per composite crop acre.
2 Proceed through the same four steps to estimate the total farm income if the minimum depth to water is kept at 2 ft. The best guide to cropping pattern as a function of depth to water is regional cropping practice in similar situations.
3 Continue the analysis to determine net income with minimum depths to water at 2-ft intervals until the bottom of the root zone is reached (steps to this point are illustrated in Ex. 11-2).
4 Add the other appropriate benefits (Secs. 8-6 through 8-11) to each estimated value of direct primary benefits.
5 Plot the estimated total and marginal benefits vs. minimum depth to water.

---

[1] Glen O. Schwab et al., "Soil and Water Conservation Engineering" (New York: John Wiley & Sons, Inc., 1966).

EXAMPLE 11-2

A land drainage project is contemplated for lowering the water table within a 5,500-acre area. A survey of existing cropping conditions reveals two crops being grown on two classes of soil with acreages and net incomes as indicated below:

Depth to water table	SOIL CLASS 1		SOIL CLASS 2	
	Crop A	Crop B	Crop A	Crop B
Surface, acres	50		50	
Net income per acre	0	0	0	0
Acreage fraction	0	0	0	0
0–2 ft, acres	200		300	
Net income per acre	0	2	0	0
Acreage fraction	0	0.30	0	0
2–4 ft, acres	700		1,000	
Net income per acre	10	12	0	8
Acreage fraction	0.10	0.90	0	0.90
4–6 ft, acres	900		1,200	
Net income per acre	50	15	20	12
Acreage fraction	0.50	0.50	0.20	0.80
6–8 ft, acres	400		200	
Net income per acre	80	18	60	16
Acreage fraction	0.75	0.25	0.60	0.40
Over 8 ft, acres	300		200	
Net income per acre	100	20	80	18
Acreage fraction	0.90	0.10	0.80	0.20

By assuming cropping patterns and incomes would shift to those indicated by the current depth to water through providing drainage, estimate project benefits by soil class per acre drained as a function of minimum depth to water achieved.

1 Current income (not necessary to solution):

Soil 1:

$$200(2)0.3 + 700(10)0.1 + 700(12)0.9 + \cdots + 300(20)0.1$$
$$= \$91,030$$

Soil 2:

$$1,000(8)0.9 + 1,200(20)0.2 + 1,200(12)0.8 + \cdots + 200(18)0.2$$
$$= \$45,520$$

2 Additional income by draining surface water:

Soil 1:

$$50(2)0.3 = 30 \qquad \$0.60 \text{ per acre}$$

Soil 2:

$$0 \qquad \$0 \text{ per acre}$$

3   Additional income by draining to 2 ft:

Soil 1:

$$250[10(0.1) + 12(0.9) - 2(0.3)] = 2,800 \qquad \$11.20 \text{ per acre}$$

Soil 2:

$$350(8)0.9 = 2,520 \qquad \$ 7.20 \text{ per acre}$$

4   Additional income by draining to 4 ft:

Soil 1:

$$950[50(0.5) + 15(0.5) - 10(0.1) - 12(0.9)] = 19,665 \qquad \$20.70 \text{ per acre}$$

Soil 2:

$$1,350[20(0.2) + 12(0.8) - 8(0.9)] = 8,640 \qquad \$ 6.40 \text{ per acre}$$

5   Additional income by draining to 6 ft:

Soil 1:

$$1,850[80(0.75) + 18(0.25) - 50(0.5) - 15(0.5)] = 59,200 \qquad \$32.00 \text{ per acre}$$

Soil 2:

$$2,550[60(0.6) + 16(0.4) - 20(0.2) - 12(0.8)] = 73,440 \qquad \$28.80 \text{ per acre}$$

6   Additional income by draining to 8 ft:

Soil 1:

$$2,250[100(0.9) + 20(0.1) - 80(0.75) - 18(0.25)] = 61,875 \qquad \$27.50 \text{ per acre}$$

Soil 2:

$$2,750[80(0.8) + 18(0.2) - 60(0.6) - 16(0.4)] = 69,300 \qquad \$25.20 \text{ per acre}$$

Total project benefits (on an annual basis):

Depth	0	2	4	6	8
Soil 1, $:	30	2,830	22,495	81,695	143,570
$/acre:	0.60	11.32	23.68	44.16	63.81
Soil 2, $:	0	2,520	11,160	84,600	153,900
$/acre:	0	7.20	8.27	33.18	55.96

Separate demand curves should be developed for each area defined by a prevailing fairly homogeneous soil type. Different soils will be suited to different crops having different drainage requirements and thus will have different optimum drainage depths. Some soil may be too impermeable for drainage to be feasible.

Project Feasibility

11-9 ECONOMIC FEASIBILITY   The large fixed cost of project analysis and the smallness of most drainage projects often make the detailed marginal analysis used for the economic evaluation of other types of water resource development projects impractical. A more satisfactory approach, as has already been suggested for culvert design (Sec. 11-7), is to complete an economic analysis for a series of drainage projects covering a wide range of situations and then develop rules or standards relating economic design to characteristics of a particular site.

Economic analysis should consider the effects of drainage projects on available water supply and fish and wildlife. Thorough drainage will reduce ground-water recharge, so more runoff will occur during flood peaks and less during low-flow periods. The decreased natural storage will increase the downstream storage required to develop a given water supply. Increased flood runoff wasted downstream is a consumptive use. Both the value of the water lost and the increased cost of supply development should be weighed in drainage project analysis. Evaluation of adverse effects on fish and wildlife is discussed in Chap. 17.

11-10 FINANCIAL FEASIBILITY   Storm drainage facilities are normally designed, installed, and maintained by local urban governments and financed by general tax revenues. However, a subdivider or developer is often required to pay for the facilities serving new subdivisions or major urban development projects, and assessment bonds (Sec. 22-9) are sometimes used to finance new facilities for older or heterogeneously developed areas. While local financing dampens uneconomic demand, the vague relationship between the tax bill and storm drainage in the mind of most taxpayers magnifies pressure on local officials to improve facilities.

Highway drainage facilities are normally financed by the jurisdictionally responsible highway agency which is often reimbursed in part by a higher level of government. Since drainage is only part of total highway cost and those who benefit from a conservative design often fail to realize the cost, the incentive to apply recently refined hydrologic and economic principles of culvert design has been limited. Culvert design practice still falls substantially short of making the best use of the highway dollar.

Land drainage has been largely financed by individual land owners with the help of loans and technical advice obtained through the Department of Agriculture. Collection ditches, levees, and outlet pumps may be financed by drainage associations (unincorporated groups of voluntary members). Larger collective efforts are usually organized and financed by a legal subdivision of government called a *drainage* or a *reclamation district* which assesses local landowners proportionally to acreage, land value, or some index of benefit received. Overall, the financial arrangements for land drainage are among the best of any water resource project purpose for encouraging optimum economic development.

SELECTED REFERENCES

Bauer, W. J.: Economics of Urban Drainage Design, *Proc. ASCE*, vol. 88, no. HY 6 (November, 1962).

Kirkham, Don.: Steady-state Theories for Drainage, *Proc. ASCE*, vol. 92, no. IR 1 (March, 1966).

Linsley, Ray K., and Joseph B. Franzini: "Water-resources Engineering" (New York: McGraw-Hill Book Company, 1964), pp. 490–533.

Luthin, James N. (ed.): "Drainage Engineering" (New York: John Wiley & Sons, Inc., 1966).

Rowe, R. Robinson: Philosophy of Culvert Design, *Proc. ASCE*, vol. 92, no. HW 1 (March, 1966).

PROBLEMS

11-1   Use the information in the accumulated-runoff curve example to plot a curve of required sump capacity vs. sump release rate. The sump outlet pipe is 1,000 ft long and has a friction factor of 0.02, and a 10-ft headloss is permissible. The cost per foot of pipe is $5d^{1.5}$, where d is the pipe diameter in feet. The cost per acre-foot of sump storage is $15(25 - \sqrt{\text{acre-feet}})$. How large a sump and how large a pipe should be used?

11-2   What would be the effect of a 5-year buildup period on the average annual benefits of Ex. 11-2? Assume a uniform buildup rate, 5% discount rate, 50 year life.

11-3   Reevaluate Ex. 11-2 if a third crop could be grown on soil class 1 ments to:

	6–8 FT			OVER 8 FT		
	Crop A	*Crop B*	*Crop C*	*Crop A*	*Crop B*	*Crop C*
Net income per acre:	80	18	150	100	20	250
Acreage fraction:	0.50	0.25	0.25	0.40	0.10	0.50

11-4   A farmer plans the installation of tile drains in a field in which the soil permeability is 500 gpd*/sq ft. An impermeable stratum exists about 10 ft below the soil surface. Use the Donnan formula for tile drain spacing[1] to plot a curve of feet of tile drain required per acre vs. minimum acceptable depth to water.

*   Gallons per day.
[1]   Linsley and Franzini, *op. cit.*, p. 511.

CHAPTER TWELVE

WATER SUPPLY

The Planning Context

12-1 DEFINITION Man uses water for a multitude of purposes. Some, such as drinking, are essential to his life. Others, such as the hosing of leaves, could readily be accomplished by other means and can economically occur only with an abundance of low-cost water. Water supply consists in making water available for agricultural or urban use. Agricultural use includes irrigation, livestock watering, and farm household use. Irrigation is the application of water to farmland in order to increase crop yield or shift to production of a higher-valued crop. Urban water is used in household, industrial, commercial, public, or other activities. Historically, urban and agricultural water have been supplied by separate projects, but proper planning requires coordinated provision of total water requirements. The California Water Project is one of a growing number of large-scale water projects designed to provide both agricultural and urban water.

12-2 HISTORICAL DEVELOPMENT Isolated farm families have traditionally obtained the water needed for domestic or livestock use from a nearby surface water (stream) or groundwater (well or spring) supply. Most urban communities and irrigators initially used the same convenient nearby sources. Water was inexpensive because the demand was limited and the supply was abundant. However, the demand has been increasing through the years, while the supply has remained constant or even been reduced by growing quality constraints. Irrigated agriculture has expanded to provide the food and fiber needs of a growing population while simultaneously encouraging settlement of desert areas. Increasing urban population and increasing per capita water use caused by technological advancement has caused urban water use to expand even more rapidly. The ratio of irrigation to total use can be expected to decline steadily in future years. In 1965, irrigation comprised 41 percent of all water used and 83 percent of all water consumed in the United States. A consumption percentage of 70 has been projected for the year 2000.[1] The difference between consumption and use percentages is because a much higher percentage of urban than of agricultural water is returned to the stream after use.

A geographically concentrated demand for water for urban or irrigation use has several consequences. Local sources are gradually depleted. Long-term storage is required to provide a supply during droughts. The hydrologic interrelationship between ground and surface water supply becomes increasingly evident. Full resource utilization requires conjunctive development of surface and underground water supplies. When even an efficiently operated local source begins to run short, the community is forced to bring water in from the outside. As the concentration of urban population and irrigated agriculture becomes larger, so do the distance to a sufficient supply, the magnitude of the required water supply project, and the cost of water.

The increase in water supply project scale through the years has changed the institutional setting from small diversion dams or wells conceived, constructed, and financed by individuals to vast project complexes carrying water great distances and largely financed through the Federal government. However, the bulk of the irrigated acreage as of 1970 is still supplied by small systems serving only a few farmers. As projects have gradually become larger in size, they have progressively required a larger federal financial contribution.

Even though the economic cost of providing additional water has been mounting in arid areas, the structure of domestic, agricultural, and industrial water use continues to be largely grounded on the premise of an abundant and inexpensive supply. However, it would be a mistake to project future water requirements from current per capita usage. A low charge for water encourages users to increase their consumption until the marginal value added by use of the water drops to the price. As demand increases, water can no longer be economically applied to such usage. Available supplies will have to be rationed administratively. The economic gain to the community of shifting the limited supply to more productive uses can be expected to mount until political forces achieve a procedure for reallocation (Sec. 7-7). The perpetual water shortage in arid areas is a manifestation of the forces acting to reallocate water to more productive

---

[1]   United States Water Resources Council, "The Nation's Water Resources" (Washington: USGPO, 1968), p. 4-1.

uses and to encourage development of industrial technology, irrigation practices, and urban landscaping with less water. The economic pressure for restructuring water-usage practice develops first in arid areas but is found wherever sufficient water is no longer available to satisfy the full demand for low-cost water.

Developing the Supply

12-3 FRESH WATER Precipitation is the ultimate source and thus establishes an upper limit to the available supply of fresh water. A water supply may be taken directly from streamflow, but low flows limit the dependable supply unless reservoir storage (or storage in a ground-water acquifer) is used to retain peak flows for use during drier periods. Reservoir yield (volume per year) is the net increase in dependable supply (firm yield) achieved by such storage. Firm yield estimates are based on a design drought. Past practice has been to use the driest period of record (a 50- to 100-year event in most areas), but the best practice is to specify a drought by frequency (Sec. 10-3) according to an acceptable risk of shortage.

Firm yield is estimated by an operation study with flow sequences and a reservoir of preselected capacity operated according to prescribed rules (Ex. 12-1).

EXAMPLE 12-1

Estimation is desired of the firm yield which can be developed by a 10,000 acre-ft reservoir at a site having its most severe low-flow sequence from February, 1932, through February, 1936, when the streamflows, rainfalls, and pan evaporations in Table 12-1 were recorded. Monthly values of the required fraction of the total annual demand (estimated from the regional pattern of monthly water requirements in the intended usage), pan coefficient (estimated from climatological data[1]), and runoff coefficient (average recorded runoff divided by average recorded watershed precipitation) are:

	J	F	M	A	M	J
Demand fraction f:	0.03	0.04	0.05	0.08	0.12	0.14
Pan coef. e:	0.70	0.60	0.50	0.55	0.65	0.70
Runoff coef. r:	0.40	0.50	0.50	0.40	0.30	0.20

	J	A	S	O	N	D
Demand fraction f:	0.14	0.13	0.12	0.08	0.04	0.03
Pan coef. e:	0.75	0.75	0.80	0.85	0.80	0.75
Runoff coef. r:	0.20	0.10	0.20	0.20	0.30	0.40

[1] Ray K. Linsley, Max A. Kohler, and Joseph L. H. Paulhus, "Hydrology for Engineers" (New York: McGraw-Hill Book Company, 1958), fig. 5-5.

TABLE 12-1 Tabular Operation Study

(1) Month	(2) Precip., ft. Rain gage	(3) Pan evap., ft. Evap. pan	(4) Inflow, acre-ft. Stream gage	(5) Release, acre-ft. Water rights	(6) Precip., acre-ft. $(1-r)(2)(11)$	(7) Evap., acre-ft. $e(3)(11)$	(8) Demand acre-ft. $4,000f$	(9) Spill, acre-ft. Storage over 10,000	(10) End of month storage, acre-ft. (10) prev. $+(4)+(5)+(6)+(7)+(8)+(9)$	(11) Acres, $5\sqrt{(10)}$
Nov., 1931	.....	.....	.....	.....	.....	.....	.....	.....	0	0
Dec., 1931	1.062	0.060	3,440	−40	0	0	−120	0	3,280	286
Jan., 1932	0.379	0.079	2,030	−40	65	−16	−120	0	5,199	362
Feb., 1932	0.390	0.111	5,010	−40	71	−24	−160	−56	10,000	500
Mar., 1932	0.042	0.199	96	−40	10	−49	−200	0	9,817	495
Apr., 1932	0.062	0.294	11	−11	18	−80	−320	0	9,435	485
May, 1932	0.018	0.411	11	−11	6	−130	−480	0	8,831	470
June, 1932	0	0.482	0	0	0	−159	−560	0	8,112	450
July, 1932	0	0.500	0	0	0	−169	−560	0	7,383	429
Aug., 1932	0	0.450	0	0	0	−145	−520	0	6,718	409
Sept., 1932	0	0.385	0	0	0	−126	−480	0	6,112	391
Oct., 1932	0.034	0.252	0	0	11	−84	−320	0	5,719	378
Nov., 1932	0.066	0.137	0	0	17	−41	−160	0	5,535	372
Dec., 1932	0.381	0.074	6	−6	85	−21	−120	0	5,479	370
Jan., 1933	0.745	0.083	1,090	−40	165	−22	−120	0	6,552	405
Feb., 1933	0.100	0.102	33	−33	21	−25	−160	0	6,388	399
Mar., 1933	0.280	0.210	347	−40	56	−42	−200	0	6,509	403
Apr., 1933	0.021	0.274	12	−12	5	−61	−320	0	6,133	391
May, 1933	0.155	0.398	11	−11	43	−101	−480	0	5,595	374
June, 1933	0	0.499	3	−3	0	−131	−560	0	4,904	390
July, 1933	0	0.547	0	0	0	−144	−560	0	4,200	324

Month										
Aug., 1933	0	0.465	0	0	0	−113	−520	0	3,567	298
Sept., 1933	0	0.384	0	0	0	−92	−480	0	2,995	273
Oct., 1933	0.158	0.240	0	0	34	−56	−320	0	2,653	257
Nov., 1933	0	0.140	0	0	0	−29	−160	0	2,464	247
Dec., 1933	0.577	0.079	3	−3	86	−15	−120	0	2,415	245
Jan., 1934	0.110	0.080	66	−40	16	−14	−120	0	2,323	241
Feb., 1934	0.455	0.098	332	−40	55	−14	−160	0	2,496	249
Mar., 1934	0	0.201	14	−14	0	−27	−200	0	2,271	238
Apr., 1934	0.056	0.266	8	−8	8	−35	−320	0	1,924	219
May, 1934	0.054	0.392	5	−5	8	−56	−480	0	1,396	186
June, 1934	0.046	0.480			7	−63	−560	0	780	139
July, 1934	0	0.507	0	0	0	−53	−560	0	167	61
Aug., 1934	0	0.450	0	0	0	−21	−520	0	0	0
Sept., 1934	0.079	0.370	0	0	0	0	−480	0	0	0
Oct., 1934	0.084	0.250	0	0	0	0	−320	0	0	0
Nov., 1934	0.434	0.126	1	−1	0	0	−160	0	0	0
Dec., 1934	0.304	0.079	1,820	−40	0	0	−120	0	0	0
Jan., 1935	0.755	0.068	18	−18	0	0	−120	0	1,660	204
Feb., 1935	0.108	0.088	1,620	−40	11	−11	−160	0	1,500	194
Mar., 1935	0.491	0.213	3,680	−40	48	−21	−200	0	2,907	270
Apr., 1935	0.486	0.258	23	−23	79	−38	−320	0	6,268	396
May, 1935	0	0.390	8	−8	0	−100	−480	0	5,688	377
June, 1935	0	0.494	1	−1	0	−130	−560	0	4,998	353
July, 1935	0	0.515	0	0	0	−136	−560	0	4,302	328
Aug., 1935	0.025	0.447	0	0	7	−110	−520	0	3,679	303
Sept., 1935	0.019	0.360	0	0	5	−87	−480	0	3,117	279
Oct., 1935	0.065	0.244	0	0	15	−58	−320	0	2,754	262
Nov., 1935	0.037	0.140	8	−8	7	−29	−160	0	2,572	254
Dec., 1935	0.288	0.068	533	−40	44	−13	−120	0	2,483	249
Jan., 1936	0.228	0.074	8,970	−40	34	−13	−120	0	2,877	268
Feb., 1936	0.515	0.080		−40	69	−13	−160	−1,703	10,000	500

A curve of reservoir storage vs. surface area was developed from topographic maps and approximated by $A_c = 5$ (acre-ft)$^{0.5}$. Downstream water rights require release of full reservoir inflow up to 40 acre-ft/month. An initial-trial firm yield of 4,000 acre-ft/year was selected and the reservoir was assumed empty on November 30, 1931.

The reservoir has a firm yield less than 4,000 acre-ft/year, as it would have run 1,454 acre-ft short during the fall of 1934. Since the demand during the drawdown period equals 2.93 (January and February excluded) times the annual value, the initial-trial firm yield should be reduced by about (1,454/2.93) 496 acre-ft/year. Because a fuller reservoir has greater evaporation losses, the actual firm yield turns out to be 3,441 acre-ft/year.

The repetitive computations are easily adapted to a digital computer. While the operation study may use the entire flow sequence, a plot of reservoir storage vs. time (Fig. 12-1) will reveal the critical drawdown period which limits available firm yield. Detailed analysis can be confined to potential critical drawdown cycles.

The operation study (Table 12-1) requires estimated streamflows for the reservoir site. Because long-term records are seldom available at the required location, it is often necessary to estimate the historical flow sequence from nearby streamflow records or, with less reliability, from climatological data and watershed characteristics.[1] The historical sequence

[1]   Norman H. Crawford and Ray K. Linsley, "Digital Simulation in Hydrology: Stanford Watershed Model IV" (Stanford, Calif.: Stanford University, Department of Civil Engineering Tech. Rept. 39, 1966).

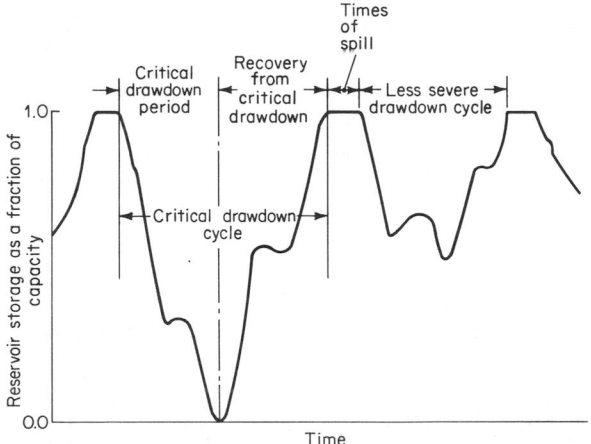

FIGURE 12-1   Time variation in reservoir storage.

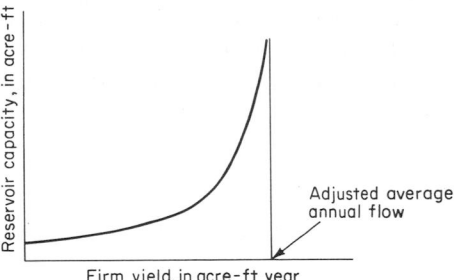

FIGURE 12-2 Reservoir capacity vs. reservoir yield.

may be used directly in the operation study to estimate the firm yield against a drought having a return period approximately equal to the length of record. However, a much better estimate of firm yield as a function of design drought frequency may be obtained through use of a long flow sequence generated from the statistical properties of the historical sequence (Sec. 20-11). The firm yield through the drought ranked m in order of decreasing severity from analysis of n years of generated synthetic record would have the frequency estimated by Eq. (10-1). A shortage would develop during more severe droughts and would require temporary restrictions in water use or supply from some other source. An operation study using synthesized flows requires monthly precipitations estimated by correlations with streamflow and average evaporations by months of the year.

Operation studies may be repeated for a number of capacities to determine firm yield as a function of reservoir storage. Figure 12-2 is a typical curve for a reservoir site on a stream which occasionally runs dry. For a site on a perennial stream, run-of-the-river firm yield causes the curve to intersect the horizontal rather than the vertical axis. The curve asymptotically approaches a vertical line equivalent to the average annual flow corrected for required releases, evaporation losses, and reservoir precipitation. The length of the critical dry period increases with distance from the origin on the curve. It begins at the duration of zero flow, for the drought design frequency, and becomes indefinitely long as the capacity-yield curve becomes nearly vertical. A curve of storage cost vs. firm yield may be developed from the capacity-yield curve and construction quantities.

The total firm yield from a group of reservoirs operated conjunctively to serve a large area exceeds the sum of the individual firm yields with each reservoir's serving its own smaller area. If critical dry periods do not coincide, withdrawal from one reservoir may be increased to avoid shortages at another. If use patterns do not coincide, peak use in one area will occur at a time of lesser use in another. The firm yield from a group of reservoirs

as a function of system cost may be estimated by first determining a group
of reservoirs representing a commensurate degree of site development
and then performing an operation study with the reservoirs as a group in
the following procedure:

1 Determine the yield-capacity curve (Fig. 12-2) for each reservoir in the
 system operated individually.
2 Determine the cost-capacity curve for each reservoir in the system from
 cost estimates for a sequence of reservoir sizes at the site. In order to
 make the costs at the various sites comparable, each should include
 delivery to an equivalent point.
3 Combine each pair of yield-capacity and cost-capacity curves to get
 a yield-cost curve.
4 The slope of a tangent to the yield-cost curve has the unit dollars per
 acre-foot of yield. Tangents of an identical slope may be drawn to each
 yield-cost curve. Each point of tangency defines a yield, cost, and hence
 reservoir size which should be built to obtain water at a marginal cost
 defined by the tangent slope. The sum of the yields and the costs for
 the points of tangency for all the reservoirs in the system defines one
 point on the system yield-cost curve (Fig. 12-3). The balance of the
 curve is obtained by selecting additional tangent slopes.
5 The sum of the individual yield-cost curves must be adjusted for the
 increased yield from coordinated operation. In order to estimate the
 increased yield, the sizes of the individual reservoirs making up the
 systems represented by points on the curve must be established. A
 point (A in Fig. 12-3) is selected, and the slope of the tangent to the
 curve at that point is determined. A line of the same slope is plotted
 tangent to each individual reservoir yield-cost curve, and the point of
 tangency determines the cost and (from the associated cost-capacity
 curve) the capacity of each reservoir included in the system. At this
 point, one knows the size of each reservoir in the system represented
 by point A.

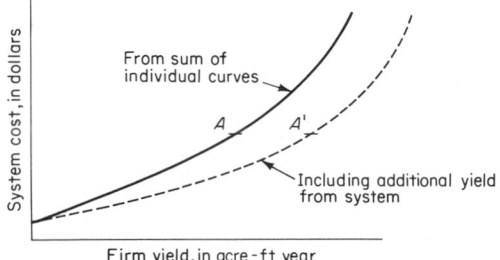

FIGURE 12-3 Cost of res-
ervoir system
vs. yield.

6 By using simultaneous streamflows and climatological data (Sec. 20-13) and a combined demand pattern, an operation study is completed for the system as a whole. The total system release is divided among reservoirs according to an appropriate operating rule (Sec. 20-7). The estimated system yield is increased from the sum of the individual reservoir yields by trial and error until the systemf firm yield which exactly empties the reservoir system at the end o the system critical dry period is established. The system firm yield is plotted as point A' (Fig. 12-3).

7 The curve of system firm yield as a function of cost is the locus of points established in the same manner as A'.

Reservoirs may be used to supply water in excess of firm yield. Since such secondary yield is available in varying quantities and will periodically be unavailable, it is best supplied only to those who can economically suspend their use of water or who have some alternative but more expensive source of temporary supply. For example, secondary surface water may be developed to reduce ground-water withdrawals. Potential secondary yield equals the water spilled during reservoir operation in supplying only firm yield. Even though a reservoir may not be large enough to hold water long enough to guarantee delivery during a critical dry period, it may be able to hold water long enough to be put to some beneficial use. The secondary yield decreases as firm yield increases because reservoir inflow is fixed. Thus the ratio of secondary to firm yield decreases with increasing capacity in a single reservoir (Fig. 12-6) or the number of reservoirs in a reservoir system. It is essentially zero for large reservoirs or systems.

The availability of secondary water may be determined by a modified operation study. At all times other than the critical drawdown period (Fig. 12-1), water in excess of the firm yield could be withdrawn from the reservoir or reservoir system without endangering the dependability of the firm water supply. However, one has to be careful not to withdraw so much secondary water that the reservoir subsequently runs dry while supplying firm yield. The rules of reservoir operation (Sec. 20-3) to supply secondary water must ensure that the probability of being able to supply the firm yield will not be materially decreased and that the secondary water should be provided in the time pattern having the greatest economic benefit. The upper limit of secondary withdrawals at any time should equal the maximum amount of water which can be put to beneficial use. The modified operation study uses the rules governing secondary release to make monthly estimates of annual secondary yield rate. Secondary yield as a function of the fraction of the time it is available (Fig. 12-4) may be plotted from the series of monthly estimates.

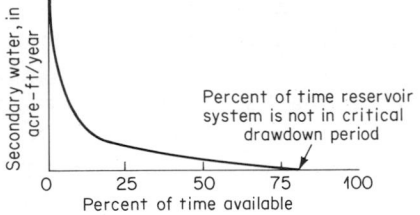

FIGURE 12-4   Annual availability of secondary water.

The unit value of secondary water increases with the fraction of the time it is available. When secondary water becomes unavailable, those who were using it will either have to obtain an alternate supply or suffer a loss. The value of secondary water may be evaluated as the value of firm water less the cost of a supplementary supply or the amount of benefit lost during service interruptions, whichever is smaller. If the secondary water is available so infrequently that no net benefit can be obtained through its use, the value of the secondary water is zero. Figure 12-5 indicates the trend in the value of secondary water with the percentage of time it is available.

Figures 12-4 and 12-5 may be combined by plotting the products of the quantity of secondary water available and the unit value of the water for corresponding time percentages (Fig. 12-6). The area under the curve is the amount of firm yield having equivalent value of the available secondary yield. The total adjusted yield for a given system of one or more reservoirs equals the sum of the individual reservoir firm yields (point A, Fig. 12-3), the additional system firm yield (point A', Figs. 12-3 and 12-7), and an amount of firm yield equivalent in value to the secondary yield (point A'', Fig. 12-7). The curve of system cost vs. total adjusted yield (Fig. 12-7) is the locus of points established by adding these three components for systems covering a range of sizes.

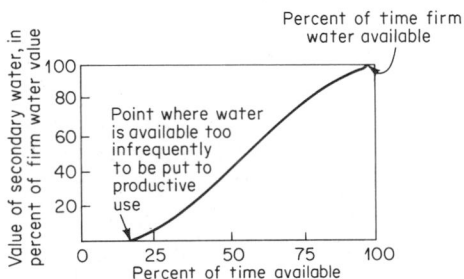

FIGURE 12-5   Value of secondary water by availability.

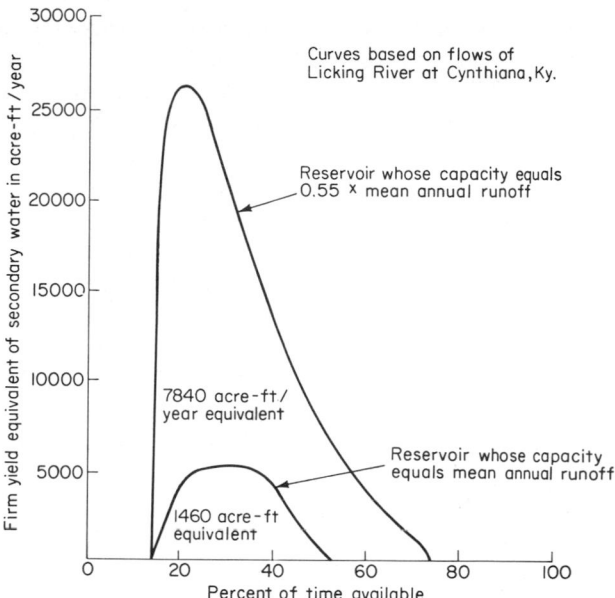

FIGURE 12-6   Curve for estimating firm-yield equivalent of secondary water.

12-4   SALINE WATER   Where the available water supply is too salty for its intended use, desalination is a possibility.[1] Water may be classified according to salt content as brackish (dissolved salts 1,000 to 3,000 mg/liter), saline (3,000 to 30,000 mg/liter), or sea water (average 35,000 mg/liter). Certain lakes and underground waters contain brine

[1]   K. S. Spiegler, "Principles of Desalination" (New York: Academic Press, Inc., 1966).

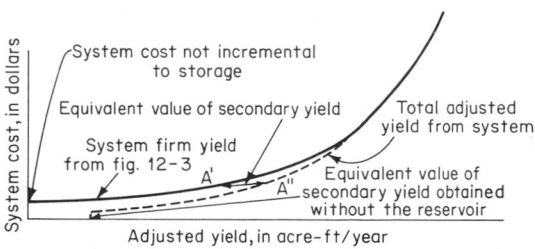

FIGURE 12-7   Cost of reservoir system vs. adjusted yield.

having a higher salt content than sea water. One of the two basic desalination processes is distillation whereby fresh water is extracted from the solution. Distillation involves applying heat to convert the water to vapor, disposing of the residual brine, and condensing the vapor. The operation becomes more economical if the heat energy dissipated during condensation is used to generate electric power. The most promising desalination proposals are those combined with a large nuclear power generating facility. The cost of distillation does not vary much with salt content and as of 1965 was about $300 per acre-foot.

The second basic type of desalination process is to extract the salt from the water. The three major processes are freezing to form ice crystals of relatively pure water and then draining the brine, demineralization by removing salts through hydrogen cation exchange, and electrodialysis with membranes which are selectively permeable to different ion types. Because the cost of extraction increases directly with salt content, distillation is the most economical process for water having a high salt content and salt extraction is more economical for less saline water. The break point is around 7,000 mg/liter. The cost per acre-foot of water produced is reduced by mixing treated with raw water until an acceptable salt content is reached.

Desalination as of 1965 was less expensive than fresh water supply development only in arid areas or on small islands where fresh water is very scarce and saline water is plentiful. However, technological advances may reduce relative cost. The economic cost of water supply by desalination also includes the cost of pumping to its point of use, obtaining the saline water, and brine disposal. Brine disposal is a major problem in inland areas where contamination of soil and ground water must be avoided, but along the coast, brine may be directly returned to the ocean. While the marginal productivity of agricultural water is generally too low to justify desalination, experimental irrigation of coarse-grained soils with brackish or saline waters by using large amounts of leaching shows promise, particularly for grass and pasture crops.[1]

12-5 LAND TREATMENT Farm ponds, grade-stabilization structures, terrace or contour tillage, and measures to improve forest and range cover dampen watershed response to storm events. Lower flood peaks reduce reservoir spills during major storms, and higher low flows reduce the reservoir storage required to achieve a given yield. The effectiveness of land treatment decreases with higher ratios of annual rainfall to potential

---

[1] Hugo Boyko, Salt Water Agriculture, *Sci. Am.*, vol. 216, no. 3 (March, 1967), pp. 89–96.

evapotranspiration.[1] The key to increasing watershed yield is reduction of evapotranspiration losses.

About 70 percent of all precipitation returns to the atmosphere through evapotranspiration, vast quantities from plants having minimal economic value. Substantial water may be saved by destroying non-economic plants. Spraying economic plants to reduce transpiration is still in the experimental stage. Paving minimizes evapotranspiration losses but is too costly from both the economic and esthetic points of view to be practical for large areas. Chemicals producing monomolecular films may be applied to reduce evaporation from free water surfaces. The resulting monolayers reduce surface tension, form a partial diffusion barrier, and increase water surface temperature.[2] The higher temperature increases evaporation enough when the film is broken to make it difficult to achieve long-term evaporation suppression. Possible upsetting effects to the biological environment of the water surface should also be considered.

12-6   DISTRIBUTION SYSTEM   Surface distribution of agricultural water requires conveyance to individual farm headgates. Water may be taken directly from the storage reservoir or released into a river and withdrawn from a downstream diversion dam. A small terminal reservoir or ditch tenders empowered to regulate the time and amounts of delivery to individual farms help control usage peaks. Unlined canals have the lowest construction cost, but lining reduces water losses and maintenance cost for scour or for weed or rodent control. Pipes reduce maintenance cost and conveyance losses to a bare minimum, avoid all hazard to the safety of children, and allow overlying land to be put to alternate uses.

Ground-water aquifers provide an alternative means of distribution from storage reservoirs to points of use and thus save the cost of surface distribution facilities. For the method to be successful, the aquifer must extend under the demand area at an elevation not requiring excessive pumping lifts, have sufficient cross sectional area and permeability to transmit water at a reasonable rate, and not have a mineral content which will cause water quality deterioration. Natural recharge may be augmented by such methods of artificial recharge as flow regulation to keep flow about equal to natural channel percolation capacity and the development of artificial spreading areas or recharge wells, pits, or shafts.[3]

---

[1]   A. L. Sharp, A. E. Gibbs, and W. J. Owen, Development of a Procedure for Estimating the Effects of Land and Watershed Treatment on Streamflow, *U.S. Dept. Agr., Tech. Bull.* 1352 (March, 1966).

[2]   Quentin L. Florey, Progress in Bureau of Reclamation Evaporation Reduction Research, *U.S. Bur. Reclamation* (May, 1966).

[3]   Information on recharge cost components is found in David K. Todd, Economics of Ground Water Recharge, *Proc. ASCE*, vol. 91, no. HY 4 (July, 1965), pp. 249–270.

Where recharge is limited, ground water may be mined. The maximum mining yield is the total volume of water which is available underground. Mining can be justified if the value of water in use exceeds pumping ing cost plus its discounted future value in use net of discounted future pumping cost. However, economic development based on mined water is made temporary by the fact that the withdrawal rate cannot be permanently maintained.

The cost of surface distribution should be compared with that of ground-water development (recharge plus pumping) to determine which is less expensive. The variation of surface-distribution cost with distance from the water source and with elevation may be expressed by plotting lines of equal cost on a map of the service area. A similar map of ground-water cost may be plotted from pumping cost as determined by aquifer properties. By overlaying one map with the other, the least-cost distribution may be found for each area. A final check should be made to be sure economies of scale do not make supplying the whole area by the same means less expensive.

The distribution of urban water is accomplished by a network of pipes capable of delivering to the individual consumer the required quantity of water under a satisfactory pressure. The distribution system should be designed to minimize the annual cost of the reservoirs, pipe network, and pumping required to maintain selected delivery standards. Urban distribution facilities account for about half of total urban water cost.

Urban water supplies are treated to produce a safe and preferably a pleasant-tasting drinking water. The water treatment plant may contain sedimentation or filtration facilities to remove suspended particles, chlorination to kill harmful bacteria, aeration to lessen unpleasant tastes and odors, and softening to remove hardness. The treatment method selected depends on the characteristics of the water supplied, with sedimentation and chlorination being the primary processes for surface supplies. Ground water more often requires treatment to reduce hardness or, in severe cases, salinity. The water treatment should be designed to obtain the required standards at least cost. Since treatment cost varies with treatment plant size,[1] economy may be achieved by combining small plants until marginal-treatment costs no longer exceed marginal-distribution costs. Some cities attempt to minimize pollution of their water supplies and thus reduce treatment costs by restricting human use of the supply reservoirs or even the entire tributary watershed, but the practice cannot be justified from economic considerations.

The cost of urban and agricultural distribution systems may be

[1] Based on data from G. T. Orlob and M. R. Lindorf, Cost of Water Treatment in California, *J. Am. Water Works Assoc.*, vol. 50 (1958), pp. 45–55.

considered in project optimization by including, in the system cost of Fig. 12-7, the cost of the mains connecting the supply reservoirs with equivalent points near the demand location. Remaining distribution cost may be deducted from the value of the water indicated by the demand curve.

12-7 USER DISTRIBUTION The urban user is responsible for taking the water from the main to the various points of use. The distribution plumbing must conform to building codes. In each case the user's distribution cost should be estimated and deducted from the value received from use of the water.

Irrigation water may be applied by flooding, furrows, sprinkling or subirrigation. Flooding is turning water loose in checks confined by leveed borders. Furrow irrigation is running the water down miniature ditches between rows of plants. Sprinkler irrigation utilizes a network of pipes and sprinkler heads and has been made possible by the development of lightweight pipe with quick couplers which can be readily moved from field to field during irrigation. Sprinkling is particularly advantageous on unusually pervious, shallow, or steep soils or where a high water cost requires minimum water loss. Because the land preparation cost required by other methods cannot be justified for occasional irrigation, sprinkling has become the most popular method in humid areas. Subirrigation provides water to seep under fields from adjacent ditches. The irrigation method should be adapted to the crops and other local conditions and selected after consultation with farm advisers. Often the best method turns out to be a coordinated combination of surface and sprinkler irrigation for the same field.[1] Economic analysis of the alternatives requires estimating the annual cost of each method and the farm water losses which result.

The farmer must provide a system of canals, ditches, or pipes to take the water from the farm headgate to the various fields. Pumps may be required to provide the head to raise water to higher fields or provide for sprinkling. For project planning, on-farm distribution costs can be estimated from a curve of cost per acre as a function of farm size based on local conditions and practice. On-farm irrigation and distribution costs should be deducted from the value received from the water to determine its net worth.

12-8 RETURN FLOWS The water not consumed in use must be collected and returned to a satisfactory disposal point. Urban waste

[1] Josef D. Zimmerman, "Irrigation" (New York: John Wiley & Sons, Inc., 1966), pp. 162–165.

water is usually collected by a sewerage system, treated to maintain the quality of the receiving water, and returned to the stream. Agricultural waste water is returned untreated (Sec. 11-5).

As the marginal cost of fresh water available to satisfy marginal demands increases (Sec. 12-2), increasing amounts of waste water will be reclaimed by treatment for reuse before disposal. Reclamation becomes economical when it becomes less expensive than the marginal cost of additional outside water. Industrial cooling water may be reclaimed by lowering its temperature. Domestic waste water is generally less expensive to reclaim than industrial-process water because standardized treatment methods can be applied. Agricultural waste water may be reused for downstream irrigation; but as salinity increases through the evapotranspiration loss of fresh water, a point will be eventually reached where reclamation is only possible through desalination.

The cost of waste-water disposal may be divided between the disposal cost (Sec. 11-5) downstream from a common collection point and the collection cost to get it to that point. The disposal cost is more easily included in the supply curve, and the collection cost is more easily included in the demand curve. The amount of water supplied determines the waste-water quantity. A random point A'' can be selected on the cost-yield curve (Fig. 12-7). The quantity of waste water produced if this amount of water is supplied and the cost of disposing of it (including treatment for urban water) are estimated. This cost is the distance $A'' - A'''$. The locus of like points provides the balance of the total-cost curve including drainage facilities (Fig. 12-8). Marginal water supply cost is developed by plotting the slope of the total-cost curve vs. annual quantity of water supplied.

The collection cost can be handled in the economic analysis in a manner analogous to that used for distribution cost. Collection cost is for on-farm collection and a feeder system taking the water from the user to a common disposal point. Collection cost, along with distribution

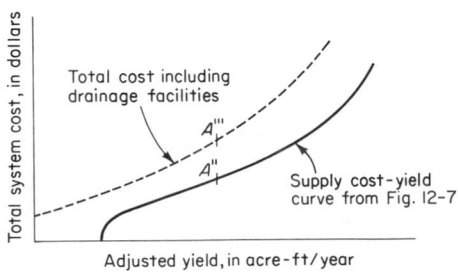

FIGURE 12-8   Cost of supply and drainage system vs. adjusted yield.

cost, should be subtracted from the value received from use of the water. A useful way to show cost information is on a map locating areas by the total of the distribution and collection cost required to serve them.

Estimating Irrigation Demand

The benefits from irrigation are determined by the net increase in income from the land made possible by irrigation. Economic analysis must thus begin by projecting cropping patterns and yields with and without the irrigation project.

12-9 CROPPING PATTERN For practical purposes, the cropping pattern without the irrigation project may be taken as that before the project unless there is substantial reason to anticipate improved dry farming practice. If without the project the area will be irrigated with water from an alternative more expensive source, the resultant cropping pattern should be used, but the cost in water supply made unnecessary by the project may be added to project benefit. The difference between the with-and-without cropping patterns will vary from a change from limited grazing to intensive agriculture in desert areas to almost no change for occasional supplemental irrigation in humid areas.

The cropping pattern which will develop with irrigation depends on the agricultural productivity of the land. Much of the needed information may be obtained through soils mapping from the Soil Conservation Service and related state agencies. Important soil characteristics include ability to hold water between irrigations but still allow excess water to drain freely, workability, depth, salt accumulation, natural fertility, and slope. Climate also determines the crops which can be grown on a soil. The results may be summarized on a map locating the potentially irrigable land by five or six groups of land classes. Economies of scale favor irrigating a large compact area of high-quality land.

Ideally, the farmer will specialize in a few crops which maximize his net income as determined by commodity markets, land classification, and local farming practice. Crop patterns which have developed in similar irrigated areas provide the best guide for projecting crop patterns by soil class, but they should be modified to fit local conditions. If a major portion of project benefits result from a few high-value crops, special scrutiny is required to confirm that these crops would actually be grown in the projected quantities. Acreage and production controls must be considered before projecting regulated crops into the project area. Changing market conditions vary cropping patterns over project life so that expected values under normal conditions should be used (Sec. 9-7). The with-and-without crop patterns are best summarized on tables showing the percentage of land within each soil class devoted to each crop.

12-10   CROP INCOME   Farm budgets (Sec. 10-11) are used to estimate crop income as a function of yield. Separate budgets are needed for each crop and may be needed for the same crop in different soil types. The yields without the project can be estimated from dry farming conditions. Yields with the project depend on the amount of irrigation water applied, as described in the following sections.

Market prices (Sec. 9-7) are used to determine income from crops for which the project provides a small portion of national production. However, market analysis is required to determine the effect of project production on market price where the project would provide a major portion of the production and to determine the economic value of government-supported commodities.

12-11   CROP WATER REQUIREMENT   Economically, additional irrigation water should be applied until its marginal physical product is reduced to the ratio of marginal benefit to marginal cost [Eq.(4-22)]. The benefit from applying water stems primarily from increased yield, but effects on crop quality and control over growing and harvesting conditions may be important. Occasionally the benefit may be in the form of reduced frost damage.

Consumptive use is the amount of water required by the plant to produce maximum yield. Part of this water is supplied by precipitation. Irrigation provides a supplementary moisture source when precipitation is insufficient. However, only in the case of *free* water is it economical to apply the entire difference between consumptive use and available precipitation, as to do so would reduce the marginal physical product of additional water to zero.

Except for differences caused by deep percolation, crops incompletely covering the soil at certain stages of their growth, and leaf glossiness, all crops have an essentially equal consumptive use per day of growing season.[1] Plants transpire water to discharge heat for temperature control, with solar radiation and wind being the primary causes of heat buildup, and all commercially grown crops have essentially equal temperature

---

[1]   Colin Clark, "The Economics of Irrigation" (Oxford: Pergamon Press, 1967), pp. 4–18.

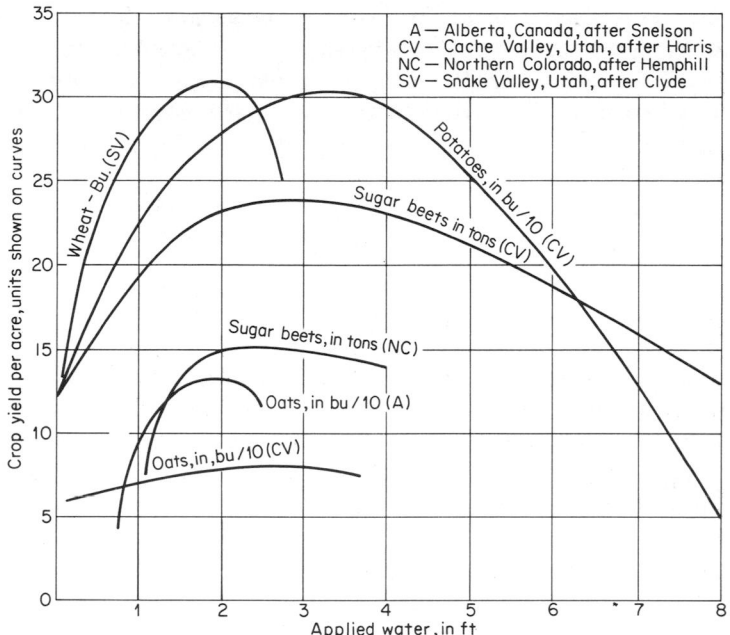

FIGURE 12-9   Some examples of the variation of crop yield with applied water. [*From Ray K. Linsley and Joseph B. Franzini, "Water Resources Engineering," (New York: McGraw-Hill Book Company, 1964), p. 382. By permission of the publishers.*]

requirements. Consumptive use does vary with geographical location and with seasonal and temporary weather fluctuations at a given location. These facts imply that irrigation should be used to produce the crop generating the highest net economic value (product of salable weight and unit price less growing expense) per unit of area and unit of time. Economic value varies widely, while consumptive use does not.

The crop water requirement may be determined from data collected on yield vs. applied water for fields or small experimental test plots for a specific crop in a specific locale having characteristic values of consumptive use and effective precipitation (Fig. 12-9). The crop-yield–water-use curve actually varies erratically among plants in a given population because plants are by nature inhomogeneous.[1] Microclimate

---

[1]   J. Ian Stewart and Robert M. Hagan, Predicting Effects of Water Shortage on Crop Yield, *Proc. ASCE*, vol. 95, no. IR 1 (March, 1969), pp. 91–104.

may vary over a field. Weather patterns and the timing of moisture deficiency with respect to phases of plant growth cause changes from year to year. A single curve must plot expected values. It is seldom practical to collect the necessary experimental data for planning a particular project, but published data are available for many crop-region combinations.

The crop water requirement is determined from the curve of yield vs. applied water by maximizing farm income in dollars per acre as expressed in the relationship

$$I = P_c Y - P_w Q - V_c Y - F_c \qquad (12\text{-}1)$$

where P_c is the unit price received for the crop, Y is the crop yield in units per acre, P_w is the value of water in dollars per acre-foot, Q is applied water in acre-feet per acre, V_c is the variable cost of producing the crop in dollars per unit of crop yield, and F_c is the fixed cost of crop production in dollars per acre. Fixed cost does not affect the optimum irrigation water application but does affect whether the crop can be profitably grown. Farm budgets may be used to estimate F_c and V_c, P_c is determined from crop-market analysis, and curves relating Y to Q* are shown in Fig. 12-9.

If sufficient experimental data are not available to develop water-yield curves for the crop-soil-climate combination to be evaluated, a more indirect procedure must be used. Consumptive use for the project location may be estimated from values known for another location by assuming consumptive use proportional to lake evaporation (the production of pan evaporation and the pan coefficient).[1] Also widely used is the Blaney-Criddle method based on correlation of measured consumptive-use data with monthly temperature, percent of daytime hours, precipitation, or growing period.[2] A more approximate approach is correlation by temperature data alone with a formula of the type

$$U_c = a + b \, \Sigma \, T \qquad (12\text{-}2)$$

where U_c is the average annual consumptive use in feet, a and b are constants which can be determined if consumptive-use data are available for a given crop at two locations, and ΣT is the average annual sum of

---

* Quadratic parabolic equations to fit experimental data are found in Nathan Buras, Conjunctive Operation of Dams and Aquifers, *Proc. ASCE*, vol. 89, no. HY 6 (November, 1963), pp. 121–123.

1 The decrease in irrigation demand because of the increase in atmospheric humidity over large irrigated areas should be considered in planning irrigation of scattered fields in arid climates. See R. O. Slatyer and J. A. Mabbutt, Hydrology of Arid and Semiarid Regions, in Ven Te Chow (ed.), "Handbook of Applied Hydrology" (New York: McGraw-Hill Book Company, 1964), p. 24–38.

2 Harry F. Blaney and Wayne D. Criddle, Determining Consumptive Use for Planning Water Developments, "Methods for Estimating Evapotranspiration" (New York: American Society of Civil Engineers, 1966), pp. 1–34.

the excess of daily maximum temperatures over 32°F during the growing season, the interval between the last date in spring and the first date in the fall on which the temperature falls below 28°F. Numerous other formulas based on climatological data have been applied by irrigation engineers.[1]

Once the consumptive use has been estimated from a known value for another location corrected to project climatological conditions, the maximum yield may be estimated from local farm statistics. With the peak point established, the balance of a curve relating applied water to yield may be approximated from the shape found for the same crop at another location. This curve (Fig. 12-9) may then be used to develop a demand curve, as shown in Ex. 12-2.

EXAMPLE 12-2

If sugar beets grown in the Cache Valley of Utah could be grown for a fixed cost of $150 per acre and a variable cost of $5 per ton to sell for $14 per ton, develop a demand curve for irrigation water based on Fig. 12-9.

$$MPP_{ij} = \frac{MC_i}{MB_j} \qquad\qquad (4\text{-}22)$$

or the slope of the rising limb of the crop-yield–applied-water curve equals

$$\frac{P_w}{P_c - V_c} = \frac{P_w}{14 - 5} = \frac{P_w}{9}$$

Tabulated Computations

ASSUMED		READ FROM FIG. 12-9		EQ. (12-1)
P_w,	$\dfrac{P_w}{9}$,	Q,	Y,	I
$/acre-ft	$/acre-ft	acre-ft/acre	tons/acre	$/acre
0	0	2.9	23.8	64.2
9	1	2.6	23.5	38.1
18	2	2.1	23.0	19.2
36	4	1.4	21.0	−11.4
54	6	0.9	18.3	−33.9
72	8	0.3	14.0	−45.6
90	10	0.0	11.5	−46.5

By interpolation, growing sugar beets becomes unprofitable when P_w is above $29 per acre-foot. Demand curve is plotted on Fig. 12-10.

[1] J. E. Christiansen, "Estimating Pan Evaporation and Evapotranspiration from Climatic Data" (Logan: Utah State University, Water Res. Lab., 1966).

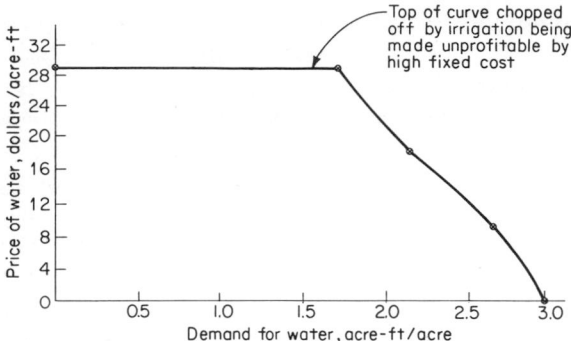

FIGURE 12-10   Demand curve for irrigation water for
sugar beets, Cache Valley, Utah.

This demand curve must then be corrected for effective precipitation P_f. Effective precipitation is the precipitation contributing to crop moisture supply and may be estimated as the average annual difference between recorded precipitation and recorded cropland runoff by using data from nearby rainfall and streamflow gages. When this data is not available, soil-moisture accounting procedures may be used.[1] The demand curve developed for irrigation water at a drier location may be corrected to a wetter location by truncating the left portion of the curve as shown in Fig. 12-11. If the correction is from a wetter to a drier location, the demand curve must be extrapolated to the left. A more refined analysis would determine the probability distribution of P_f and combine with demand curves developed from water-yield curves which follow another probability distribution to obtain a set of demand curves on an expected-value basis. Such a procedure would permit recognition of the tendency of peak water requirements to come during low-flow years. Whatever procedure used in their development, separate demand curves are needed to express water requirement as a function of price for each crop in each major soil type in the project area.

12-12   *MONTHLY CROP WATER REQUIREMENT*   The design capacity of irrigation-distribution facilities and monthly irrigation fractions for use in the reservoir operation study may be estimated from monthly consumptive use and effective-precipitation data. Monthly consumptive use may be estimated from data on crop moisture use in

---

[1]   Vaughn E. Hansen, Unique Consumptive Use Curve Related to Irrigation Practice, *Proc. ASCE*, vol. 89, no. IR 1 (March, 1963), pp. 43–50.

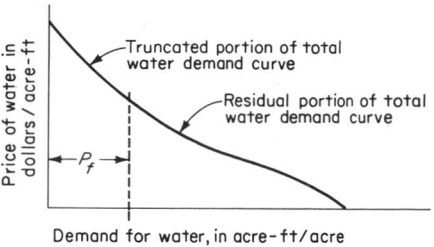

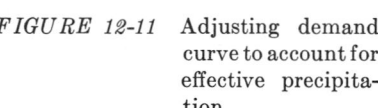

FIGURE 12-11 Adjusting demand curve to account for effective precipitation.

local test plots or more approximately by dividing the annual quantity proportional to monthly lake evaporation net of monthly effective precipitation. Data on the seasonal distribution of consumptive use show variation with plant growth from increasing values during the vegetative growth stage to high values during the flowering stage to decreasing values during the fruiting stage.[1] The monthly ratio of the economic irrigation application to consumptive use net of effective precipitation may be assumed to equal the annual ratio.

The distribution system may be designed to handle the average rate of irrigation usage during the maximum demand month. For a peak month with a demand of 5.0 in., this equals

$$\left(5\,\frac{\text{in.}}{\text{mo.}}\right)\left(\frac{1}{12}\,\frac{\text{ft}}{\text{in.}}\right)\left(\frac{1}{31}\,\frac{\text{mo.}}{\text{day}}\right)\left(\frac{1}{2}\,\frac{\text{cfs-days}}{\text{acre-ft}}\right) = 0.0067\,\frac{\text{cfs}}{\text{acre}}$$

For this month, 1.0 cfs of continuous flow provides water for 150 acres, but if water losses are accounted for, an average figure is 1.0 cfs continuous flow provides for 80 acres.

[1] *Ibid.*

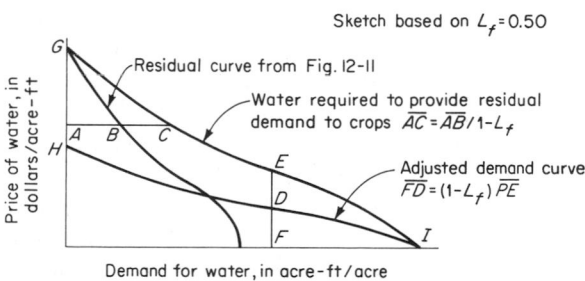

FIGURE 12-12 Adjusting demand curve to account for farm losses.

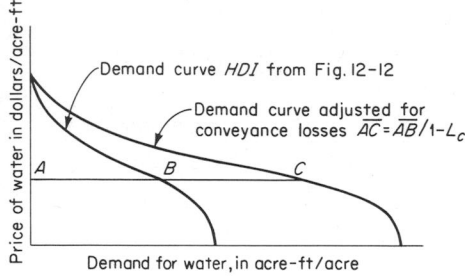

FIGURE 12-13 Adjusting demand curve to account for conveyance losses.

12-13 DISTRIBUTION LOSSES A farmer cannot irrigate without losing water between the farm headgate and the crop by deep seepage, surface runoff, or evapotranspiration from ditches and weeds. The amount of loss depends on the method of irrigation, the nature of the on-farm distribution system, and soil characteristics. Economic forces should be considered in distribution system design, but Hudson found that many farmers respond slowly to changing economic conditions because of shifting land tenure, fixed water rights, and limited information.[1] Farm losses range between 90 and 20 percent of the headgate water, with 50 percent being a reasonable mean for well-managed farms.

The demand curve is adjusted for farm losses by a two-step process (Fig. 12-12). It is first expanded horizontally to determine how much water the farmer must take at his headgate to supply the demand-curve amount to this crop by dividing the demand at each price by $1 - L_f$, where L_f is the fraction of the water lost. The result is then retracted vertically because the farmer can afford less water at a given price if some of it is lost than he can if it is all applied to crops. The effective price of water becomes $P_w/1 - L_f$, and replotting the curve on this basis is equivalent to multiplying the price for each demand by $1 - L_f$.

Additional water losses will occur upstream from the farm headgate from evapotranspiration along canals, seepage, and operational waste. The amount of loss depends on the length and type of distribution facilities and soil permeability and must be estimated for specific project conditions. Conveyance losses range from 2 percent for an all-pipe system to 40 percent for long, unlined, open ditches. The demand curve is adjusted to account for conveyance losses by the horizontal expansion process of dividing the demand at each price by $1 - L_c$, where L_c is the fraction of the water lost (Fig. 12-13). On-farm water use is governed by price, and the expanded curve indicates the diversion quantity needed to get this much to the consumer.

[1] James Hudson, "Irrigation Water Use in the Utah Valley, Utah" (Chicago: The University of Chicago Press, Department of Geography Res. Paper 79, 1962).

The project and on-farm distribution systems should be designed so that the marginal value of the water lost equals the net marginal cost of improving the system to prevent the losses. Most improvements increase construction cost, reduce maintenance cost, and cause a net increase in discounted average annual total cost. Bandini has developed a methodology for economic evaluation of canal losses.[1] Measures for evaporation, suppression, and seepage control and phreatophyte elimination should be justified by this principle. Through a series of estimates of the costs of distribution systems and the associated water losses, the marginal price of water required to justify a specific improvement may be estimated as the average annual improvement cost, corrected for differences in maintenance cost and right-of-way requirements, and divided by the amount of water saved. The results will show optimum farm and conveyance losses to vary with price as plotted in Fig. 12-14. The adjustments to the demand curve (Figs. 12-12 and 12-13) can be improved by using the values of L_f and L_c corresponding to each demand-curve price. Project optimization will produce the optimum price and quantity of water used and will thus imply specific values of L_f and L_c and a specific design required to achieve these values.

12-14 OTHER WATER REQUIREMENTS Sometimes extra irrigation water must be applied to control salinity. The excess water dilutes the concentration of soil salts and washes them downward through the soil so that they will not cake at the soil surface. The allowable salt concentration in the soil moisture [C_s in parts per million (ppm)] varies among crops and in theory could be determined by using Eq. (12-1), a curve relating crop yield to soil salt concentration,[2] and the cost of leaching water. However, the complexity of the relationship between plant

---

[1] Alfredo Bandini, Economic Problem of Irrigation Canals: Seepage Losses, *Proc. ASCE*, vol. 92, no. IR 4 (December, 1966), pp. 35–57.

[2] A literature survey with curves plus discussion is found in M. Glade Pincock, Assessing Impacts of Declining Water Quality on Gross Value Output of Agriculture: A Case Study, *Water Resources Res.*, vol. 5, no. 1 (February, 1969), pp. 1–12.

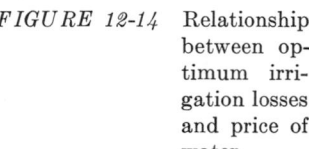 *FIGURE 12-14* Relationship between optimum irrigation losses and price of water.

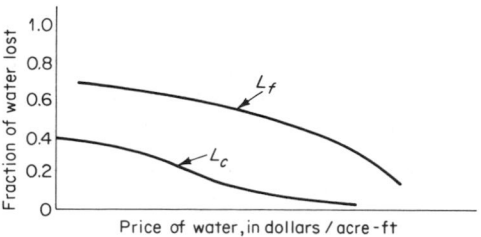

growth and soil salt accumulation complicates definition of the yield–salt-accumulation curve. An alternative approach is to select a tolerable limit for C_s and take the cost of leaching water required to maintain it as a fixed cost of crop production. If the salt concentration in the available leaching water is C_w, the quantity of water required for leaching is

$$Q_w = \frac{C_s}{C_s - C_w} Q_d \qquad (12\text{-}3)$$

where Q_w is the amount of leaching water required and Q_d is the amount of water which would be required were no leaching necessary.[1] Because the farmer must buy the leaching water, it may be incorporated in the demand curve by substituting $(C_s - C_w)(1 - L_f)/C_s$ for $(1 - L_f)$ in the adjustment of Fig. 12-12.

A supply augmented by recirculating return flows (coming from farm losses and used leaching water) will contain higher salt concentrations and will thus increase downstream leaching-water requirements. The value of recirculation is lost when the excess water required for leaching exceeds the net addition to the supply by recirculation. Because the leaching requirement depends on the crop, the recirculation of irrigation water should be considered in projecting crop distribution between upstream and downstream areas.

Additional irrigation water may be applied to cool the plants and the soil during hot periods. Also, irrigation during cold periods may reduce frost damage. Irrigation may also be used to aid germination, for pest control, or to improve crop quality. All types of irrigation should be considered in estimating project water requirements and should be employed if the expected increase in crop value exceeds the value of water used.

12-15 DEMAND CURVE The irrigation demand or marginal-benefit curve must be adjusted for the indirect or secondary benefits associated with the project (Secs. 8-6 to 8-11). Thorough analysis of such benefits requires a detailed survey of technological and pecuniary spillover effects, but the prevailing practice is to evaluate them as a fixed fraction F_i of the direct primary benefits. The fraction will vary with crops, local economic conditions, project timing with respect to employment cycles, and other spillover effects. The demand curve indicating marginal project benefit to the community is developed through expanding

[1]   Ray K. Linsley and Joseph B. Franzini, "Water-resources Engineering" (New York: McGraw-Hill Book Company, 1964), pp. 390–392.

the demand curve of marginal benefit to the user by multiplying the unit value of each demand by $1 + F_i$ (Fig. 12-15).

The series of steps outlined above can provide a demand curve for water to irrigate each crop (divided by soil type if necessary) in the projected crop pattern. The project-water-demand curve is developed from the crop-water-demand curves; the map indicating the sum of the distribution cost to provide water to, and the collection cost (Sec. 12-6) to collect waste water from, each portion of the service area; and the projected crop pattern (Sec. 12-9). Subareas of approximately equal water-distribution and waste-collection cost are outlined on the map, and a demand curve for each subarea is developed by multiplying the water used per unit area at a given price, as indicated by the crop-demand curve, by the number of acres of that crop grown within the subarea and then summing horizontally to include all the crops. The subarea-demand curve is adjusted by subtracting from each value of water the subarea sum of distribution and collection cost in dollars per acre-foot. Increasingly large amounts will be truncated from the base of the subarea-demand curve as locations become more remote, until the whole curve disappears outside the economic service area.

The irrigation-project-demand curve is the horizontal sum of the subarea-demand curves. For the intercept of the project-demand curve and the horizontal axis, the demand for zero-cost water in each subarea is determined from the individual-demand curves, and all the subarea demands are summed to get the project demand for zero-cost water. The process is repeated for increasingly higher water costs until the entire project-demand curve is developed. As an alternate to the detailed analysis outlined above, many approximate methods for developing

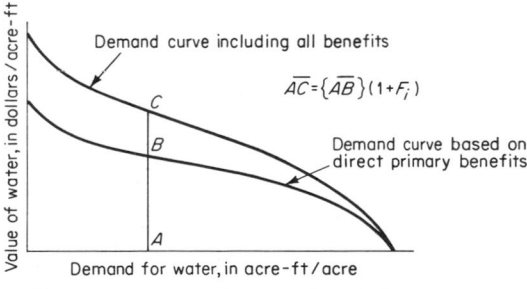

FIGURE 12-15 Adjusting demand curve to account for nonprimary benefits.

irrigation-demand curves are available for use in preliminary studies or as a check against serious error.[1]

Estimating Urban Demand

The benefits from urban water supply are determined by the value of the additional water provided as implied from data relating use and price for municipal users.

12-16   URBAN USE AT BASE PRICE   A given city has a water use record from which per capita use and prices can be estimated for a series of historical years. Average daily urban use in the United States is 140 gallons per capita per day (gpcd), with individual communities ranging between 50 and 500 gpcd. Urban use is larger in warm, dry climates than in cool, humid ones. It increases with the standard of living and with the pressure maintained in the lines. Other factors affecting water use are metering, water quality, the extent of the sewerage system, and the efficiency of system management. While future water use may be predicted as the product of projected community population and per capita use based on current practice, better results can be obtained by subdividing users into types.

Where water metering records are available, historical use may be divided among households, industry, commercial establishments, and public facilities. Household use depends on climate, the number of people per household, the economic status of the population, whether the water is metered, and if it is on water rates. The normal range is 70 to 90 gpcd, but an analysis of 39 residential study areas disclosed a range of 47 to 437 gpcd average annual use with a range in the ratio of peak hour to average use of 2.47 to 16.50.[2] Higher peak-to-average ratios were found where substantial lawn sprinkling is practiced, because sprinkling is seasonal, while indoor use remains more constant over the year.

Industrial use varies widely among industries, and statistics on average use per unit of production are available for a number of them

---

[1]   John Ernest Flack, "Water Rights Transfers: An Engineering Approach" (Stanford, Calif.: Stanford University, Institute in Engineering Economic Systems (EEP-15, 1965), pp. 66–96.

[2]   Charles W. Howe and F. P. Linaweaver, The Impact of Price on Residential Water Demand and Its Relation to System Design and Price Structure, *Water Resources Res.*, vol. 3, no. 1 (1st Quarter, 1967), pp. 13–32.

(Table 12-2).[1] The wide range of values shown for a given product indicates the degree to which other factors of production can be substituted for water as price increases.

Commercial use includes water used by office buildings, warehouses, and stores. Average demand for such areas is about 25 gpcd. A more refined estimate can be made from the sum of the products of the number of commercial establishments and unit water use by establishment type.

Public use includes water supplied to parks, golf courses, schools, hospitals, churches, and other public facilities. A typical city uses about 25 gpcd. The greatest variation is in the amount used for watering parks and golf courses, which is governed by the amount of land devoted to these purposes. The consumptive use by grass may be estimated by the methods used for agricultural crops.

A given city can determine its current per capita use, adjust it for expected changes in local demand, and multiply by projected population (Sec. 9-2) to estimate water requirements for a series of future dates (Fig. 12-16). The approach might be refined by establishing separate requirements by the four major types of use and summing. If the resulting water requirements as a function of time are viewed by the planner as a fixed quantity of water which must be supplied, economic analysis is only a search for the least costly supply. New projects must be built with sufficient lead time to keep projected requirements from surpassing the avail-

[1] Industrial Research and Extension Center, "Industrial Water Requirements" (Little Rock: University of Arkansas College of Business Administration, 1963), pp. 14–17.

TABLE 12-2   Ranges of Gross Water Use per Unit of Product

Product	Unit of production	Typical water use, gal/unit
Beet sugar	100 lb	76–3,200
Salt	Ton	6–640
Distilling	Proof gallon	125–167
Soap	Case	3–100
Detergents	Drum	33–38
Tanning	Square foot	0.2–64
Petroleum refining	Barrel	500–3,247
Steel	Ton	3,544–24,798
Coal	Ton	1–1,000

SOURCE: Charles W. Howe, Crises Decision Making in American Water Development, "Eleventh Annual New Mexico Water Conference" (University Park, N. M.: Water Resources Research Institute, New Mexico State University, 1966), p. 38.

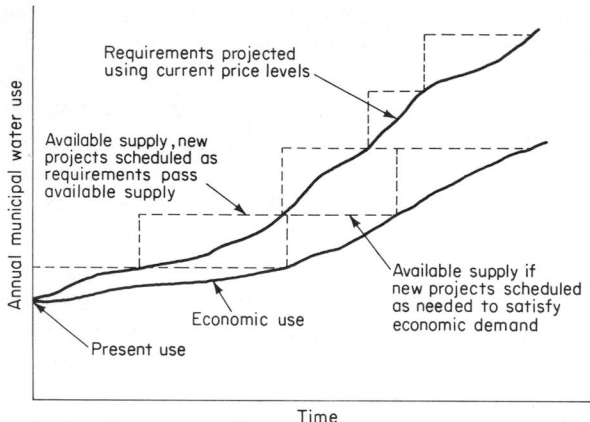

FIGURE 12-16 Projection of municipal water use.

able supply. However, the requirements approach as commonly used overlooks the relationship between per capita demand and price and thus ignores the question of optimum per capita water use. It has encouraged the "carefree impression that water is practically free, and the frequently mistaken premise that additional supplies cost less than would measures of economy."[1] By the law of supply and demand, water will be inexpensive when it is abundant and expensive when it is scarce. People will use less water as it becomes more expensive. It makes little sense to project future use of expensive water from per capita figures for the present use of the inexpensive water. It is no wonder that projected water use based on the requirements approach indicates a severe future water shortage.

12-17   DEMAND CURVE   Economic efficiency is only going to be achieved if the projected water requirement is viewed as but one point on a demand curve, the usage for the current price of water. Usage will increase at lower prices and decrease at higher prices. While research in developing demand curves for urban water is still in the formulative stage, empirical studies based on cities of comparable climatological and industrial setting but charging different water rates or studies based on usage changes in a given city after a change in rates provide a helpful starting point.

[1]   Hans H. Landsberg, "Natural Resources for U.S. Growth" (Baltimore: The Johns Hopkins Press, 1965), p. 126.

The elasticity of demand for household water (Sec. 3-4) seems to stem primarily from quicker repair and reduced yard watering, as use inside the home does not change much. Investigators have found the price elasticity of demand for residential water to be about -0.35.[1] When subdivided by use type, the price elasticity of demand was found by Howe and Lina-weaver to be about -0.23 for domestic water, -0.7 for sprinkling demand in arid areas, and -1.6 for sprinkling demand in humid areas. Thus, residential water demand is much more elastic in humid than in arid climates, but price does have a significant effect on water use in either kind of area.

As an alternative approach for industrial water use, a demand curve might be developed from the industry's production function (Sec. 4-2). When the price of water gets high enough to make it worthwhile, industry will recirculate greater quantities of water and substitute non-water-using procedures in the production process.[2] A steel mill in California reduced its water requirements from 35,000 to 1,400 gal/ton of steel by recirculation. About 80 percent of all industrial consumption is for cooling, for which saline water or air may be substituted. Petroleum refining is rapidly substituting air cooling. A demand curve of the water required by a particular industry is estimated by studying the function of water usage in alternative production processes and the degree to which processes using less water can be substituted.

If requirement projections indicate a water usage Q_b at price P_b for a use where the price elasticity of demand is estimated to be E, Eq. (3-1) can be integrated to obtain the demand curve for the range of values in which elasticity can be assumed to remain constant.

$$\int \frac{dP}{P} = -\frac{1}{E} \int \frac{dQ}{Q} \tag{12-4}$$

$$\ln P = -\frac{1}{E} \ln Q + C_1 \tag{12-5}$$

By taking the exponential of both sides of the equation and setting the integration constant so the curve will pass through the known point Q_b, P_b,

$$P = P_b \frac{Q_b^{1/E}}{Q^{1/E}} \tag{12-6}$$

Where separate demand curves are developed by urban use, they may be combined by the horizontal summation process used to combine

---

[1] Studies which have been made to determine the effect of price on urban water use are summarized in Flack, *op. cit.*, pp. 49–63.

[2] Blair T. Bower, The Economics of Industrial Water Utilization, in Allen V. Kneese and Stephen C. Smith (eds.), "Water Research" (Baltimore: The Johns Hopkins Press, 1966), pp. 143–173.

demands for market goods (Sec. 3-12). The combined curve must be corrected for conveyance losses, which average 15 percent of demand (Fig. 12-13). The urban demand curve must also be adjusted for the ratio of other benefit to direct primary benefit, as shown in (Fig. 12-15). The rules developed for flood control (Sec. 10-12) may be applied to estimate benefits to new development that is attracted by a better water supply. Distribution and sewerage costs may be handled by dividing the total urban area into subareas in the same manner used for irrigation demand.

12-18 BENEFITS FROM URBAN WATER SUPPLY As a more reasonable alternative to the requirements approach of projecting demand from current usage rates and estimating the benefit as the cost of the second-least-expensive supply, the benefits of a project to increase the level of municipal water supply can be estimated as the area under the demand curve from the usage without the project, Q_1, to that with the project, Q_2, ideally the economic use (Fig. 12-17).

$$B = \int_{Q_1}^{Q_2} P \, dQ = \int_{Q_1}^{Q_2} P_b Q_b^{1/E} \frac{dQ}{Q^{1/E}} \tag{12-7}$$

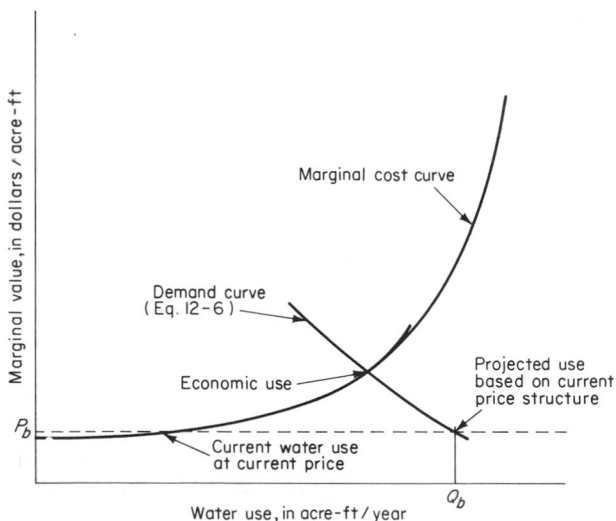

FIGURE 12-17 Typical marginal curves for municipal water supply.

If E is not equal to 1, integration gives

$$B = \frac{P_b Q_b^{1/E}}{1 - 1/E} \left(\frac{Q_2}{Q_2^{1/E}} - \frac{Q_1}{Q_1^{1/E}} \right) \tag{12-8}$$

If E equals 1, the result is

$$B = P_b Q_b \ln \frac{Q_2}{Q_1} \tag{12-9}$$

EXAMPLE 12-3

The long-run marginal cost (dollars per acre-foot) of supplying water to users in a city of 5,000 population equals $10 - 0.002A + 0.000003A^2$, where A is the annual water usage in acre-feet. The city currently supplies about 1,000 acre-ft annually at a price of \$10 per acre-foot. A period of rapid growth over the next few years is expected to increase annual usage to 4,000 acre-ft based on the current price. Annual use is then expected to stabilize for many years. However, the community's price elasticity of demand for water is estimated to be 0.4. The fixed annual cost of a water supply project is estimated to be \$50,000. In the following calculations, conveyance losses and other than direct primary benefits are neglected.

1 What would be the marginal cost if all 4,000 acre-ft were supplied?

$10 - 0.002(4,000) + 0.000003(4,000)^2 = \$50$ per acre-foot

2 What would be the cost of supplying the additional 3,000 acre-ft?

$$C = 50,000 + \int_{1,000}^{4,000} (10 - 0.002A + 0.000003A^2)\, dA$$

$\quad = 50,000 + 10(4,000) - 0.001(4,000)^2 + 0.000001(4,000)^3$
$\qquad\qquad\qquad\quad - 10(1,000) + 0.001(1,000)^2 - 0.000001(1,000)^3$

$\quad = 50,000 + 4,000 - 16,000 + 64,000 - 10,000 + 1,000 - 1,000$

$\quad = \$128,000$ per year

3 Assuming constant demand elasticity over this range, what would project benefits be?

$$B = \frac{10(4,000^{2.5})}{1 - 2.5} \left(\frac{4,000}{4,000^{2.5}} - \frac{1,000}{1,000^{2.5}} \right) = \$186,700 \text{ per year} \tag{12-8}$$

4 What is the optimum project size for supplying additional water?
For optimum project size, $MC = MB$ [Eq. (12-6)],

$$10 \frac{4,000^{2.5}}{Q^{2.5}} = 10 - 0.002Q + 0.00003Q^2$$

Trial and error solution for Q gives 2,706 acre-ft/year. Supply 1,706 acre-ft/year at $P = \$26.56$ per acre-foot.

5 What are the cost and benefits of the optimum supply project?

$$C = 50,000 + \int_{1,000}^{2,706} (10 - 0.002A + 0.000003A^2)\, dA = \$79,600$$

per year

$$B = \frac{10(4,000^{2.5})}{1 - 2.5} \left(\frac{2,706}{2,706^{2.5}} - \frac{1,000}{1,000^{2.5}} \right) = \$165,400 \text{ per year}$$

Net benefits are increased from $58,700 per year to $85,800 per year when compared with the requirements approach.

6 If conveyance losses amount to 15 percent and community benefits equal 25 percent of direct benefits, what would be the optimum project size?

The benefits are increased by 25 percent and the required water development by 15 percent to change the marginal equation to

$$12.5 \frac{4,000^{2.5}}{Q^{2.5}} = 10 - 0.002(1.15Q) + 0.000003(1.15Q)^2$$

Trial-and-error solution for Q gives $Q = 2,713$ acre-ft/year. Supply 1,713 acre-ft/year additional water.

$2,713(1.15) = 3,120$ acre-ft/year required from source.

For $Q = 3,120$, $P = 32.96(1.15)/1.25 = \$30.32$ per acre-foot.

Example 12-3 illustrates how marginal economic analysis can be used to estimate benefits from municipal water supply. The elasticity used should be weighted according to the distribution of water use among use types. Alternatively, separate demand curves and elasticities could be developed by use type and horizontal summations made to estimate total demand. The procedure only assumes the price elasticity of demand to be constant over the range of the proposed additional water supply and thus avoids the difficulties in estimating elasticity as the total supply drops toward zero, as would be required to estimate the total value of a water supply to a community.

A typical community in planning for its future water supply is faced with increasing long-run marginal costs as it must go greater distances to obtain a suitable supply. Simultaneously population growth and technological innovation are increasing water requirements. Projected future water usage based on the requirements approach provides reasonable results as long as water is sufficiently plentiful so that the marginal-cost curve is not rising too rapidly. Severe overdesign results as the shortage of local water becomes more severe. The economic use is less than the use projected on a requirements basis (Fig. 12-17). Economic use when plotted against time will lag behind requirements projections (Fig. 12-16). The alternative cost approach to project justification will lead to projects' being built too big and too soon.

While the demand-curve approach suffers from a shortage of data relating urban water use to price, it provides the only real promise of realistic benefit evaluation. Much better information is needed on water usage and price elasticity of demand by type of use so that better demand curves can be constructed.

Project Feasibility

12-19 ECONOMIC FEASIBILITY The optimum scale of a water supply project is determined by equating the marginal cost of providing the water with the marginal benefit received. The irrigation-demand curve typically includes large amounts of low-value water, while the urban-demand curve typically includes smaller amounts of high-value water (Fig. 12-18). The two demand curves are combined by horizontal addition as a given volume of water can only be put to one of the two uses. Project cost is represented by the area under the marginal-cost curve to the left of its intersection with the combined marginal-benefit curve. Irrigation benefit is represented by the area under the irrigation-marginal-benefit curve to the left of the point where the curve crosses the equilibrium value.

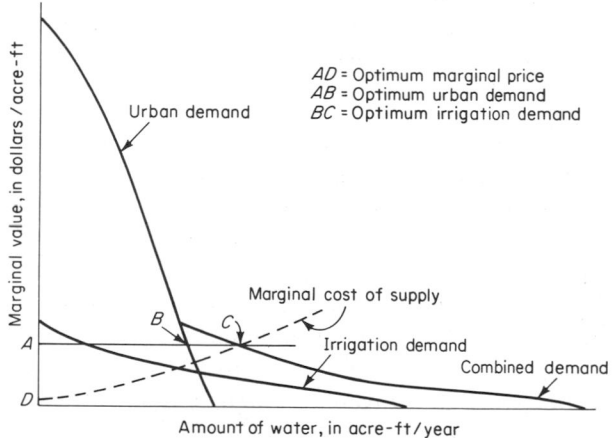

FIGURE 12-18 Typical combination of supply and demand curves.

Urban water supply benefits are correspondingly represented by their marginal-benefit curve. One can complete the design of the optimum project by going backward through the procedures by which the marginal curves were formed to find the supply facilities and satisfied demands associated with the optimum point.

Because of the relative shapes of the demand curves for urban and irrigation water, the average value of urban water tends to be much higher than the average value of irrigation water even when their marginal values are equal. A study of the Rio Grande Basin in New Mexico found the average value of irrigation water to be about $48 and the average value of industrial water to be about $3,500 per acre-foot.[1] While the older and thus higher-priority appropriation water rights possessed by irrigators cause the marginal value of urban water to exceed that of irrigation water, it does not necessarily follow that municipalities could profitably absorb all the water used by agriculture. A thorough analysis of the respective demand curves is required to determine the economically efficient allocation of water among alternative uses.

When a project diverts water from alternative uses (even including incidental use for wild flooding, waste dilution, or fish and wildlife), the marginal cost is the cost of developing the supply plus the opportunity cost of the appropriated water. The opportunity cost of water is the value realized through the use it would have were the development works not built. If the alternative use were secured by transferable water rights, the value of the water would be the cost for which the rights could be purchased. The value of water diverted from many uses may be estimated by benefit analysis appropriate to the particular use. Opportunity cost is more difficult to evaluate for water used for waste carrying, fish and wildlife, esthetics, and incidental wild flooding.

12-20   FINANCIAL FEASIBILITY   Current federal policy for project repayment[2] has allowed irrigators to pay as little as 10 percent of the marginal cost of supply. Irrigators are not required to pay interest cost. They need not repay separable irrigation costs (Sec. 23-7) if these can be paid from hydroelectric power revenues or by excess revenues generated by older projects which have been highly successful financially (basin accounts). Charges may be reduced even further if they would otherwise exceed the net benefit to irrigators less an incentive income to induce conversion from dry farming to irrigated agriculture. Estimation of incentive

---

[1]   Nathaniel Wollman (ed.), "The Value of Water in Alternative Uses" (Albuquerque: University of New Mexico Press, 1962).

[2]   Repayment of Project Costs, "Project Planning, Part 116: Economic Investigations," *U.S. Bur. Reclamation*, Ser. 110, chap. 6 (July, 1959).

income and thus repayment capacity is obtained from increased farm income less a fair return on farm investment, labor, and management. The practice of charging less than marginal cost to reduce charges to irrigators is also followed by irrigation districts as they sell power or collect property taxes. In practice, the financial feasibility of an irrigation project is determined by ability to reach a mutually acceptable compromise between irrigators' willingness to pay and federal rules limiting maximum subsidies.

Urban water charges may also be reduced by assumption of part of the financial obligation by tax revenues or by income from other municipal utilities. In other cases, high water rates are used to pay for many other municipal services. Municipal and industrial water developed in federal projects must pay for its full cost at the federal discount rate except that where the water is reserved for future use, no interest need be paid for up to 10 years. A common practice is for a water supply agency to charge more for urban than for irrigation water. Charging less than marginal cost encourages uneconomic overuse of developed water supplies and contributes to water shortages.

SELECTED REFERENCES

Bowden, Leonard W.: "Diffusion of the Decision to Irrigate" (Chicago: The University of Chicago Press, Department of Geography Res. Paper 97, 1965).

Bower, Blair T.: The Economics of Industrial Water Utilization, in Allen V. Kneese and Stephen C. Smith (eds.), "Water Research" (Baltimore: The Johns Hopkins Press, 1966), pp. 143–173.

Clark, Colin: "The Economics of Irrigation" (Oxford: Pergamon Press, 1967).

Davis, R. K.: Water Supply Economics in the Potomac River Basin, *J. Am. Water Works Assoc.*, vol. 56 (1964), p. 257.

Eckstein, Otto: "Water Resource Development: The Economics of Project Evaluation" (Cambridge, Mass.: Harvard University Press, 1958), pp. 192–236.

Flack, John Ernest: "Water Rights Transfers: An Engineering Approach" (Stanford, Calif.: Stanford University, Institute in Engineering Economic Systems, EEP-15, 1965).

Houk, Ivan E.: "Irrigation Engineering" (New York: John Wiley & Sons, Inc., 1956).

Howe, Charles W., and F. P. Linaweaver: The Impact of Price on Residential Water Demand and Its Relation to System Design and Price Structure, *Water Resources Res.*, vol. 3, no. 1 (1st Quarter, 1967), pp. 13–32.

Huffman, R. E.: "Irrigation Development and Public Water Policy" (New York: The Ronald Press Company, 1953).

Kuiper, Edward: "Water Resources Development: Engineering, Economics and Planning" (Washington: Butterworth & Co. (Publishers), Ltd., 1965), pp. 339–365, 387–404.

Milliman, J. W.: Policy Horizons for Future Urban Water Supply, *Land Economics*, vol. 39 (May, 1963).

Spiegler, K. S.: "Principles of Desalination" (New York: Academic Press, Inc., 1966).

Todd, David K.: Economics of Ground Water Recharge, *Proc. ASCE*, vol. 91, no. HY 4 (July, 1965), pp. 249–270.

Wollman, Nathaniel (ed): "The Value of Water in Alternative Uses" (Albuquerque: University of New Mexico Press, 1962).

PROBLEMS

12-1 Use a series of monthly streamflows and the methodology of Ex. 12-1:

a Develop a curve of firm annual yield vs. reservoir capacity (Fig. 12-2).

b For three selected reservoir capacities and based on the rule that secondary water can be withdrawn from the reservoir as long as the remaining storage does not drop below that of the corresponding month of the critical dry period, develop curves of secondary yield vs. percent of time available (Fig. 12-4).

c Develop from the above results a curve of adjusted yield vs. system cost (Fig. 12-7). Use Fig. 12-5 to estimate the relative value of secondary water. Estimate the cost of the reservoir having a capacity equal to the average annual runoff of $20 per acre-foot of storage. Cost per acre-foot of storage by ratio of reservoir capacity to average annual runoff is as follows:

Ratio:	0.2	0.4	0.6	0.8	1.0	1.2	1.4	1.6	1.8	2.0
$/acre-ft:	80.0	40.0	28.0	23.0	20.0	20.5	22.0	25.0	30.0	40.0

The series of monthly streamflows may be taken from a historical record or generated on a probability basis from a historical record (Chap. 20). If a synthesized streamflow record is used, monthly rainfalls should be developed by correlation with monthly streamflows to establish a rainfall commensurate with the generated streamflow.

12-2 A farmer in the Cache Valley of Utah raises sugar beets and markets them at $14 per ton. His fixed operating costs are $100 per acre annually, and the cost of water is $3.50 per acre-foot. Using

Fig. 12-9 and a variable cost of $5 per ton, determine the total amount of water per acre the farmer should use annually for optimum return. What amount of water should be used if the water cost is $20 per acre-foot, and all other costs remain the same?

12-3   The water supply in a given area is divided between rural and urban users. The demand curve for urban water is represented by the equation $P + 9Y = 36$. The demand curve for rural water is represented by the equation $5P + Y = 50$. P is the price per acre-foot of water, and Y is the quantity in 1,000 acre-ft. The water supply costs are represented by the equation $P = 2 + Y$. How much water should be supplied to each type of user? What price should the water be sold for? For this point, what are the gross receipts? The gross benefits? The net benefits? How much of the net benefits are realized by the rural area? The urban area? The producer? What is the benefit-cost ratio of the project? If costs are allocated by the use of facilities method, what would the benefit-cost ratio for rural users be? Urban users?

12-4   A water supply reservoir is being considered to supply both irrigation and urban water. The demand curve for urban water is expressed by $2V + A_u = 1,000$, where V is the marginal value and A_u is the annual quantity supplied. The demand curve for irrigation water is expressed by $20V + A_i = 1,000$. The total annual cost of supplying the water is expressed by

$$TC = 100 + 1.0A - 0.001A^2 + 0.000001A^3.$$

a   Write the equation of the average-cost curve.
b   Write the equation of the marginal-cost curve.
c   Should the two demands be added as market goods or collective goods?
d   How much urban water should be supplied before any irrigation water is supplied at all?
e   What two equations comprise the total-demand curve?
f   What is the optimum reservoir yield?
g   How should this total be divided between urban and irrigation users?
h   What is total-project cost?

12-5   Solve Ex. 12-3, assuming projected future usage were divided with 1,500 acre-ft/year for residential use having an elasticity of 0.25 and 2,500 acre-ft/year for industrial use having an elasticity of 0.5. Assume that any available supply will be divided between the uses on the basis of equal marginal cost.

12-6   From typical statewide topography and 1964 construction costs, the first cost of reservoir construction in Illinois has been estimated on an average to equal $9161S^{0.54} + 49S^{0.87}k$, where S is storage in acre-feet and k is the cost of right-cf-way in dollars per acre.[1] Use a k of \$1,000 per acre and the data of Ex. 12-1 to develop a curve of marginal reservoir cost vs. firm yield in acre-feet per year.

12-7   Plot a curve of the elasticity of demand for irrigation water vs. price based on Ex. 12-2.

[1]   J. H. Dawes and Magne Wathne, Cost of Reservoirs in Illinois, *Illinois State Water Surv., Circ. 96* (1968).

CHAPTER THIRTEEN

HYDROELECTRIC POWER

The Planning Context

13-1 DEFINITION Electric power technology provides the generation of electrical energy at a central location, its almost instantaneous transmission to widely dispersed areas, and its conversion into motion, heat, or light for a multitude of uses in homes, offices, and factories. Advancing technology in the generation, transmission, and conversion of electrical energy has instigated some of the most revolutionary changes in modern society.

Falling water is only one possible energy source for generating electricity. The other major source is thermal energy released during the cooling phase of a steam cycle. Thermoelectric power can be classified according to the fuel used to apply heat within the cycle. Fossil fuel plants use coal or petroleum products. Nuclear plants use atomic fuel (usually the radioactive metals such as uranium, thorium, or plutonium or their compounds or various ceramic materials) in one of a number of possible different kinds of reactors. Sometimes fossil fuels are used in diesel or gas turbine plants which do not depend on a steam cycle. A small amount of electricity is generated from wind, tidal, chemical, geothermal, or solar energy.

13-2 HISTORICAL DEVELOPMENT Thermal generation began at the Pearl Street plant in New York City in 1881. The first hydroelectric plant was built the following year in Wisconsin. Thermal generation predominated during the next 30 years because losses from early inefficient transmission could be avoided by generating close to demand centers.

Improved transmission efficiency and a temporary fuel shortage encouraged the rapid development of the relatively more distant hydroelectric sites after 1910. More recently, improved steam plant efficiency and a scarcity of new hydroelectric sites has restored thermal generation to the predominate method.

Total installed capacity in the United States by generation method is given on Table 13-1 for 1966 along with figures projected by the Federal Power Commission for 1980. Also provided is the percentage of total generating capacity in hydroelectric power for selected countries. Nuclear capacity is expected to increase at the expense of fossil fuels as the efficiency of nuclear plants and the cost of fossil fuels increase. Fossil fuel use is expected to shift toward the more abundant and less costly lower-grade fuels. Economies of scale have greatly increased the optimum thermal generating plant size.

13-3   SELECTING THE METHOD OF GENERATION   The time pattern of generation must duplicate the time pattern of demand (Fig. 13-1) because electric energy cannot be economically stored on a large

TABLE 13-1   Total Generating Capacity in the United States

Type of plant	1966		1980		GROWTH	
	Capacity, million kw	Per-cent of total	Capacity, million kw	Per-cent of total	Capacity, million kw	Per-cent of total
Hydroelectric	42.6	19.1	75.8	14.5	33.2	11.0
Fossil fuel	172.1	77.3	352.0	67.3	179.9	59.9
Pumped storage	1.1	0.5	19.0	3.6	17.9	6.0
Nuclear	2.6	1.2	69.3	13.3	66.7	22.2
Other	4.3	1.9	6.9	1.3	2.6	0.9
Total	222.7	100.0	523.0	100.0	300.3	100.0

Hydro Capacity as a Fraction of Total
Generating Capacity for Selected Countries

United States	19	Philippines	35
Brazil	80	Australia	25
Argentina	10	New Zealand	80
Egypt	35	Norway	98
India	33	U.S.S.R.	20
Japan	53	United Kingdom	3
France	47	West Germany	12
Italy	72	Poland	1

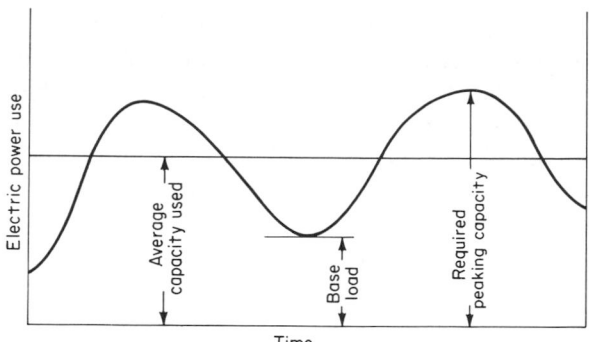

FIGURE 13-1   Typical electric-power-requirement curve.

scale. Base load is energy required continuously for many hours. Peaking power supplies the fluctuating portion of the energy requirement. Hydroelectric plants have a major advantage in that generation rates can be varied quickly and inexpensively in response to fluctuating energy usage by simply regulating the flow of water through the plant. The rate of energy transfer through the steam cycle is more difficult to vary. Large boilers must be raised to the proper temperature. Consequently, steam plants are much more expensive to maintain in a state of readiness to generate. When thermal power must be used for peaking capacity, it is less costly to use smaller diesel or gas turbine units having lower fixed cost. A smaller plant uses fuel less efficiently, but fuel cost becomes a relatively smaller portion of the total as the plant is operated less often.

Hydroelectric generation usually predominates wherever sufficient falling water is available to supply the demand. As power requirements increase, hydro plants are shifted to generate peaking power and new thermal plants are constructed to generate the base load. Where hydro sites are too few to even provide peaking capacity, pumped storage is used. A pumped-storage plant uses power generated during low-demand periods to pump water to a high reservoir for later release through the turbines to generate peaking power. Such plants are most economical where two low-cost reservoir sites are available at a high head differential.

The economic advantage between fossil and nuclear fuels is largely determined by fuel cost and the size of the generating unit. In the United States, the cost of fossil fuel ranges between 18 and 45 cents per million Btu of supplied energy. The lowest costs surround the coal fields between western Pennsylvania and northern Alabama and the oil fields of Texas and Oklahoma. The highest costs are in the Pacific Northwest and New England. With 1965 technology, nuclear generation becomes competitive at fossil fuel costs of about 25 cents per million Btu.[1] The larger the generating capacity, the relatively less economical thermal generation becomes in comparison with nuclear generation. In 1966, the break-even point in New York State was for a plant size of around 500,000 kw. The economies of scale made possible by increased use of electricity will favor nuclear-generated power. Because the cost of a nuclear power plant is relatively independent of the amount of electricity generated, the most economical operation of a combined nuclear–fossil fuel system is to save on capacity cost by using nuclear plants for the base load and to save on fuel cost by using fossil fuel plants for peaking power.

A number of factors influence the choice between thermal and hydroelectric generation. Hydroelectric plants have a much higher first cost because of the expense of the dam and appurtenances, the reservoir right-of-way, and the relocation of flooded facilities. However, annual operating costs are much higher for thermal plants. Hydroelectric plants can be operated with minimum manpower or even be automated for remote control. The cost of water is minor because the water can be used for other purposes after passing through the turbines. Pumped-storage plants have a fuel cost equal to the value of the off-peak thermal power used for pumping. Hydroelectric plants normally have smaller tax and insurance costs because they tend to be located in more isolated areas where lower tax rates apply and because a smaller portion of the plant is insurable. The greater isolation of hydroelectric plants increases the expense of transmission facilities and transmission losses. In addition, many of the best sites have considerable scenic beauty, and the lost amenities must be considered in the analysis.[2]

A thermal plant (both nuclear and fossil fuel) requires 40 to 80 gal (depending on water temperature) of cooling water for its condensers per kilowatthour of electricity generated. Thermal plants are second only to irrigation in the United States in the volume of water used, but only 1 part in 200 is consumed by evaporation losses. If the cooling water is returned directly to the stream, it increases the temperature, which is harmful to cold-water fish, reduces dissolved oxygen content and hence the capacity of the stream to assimilate degradable wastes, and limits use of the water for industrial cooling by others. However, these ill effects can be substantially reduced by discharging the warm water into a tower for atmospheric cooling and then reusing the water. About 20 percent of the cooling water used in the United States is currently recirculated through

---

[1] R. N. Bergstrom, Has Nuclear Power Become Competitive? *Civil Eng.*, vol. 35 (February, 1965), p. 32.
[2] T. A. L. Paton and J. Guthrie Brown, "Power from Water" (London: Leonard Hill Books, 1961), pp. 175–181.

cooling towers, and the percentage will increase substantially as stream temperature requirements and water supplies become more critical. Cooling towers can be economically justified by their mitigation of the adverse consequences of increasing stream heat content or by reducing transmission cost by permitting construction of a thermal plant adjacent to a smaller cooling-water supply. In short, thermoelectric generation must be coordinated with water quality management. Potential atmospheric pollution from incomplete combustion of fossil fuels or improper disposal of nuclear wastes must also be considered.

Developing the Supply

13-4 HYDROELECTRIC PLANT TERMINOLOGY Hydroelectric plants utilize the power from the kinetic energy of falling water as expressed by the equation

$$P = \frac{Q\gamma H}{550} \tag{13-1}$$

where P is the power in horsepower, Q is the flow in cubic feet per second, γ is the density of water or 62.4 lb/cu ft, and H is the head in feet. Power may also be expressed in kilowatts; 1 hp equals 0.746 kw. The capacity of a generating facility or the maximum rate at which the plant can produce electrical energy is measured in kilowatts. The generating capacity must exceed the peak rate of energy use to prevent periodic shortages. Because peaking capacity depends on the available head [Eq. (13-1)], it is advantageous to keep storage reservoirs fairly full. The energy generated in kilowatthours is represented by the area under a time plot of kilowatts produced (Fig. 13-1). The *load factor* is the ratio of the energy produced to the energy which would be produced were the plant run continuously at the peak demand rate, the ratio of average demand to peak demand. The amount of energy a hydroelectric plant can produce is limited by the volume of available water. Thus, a hydroelectric plant must have sufficient head to generate for peak rates of power usage and sufficient storage to supply water to generate long-term energy requirements.

The degree of river basin hydroelectric development may be expressed as the fraction of the energy of falling water converted into electrical energy. The potential hydroelectric power within a river basin is

$$E = \frac{\gamma}{550} \sum QHt \tag{13-2}$$

where Qt, the product of flow rate and time, equals the volume of flow. Equation (13-2) can be evaluated by dividing a stream system into reaches, determining the volume-head product for each, and summing. If all head loss occurred within power plants, the energy would be fully developed, a condition approached where the headwater of each reservoir reaches to the foot of the next dam upstream. At the end of 1962, there had been installed 38,600,000 of the 121,350,000 kw, or 31.8 percent of the potential in the United States. Over half the potential has been installed in Sweden, Switzerland, and a few other countries. On a worldwide basis, 181 million of a potential 2,724 million kw, or 6.65 percent, has been installed. Economic analysis shows that potential hydroelectric power should be developed only where a market exists for energy sold at marginal production cost and where thermal power cannot be generated at less cost.

The *firm power* capacity of a hydroelectric plant is the maximum annual rate at which energy can be generated without interruption during the critical dry period (Sec. 12-3). Firm power is supplied to all residential and commercial customers. *Secondary power* cannot be guaranteed but is available more than half the time. It is usually sold at about half the firm-power rate to industrial plants which find it less expensive to suspend operations during power shortages than to pay the higher rates for firm power. *Dump power* is available less than half the time. It is sold at very low rates to industries which can use large blocks of temporary power. Rates for secondary and dump power would ideally monotonically increase with the fraction of the time the power is available.

13-5 HYDROELECTRIC PLANT TECHNOLOGY A *run-of-river* plant depends entirely on unregulated river flow. Run-of-river plants are only practical on streams with substantial natural flow throughout dry seasons or at locations downstream from storage reservoirs. *Pondage plants* store nighttime flows to generate energy during the peak hours of the following day. *Seasonal storage plants* store wet-season flows for release during the subsequent dry season. *Cyclic storage plants* store enough water to last several years during extended dry periods.

If the powerhouse is at the foot of the dam, the water flows directly from the reservoir through trashracks, which keep out debris large enough to harm the turbine runner, into the penstock leading to the powerhouse. Often sufficient additional head to justify the required conveyance facilities can be gained by locating the powerhouse downstream from the dam to take advantage of the intervening river fall. The energy of the falling water coming through the penstock is converted into the energy of a rotating shaft by a turbine. This energy is then converted into electrical energy by an alternating-current synchronous generator. Current generated to alternate at a frequency of 60 cycles/sec is standard in the United States and must be maintained for clocks and other electric timing devices to function properly. Occasionally a lower frequency is used temporarily to conserve water during power shortages. The output of the generator is measured in kilovolt-amperes and must be multiplied by a *power factor* to get the kilowatts of output. The power factor usually is between 0.8 and 0.9 and would be 1.0 if the capacitance of the load exactly equaled the inductance, but most loads have excess inductance. Power users having very low power factors are normally required to improve the inductance-capacitance balance or pay higher rates. Downstream from the power plant, an afterbay is required to prevent the discharge hydrograph from following the evening peaks and early morning low flows characteristic of power generation.

13-6   HYDROELECTRIC PLANT EFFICIENCY   Generating efficiency is restricted by mechanical losses within each phase of the energy conversion. Overall *mechanical efficiency* equals the output of electrical energy divided by the potential energy lost by the falling water. It equals the product of the mechanical efficiencies of the individual components (penstock, turbine, and generator), usually about 75 percent. In a pumped-storage plant, efficiencies of the pump motor, the pump, and the penstock under reverse flow must also be included to give an overall mechanical efficiency of about 50 percent. Plant mechanical efficiency should be multiplied by the right side of Eq. (13-1) when estimating the power-generating capacity.

The *economic efficiency* of a pumped-storage plant is the value of the power used in pumping divided into the value of the power generated. It equals the product of the mechanical efficiency and the ratio of the unit prices of output to input power. Economic efficiency must exceed 1 for pumped storage to make economic sense, and values of 4 to 6 are not uncommon. At the margin, power of increasing incremental value should be used for pumping until incremental economic efficiency drops to 1.

13-7   POWER TRANSMISSION   Electrical energy travels from the power plant to the point of use through electrical conductors or transmission lines. The power loss in transmission is proportional to RI^2, where R is conductor resistance and I is the magnitude of the electric current. The amount of power transmitted is proportional to EI, where E is the electromotive force. Thus, an increase in E permits transmission of the same amount of power with a reduced I and hence reduced transmission losses. However, the cost of insulation and controlling adverse electromagnetic fields mount as transmission voltage is increased. Advances in the technology of high-voltage transmission have permitted construction of transmission lines carrying direct current exceeding 750,000 volts. The lower transmission losses have made economically feasible the transmission of electric power over increasingly greater distances. The day of individual generating facilities for each city and town has been replaced by the day of transcontinental electrical networks.

The economic trade-off between power losses and insulation cost is not favorable to local distribution at high voltages. Thus, distribution requires high-voltage lines from the power plants to scattered transformer stations where the voltage is reduced for local transmission and, if necessary, converted from direct to alternating current. The number and locations of the transformer stations should be selected to minimize the sum of the value of the lost power and the cost of the facilities. The generating capacity must be large enough to overcome transmission losses, which means that there is also an economic trade-off between the cost of the generating plant and the cost of transmission lines.

Transmission lines adversely affect the scenic and amenity values of the landscape. Extensive underground distribution is too expensive to be economical except in limited areas of unusual scenic value. Often, the transmission lines can be placed in concealed locations. Sometimes, special towers with greater esthetic appeal may be built. As long as electricity is used, transmission facilities are a necessity, but facility design should consider local amenities when comparing alternatives.

13-8 POWER SYSTEMS The greatest benefit of long-distance transmission is the reduction in generating capacity made possible as power can be brought in from outside during times of peak load. When each town had to install sufficient generating capacity to satisfy its instantaneous peak power demand, the total generating capacity installed by a group of towns equaled the sum of their individual peaks. As it became feasible to transmit electricity among the towns, one town during its peak demand period could borrow electrical energy from another. The second town could get the power back when it experienced a peak. The total required generating capacity could be reduced from the sum of the individual peaks to the peak of a power-requirement curve determined by adding individual requirements at corresponding times.

Diversity in the timing of peak loads results from many causes. Daily diversity occurs between industrial areas with daytime peaks and residential areas with early evening peaks. Weekly diversity occurs between areas with weekday and those with weekend peaks. Seasonal diversity occurs between areas in which summer air conditioning or irrigation water pumping predominate and areas in which winter heating and lighting predominate. Time-zone diversity occurs in an east-west direction. Random diversity is caused by chance variations in demand patterns.

Interties connecting local electrical systems cancel diversity and reduce peaking capacity requirements. The economic trade-off is between the cost of transmission lines and the cost of peaking capacity. Improved transmission technology and a growing shortage of hydroelectric sites for peak power has caused the shift to interties. The amount of energy transmitted is usually a relatively minor portion of the total energy requirement as energy need only be transmitted during periods when local demand exceeds local generating capacity.

Nations and even continents are developing a single large power pool interconnecting publicly and privately owned electric companies. Energy taken from the pool is metered, but debts are usually paid by return of equal energy to the pool. Power pools reduce the load factor to make peaking capacity a relatively smaller fraction of total generating capacity. Dump or secondary power becomes firm power and thus commands a higher price. Standby generating facilities are less important, as temporary generating failures can be overcome by withdrawing power from the pool. Individual power-producing facilities become too small to alter total power supply significantly and thus may be planned on the basis of on a horizontal demand curve at constant price.

13-9 HYDROELECTRIC PLANT HYDROLOGY The energy which can be generated by a run-of-the-river plant can be estimated from a flow-duration curve (Fig. 13-2) by the procedure illustrated in Ex. 13-1.

EXAMPLE 13-1
A run-of-the-river power plant site has the flow-duration curve shown in Fig. 13-2. Fifty feet of head may be developed at the site by a plant having a mechanical efficiency of 75 percent. How much energy could be produced by a plant having an installed capacity of 200,000 kw?

The installed capacity required to utilize 1 cfs of flow:

$$P = \frac{Q\gamma H}{550} e = \frac{1(62.4)50}{550} 0.75 = 4.25 \text{ hp} = 3.18 \text{ kw}$$

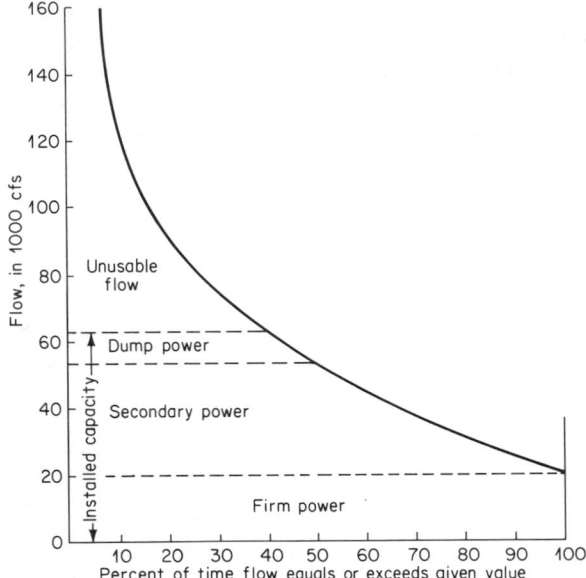

FIGURE 13-2   Flow-duration curve in run-of-the-river power-plant design.

The maximum river flow which can be utilized:

$$\frac{200,000}{3.18} = 62,900 \text{ cfs}$$

Firm power:

With flows up to 20,000 cfs (Fig. 13-2); available 100 percent of the time, or 8,760 hr/year.

Energy:

$3.18(8,760)20,000 = 558 \times 10^6 \text{ kwhr}$

Secondary power:

With flows up to 53,000 cfs (an additional 33,000 cfs); available 72 percent of the time (mean value from Fig. 13-2).

Energy:

$3.18(0.72)8,760(33,000) = 662 \times 10^6 \text{ kwhr}$

Dump power:

With flows up to 62,900 cfs (an additional 9,900 cfs); available 45 percent of the time (mean value from Fig. 13-2).

Energy:

$3.18(0.45)8,760(9,900) = 124 \times 10^6 \text{ kwhr}$

The flow-duration curve should be developed from as long a stream-flow record as possible to avoid undue influence by abnormally wet or dry periods and should be modified to correct for upstream reservoir storage. If the load factor is less than 1.00, the firm power is the product of the value calculated in Ex. 13-1 and the load factor.

If pondage is provided, daily demand diversity need not be included in relating firm energy to firm peaking capacity and the remaining load factor is much closer to 1. Firm energy is correspondingly increased. Pondage is justified economically if it costs less than the increase it produces in the value of the energy shifted from secondary to firm.

The firm energy which can be produced through long-term storage is governed by reservoir capacity, streamflow hydrology, and available head. The amount may be estimated by revising the operation study of Ex. 12-1 to include head (Ex. 13-2). Downstream water rights need not be deducted from reservoir inflows unless they exceed the power-generating water requirement or are exercised between the reservoir and the powerhouse. In the procedure, a reservoir capacity (active storage) is selected, and firm energy estimates are adjusted by trial until the reservoir just runs dry with no shortages. The procedure can be repeated over a range of reservoir capacities to plot a curve (Fig. 13-3) of active storage vs. firm energy for the site.

Dead storage is water kept in the reservoir at all times to increase the head and hence increase the energy generated by a given volume of water

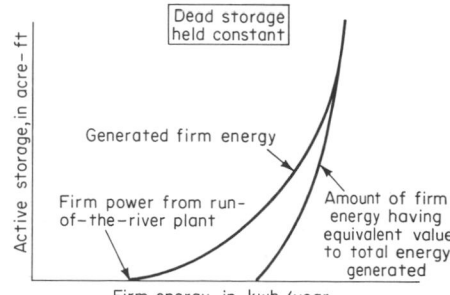

FIGURE 13-3   Active reservoir storage vs. firm energy.

passing through the turbines. Economic justification requires that the incremental cost of making the dam higher to provide dead storage not exceed the value of the additional power. Analysis requires repeating the calculations of Ex. 13-2 and plotting a series of curves like those in Fig. 13-3 for a range of dead-storage values.

EXAMPLE 13-2

Estimation is desired of the firm energy which can be developed without dead storage from an 8,000-acre-ft reservoir at the site analyzed in Ex. 12-1. Monthly energy requirements were estimated from local power use records to be the following fractions of annual energy use:

Jan. 0.12	Mar. 0.10	May 0.06	July 0.05	Sept. 0.07	Nov. 0.10
Feb. 0.11	Apr. 0.09	June 0.05	Aug. 0.05	Oct. 0.09	Dec. 0.11

A curve of head vs. reservoir surface area was developed from topographic maps and approximated by $h = 0.08$ acre $+ 15$. Power plant head in full reservoir is

$$h = 0.08(5.0)(8,000)^{0.5} + 15 = 51 \text{ ft}$$

$$\text{Kilowatthours} = 0.746 \frac{Q\gamma h}{550} et \qquad (13\text{-}1)$$

1.0 acre-ft/month $= 0.0168$ cfs   and 1.0 month contains 720 hr

$$\text{Kilowatthours} = 0.746 \frac{0.0168 \text{ acre-ft}(62.4h)}{550} 0.75(720) = 0.767 \text{ acre-ft}(h)$$

where acre-feet of water are used to generate kilowatt hours of energy per month. Downstream water rights conflict with power generation.

The initial-trial firm energy of 100,000 kwhr/year is shown by the tabular operation study (Table 13-2 on pp. 338 and 339) to be too high, and a lower estimate should be made for the next trial.

In addition to ensuring that enough water is available to generate the firm energy, it is also necessary to ensure that sufficient head is available to provide the required firm peaking capacity, the firm energy divided by the load factor. The generating facilities must be sized to provide the required peaking capacity from the minimum head. One advantage of dead storage is that it reduces the flow rate and hence the size and the cost of the water-carrying facilities.

Monthly energy usage as a fraction of annual usage is employed in Ex. 13-2. Monthly load factors (the ratio of the average rate to the peak rate of energy usage during that calendar month) may be used to estimate the peaking capacity required during each calendar month. Each capacity may be combined with the minimum head for that month to estimate the peak flow rate. The design peaking capacity should provide for the most severe monthly conditions.

Joint operation of a group of hydroelectric plants makes possible the production of more firm energy than the sum of the amounts which can be generated from the plants individually (Sec. 13-15). The firm energy from a power system may be estimated by analyzing coordinated operation of the reservoir system in response to historical or simulated inflows (Sec. 12-3). The addition of a new plant to a power system is justified if it has a cost less than the value of the incremental increase in system power that it produces.

Secondary energy may be generated by releasing additional water at all times other than during the drawdown phase of the critical dry period. The total secondary energy which could be generated may be estimated from a modified operation study (Sec. 12-3). Using the methodology followed through Figs. 12-4 to 12-6 makes it possible to plot a curve relating firm-energy equivalent to storage (Fig. 13-3).

If the hydroelectric plant is connected by interties to other generating facilities, the division between firm and secondary energy depends on the operation of the system as a whole. The operation study for a proposed new plant should be based on the operating rules which will best coordinate the power production schedule of the new plant with the balance of the system. In a predominately hydroelectric system, as in a water supply system, system expansion causes secondary power to become relatively less important as new plants are added. If a hydroelectric plant provides peaking power for a predominately thermal system, secondary power may be generated from water not needed to satisfy the energy requirements of peaks above the thermal generating capacity. System operation must decide whether it is most economical to use this water to generate secondary energy, to generate firm energy and reduce

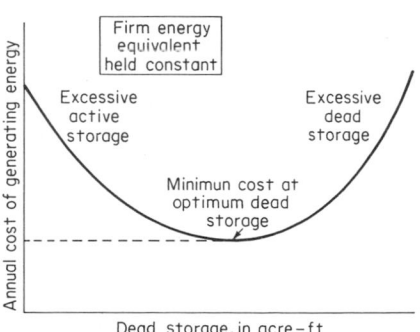

FIGURE 13-4   Annual cost of energy production vs. dead storage.

TABLE 18-2 Tabular Operation Study

(1) Month	(2) Inflow, acre-ft	(3) Precip., acre-ft	(4) Evap., acre-ft	(5) Demand, kwhr	(6) Demand, acre-ft $= \dfrac{\text{kwhr}}{0.767h}$	(7) Spill, acre-ft	(8) End of month storage, acre-ft	(9) Acres, $5\sqrt{(8)}$	(10) h, $0.08(9) + 15$
Nov., 1931	.....	....	.....	.....	.....	.....	0	0	15
Dec., 1931	3,400	0	0	11,000	−956	0	2,444	247	35
Jan., 1932	1,990	56	−14	12,000	−477	0	4,029	317	40
Feb., 1932	4,970	62	−21	11,000	−358	−682	8,000	447	51
Mar., 1932	56	9	−45	10,000	−256	0	7,764	441	50
Apr., 1932	0	16	−71	9,000	−235	0	7,474	432	50
May, 1932	0	5	−115	6,000	−156	0	7,208	424	49
June, 1932	0	0	−143	5,000	−133	0	6,932	416	48
July, 1932	0	0	−156	5,000	−136	0	6,640	407	48
Aug., 1932	0	0	−137	5,000	−136	0	6,367	399	47
Sept., 1932	0	0	−123	7,000	−194	0	6,050	389	46
Oct., 1932	0	11	−83	9,000	−255	0	5,723	378	45
Nov., 1932	0	17	−41	10,000	−290	0	5,409	367	44
Dec., 1932	0	84	−20	11,000	−326	0	5,147	359	44
Jan., 1933	1,050	161	−21	12,000	−356	0	5,981	387	46
Feb., 1933	0	19	−24	11,000	−312	0	5,664	376	45
Mar., 1933	307	53	−39	10,000	−290	0	5,695	377	45
Apr., 1933	0	5	−57	9,000	−261	0	5,382	367	44
May, 1933	0	40	−95	6,000	−178	0	5,149	359	44
June, 1933	0	0	−125	5,000	−148	0	4,876	349	43
July, 1933	0	0	−143	5,000	−152	0	4,581	338	42
Aug., 1933	0	0	−118	5,000	−155	0	4,308	328	41
Sept., 1933	0	0	−101	7,000	−223	0	3,984	316	40
Oct., 1933	0	40	−65	9,000	−293	0	3,666	303	39

Nov., 1933	0	0	−34	10,000	−334	0	3,298	287	38
Dec., 1933	0	99	−17	11,000	−377	0	3,003	274	37
Jan., 1934	26	18	−15	12,000	−422	0	2,610	255	35
Feb., 1934	292	58	−15	11,000	−409	0	2,536	252	35
Mar., 1934	0	0	−25	10,000	−372	0	2,139	231	33
Apr., 1934	0	8	−34	9,000	−356	0	1,757	209	32
May, 1934	0	8	−53	6,000	−245	0	1,467	192	30
June, 1934	0	7	−65	5,000	−217	0	1,192	173	29
July, 1934	0	0	−66	5,000	−225	0	901	150	27
Aug., 1934	0	0	−51	5,000	−241	0	609	123	25
Sept., 1934	0	8	−36	7,000	−365	0	216	73	21
Oct., 1934	0	5	−16	9,000	−558	0	0	0	15
Nov., 1934	0	0	0	10,000	−869	0	0	0	15
Dec., 1934	0	0	0	11,000	−956	0	0	0	15
Jan., 1935	1,780	0	0	12,000	−1,042	0	738	136	26
Feb., 1935	0	7	−7	11,000	−552	0	186	68	20
Mar., 1935	1,580	17	−7	10,000	−652	0	1,124	167	28
Apr., 1935	3,640	49	−24	9,000	−419	0	4,370	331	42
May, 1935	0	0	−84	6,000	−186	0	4,100	320	41
June, 1935	0	0	−111	5,000	−159	0	3,830	309	40
July, 1935	0	0	−119	5,000	−163	0	3,548	298	39
Aug., 1935	0	7	−100	5,000	−167	0	3,288	286	38
Sept., 1935	0	4	−82	7,000	−240	0	2,970	272	37
Oct., 1935	0	14	−56	9,000	−317	0	2,611	255	35
Nov., 1935	0	7	−29	10,000	−372	0	2,217	235	34
Dec., 1935	0	41	−12	11,000	−421	0	1,825	213	32
Jan., 1936	493	29	−11	12,000	−488	0	1,848	215	32
Feb., 1936	8,930	55	−9	11,000	−448	−2,376	8,000	447	51

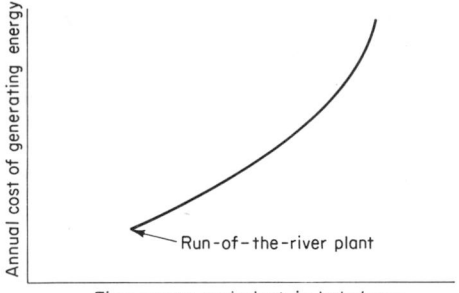

FIGURE 13-5 Annual cost of energy production vs. firm-energy equivalent.

thermal generation, or to release the water downstream without running it through the power plant.

13-10   THE SUPPLY CURVE   Derivation of the marginal-cost curve begins with a series of curves of active storage plotted against the equivalent of firm energy with dead storage held constant (Fig. 13-3). Each curve in the series provides one combination of active and dead storage which could be used to generate a selected firm-energy equivalent. Cost estimates for the reservoirs implied by each combination provide data for a curve of annual generating cost as a function of dead storage (Fig. 13-4). The low point on the characteristically U-shaped curve indicates the optimum dead storage for generating the selected firm-energy equivalent. Too little dead storage provides such low heads that the water requirement for energy generation increases the dam size by increasing the required active storage. Too much dead storage will not effect a corresponding active-storage reduction and thus will also increase dam size and cost. The low point provides a minimum dam size and cost for the first selected firm-energy equivalent. Other energy values may be selected to determine other low points to plot total annual cost as a function of

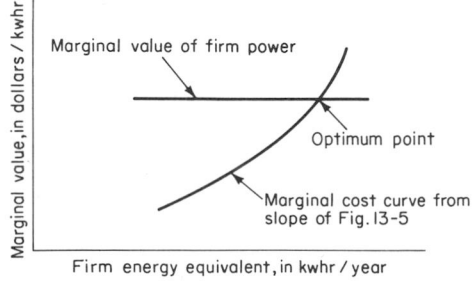

FIGURE 13-6   Marginal-cost and benefit curves for h y d r o e l e c t r i c power plants.

energy produced (Fig. 13-5). The least cost and energy would be associated with a run-of-the-river plant. The marginal-cost curve (Fig. 13-6) may then be developed from the slope of the total-cost curve.

Estimating the Demand

13-11 POWER-DEMAND CURVES Demand curves for power within a given service area could be established by projecting usage at a base price and correcting for the elasticity of demand in the manner described for urban water supply (Sec. 12-17). However, a much lower transportation cost and ability to substitute thermoelectric generation with its associated economies of scale convert the increasing marginal-cost curve typical of water supply (Fig. 12-17) to a stable or even decreasing relationship. As a result, the use projection that is based on the current price structure is a much better estimate of actual future use and may actually be too low if the requirements of new technology for electricity are underestimated. The requirements projection and the economic projection (Fig. 12-16) coalesce.

For planning a particular project, the demand curve is essentially horizontal at the current market price (Fig. 13-6). Any one project is too small to influence the price of electricity throughout a large interconnected system. The elasticity of Eq. (12-6) approaches infinity. In a properly functioning market, the marginal value of the power produced equals the marginal cost of production. In an industry having the natural-monopoly characteristics (Sec. 5-11) of electric power, the market does not automatically reach equilibrium, but state regulation attempts to achieve normative pricing.

13-12 THE POWER-MARKET SURVEY A power-market survey is a study to predict power use within a selected geographical area for a series of dates into the future. The projection utilizes per capita usage based on the existing price structure, anticipated technological changes, and projected populations. While planning to satisfy a water "requirement" obtained in this manner does not make sense in an era of increasing water scarcity, improving thermal generation technology promises to keep power costs in constant dollars relatively stable.

To eliminate the duplication of effort of many project planners surveying existing power usage and price structures, the Federal Power Commission has evaluated existing and projected demand for most regions as well as the United States as a whole. The surveys by the Federal Power Commission segregate electrical use into residential, commercial, industrial, irrigation, and electroprocess use. Existing use is estimated by category from consumption data. This use will vary from one part of the country to another with prevailing price structure, climate, economic development, and industrial base. Total use is summed from catagory use. Projections are made from estimated increases in the number of users per classification and estimated increases in per capita use. The time series of project use by date indicates when increases in generating capacity will be required. The Federal Power Commission policy against allowing firm-power shortages requires peaking capacity to be installed prior to the advent of new demand peaks. The power-market survey must anticipate new demand peaks with sufficient lead time to allow installation of additional peaking capacity.

Electroprocess industries such as aluminum and magnesium production require substantial quantities of low-cost power. Extensive power developments have been economically justified as a source of power for electroprocessing. A market analysis of the demand for the products that these industries produce and a study of the advantages and disadvantages to the industry of locating in the power service area must be made before economic justification of a hydroelectric project to provide energy for electroprocessing can be substantiated.

13-13 *THE ALTERNATIVE-COST APPROACH* If the power-market survey projects a demand exceeding available firm-power supply, the economic problem is to determine whether the need can be satisfied at less cost by thermal or by hydroelectric generation. Even though institutional factors may cause those operating the alternative thermal plant to be subject to different financial obligations than those operating the proposed hydroelectric plant, the costs must be compared by using identical tax burdens, interest rates, and depreciation accounting methods.[1] Hydroelectric power is not economically feasible if its cost advantage is only a product of preferential treatment in taxes, interests, or accounting methods. Since hydroelectric plants have much longer lives than thermal plants, they are in greater danger of becoming technologically obsolete, but the storage reservoir might be converted to some other use in this event. The comparison procedure is illustrated in Ex. 13-3.

[1] Otto Eckstein, "Water Resource Development: The Economics of Project Evaluation" (Cambridge Mass.: Harvard University Press, 1958), pp. 239–245.
Federal practice following the alternative-cost method is outlined in William Whipple, Evaluation of Federal Hydroelectric Power Projects, *Proc. ASCE*, vol. 88, PO 1 (May, 1962).

EXAMPLE 13-3

Government construction of a hydroelectric project would cost $24,400,000. The project has an annual operation and maintenance cost of $140,000 and a 50-year life; a planning discount rate of 3 percent is to be used. What is the annual cost of the project?

$$AC = 140{,}000 + 24{,}400{,}000 \left(\frac{A}{P}, 3\%, 50\right) = 140{,}000 + 950{,}000$$

$$= \$1{,}090{,}000 \text{ per year}$$

The alternative thermal project would be constructed from private funds at a first cost of $10 million, an annual cost for maintenance and fuel of $1,850,000, and a 25-year life. The private company requires a 6 percent return and pays taxes and insurance equal to 3.5 percent of the first cost per year. What is the annual cost to the private company of building this project?

$$AC = 1{,}850{,}000 + 10{,}000{,}000 \left[\left(\frac{A}{P}, 6\%, 25\right) + 0.035\right]$$

$$= 1{,}850{,}000 + 1{,}132{,}000 = \$2{,}982{,}000 \text{ per year}$$

What is the annual cost if the thermal project cost is figured on the same basis used for the public hydroelectric project?

$$AC = 1{,}850{,}000 + 10{,}000{,}000 \left(\frac{A}{P}, 3\%, 25\right) = 1{,}850{,}000 + 574{,}000$$

$$= \$2{,}424{,}000 \text{ per year}$$

What would the annual cost be if technological improvement were to decrease the cost of thermal generation at a rate of 3 percent/year so that a steam plant with the improved technology could be used when the first one must be replaced in 25 years?

Total cost reduction caused by technological improvement over 25 years:

$$(1.03)^{25} = 2.094$$

Annual cost over second 25 years:

$$\frac{2{,}424{,}000}{2.094} = \$1{,}160{,}000 \text{ per year}$$

$$AC = \left(\frac{A}{P}, 3\%, 50\right)\left[2{,}424{,}000 \left(\frac{P}{A}, 3\%, 25\right)\right.$$

$$\left. + 1{,}160{,}000 \left(\frac{P}{A}, 3\%, 25\right)\left(\frac{P}{F}, 3\%, 25\right)\right] = \$2{,}020{,}000 \text{ per year}$$

If the hydroelectric power plant has a 100-mw capacity and a 70 percent load factor, what is the average cost per kilowatthour?

$$\frac{1,090,000}{100,000(0.70)8,760} = \$0.00178 \text{ per kwhr}$$

How much would the private company have to charge per kilowatthour for energy produced in its thermal plant?

$$\frac{2,980,000}{100,000(0.70)8,760} = \$0.00486 \text{ per kwhr}$$

13-14 PROJECT BENEFITS For new electric generation to supplement power available to a large network, the unit benefit for power projected as needed by the power-market survey equals the prevailing regional price. The Federal Power Commission periodically estimates regional values. The expectation of an increase in power use if current prices continue is a judgment that value in use will exceed the price. The fact that the power is not yet used indicates its marginal value is still less than the price but is expected to pass it gradually during the planning period. The price becomes about as close an estimate of value as one can realistically develop. If a new power supply serves an isolated area or is large in comparison with the projected need, the benefit equals the area under the demand curve between the amount of power available with and that available without the project and can be estimated by the procedure outlined in Ex. 12-3. The unit benefit would approximately equal the average of the price with the project and the price without it.

Providing additional electric energy is justified if it can be delivered at a cost less than the prevailing price. Hydroelectric generation is justified if it is the least costly available production method. The cost of generation by alternative methods must be determined as a part of the search for the least costly production method, but it does not really represent a project benefit.

Project Feasibility

13-15 ECONOMIC FEASIBILITY The formulation of the optimum hydroelectric project to be integrated into the system for producing electrical energy consists in determining the optimum dead storage, the optimum active storage, the optimum installed generating capacity, and the optimum operating rules. The optimum firm-energy equivalent is represented by the point where the marginal cost of producing firm energy equals its marginal value (Fig. 13-6). The optimum dead storage is read from the curve of annual cost of energy vs. dead storage (Fig. 13-4) corresponding to the optimum firm-energy equivalent. The optimum active storage is read from the curve of active reservoir storage vs. firm-energy equivalent (Fig. 13-3) corresponding to the optimum dead storage. Based on the optimum active storage, the optimum firm energy can also be read from Fig. 13-3. The optimum installed generating capacity is estimated by dividing the optimum firm energy by the load factor.

The optimum project operating rules must be determined by trial and error to maximize power production from the hydroelectric system. Table 13-3 describes a small portion of the Tennessee Valley Authority hydroelectric system (Fig. 13-7).[1] If only the Apalachia plant were constructed, 11,700 kw of firm power could be obtained. If the three upstream plants were constructed but operated independently, 33,700 kw could be generated at Apalachia. By coordinated operation, firm power can be increased to 42,800 kw. The change from 11,700 to 33,700 illustrates how upstream storage reservoirs increase the firm-power potential of downstream plants by increasing low flows. An upstream storage facility such as that at Chatuge increases downstream power by several times the amount generated at the site. A downstream facility may depend almost entirely on upstream storage for flow regulation. The firm power could be increased further were the system operated with the sole objective of generating power rather than with additional purposes such as flood control and navigation.

[1] John V. Krutilla and Otto Eckstein, "Multiple Purpose River Development" (Baltimore: The Johns Hopkins Press, 1958), pp. 61–68.

FIGURE 13-7 Schematic diagram of power plants for Table 13-3. [*From John V. Krutilla and Otto Eckstein "Multiple Purpose River Development," published (Baltimore: The Johns Hopkins Press, for Resources for the Future, 1967). By permission of The Johns Hopkins Press.*]

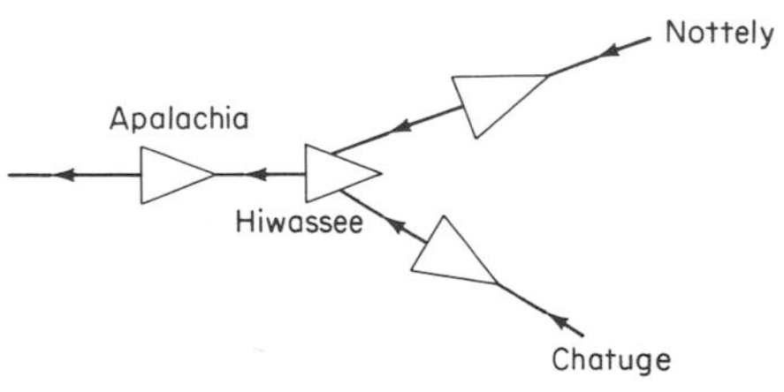

Additional peaking capacity cannot be economically justified unless the benefit derived from use of the additional power during peak demand periods exceeds the cost of increasing the generating capacity. However, current policy against planned shortages prohibits explicit limitation of peaking capacity to take advantage of this economic trade-off. Nevertheless, excessive peaking capacity to supply users with very low load factors can be avoided by charging higher rates for electrical service during peak demand periods and thus forcing more favorable load factors by economic pressure. Project optimization should thus also determine the optimum rate schedule as that which limits the demand for peaking power to amounts which can be economically justified. Higher rates for peaking power are more efficient than temporary shortages during peak demand periods because they allocate the generated electricity by a market mechanism rather than arbitrary rationing.

An addition to a hydroelectric system is likely to make it necessary to adjust the rules for operating each plant in the system. If the plants are not under common ownership, the Federal Power Commission requires each downstream private plant to pay for the benefit it receives from new upstream storage. However, upstream private storage cannot recoup benefits to downstream federal power plants. Coordinated reservoir operation is not legally enforced, but the resulting mutual advantages make it worth the while of most power producers to cooperate to maximize production.

Hydrologic and market factors cause the benefits from a given project to depend on whether it is built before or after other local projects.[1] Decreasing marginal benefits normally causes the benefits from a particular project to be progressively smaller as the project is placed later in a con-

---

[1]   John V. Krutilla, "Sequence and Timing in River Basin Development" (Washington: Resources for the Future, Inc., 1960).

TABLE 13-3   Hydroelectric Plant Contribution to System Primary Power in Kilowatts

POWER AT

Power from	Down stream	Apalachia	Hiwassee	Nottely	Chatuge	Total power from
Apalachia	600	33,700	......	.....	.....	34,300
Hiwassee	3,600	3,900	20,000	.....	.....	27,500
Nottely	1,800	1,900	1,100	3,400	.....	8,200
Chatuge	3,100	3,300	1,900	.....	2,400	10,700
Total power at	.....	42,800	23,000	3,400	2,400	

struction sequence. In system planning, the construction sequence producing maximum net benefits should be determined and followed.

13-16 GOVERNMENT REGULATION Hydroelectric development is regulated by the Federal Power Commission and by state governments. The Federal Power Commission investigates each proposed generating facility and has the power to license nonfederal power projects which serve the public interest and to deny licenses to those which do not. Licenses may be denied for undue adverse consequences to fish, the lack of an adequate market, plans by a federal agency to develop the same site, location of the proposed site in a reserved area, failure to develop a site in the economically optimum manner, or failure to coordinate properly with other water development. Each license is granted for a fixed period, not to exceed 50 years, and may be revoked because of improper operation or maintenance. River basin planning studies are made to be sure proposed projects are properly coordinated with overall basin development. The Federal Power Commission also evaluates power markets, plans interties to coordinate electrical systems, requires downstream power plants to pay for the benefit they receive from upstream storage, supervises power developments on public land, and regulates wholesale rates on interstate power transmission.

State regulation is primarily concerned with controlling power rates to prevent private power companies from taking advantage of their monopoly position to reap excess profit. State regulatory agencies analyze the financial structure of the power industry to set rates low enough to yield no more than the socially acceptable profit and high enough to continue to attract investment capital. The regulation requires continuing surveillance to adjust the rates as conditions change.

13-17 GOVERNMENT OWNERSHIP Government ownership is often suggested as a means of preventing private monopoly profit.[1] In the United States, about 20 percent of the total generating capacity is owned by local government (including general governments such as municipalities and special governments such as public utility districts), 38 percent by privately owned utilities, and 42 percent by the Federal government. In other countries, most electric utilities are owned by the national government. Most federally owned power facilities have in the past been associated with multiple-purpose projects, but thermoelectric power is becoming significant. About 50 percent of the total federal power is owned by

---

[1] The case against government ownership is summarized in Edwin Vennard, "Government in the Power Business" (New York: McGraw-Hill Book Company, 1968). The case against private ownership is found in Lee Metcalf and V. Reinemer, "Overcharge" (New York: David McKay Company, Inc., 1967).

the Corps of Engineers, 32 percent by the Bureau of Reclamation, and 18 percent by TVA.

Publicly owned (federal or local) utilities have financial advantages which make it impossible to determine their relative economic merits by comparing their rate structures with privately owned utilities. Ablin summarized the tax and interest burdens for the various types of ownership as shown in Table 13-4.[1] In the Pacific Northwest, private utilities pay 14.9 to 25.5 percent of their total electric revenues as taxes; public utility districts pay 3.5 to 7.6 percent, and federal projects pay no taxes.[2] In addition, private utilities may be required to incorporate provisions for flood control, navigation, or fish enhancement in their hydroelectric dams without compensation. A federal project would allocate the cost of these features to the purpose served. The lower financial burden allows public power generated at the same economic cost to be sold for less than private power (Ex. 13-3). As the difference between the project revenues and project cost must be recovered from other tax sources, low rates shift the financial burden from the power user to the taxpayer. "This suggests a net income transfer from other regions to the one in which the project is undertaken."[3]

The magnitude of this income redistribution or subsidy is shown in Fig. 13-8. At a fair market price, power use will be at point a. If subsidized public power lowers the price to point b, area A represents the net income redistribution to consumers paid for by increased taxes. Area B also must be paid for by increased taxes and represents the cost of producing the additional power in excess of the value realized by the consumers. The low,

[1]   Richard S. Ablin, "Misallocation of Electric Power in the Pacific Northwest," Ph.D. thesis, Department of Economics, University of Chicago, 1960, pp. 6-8.
[2]   William Whipple, Evaluation of Federal Hydroelectric Power Projects, *Proc. ASCE*, vol. 88, PO 1 (May, 1962), pp. 155-156.
[3]   Krutilla and Eckstein, *op. cit.*, p. 263.

TABLE 13-4   Ownership Variation in Tax and Interest Burden

Ownership	Interest	Local taxes	Income taxes
Federal	Low*	No§	No
Local	Higher†	Yes¶	No
Private	Highest‡	Yes	Yes

*   Paid at current planning discount rate (Sec. 6-8) but subject to certain exceptions (Sec. 13-18).
†   Higher than federal rates because of a lower credit rating but lower than private rates because interest on municipal bonds is exempt from income tax. The Rural Electrification Administration's distribution systems are subsidized at a rate below the federal planning rate.
‡   Highest borrowing rate, and opportunity cost of equity capital tends to be higher still.
§   Some payments in lieu of taxes are made to local governments.
¶   Often slightly below the private level.

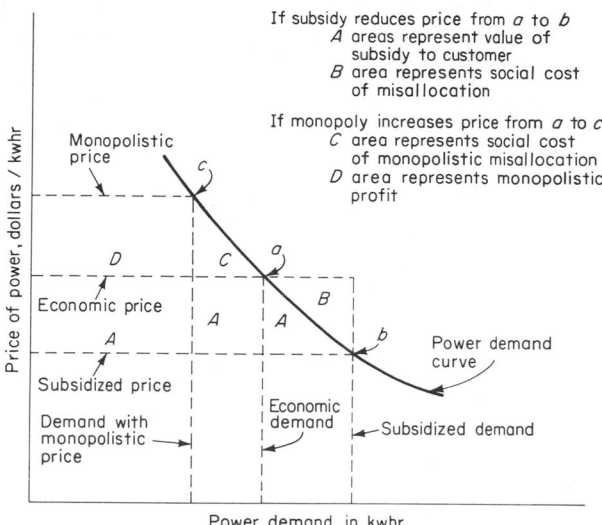

The figure contains the following labels:

If subsidy reduces price from *a* to *b*
  A areas represent value of
    subsidy to customer
  B area represents social cost
    of misallocation

If monopoly increases price from *a* to *c*
  C area represents social cost
    of monopolistic misallocation
  D area represents monopolistic
    profit

Price of power, dollars / kwhr

Monopolistic price

c

D   *C*   *a*

Economic price   *A*   *A*   *B*

A   Power demand curve   *b*

Subsidized price

Demand with monopolistic price   Economic demand   Subsidized demand

Power demand, in kwhr

FIGURE 13-8 Results of power subsidies.

public-power rates thus cause a net reduction in national income amounting to area *B*. If state regulation of public utilities does not overcome monopolistic pricing, the net loss in national income will be represented by area *C*.

Power produced by the Federal government has been sold to publicly owned utilities in preference to privately owned ones, but the nationwide intertie network is causing this policy to be modified. Public preference clauses discourage economic efficiency by establishing criteria for sale other than the value of the power to the customer.

13-18 FINANCIAL FEASIBILITY The role of revenue obtained from hydroelectric power, the most lucrative output of water resource projects, has been the center of continual controversy. Power rates based on the federal financial burden (Table 13-4) often raise less than the full cost of the power facility. However, the portion of the revenues covering the interest cost on hydroelectric plants was used to pay for the irrigation features of multipurpose systems until 1952. In that year, the Cullbran formula was adopted, stating that only revenues in excess of those required to pay 3 percent interest on the hydroelectric facilities could be used to pay for irrigation water.[1] As controversial as such juggling of funds may

---

[1] Otto Eckstein, "Water Resource Development: The Economics of Project Evaluation" (Cambridge, Mass.: Harvard University Press, 1958), pp. 226–236.

be, the disposition of project revenue does not relate to optimum project selection according to economic efficiency.

SELECTED REFERENCES

Creager, William P., and Joel D. Justin: "Hydroelectric Handbook" (New York: John Wiley and Sons, Inc., 1950).

Eckstein, Otto: "Water Resource Development: The Economics of Project Evaluation" (Cambridge, Mass.: Harvard University Press, 1958), pp. 237–258.

Galloway, D. C., L. K. Kirchmayer, W. D. Marsh, and A. G. Mellor: An Approach to Peak Load Economics, *Trans. AIEE*, vol. 79, pt. 3 (1960).

Kirchmayer, Leon K.: "Economic Operations of Power Systems" (New York: John Wiley & Sons, Inc., 1958).

Krutilla, John V.: "Sequence and Timing in River Basin Development" (Washington: Resources for the Future, 1960).

Kuiper, Edward: "Water Resources Development: Planning, Engineering and Economics" (Washington: Butterworth & Co. (Publishers), Ltd., 1965), pp. 264–338.

Linsley, Ray K., and Joseph B. Franzini: "Water-resources Engineering" (New York: McGraw-Hill Book Company, 1964), pp. 323–359, 448–467.

Whipple, William: Evaluation of Federal Hydroelectric Power Projects, *Proc. ASCE*, vol. 88, PO 1 (May, 1962).

PROBLEMS

13-1 Use the same series of monthly streamflows as in Prob. 12-1 and the data of Ex. 13-2, as needed, to:

    a. Develop a curve of firm annual energy vs. reservoir capacity.

    b. Use the cost data of Prob. 12-1 to develop a curve of firm annual energy produced vs. cost per kilowatthour.

    c. Add a volume of dead storage equal to the average annual runoff, and repeat steps *a* and *b*.

13-2 A pumped-storage installation uses two 8,100-hp centrifugal pumps of 87 percent efficiency to pump water through 500 ft of 72-in. penstock ($n = 0.015$) to an elevation of 375 ft above tail water level. This water is then discharged through the same penstock to a 33,000-hp turbine whose efficiency is 91 percent. The generator efficiency is 89 percent, and that of the pump motors is 85 percent. If all water used in the turbine is pumped, what is the overall efficiency of the system? If the pumps utilize dump power with an increment cost of 1 mill/kwhr and the generator produces prime power selling at 9 mills/kwhr, what is the economic efficiency of the plant when all the water is pumped?

13-3   Electric power must be provided to serve a power load distributed as follows:

Load, 1,000 kw:	200	180	160	140	120	100	80	60
Fraction of time exceeded:	0	20	33	43	62	85	95	100

At an available hydroelectric site, a continuous firm flow of 5,300 cfs can be guaranteed to a plant having a head of 68 ft and an efficiency of 0.82 and costing $62.80 annually per installed kilowatt. A thermoelectric plant can be developed for $65.00 per installed kilowatt and a fuel cost of 0.1 cent per kilowatthour of energy generated.
a Determine the optimum installed capacity for each plant.
b Determine the cost per kilowatthour of energy generated at each optimum plant.

13-4   A proposed hydroelectric plant site has available a firm flow of 140 cfs at a head of 800 ft. A power plant having an efficiency of 75 percent and a 50-year life can be built for $2 million and operated (including taxes and insurance) for $100,000 annually by a power company having a minimum acceptable rate of return of 7 percent. The power can be sold for 0.6 cents per kilowatthour.
a What net revenue will an economically motivated power company realize?
b What is the annual cost of generating energy?
c Once the plant is constructed, to what value would the sale price of electrical energy have to drop to make continued operation unprofitable?

CHAPTER
FOURTEEN

NAVIGATION

The Planning Context

14-1 DEFINITION In the context of water resources planning, navigation refers to the transportation of freight or passengers on inland waterways. Ocean transport is only indirectly related to the development or planning of water resource projects. In planning, navigation facilities should be coordinated with the total transportation system in order to determine where water carriers have an economic advantage and to develop proper facilities at the interface between land and water transport.

Navigation on inland waterways has several distinct forms. Ocean-going vessels may travel to inland ports through enlarged ship channels. Recently completed projects include the St. Lawrence Seaway and the Sacramento ship channel. Navigation by smaller craft may be extended further inland on routes mostly following major rivers and other natural waterways. Navigation to such inland cities as Tulsa, Oklahoma, Lewiston, Idaho, and Fort Benton, Montana, is already possible or being seriously studied. Freight is moved through inland river or canal systems by barge tows. Inland waterway passenger travel occurs on small pleasure craft and in group cruises on bigger vessels but primarily for relaxation rather than to reach a specific destination.

14-2 HISTORICAL DEVELOPMENT Before the advent of the steam engine and the construction of railroads, transportation was much easier by water than by land. All the major trade routes were by water, and as a result, nearly every major city was founded on a navigable water-way. The first attempt at water resources planning in the United States dates to the Gallatin report of 1808 on inland waterway navigation. The 1820s witnessed a great canal-building program to provide water transportation to inland areas. The canals were of small cross section, lay over surprisingly rough topography, contained numerous locks to raise or lower vessels, and used animal power to move the barges. Many state governments overextended themselves by building canals which could be neither economically nor financially justified. Within 20 years, the slower and more costly inland waterway transport was no longer able to compete with the growing railroad network. Only a few canals remained in operation. The financial loss suffered by many states was so great that some state constitutions retain to this day restrictions against borrowing for public works projects.

Railroads have been losing their dominance during the twentieth century. Regulation by the Interstate Commerce Commission seeks to prevent any railroad from cutting rates below marginal costs to force waterway competition out of business. In 1907, President Theodore Roosevelt appointed the Inland Waterways Commission to study the multiple-purpose development of inland waterways. The Corps of Engineers expanded its program of inland waterway improvement to help cut transportation cost. Finally, low cost, the ability to carry heavy items, and the ability to take advantage of storage en route to cut inventory cost made navigation the most economical form of transport for many items. Costs in 1969 averaged only 0.3 cent per ton-mile. This compares with 1.5 cents by rail and 6.5 cents by truck.[1] The low cost of water transport results from a high ratio of cargo to deadweight (up to 4) and the relatively lower motive force required to overcome fluid friction. The force per unit weight of freight is about one-tenth of that by rail for normal inland waterway traffic and becomes progressively less as shipment in larger vessels is possible. Offsetting disadvantages include very slow speeds (averaging 6 mph), ice closure in winter plus periodic closure during droughts or floods, the limited number of points served by water and therefore prevention of door-to-door service to most customers, routes which are very circuitous, and the need for expensive port facilities.

14-3 TYPES OF FACILITIES Navigation facilities include the waterway, the harbor, and the vessel. The three basic types of inland waterway are lakes, rivers, and canals. Natural lakes have a large depth and width with little current but are often poorly located for transportation routes and more exposed to storms and winds. The Great Lakes are the

---

[1] Braxton B. Carr, Barge Transportation—Energizer of Production and Marketing, *Proc. ASCE*, vol. 95, no. WW 2 (May, 1969), pp. 163–165.

most extensively used for navigation of the natural lakes in the world. Rivers with substantial year-round flows provide the basic inland water transportation arteries, and their use is greatly enhanced by the riverfront location of most major cities. They provide ready-made routes which can be provided and maintained at a relatively low cost. Local measures required to handle rapids, snags, or sandbars are relatively inexpensive. As of 1965, there were 25,380 miles of improved waterways in the United States, with the Mississippi-Ohio River System carrying the bulk of the river freight. About 60 percent of the system can accommodate vessels having a 9-ft draft.[1]

Navigation canals connect natural inland waterways or an inland waterway and the sea. Canal construction is too costly to be justified other than to extend the length of, or connect, natural waterways and thus minimize the costly process of shifting back and forth between land and water transport. Canals may parallel rivers to avoid navigation hazards, provide shorter alignments, speed upstream travel, cut waterway maintenance cost, and enhance the recreational and esthetic values of the river. Canals are relatively free from flood-caused water-surface fluctuations and excessive currents and have lower low-flow water requirements. Canals are also built parallel to the coast so that cargo will not have to be transferred from the barge flotilla to vessels capable of withstanding the waves of the open sea. Canals extend along most of the Atlantic and Gulf Coasts of the United States. Because transport by oceangoing vessel is less costly per ton-mile than transport by barge, an economic trade-off must be made between savings in vessel operation and the cost of transferring goods already brought downriver by barge to oceangoing vessels in order to determine the minimum economic haul distance between coastal ports for oceangoing vessels. The Coast Guard reviews navigation improvements that are proposed and recommends navigation aids for vessel safety.

Harbor facilities are required at each interface between land and water transport or between two types of water transport. Provision is needed to allow railroad cars and trucks to come as close to the vessels as possible. Dock space is needed for the movement and temporary storage of freight during loading and unloading, and space alongside the dock is needed for berthing the vessel. Additional space is needed to service, maintain, or repair vessels. Ever-increasing labor costs are causing loading and unloading to shift to more capital-intensive but labor-saving methods. Large containers, which can be shifted from boat to truck to train by a single man in a few minutes, reduce labor costs and pilferage losses. The technology for mechanized loading and unloading is rapidly developing and can substantially lower marginal harbor cost where the

[1] *Ibid.*

larger fixed cost can be justified by shipping large volumes of bulk commodities.

The high cost of mechanized loading equipment and the vessel delay caused by too many stops favor a few large terminals rather than many small ones. Many large private firms maintain their own terminals, but economic utilization of the waterway requires, in addition, well-equipped public terminals closely coordinated with land-transportation facilities.

The most common inland water vessel is a flotilla of shallow-draft barges tied together and propelled by a small tug. Standard barges in the United States are 35 ft wide by 195 ft long and are designed for a 9-ft draft at full load. These dimensions allow maximum-load cargo per barge of 1,570 short tons; however, an 8.5-ft draft and 1,400-ton load are more typical. Standard European barges are 31 ft wide by 262 ft long with a design draft of 8.25 ft. Flotillas vary in size up to 20 or even as many as 40 barges on large rivers. Small pleasure craft are becoming more numerous on many waterways and are beginning to conflict with commercial users as they create channel and lock congestion and object to waves created by larger vessels.

Developing the Supply

14-4 TRIAL DESIGN The goal of navigation planning is to determine the plan for waterway and harbor improvement which maximizes net benefit. The marginal-cost curve, used to equate marginal benefits with marginal cost, must be derived from a curve of total cost vs. a series of freight volumes. The design represented by each point on the total-cost curve should, for the indicated freight volume, minimize the overall cost of transportation, C_f:

$$C_f = C_{wv} + C_{wf} + C_{hv} + C_{hf} \tag{14-1}$$

or the sum of the cost of the waterway, C_{wf}, and of the vessels moving through the waterway, C_{wv}, plus the sum of the cost of the harbor, C_{hf}, and of the vessels moving through the harbor, C_{hv}. Costs may be expressed either in dollars per ton-mile or dollars per ton shipped through the facilities. Project optimization (Sec. 14-17) thus requires determining the minimum cost facility for a series of specified annual freight volumes as a step in determining which minimum cost design maximizes benefits.

Specific navigation projects may deal only with improvements to a waterway or to a harbor so that only two of the four terms on the right side of Eq. (14-1) apply. However, it is essential for harbor and waterway facilities to be coordinated to handle vessels of the same size and type. Periodic evaluations are necessary to make sure existing or proposed systems handle freight volumes at minimum cost.

14-5   HARBOR CAPACITY   Development of the marginal-cost curve needed to pick the optimum degree of harbor development requires that the total harbor cost C_{hf}, associated with the least sum of C_{hv} and C_{hf}, be plotted vs. some index of facility size. This index may be defined as the capacity. It may be measured in purely physical units, such as the number of docking berths, and reflect the volume of traffic the physical facilities can accommodate at minimum average vessel cost. It may be measured as an annual design traffic volume and represent the facilities which can handle that volume at least cost under prevailing seasonal patterns of adverse weather and freight movement. The probabilities of strikes, mechanical failures, and other traffic disruptions should also be considered. The relationship between facilities and freight movement used in planning should be based on observed movement of comparable freight through facilities comparable to those being planned. Depending on prevailing costs, the optimum design may vary from guaranteed unloading on arrival to a high probability of having to wait in line before unloading can begin. The sole purpose of specifying capacity is to index alternative degrees of facility development as an intermediate step in benefit maximization.

The practical capacity of a given harbor is normally governed by a specific bottleneck. Often, the total harbor capacity can be increased just by improving this one component of the total facility. With sufficient improvement, secondary bottlenecks also develop, and they too must be improved. A new harbor may be planned with a balanced design having all facilities of equal capacity. However, facility differences in the economy of stage construction typically favor initial construction of some facilities with a smaller capacity than others.

14-6   HARBOR COST   A harbor is located on a waterway accommodating vessels of known size and type. Some of the vessels will want to stop at the harbor, as determined by quantities of freight needing to be loaded or unloaded or the vessels' need for maintenance or repair. The optimum harbor provides the facilities which minimize the sum of the cost of the harbor plus the cost of the vessels within the harbor.

The harbor includes an area protected from winds and waves by jetties and breakwaters, an entrance channel, interior channels to anchorage areas and berthing areas along docks, turning basins, facilities to provide vessels with fuel and minor repairs, and facilities for transferring cargo to or from other types of transportation carriers. The greater the capacity of the harbor facilities for berthing ships, moving cargo onto and off of ships, moving cargo out of the port area by other transport modes, and storing cargo, the quicker the vessels can move through port. The harbor cost increases as greater capacity is provided, but the cost of waiting vessels is decreased. Vessel waiting cost consists of the value of lost vessel time, crew wages during the waiting period, and customer losses in receiving slower delivery.

Harbor planning requires the sizing of each harbor component. The degree of protection best provided by jetties and breakwaters depends on an economic trade-off between construction cost and expected storm damage. The optimum size of the channel, anchorage, and berthing areas depends on an economic trade-off between harbor cost and vessel waiting time. Plumlee has developed a computer model from queueing theory (Sec. 19-4) for determining the optimum number of berths in a harbor facility.[1] The selection of harbor equipment for loading or unloading depends on freight volumes and the cost of the equipment. Mechanized equipment has a high fixed but a low variable cost per unit of freight. Manual loading or unloading has a low fixed and a high variable cost. Mechanized equipment can be justified when it can be used to move freight through the harbor at a total cost less than that with a less mechanized procedure.

14-7 WATERWAY IMPROVEMENT ALTERNATIVES Inland waterways may be improved, in order of increasing costliness, by open-channel methods, lock and dam methods, or canalization. The appropriate method varies from place to place within a navigation system. Open-channel methods improve a natural river channel. One open-channel method is to use reservoir yield to augment low flows and reservoir storage to control channel-damaging floods. Low flows should be augmented when the cost of the required reservoir yield does not exceed the resulting benefit to navigation (Sec. 14-10). The amount of augmentation should be increased until the marginal cost of the water equals the marginal savings in transport cost. As the distance between the reservoir and the navigation channel increases, releases must be increased to allow for intervening seepage and evaporation losses, channel storage, and difficulty in synchronizing reservoir releases and downstream requirements.

Channel obstructions or snags such as tree stumps, rocks, or roots must be removed from the navigation channel. Dredging to remove

[1] Carl H. Plumlee, Optimum Size Seaport, *Proc. ASCE*, vol. 92, no. WW 3 (August, 1966), pp. 1-24.

sediment must be repeated regularly as deposition accumulates. It is not unusual for annual dredging cost to be several times the amortized construction cost. The Corps of Engineers has found required channel dredging to depend on the severity of low flows because it is harder to keep the channel open and more deposition occurs.[1] In colder climates, annual maintenance cost may include forecasting of freezing and thawing to maximize waterway use during the ice-free season, measures to hasten spring thaws, and blasting of ice jams.

Contraction works (dikes, groins, or jetties) concentrate flow in order to scour out a narrower and deeper central channel while depositing excess sediment in slack water along the shore to increase bank stability. Banks may also be stabilized by using revetments for mechanical protection, particularly along the outside bank at bends. A cutoff channel eliminates sharp meanders, but bank stabilization is required to prevent the meandering from becoming reestablished. In many situations, bank stabilization will enhance flood control and land drainage as well as navigation benefits.[2]

Lock and dam methods provide navigation by converting the river into a stair-stepped series of lakes. Dams form the lakes on which the vessels can navigate, and locks are built at the side of each dam for vessel bypass. When compared with open-channel methods, the greater costs of installing the locks and dams, additional bridge lengthening and raising, the additional right-of-way that will be flooded, and the consequences of a probable reduction in water quality must be balanced against lower vessel operating costs through slack water and deeper and wider channels, lower channel maintenance cost, and lower water requirements equaling only lockage water and evaporation losses. Higher dams reduce most vessel cost but increase problems of marking the sailing line and exposure to winds and waves. Safety harbors at approximately 5-mile intervals are required to provide shelter during adverse weather and a place for mechanical repair. The current trend on major rivers is to replace many low dams with fewer high ones.

Locks consist of two longitudinal retaining walls with gates at each end through which vessels can enter or leave. Vessels steer more easily toward locks providing the maximum straight approach channel with minimum cross currents in both directions. The water level in the lock is varied between upstream and downstream water elevations as the vessel passes. The most common lock size on the Mississippi River navigation

[1]   Mississippi River Commission, "Mississippi River Reservoir Benefit Study" U.S. Army Corps of Engineers (1963), p. 19.
[2]   Walter C. Carey, Comprehensive River Stabilization, *Proc. ASCE*, vol. 92, no. WW 1 (February, 1966), pp. 59–86.

channel system is 110 ft wide by 600 ft long. Typical lock heights vary between 15 and 50 ft. Auxiliary locks are needed so that traffic can continue to move when a lock must be closed for maintenance or repair; however, this can usually be done in the winter in cold climates.

Canal construction requires excavation of the entire waterway. Riprap or other stabilization is needed to protect the banks against erosion from vessel waves. Controlled flows tend to make flow velocities and maintenance cost lower for canals than for natural channels. The lower flow velocities and straighter channel alignment also reduce vessel travel time.

Navigation improvements require the raising of bridge crossings or the installation of draw bridges. The Tennessee Valley Authority requires 57 ft from the water surface to the bridge deck bottom and 350 ft between bridge piers. Navigation projects may increase the cost of land transportation by requiring more expensive bridges with greater clearances, greater bridge maintenance cost, greater vehicle operating cost in climbing up and over a bridge or stopping for a wait and starting again, and delays for bridge openings.

14-8 WATERWAY CAPACITY Determination of the optimum degree of waterway improvement requires that the total waterway cost C_{wf}, associated with the least sum of C_{wv} and C_{wf} (Sec. 14-9), be plotted vs. capacity or some other index of facility size. The capacity of an open channel or canalized system to transport freight is normally governed by channel dimensions, alignment, and flow conditions at the most restrictive bottleneck. The capacity of a lock and dam system is normally governed by the locks. Harbor facilities control movement through large bodies of water.

The capacity of each facility has a physical upper limit. Maximum waterway capacity would be realized under the ideal conditions of uniformly spaced, fully loaded tows traveling at the maximum uniform speed commensurate with prevailing current velocity (Ex. 14-1).

EXAMPLE 14-1
A waterway is wide enough to accommodate movements in both directions of flotillas two barges wide and three barges long. Prevailing current velocity is 5 mph. If flotillas can move 10 mph through still water at a spacing of one flotilla length, what is the maximum capacity of the waterway?

Capacity will be governed by movement in the upstream direction in which flotillas can only move 5 mph and equals

$$1,570(\text{tons/barge})[6(\text{barges/flotilla})]\,\frac{1}{2(3)195}\,(\text{flotilla/ft})$$
$$\times\,5,280(\text{ft/mile})[5(\text{miles/hr})]24(365)(\text{hr/year})$$
$$=\,1.86\,\times\,10^9\,\text{tons/(year)(direction)}$$

Maximum lock capacity equals the product of the capacity pay load per barge, the number of barges which will fit into the lock, and the lockage intervals per year. The lockage interval is the time required for tows to enter and be arranged within the lock, the gates to be closed, the water surface to be raised or lowered, the gate to be opened, and the outgoing tows to depart and sufficiently clear the lock area for the incoming tows to enter. If entry and exit are congested, capacity may be increased by employing four or five consecutive up lockages followed by four or five consecutive down lockages. Lock dimensions may require a different arrangement of barges within the tow than that used in the waterway.

The demand for waterway transportation is often seasonal so that waterway capacity is only taxed during periods of peak use. Peak rates of actual freight movement seldom exceed a practical capacity of about 25 percent of maximum capacity.[1] The demand may be directional so that empty barges must be backhauled. Loading difficulties may prevent filling barges to capacity. Service may be interrupted by breakdowns of tows or locks or by adverse weather or stream conditions. From the economic point of view, waterway capacity is reached when the expense of enlarging the facility to relieve congestion no longer exceeds the expected resultant savings in lower vessel operating cost.

14-9 WATERWAY AND VESSEL COST   A bigger waterway can accommodate larger vessels able to transport freight at a lower cost per ton-mile. It also reduces fluid friction and thus the operating cost of a vessel of given size. Congestion is decreased. However, a bigger waterway costs more. The optimum waterway to handle a given traffic volume minimizes the sum of waterway and vessel costs (Fig. 14-1). Both costs include the discounted average annual installation cost plus annual operation and maintenance.

[1]   Eric E. Bottoms, Practical Tonnage Capacity of Canalized Waterways, *Proc. ASCE*, vol. 92, no. WW 1 (February, 1966), pp. 33–46.
John P. Davis, Tonnage Capacity of Locks, *Proc. ASCE*, vol. 95, no. WW 2 (May, 1969), pp. 201–213.

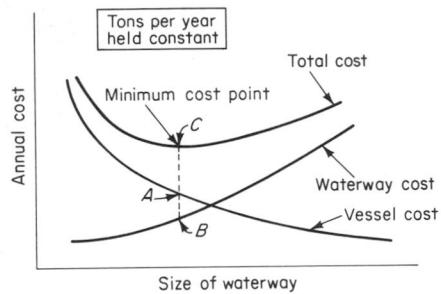

FIGURE 14-1   Waterway optimization.

Wider channels allow more barges to be tied together, increase barge-tow maneuverability, and permit tows going in opposite directions to pass each other on curves. Fewer tugs are needed per ton of freight. Barge tows are difficult to steer accurately, especially during storms or high winds. The optimum channel width is greater on curves than on tangents. A typical minimum width in the United States is 300 ft or a little more than twice flotilla width.

Most major North American navigation channels have design depths of 9 or 12 ft, while a 4-meter depth is most common in Europe. Increased depth reduces fuel cost for a given vessel size by reducing viscous drag. It also reduces vessel cost by permitting passage of larger vessels, which realizes economies of scale in operation. An idea of the vessel economy realized through increased channel depth and width is provided for a vessel of given size by the figures in Table 14-1. A greater economy could be realized by shifting to vessels of greater draft, provided the increased depth is extended throughout the waterway system so freight does not have to be moved back and forth among vessels of different size.

Vessel cost includes the cost of vessel ownership and the cost of vessel operation. The cost of vessel ownership V_o equals

$$V_o = (V_f - V_s)\left(\frac{A}{P}, i\%, N\right) + V_s i + V_a \qquad (14\text{-}2)$$

where V_f is the first cost, V_s is the salvage value of the vessel, and V_a is the average annual expense by the owner, which is independent of the amount of use (insurance, property taxes, etc.). The owner attempts to recover his cost of ownership by charging for use of his vessel to transport goods. The hourly cost equals V_o divided by the number of hours the vessel is available during the year. Congestion tends to slow vessel velocity by making navigation more complicated and to increase waiting. Congestion cost equals the congestion-caused hours of delay in vessel movement times the hourly ownership cost.

The cost of vessel operation is largely determined by the effective push required from vessel engines. Empirical relationships (Table 14-1) are available for estimating the increase in vessel operating cost caused by more restrictive channel dimensions and greater speed,[1] both factors increasing friction-resistance loss. Smaller waterways increase both congestion and operating cost, and the two should be added in economic analysis.

Straighter channel alignment shortens routes to reduce travel time and required curve widening, but it also increases channel slopes to produce greater water velocities. Faster stream velocity reduces the cost of transporting goods downstream but increases the cost of transporting goods upstream far more. For a 300-mile-long channel and a 10 mph barge speed in still water, an increase in river velocity from 2 to 5 mph would decrease downstream travel time by 5.0 hr, but increase upstream travel time by 22.5 hr. Current velocities in excess of 4 mph make navigation prohibitively slow. The cost of increased transit time must be considered in the analysis.

[1] Charles W. Howe, Methods for Equipment Selection and Benefit Evaluation in Inland Waterway Transportation, *Water Resources Res.*, vol. 1 (1st Quarter, 1965), pp. 25–39.
Charles W. Howe, Mathematical Model of Barge Tow Performance, *Proc. ASCE*, vol. 93, no. WW 4 (November, 1967), pp. 153–166.

TABLE 14-1   Effects of Depth on Tow Performance

Vessel draft, ft	8.5	8.5
Vessel horsepower	4,500	4,500
Vessel width, ft	144.8	144.8
Channel width, ft	200	300

Channel depth, ft	$/ton-mile	$/ton-mile
12.0	0.00121	0.00103
18.0	0.00102	0.00087
24.0	0.00094	0.00080
30.0	0.00088	0.00075
36.0	0.00083	0.00071
42.0	0.00079	0.00067
48.0	0.00076	0.00064
342.0	0.00033	0.00028

SOURCE: Charles W. Howe, Methods for Equipment Selection and Benefit Evaluation in Inland Waterway Transportation, *Water Resources Res.*, vol. 1 (1st Quarter, 1965), p. 37.

When the locks used to transfer vessels from one water level to another are small, flotillas must be broken up to pass through at a substantial increase in transit time. Even where this is not necessary, each lock means vessel delay, operating and maintenance expense, and lockage water loss. Alternative combinations of lock size and lock spacing need to be considered to find the one with least cost.

Simulation (the generation of typical barge traffic patterns by applying random numbers and known probabilities) provides a valuable tool for finding the size of waterway or harbor that minimizes the sum of facility and vessel costs. An annual freight volume can be selected. A waterway size can be picked. An appropriate maximum vessel size can be established from the size of the waterway and connecting channels and harbors. Movement of the selected freight volume through the waterway in the vessels can be simulated in the context of local weather, streamflow, and traffic conditions. Operation and congestion costs can be estimated and summed to get C_{wv}. If the vessel size for a particular project is not predetermined by connecting facilities, alternative vessel sizes may be studied to find the one moving the traffic through the waterway at least cost. The results provide one point on each of the three curves of Fig. 14-1. Other waterway sizes can be selected and the procedure repeated to complete the curves and determine the minimum cost point for the selected freight volume. The whole process can be repeated for a sequence of freight volumes to obtain additional points to complete the total-cost curve. Because the analysis is seeking the optimum facility design, the total-cost curve would plot facility cost vs. freight volume (the economic channel capacity) and thus be the locus of points such as B in Fig. 14-1 plotted against associated tons per year.

Estimating the Demand

14-10 NAVIGATION BENEFIT Navigation projects benefit the economy by reducing transportation cost. The savings equals the difference between the transportation cost by the mode used without the project and that by inland water. For a given commodity shipped between two given points

$$C_s = C_a - C_{wv} - C_{hv} - C_p \tag{14-3}$$

where C_s is the savings, C_a is the cost which would be required to ship the commodity by the least costly alternative transport mode, C_{wv} is the cost of moving the good through the waterway, C_{hv} is the cost of moving the good through the harbor, and C_p is the premium shippers are willing to pay for the superior service of the alternative mode. The costs C_{wf} and C_{hf} are not included in demand analysis because they are incorporated in the supply curve. All costs may be expressed in dollars per ton. Evaluation of navigation benefit requires estimation of values for each of these terms for each commodity likely to be shipped through the facilities.

14-11 TRANSPORTATION COST ANALYSIS Freight shipped through an improved waterway would, without the improvement, be shipped by some other transport mode, be shipped on the unimproved waterway, or not be shipped at all. Whether a good would be shipped depends on its value in use at its potential destination. If the user would be willing to pay the additional transportation charge, C_a is the marginal cost of shipping by the alternative mode. Otherwise, C_a is some lesser amount determined as the maximum shipping charge the user would be willing to pay and estimated by analysis of his use of the commodity, and C_p is zero. If without the project a good would be shipped on the unimproved waterway, C_a equals $C_{hv} + C_{wv}$ for that waterway.

The alternative mode would normally be by rail but can be determined in a given case from analysis of available facilities. The marginal cost of shipping via the alternative mode is the cost of using its facilities to get the commodity from its origin to its destination that would not accrue were the commodity not shipped. Direct analysis from railway cost records would be the best way of estimating this value were not railway cost structure so complex. In the absence of better information and as an approximate overall average, the marginal cost may be taken as 75 percent of the published rate[1] when evaluating a presently nonexistent waterway and 100 percent when evaluating a waterway improvement.

An adjustment is needed if diversion of the good to the waterway will alter the marginal cost for shippers still using the alternative mode. An increase in cost to remaining shippers because of loss of economies of scale should be deducted from project benefit. A reduction in cost because of reduced congestion should be added to project benefit.

The cost of moving a commodity through the waterway varies with the size of the waterway and the total quantity of freight being moved. The long-run marginal cost C_{wv} of moving a given volume of freight through a given waterway can be read from the appropriate curve as in Fig. 14-1 (point A). Once a waterway is constructed, the much smaller

[1] Otto Eckstein, "Water Resource Development: The Economics of Project Evaluation" (Cambridge, Mass.: Harvard University Press, 1958), pp. 172–173.

short-run marginal cost (capital recovery of sunk cost no longer applies) determines use levels. As traffic increases with time, congestion will increase the short-run marginal cost until it eventually exceeds long-run marginal cost, an indication that expansion is justified.

The cost of moving a commodity through the harbor varies with the available harbor facilities. The vessel long-run marginal cost C_{hv} may be determined for a specified level of harbor improvement through the same procedure used to determine the analogous terms for waterways. For commodities whose origin or destination is located at a distance from the harbor, the cost of transporting them to or from the harbor should be added to C_{hv} in Eq. (14-3).

Because waterways provide slow service subject to seasonal interruptions, most shippers would be willing to pay a premium C_p for the higher-quality service offered by the other modes. The amount of the premium depends on the value gained through a shorter transit time. It may be estimated by comparing transit time by inland waterway with that by the alternative transport mode and analyzing the importance of quicker delivery. It may be expected to vary from about 10 percent of C_a for most bulk commodities to a prohibitively large value for perishable goods. Negative values may be used where the project improves and thus provides better service through an existing waterway by reducing congestion.

14-12 COMMODITIES SHIPPED Theoretically, Eq. (14-3) could be applied to the full range of commodities needing to be moved between points connected by a waterway or to or from an area served by a harbor. All goods having a positive value of C_s should be moved through the navigation facilities. As a more approximate but more practical approach, the commodities most likely to be shipped on a prospective waterway can be estimated from past experience on similar waterways or from questionnaires submitted to prospective shippers. Usually 10 to 20 goods comprise over 95 percent of the traffic, and these are the goods for which a detailed analysis is required. The tonnage of each good to be shipped is estimated from the existing demand and projections of regional industrial activity, which are best obtained with input-output growth models (Sec. 9-3). Silberberg has developed a linear programming model for estimating volumes of coal moved by barge as a function of regional industrial activity and rail and barge freight rates.[1] The model is especially helpful in determining the effects on navigation traffic resulting from changes in any of these parameters.

[1] Eugene Silberberg, The Demand for Inland Waterway Transportation, *Water Resources Res.*, vol. 2 (1st Quarter, 1966), pp. 13–29.

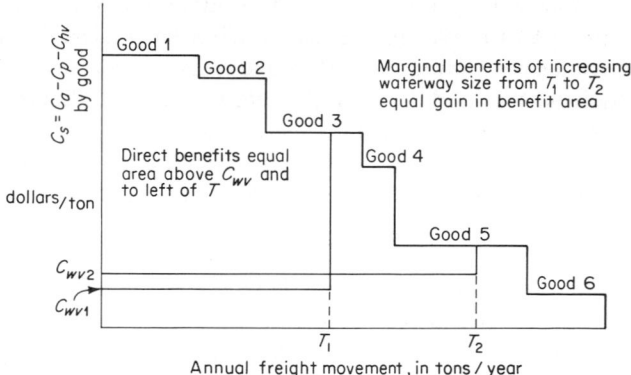

FIGURE 14-2   Navigation benefits.

The costs represented by the terms in Eq. (14-3) need only be evaluated in detail for the commodities comprising a significant portion of the projected traffic. Special care is needed in evaluating a few primary commodities. Even for a project as large as the St. Lawrence Seaway, 40 percent of the benefits depend on a single commodity, iron ore.

14-13 DEMAND FOR WATERWAY FACILITIES   The demand for waterway facilities is estimated by developing a marginal-benefit curve based on a known set of harbor facilities. Values of C_a, C_{hv}, and C_p and expected tonnage are estimated for each commodity expected to move through the waterway. The value of $C_a - C_p - C_{hv}$ may then be estimated, and the commodities may be arranged in descending order, beginning with the one for which the greatest transport savings is realized by waterway shipment. The benefit resulting from a waterway having any desired economic capacity can be determined from a plot of $C_a - C_p - C_{hv}$ vs. the cumulative tons per year having equal or greater transport savings (Fig. 14-2). The analysis proceeds one by one through each of the family of waterway optimization curves (Fig. 14-1) by using its annual freight volume T and vessel cost associated with the optimum design, C_{wv}, to estimate a total direct benefit as shown in Fig. 14-2. Indirect or secondary benefits may be added as warranted. The total-benefit curve is a plot of total benefit vs. a series of selected capacities. The slope of this curve gives benefits marginal to increasing waterway size.

14-14 DEMAND FOR HARBOR FACILITIES   The demand for harbor facilities is based on a known set of waterway facilities. Values of

C_a, C_{wv}, and C_p and expected tonnage are estimated for each commodity expected to move through the harbor so that savings may be plotted vs. cumulative annual freight movement. For a selected harbor capacity, C_{hv} is determined. The total benefit is the area between the savings curve (Fig. 14-2) and C_{hv} of the selected harbor capacity. The total benefit may be plotted vs. a series of harbor capacities. The slope of this curve gives benefits marginal to increasing harbor size.

14-15 DEMAND FOR COMBINED HARBOR AND WATERWAY IMPROVEMENT If both waterway and harbor facilities are to be improved in the same project, total demand must be estimated from a combined marginal-benefit curve. Values of C_a, C_p, and expected tonnage are estimated for each commodity expected to move through the facilities. The required cost curves (Fig. 14-1) represent $C_v = C_{hv} + C_{wv}$ and $C_f = C_{hf} + C_{wf}$. A given facility capacity may then be selected and the corresponding value of C_v determined. For each commodity, C_s may then be calculated in the customary manner, and the procedure is completed as before, to get benefits marginal to increasing combined facility size.

14-16 RECREATION DEMAND The use of navigable waterways by pleasure craft is becoming large enough to necessitate provision for these vessels in project planning. Under the current practice of not improving waterways solely for pleasure craft, the cost would be for the additional facilities required to prevent these craft from congesting the waterway. Special small-craft harbors are also needed. The benefit derived is recreational in character and may be analyzed in user days (Sec. 16-12). Small-craft harbors might alternatively be justified by returns reasonably expected from operating boats for hire.

Project Feasibility

14-17 ECONOMIC FEASIBILITY The marginal cost of providing for additional freight transport is compared with the resulting marginal benefit to determine the capacity for providing freight transport which can be economically provided. The waterway optimization curve (Fig. 14-1) for this freight volume provides a waterway cost (point B) and thus indirectly the optimum design. Waterway dimensions determine vessel size. The resulting project is economically justified if total benefit exceeds total cost.

14-18   FINANCIAL FEASIBILITY   Since Congress abolished all tolls on government improved waterways in 1884,[1] federal funds (approximately $6,500 million) have been used to finance construction, operation, and maintenance; local funds (approximately $3,500 million) to finance right-of-way (including that for spoil material), utility relocations, and most terminal facilities; and private funds to finance the vessels and the remaining terminal facilities. Local funds may be required to pay all construction expenditures in excess of a prescribed federal limit. Barge tows pay certain lockage and other fees.

The provision of waterways almost free to the user amounts to a substantial subsidy of waterway transportation. The effect of the subsidy is to promote inefficient use of the total transportation system by diverting traffic to waterway facilities which are made artifically inexpensive to the shipper. However, the rates charged for shipping by other transportation modes also departs from marginal costs. Trucks do not pay marginal highway cost, considering their contribution to highway congestion. Railway rates probably vary widely on both sides of marginal cost. Many airlines receive direct subsidies, and all receive below-cost use of airport facilities. A more efficient allocation of freight traffic among the transport modes would result if each paid its own full share of the marginal transport cost.

The Interstate Commerce Commission regulates rates of all goods (such as manufactured products) which must be carefully placed in a barge for shipment. Barge owners must charge the published rates for each good between each pair of terminals. Bulk commodities which can be dumped into barges without further handling are exempt from regulation unless more than three such commodities are transported on a barge flotilla or are transported on the same flotilla with regulated commodities. Also exempt are private carriers (carriers who own both the barge and the freight) and contract carriers (barge owners hauling freight by contract for a particular party) when it is ruled that the inherent nature of the commodity means the contract carrier is not competitive with common carriers (barge owners serving the general public). Normally, the barge lines charge the specific rates listed between specific terminals for specific commodities. High group rates may be used for commodities for which no specific rates are listed between the terminals in question, but they are usually replaced by new specific rates established by direct bargaining.

[1]   U.S., *Statutes at Large*, XXIII, 133.

SELECTED REFERENCES

Eckstein, Otto: "Water Resource Development: The Economics of Project Evaluation" (Cambridge, Mass.: Harvard University Press, 1958), pp. 160–191.

Howe, Charles W.: Methods for Equipment Selection and Benefit Evaluation in Inland Waterway Transportation, *Water Resources Res.*, vol. 1 (1st Quarter, 1965), pp. 25–39.

Kuiper, Edward: "Water Resources Development: Engineering, Economics, and Planning" (Washington: Butterworth & Co. (Publishers), Ltd., 1965), pp. 366–386.

Linsley, Ray K., and J. B. Franzini: "Water-resources Engineering" (New York: McGraw-Hill Book Company, 1964), pp. 468–489.

Locklin, P. D.: "Economics of Transportation" (Chicago: Richard D. Irwin, Inc., 1966), pp. 712–761.

Nicolaou, Stavros N.: Berth Planning by Evaluation of Congestion and Cost, *Proc. ASCE*, vol. 93, no. WW 4 (November, 1967), pp. 107–132.

Plumlee, Carl H.: Optimum Size Seaport, *Proc. ASCE*, vol. 92, no. WW 3 (August, 1966), pp. 1–24.

Quinn, Alonzo DeF.: "Design and Construction of Ports and Marine Structures" (New York: McGraw-Hill Book Company, 1961).

Silberberg, Eugene: The Demand for Inland Waterway Transportation, *Water Resources Res.*, vol. 2 (1st Quarter, 1966), pp. 13–29.

PROBLEMS

14-1 A certain navigation channel has a 300-ft bottom width, bottom slope of 0.00004, side slope of 4:1, and Manning's n of 0.025. Assuming a minimum clearance of 0.5 ft between the barge bottom and channel bottom and a practical capacity equal to 25 percent maximum capacity, plot a curve of flow rate vs. practical capacity from depths of 4.0 to 9.0 ft? What would be the practical capacity and flow rates for barges of 8.5-ft draft with a water depth of 12.0 ft? 18.0 ft? What value per acre-foot has the water that is necessary to provide this extra depth, based on Table 14-1 (assume negligible congestion cost)?

14-2 A navigation channel is proposed which would have the primary function of transporting sand and gravel. Rail freight charges are $2.00 per ton, while water transport costs $0.80 per ton. The project has a first cost of $100,000 and an annual operation and maintenance cost of $5,000. Estimated traffic is 10,000 tons/year. With a 50-year life and 3 percent interest, what would be the benefit-cost ratio of the project be if rail freight rates were assumed to equal

1.33 times marginal cost? What would the benefit-cost ratio be if, in addition, railroads were entitled to a 10 percent higher rate than water transport because of better-quality service?

14-3   Outline the specific information you would need to simulate a Fig. 14-1 graph for a navigation project to connect two navigable waterways with a 50-mile canal of the dimensions given in Prob. 14-1.

14-4   A coal company is considering construction of a slack-water-navigation canal leading 10 miles from a major navigable waterway into a newly developed coal field. Excavation depth would vary from $4 + d$ ft at the river end to $10 + d$ ft at the upstream end. Total excavation cost (including engineering) equals $2.50 per cubic yard. Right-of-way costs $300 per acre. The canal is to be constructed with 4:1 side slopes. Annual operation and maintenance equals 0.7 percent of excavation cost, L is 50 years, and i is 7 percent. Barges used in the river have a deadweight of 300 short tons, length of 195 ft, width of 35 ft, maximum draft of 8.5 ft, and a 10 mph speed in still water. The coal is to be shipped 40 miles downriver to a steel plant. The cost of moving a barge is 0.3 cents per ton-mile including deadweight. Minimum clearance from barge to stream bottom is 0.5 ft. The coal can be shipped to the steel mill for 50 cents per ton by rail. The coal will be loaded directly into the barge at the upstream end at about the same cost it would take to load a railroad car. Barges will not be reloaded once they reach the deeper water of the river. The company places no value on faster rail service. Assume a flotilla is twice as many barges long as wide, and at maximum capacity flotillas are spaced one flotilla length apart. Practical capacity equals 25 percent of maximum capacity.

a. How much coal must the company sell to the steel mill annually to make the minimum project economical ($d = 4.5$ ft, $b = 100$ ft)?

b. How much coal must be sold annually to justify increasing the channel depth to 6.5 ft? to 8.5 ft?

c. How much coal must be sold annually to justify increasing the width of the 8.5-ft-deep channel to 200 ft?

CHAPTER FIFTEEN

WATER QUALITY CONTROL

The Planning Context

15-1 DEFINITION If water is withdrawn from the stream, it may be used in homes, industries, or farms. If the water is left in the stream, it serves as a transportation artery, a source of power, a place to fish, boat, or swim, and contributes to the environment which makes a community a pleasant place to live in. Finally, streamflow may be used to carry waste material away from homes, factories, or mines. Streamflow has a value in use, a value in transit, and a value as a waste carrier. The first two functions compete with the third because a waste load infringes on the value of water in other uses.

Water quality planning requires selection and preservation of water quality standards, the rules specifying the kinds and quantities of waste material which will be permitted to enter the stream. It is not in the public interest to allow everyone to discharge waste material freely into streams, but it is equally unwise to outlaw all use of the stream as a waste carrier. Optimum water quality control lies at the point between these two extremes where the sum of the value of the water in the three uses is a maximum. At the optimum water quality standard, the marginal decline in the sum of the values of the water in use and transit which would be caused by the discharge of additional waste material equals the marginal cost incured in waste treatment or nonstream disposal to maintain the standard.

15-2 TYPES OF POLLUTION The impurities in water can be divided between *degradable* (nonconservative) wastes, which decompose into harmless substances or are otherwise removed from the stream by natural biological, chemical, or physical processes, and *nondegradable* (conservative) wastes, which are not altered by such processes. The first class includes domestic sewage, heat, plant nutrients, most bacteria and viruses, and noncolloidal sediments. The second includes salts and other inorganic chemicals, radiological waste products, persistent organic chemicals including many detergents and agricultural chemicals, and colloidal suspensions. Contamination refers to impurities posing a hazard to human health.

The concentration of the pollutant is usually expressed in parts per million (ppm); 1 ppm is one pound of pollutant per one million pounds of water. The only natural process mitigating the adverse effects of non-degradable wastes in the stream is dilution. Their concentration at any point can be predicted by dividing the weight of waste material entering the stream by the quantity of diluting water [Eq. (15-1)].

The concentration of a degradable waste is much more difficult to predict because it is reduced by natural processes as the waste travels downstream. Organic-pollution load is measured by biochemical oxygen demand (BOD), the oxygen in parts per million which would have to be withdrawn from the stream to oxidize all the organic material into relatively harmless compounds. Stream oxygen balance depends on the rate that oxygen is withdrawn from the stream to oxidize the organic material (deoxygenation) and the rate oxygen dissolves in the stream from the air (reoxygenation).[1] If the BOD completely depletes the stream of dissolved

---

[1]   Nelson L. Nemerow, "Theories and Practices of Industrial Waste Treatment" (Reading, Mass.: Addison-Wesley Publishing Company, Inc., 1963), pp. 22–48.

TABLE 15-1   Variation in Stream Environment and Biota past a Typical Point of Pollution-load Entry

Stream, miles	Dissolved oxygen, ppm	BOD, ppm	Number of species	Av. species population, $1,000$ sq ft^{-1}
−1	7.5	2.0	40	1.0
0	7.5	20.0	40	1.0
12	3.5	15.0	9	4.0
24	2.0	11.5	1	8.0
48	3.5	6.5	2	10.0
72	5.0	3.5	10	7.5
96	7.0	2.5	26	3.5
120	7.5	2.0	40	1.0

SOURCE: William M. Ingram and Kenneth M. Mackenthun, The Pollution Environment, in Kenneth L. Bowden (ed.), "Proceedings of the Second Annual American Water Resources Conference" (Urbana, Ill.: American Water Resources Association, 1966), pp. 115–133.

oxygen, the resulting anaerobic conditions retard decomposition, produce objectionable odors, and kill fish and other water life. Table 15-1 indicates a typical variation in stream environment past a point of severe organic pollution. As BOD exhausts the dissolved oxygen, most species disappear, but such remaining species as sludge worms become very numerous. Because the solubility of oxygen in water varies inversely with temperature, the danger of anaerobic conditions is greater in summer than winter and greatest during summer low-flow periods. Heat pollution, primarily caused by use of the water for industrial cooling, aggrevates deoxygenation.

By oxidizing organic matter, waste-water treatment liberates the mineral constitutents. These dissolve in the effluent and fertilize aquatic vegetation, particularly unicellular algae. Phosphates are the biggest offender. The luxuriant vegetation in the receiving waters produces obnoxious ordors, clogs intake structures, and may become toxic to desirable plants and animals. The resulting esthetic and economic degradation is called *eutrophication* and is rapidly becoming the major fresh-water-quality problem.

Sediment may be either rolled along the stream bed or carried in suspension within the flow. The carrying capacity of the stream increases with flow velocity, and the susceptibility of particles to movement is inversely related to the size of nonplastic soil particles and the plastic index of cohesive soils. Sediment-transport theory provides methods for estimating both suspended- and bed-load movement.[1]

15-3   COORDINATION   WITH   OTHER   PROJECT   PURPOSES
Each water use has distinct water quality requirements and distinct effects on the quality of the water it uses. Water used for domestic supply must be free from disease-causing bacteria and viruses as well as toxic chemicals and must contain a minimum of unattractive tastes, odors, or colors. Corrosive or hard waters may harm household appliances or plumbing and increase soap use. Domestic water quality requirements are primarily to preserve human health, make water psychologically more pleasing to the user, and reduce the cost of household appliances and plumbing. Only the third requirement can be evaluated economically (for example, proposals for municipal water softening have been subjected to benefit-cost analysis based on soap saved) as extramarket values control the first two. Waste water from residential areas contains large quantities of degradable waste, bacteria, and nondegradable household chemicals.

About 80 percent of industrial water use is for cooling, and about 20 percent is for use in other industrial processes. Cooling water should have a

[1]   Hans Albert Einstein, Sedimentation Part II: River Sedimentation, in Ven Te Chow (ed.), "Handbook of Applied Hydrology" (New York: McGraw-Hill Book Company, 1964), pp. 17-35–17-67.

low temperature and be free from corrosive and scale-forming materials. Process uses tend to be more sensitive to water quality than cooling uses are, but the exact water quality requirements depend on the nature of the process. As examples, iron, manganese, and carbon dioxide interfere with paper-making processes; and steel rolling mills are damaged by high choloride concentrations. The primary effect of the cooling use on water quality is the addition of heat, which limits cooling use by others and reduces stream oxygen content. Industrial-process wastes are widely varied, and some are extremely toxic or otherwise objectionable. A single food- or paper-processing plant may produce as much waste as a medium-size city.

Irrigation requires water free from chemicals or bacteria toxic to plants or to persons or animals who eat the plants and from chemicals which react with the soil to produce unsatisfactory moisture characteristics. Boron concentrations over 4 ppm harm most crops. Selenium is absorbed in the plant and is toxic to livestock. When sodium cations exceed about 10 percent of the total, the aggregation of soil grains begins to break down to make the soil less permeable and crust when dry and to cause its pH to rise above tolerable limits. Crusting restricts soil drainage and aeration. Total dissolved solids in excess of 700 ppm restrict plant osmotic activity and absorption of soil nutrients. Water quality requirements vary greatly among plant species and become more restrictive for soils of lower permeability or in areas of high water table. A given crop is more salt tolerant in cool than in warm climates. The salt tolerance of a specific crop depends on the sensitivity of the plant to increased osmotic pressure.[1] Bacterial contamination is a threat to public health when severely contaminated water is used to irrigate vegetables customarily eaten raw.

Irrigation return flows are normally more saline than the applied water, because of evapotranspiration losses and the use of the water for leaching soil salts.[2] Agricultural chemicals occasionally contaminate return flows and add phosphates to intensify eutrophication. Quality improvements include lower temperatures, turbidity, and coliform bacteria counts. Drainage flows from humid areas are normally less saline than irrigation return flows but may contain toxic agricultural chemicals.

Surface mining, logging, heavy construction, and forest fires destroy soil cover and substantially increase the sediment content of runoff until the cover is restored. Haul roads constructed for forest access multiply sediment content severalfold unless special measures are taken to stop

---

[1] R. O. Slatyer and J. A. Mabbutt, Hydrology of Arid and Semiarid Regions, in Ven Te Chow (ed.), "Handbook of Applied Hydrology" (New York: McGraw-Hill Book Company, 1964), pp. 24-41–24-42.

[2] For a detailed analysis of the effect of irrigation return flows on the quality of the North Platte River, see Joe Kendall Neel, Certain Limnological Features of a Polluted Irrigation Stream, *Trans. Am. Microscop. Soc.*, vol. 72, no. 2 (April, 1953).

gully erosion. Coal and mineral ore mines may discharge acid or other harmful chemicals into the water. Petroleum production brings brackish water to the surface that may enter the stream if it is not returned to underground aquifers.

Fish require a minimum of dissolved oxygen of about 4 ppm, and no water-related wildlife, including ducks, frogs, and shellfish, can tolerate anaerobic conditions. Many agricultural and industrial chemicals are toxic. Any activity which disturbs the natural ecological environment of the stream is detrimental to natural habitats. Since specific fish species require specific salinity and temperature ranges, slow changes may cause a habitat to shift from one species to another, and fluctuations too rapid for biological adjustment will eliminate most species. Trout, for example, require long-term water temperatures below 22°C and cannot survive temperatures over 25°C.[1] Waterfowl may be harmed by pollution of their breeding and feeding grounds. Shellfish grown in polluted waters may spread disease as they are eaten.

Recreation requires water free from disease-causing bacteria or viruses or poisons causing bodily harm upon internal or external contact and is enhanced by the absence of esthetically uninviting colors, odors, or turbidity in the water. Skin and respiratory diseases may be transmitted by body wastes which accumulate within recreational water. Recreation-site amenity usually imposes more severe water quality standards than public health factors do. Lower quality standards may be applied to recreational water from which bathing is excluded. Boats with toilet or kitchen facilities may create a health hazard if the refuse is dropped directly into the water, and beaches may be impaired by the oil residue left by motor boats.

Many municipalities restrict the recreational use of their water supply reservoirs and even of the tributary watersheds through fear of pollution. It is true that increased recreational use may increase the danger of bacteria's getting into the water or of watershed fires. However, chlorination is required to ensure the biological safety of any public water supply. The additional cost of water treatment required by recreational-caused pollution has not been shown to be significant and is certainly far less than the recreation benefit. Forest fire danger can be minimized by restrictions in recreational use of the watershed during high-hazard periods. The trend has been toward opening municipal reservoirs for multiple use as long as the facilities are properly maintained and adequate waste-disposal methods are provided and used.[2]

---

[1] Louis Klein, "River Pollution, Vol. II: Causes and Effects" (London: Butterworth & Co. (Publishers), Ltd., 1962), p. 49.

[2] Byron Beattie, Municipal Watersheds and Recreation Can Be Compatible, in Roma K. McNicle (ed.), "Water: Development, Utilization, Conservation" (Boulder: University of Colorado Press, 1964), pp. 37–45.

The water quality requirements for navigation and hydroelectric power projects are minimal. Turbines or propellers may be harmed by unusually large sediment or debris and various corrosive chemicals. Chemical cleaning residue may be left in the water, and reservoir storage may significantly reduce stream waste-carrying capacity.

Flood control works are unlikely to reduce water quality, but flood damages are higher when there is inundation by low-quality water. High sediment contents are particularly harmful. Toxic chemicals or organic wastes may contaminate public water supplies but are unlikely to be present in significant concentrations during flood flows unless the flood inundates and washes away material from sewage-treatment plants or warehouse or storage areas.

Reservoirs affect downstream water quality in a number of ways.[1] A net evaporation loss increases average downstream salinity; but salinity peaks may be reduced by low-flow augmentation. The leaching of salts from soils within the reservoir may also increase salinity during the early years of reservoir life. Sediment deposition in the reservoir reduces downstream turbidity and increases downstream scour; however, this effect may be offset by a reduction in scour-producing flood peaks. Reservoirs tend to delay river temperature rise in the spring and decline in the fall and dampen high and low temperature extremes. Reservoir stratification will reduce the dissolved oxygen content of the released flows, and slack water caused by back-to-back reservoirs will retard reaeration. Stratification is intensified by use of reservoir water for industrial or thermal electric plant cooling.[2] Degradable wastes change much more slowly in ponded than in flowing water. Inadequate clearing of organic material from a reservoir site may have a number of undesirable effects on water quality.[3]

15-4 HISTORICAL DEVELOPMENT   The need for waste disposal and the external diseconomies caused by using water as a waste carrier increase with population and industrial growth. Eventually, enforced minimum water quality standards are required to protect third parties. Prior to 1940, few states did more than provide advice on water quality control; but since then, most states have passed legislation to regulate pollution. Interstate compacts have been formed to regulate water

[1]   Joe Kendall Neel, Impact of Reservoirs, in David G. Frey (ed.), "Limnology in North America" (Madison: The University of Wisconsin Press, 1963).
[2]   Peter A. Krenkel, William A. Cawley, and Virgil A. Minch, The Effect of Impounding Reservoirs on River Waste Assimilative Capacity, *J. Water Pollution Control Federation*, vol. 37 (September, 1965).
[3]   Robert O. Sylvester, The Influence of Reservoir Soils on Overlying Water Quality, in O. Jaag (ed.), "Advances in Water Pollution Research," vol. 1, (London: Pergamon Press, Ltd., 1965), pp. 327–344.

quality in such river basins as the Delaware, Hudson, Potomac, and Ohio. Public Law 845 (1948) marked the first exercise of federal power to regulate pollution, and in more recent acts (1956, 1962), federal programs to aid pollution control measures financially have been instigated. In 1965, legislation was passed to give the United States government power to establish and enforce minimum water quality standards on interstate streams within states which should fail to put acceptable standards into effect by June 30, 1967.

The most widely used water quality control measure is waste-water treatment. As rivers and streams have been subjected to increased waste loads, cities and industries have been forced to treat their wastes to remove objectionable impurities. Even greater waste loads have required the development of new treatment methods to remove more waste material or to treat the wastes of new industrial processes.

Water quality control as an expressed purpose of a large-scale water resources project first occurred with construction of Shasta Dam in California in 1945 to provide low-flow augmentation to preserve a permanent velocity gradient toward the sea. In any river system without this gradient, salt water will travel upstream to the point where the stream bottom falls below sea level. An alternative method for preventing salt-water intrusion is to prevent reverse flows by a physical barrier. Both barriers and seaward velocity gradients have been used to prevent salt-water intrusion of ground-water aquifers adjacent to salt-water bodies. Use of reservoir yield for low-flow augmentation for waste dilution promises to become a major purpose of future water resource project construction.

Developing the Supply

A great many methods must be coordinated in formulating the optimum water quality control system. The technical design of system elements is described in sanitary engineering literature,[1] but it is necessary to review the basic approaches briefly in order to understand how they may be coordinated effectively.

15-5 WASTE-WATER TREATMENT   Waste-water-treatment plants improve the quality of waste water before it is discharged into the stream.

---

[1]   Gordon M. Fair, John Charles Geyer, and Daniel A. Okun, "Water and Waste Water Engineering" (New York: John Wiley & Sons, Inc., 1966) is a standard introductory text.

Most communities remove degradable organic wastes by primary treatment (screening and sedimentation) supplemented by secondary treatment (use of biological processes) to accelerate the self-purification which occurs in .natural waters. New tertiary processes are being developed to further purify the effluent from secondary treatment. Where the use of water as a waste carrier conflicts with its value in use rather than with its value in transit, the water may be treated as it is withdrawn (Sec. 12-6).

Unit treatment costs vary with:[1]

1 *The volume of waste flow to be treated.* Economies of scale reduce unit treatment cost with increasing volume.
2 *The variability of the rate of incoming waste flow.* The size and cost of the treatment facilities depends on the peak flow entering the plant. Thus cost per volume of water treated increases with the peak-to-volume ratio.
3 *The concentration of the waste.* The more concentrated the waste, the higher the cost will be.
4 *The character of the waste.* Commonly encountered waste materials can be handled by conventional treatment processes, while extraordinary waste materials require special, more costly treatment.
5 *The required degree of waste removal.* Cost increases with the purity of the required effluent.

Water may be taken from a river, used, and returned with a waste load several times on the way to the sea. The cost of required treatment before use is reduced by natural purification within an intervening river reach. Popular esthetic objections to direct recirculation of treated waste water into urban supplies (Sec. 12-8) also diminish if the natural purification processes of streams or aquifers are used.

Within a recirculation system, economic trade-off possibilities exist between waste and water supply treatment. The more completely wastes are treated before being discharged into a stream, the less completely water supplies must be treated after they are withdrawn. In analyzing the trade-off, Frankel found the savings in downstream water treatment costs were seldom as high as 10 percent of the upstream waste treatment cost.[2] His finding means, at least for degradable wastes, treatment before discharge into the stream must be largely justified

1 Bernard Charles McBeath, "A Study of Economic Effects of Treatment Plant and Stream Parameters on Waste Water Disposal (Stanford, Calif.: Stanford University, Institute in Engineering Economic Systems, EEP-21, 1966).
2 Richard J. Frankel, Water Quality Management: Engineering-Economic Factors in Municipal Waste Disposal, *Water Resources Res.*, vol. 1 (2d Quarter, 1965), pp. 173–186.

by losses to value in transit rather than by losses to downstream water users. Because the primary value in transit is from recreational and fishing use, economic justification for controlling stream pollution is highly dependent on recreation benefits. The optimum combination of waste and water supply treatment is that which maintains the desired water quality standards for water in use and water in transit at least cost.

Smaller communities and industries may realize economies of scale in combining to build one large, rather than many small, treatment plants. Treatment-plant construction cost per volume of water treated declines with plant size. Larger plants can afford more highly skilled operators who are able to run the treatment process more efficiently. Both savings may be offset by the increased cost of a collection system which must bring the wastes from greater distances and difficulties with objectionable chemical reactions or odors in transit. The economically optimum plant size has the minimum sum of plant costs and collection costs.

15-6 WASTE-WATER DILUTION Since the harmful effects of pollution increase with waste concentration, damages may be reduced by bringing the time patterns of waste discharge and streamflow more in line with one another. One method is low-flow augmentation by which reservoirs provide water for supplementing flows during dry periods. An alternative approach is to build storage facilities to contain the wastes during dry periods for release into the stream during times of higher flow. The two approaches may be combined in a search for the least-cost combination. Streamflow regulation is most profitable for increasing extreme low flows, and waste-storage facilities are most profitable for dampening peak rates of waste accumulation.

15-7 WASTE-WATER SEPARATION Many cities have long provided separate systems for collecting their storm runoff and their sanitary wastes. More recently, large-scale specialized channels to carry non-degradable wastes, which cannot be removed at reasonable cost by treatment, and to provide waste collection to take advantage of the economies of scale of large treatment plants have been proposed. Such channels or pipes can also be used to distribute outlet points into the receiving water geographically in the manner best promoting water quality management objectives. The Emscher River in Germany is concrete lined for use entirely as a waste carrier, and the entire flow is treated in a large plant before discharge into the Rhine. Plans are under way for construction of a channel to carry saline irrigation return flows parallel to the San Joaquin River in California to a salt-water outlet. Economic pressure for special channels to carry waste is particularly acute where the amount of waste material is very large compared with stream-flow. In Germany, the need is created by the large amounts of waste produced by a highly industrialized area. In California, the need is created by streamflow depletion for irrigation having highly saline return flows. Some treatment is required before discharging industrial or municipal wastes into a specialized channel to prevent degradable wastes from producing particularly undesirable odors or appearances. Lining may be required to prevent the waste material from contaminating the ground water. The cost of waste transport includes the value of the water required to transport the wastes. A major advantage of carrying more concentrated wastes in a separate channel is the resulting savings in water used.

15-8 INDUSTRIAL PROCESS MODIFICATION Pollution dam-ages may also be reduced by process adjustments by industries who discharge their wastes into the stream or who use the stream for water supply. An industry discharging wastes might shift to an industrial process producing smaller quantities of a less obnoxious type of waste material, or it might reschedule its operations so more of the waste would be produced during high-flow seasons. A water-using industry might shift to an industrial process less sensitive to poor water quality or reschedule its more sensitive processes during high-flow periods. It might store high-quality flows for use during periods of low-quality flow or develop an alternative ground-water supply for temporary use. A cost analysis is needed to evaluate each potential adjustment. Water pollution damages may also be reduced by incorporating water quality considerations in industrial location decisions. Industries requiring a high-quality water supply should locate in upstream areas, and industries discharging an extremely low-quality effluent should locate downstream.

15-9 THE SUPPLY CURVE The supply curve must be developed from a curve of total cost of achieving a given water quality standard against that standard usually expressed as a concentration. The alternative measures for providing water quality control are so many and so varied as to require an extensive effort in economic systems analysis to pick the optimum combination. Within a treatment plant, the optimum of many alternative flow patterns through treatment processes must be selected.[1] The optimum treatment plant must then be combined with the optimum combination of low-flow augmentation, effluent storage,

---

[1] Walter R. Lynn, John A. Logan, and A. Charnes, System Analysis for Planning Wastewater Treat-ment Plants, *J. Water Pollution Control Federation*, vol. 34 (1962), pp. 565–581.

and other measures.[1] The most general mathematical models analyze the interrelationships among water quality control programs and pertinent physical, economic, and administrative factors. The form of the analysis generally follows a pattern analogous to that discussed for flood control (Sec. 10-9).

Estimating the Demand

Engineering measures for water quality control are economically justified if they reduce the damage caused by poor water quality by an amount in excess of their cost. Benefit evaluation thus requires evaluation of damages with and without specific measures.

15-10 DAMAGE EVALUATION   The value of water in use and in transit decreases with deteriorating water quality. Each user may suffer the loss inflicted by using poor-quality stream water, adjust his water use pattern so that sensitive uses do not occur during periods of low water quality, develop an alternative supply to avoid using low-quality water, or treat the water. The damage he suffers from a given decline in water quality is the sum of the costs of the least-expensive combination of measures available to him. The damage may then be summed for all users and added to the loss of value in transit, where the only alternative is to suffer the loss. For a given pollutant, the analysis can be used to develop a curve of annual damage vs. waste-water concentration (Fig. 15-1). Where the damage caused by one pollutant depends on damage caused by other pollutants, several curves expressing damage as a function of the concentration of the first pollutant are needed, with damages suffered from other types of pollution as the third parameter.

---

[1] M. Mead Montgomery and Walter R. Lynn, Analysis of Sewage Treatment Systems by Simulation, *Proc. ASCE*, vol. 90, no. SA 1 (February, 1964), pp. 73–97.

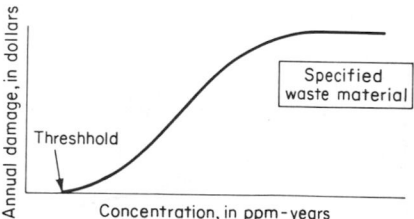

FIGURE 15-1   Damage-concentration curve.

The best way of developing a damage-concentration curve for a given river reach is to aggregate by vertical-addition curves derived individually for the major user groups, including municipalities, several classes of industry, irrigators, fish and wildlife, and recreation. A practical method of handling the time variability of stream water quality and water use patterns is to base the user damage-concentration curves on a standardized curve plotting the annual damage per acre-foot of water used which would occur if the pollution concentration in the water supplied the user were to remain constant over the course of the year. A standardized curve is needed for each combination of pollutant and user type. The appropriate standardized curve may be converted into a user damage-concentration curve by multiplying the damage per unit of water volume by the number of acre-feet used per year.

Damage-concentration curves are normally S-shaped with no damage inflicted until the waste reaches a threshold concentration, then a range in which damages increase rapidly with increasing concentration, and finally a range in which the water quality is already so bad that greater concentration can do little more harm. The selection of an inflexible water quality standard specifying a maximum allowable concentration implies a damage-concentration curve rising vertically from zero to infinity at the selected concentration.

The aggregate damage concentration curve may be used to estimate average annual water quality damages by combining with a curve relating concentration to streamflow (Fig. 15-2). The curve may be developed by plotting sampled water quality against simultaneous streamflow. Alternatively, the curve may be computed from the time pattern of nondegradable waste discharge and streamflow hydrographs by

$$QC = 0.186W \qquad (15\text{-}1)$$

where Q is the streamflow in cubic feet per second, C is the concentration in parts per million, and W is the rate of upstream waste discharge in pounds per day. Concentrations tend to be greatest at the beginning of the wet season when accumulated wastes are being flushed from the watershed. This relationship may require seasonal concentration-flow curves. The

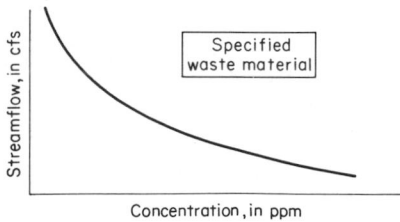

FIGURE 15-2   Concentration-flow curve.

FIGURE 15-3 Damage-flow curve.

concentration-flow relationship is much more complicated for degradable wastes, as concentration decreases downstream in a manner depending on the availablity of dissolved oxygen.

The curves of Figs. 15-1 and 15-2 may be combined to obtain a damage-flow curve (Fig. 15-3) for each waste material. It is necessary to account for the variability of streamflow by combining Fig. 15-3 with a flow-duration curve developed from historical or synthetic streamflow records (Fig. 15-4). Finally, Figs. 15-3 and 15-4 may be combined to obtain a damage-frequency curve (Fig. 15-5). After curves like those in Fig. 15-5 have been developed for each damage-causing pollutant, total average annual damages are estimated by summing the areas under the individual curves.

The above methodology assumes water quality damage to be directly proportional to the duration that pollution concentration remains above a given level. Flood damage differs from water quality damage in that the amount of damage depends more on the extreme event during the year and less on its duration. While estimating water quality damages from the frequency of extreme events has been suggested,[1] it seems more

---

[1] Allen V. Kneese, "The Economics of Regional Water Quality Management" (Baltimore: The Johns Hopkins Press, 1964), p. 131.

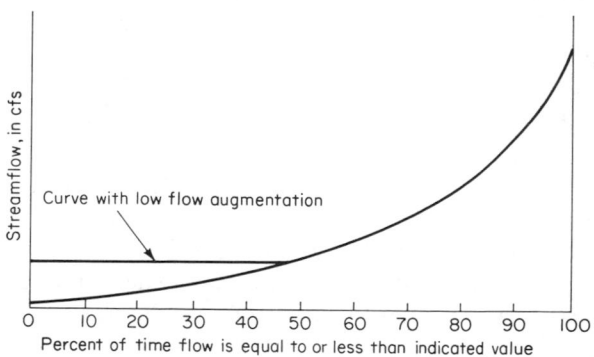

FIGURE 15-4 Flow-duration curve.

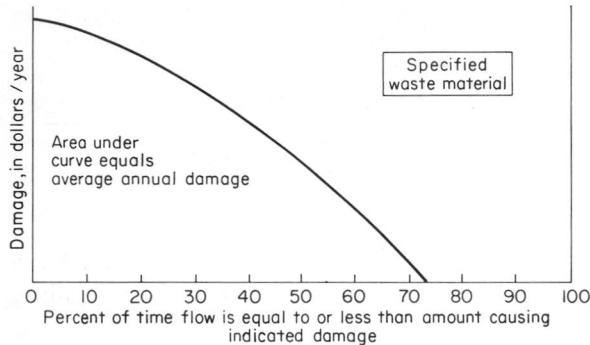

FIGURE 15-5   Damage-frequency curve.

reasonable to assume the duration of low-quality flows to be the primary factor.

15-11 PROBLEMS IN DAMAGE MEASUREMENT   The basic data required to estimate water pollution damages are contained in Figs. 15-1, 15-2, and 15-4. The flow-duration curve (Fig. 15-4) is readily developed from stream-gage data as long as the period of record is long enough to include dry as well as wet years. Streamflow records are available on most streams large enough to have the year-round flows required for waste disposal. The concentration-flow curve (Fig. 15-2) may be developed from water quality data or from waste-disposal records. Since these records are less readily available than streamflow data, one may have to initiate a program of data collection and analysis. Suitable data may normally be obtained from short periods of record.

The most critical step in estimating water quality damages is developing Fig. 15-1. Research to establish concentration-damage relationships is essential for planning measures for water quality control and is particularly important because water quality control is slated to become a major function of future water resource development.

Damages from pollution of industrial water supplies may be estimated by analyzing individual industrial processes to determine how they are affected by various levels of water quality. An alternative approach is to interview industries which have suffered through a deteriorating water quality situation, to determine the costs they incurred.[1]

[1]   Rolf Eliassen and Walter Rowland, "Industrial Benefits Derived from Improved Raw Water Quality in the Contra Costa Canal" (Stanford, Calif.: Stanford University, Institute in Engineering Economic Systems EEP-4, 1962).

The loss in crop income inflicted by poor-quality irrigation water depends on accumulated soil salinity (Sec. 12-14). Occasional irrigation by highly saline water may not prove harmful if salt accumulation is prevented by later leaching. On the other hand, farmland may eventually become unproductive if consistently irrigated with relatively good-quality water without leaching. The need for as many salts to be carried away by return flows as are brought in by the irrigation water suggests that damages caused by low-quality irrigation water may be estimated from the value of the additional irrigation water required for leaching. Additional damages occur where the poor water quality forces farmers to grow a lower-value but more salt-resistant crop.

Attempts have been made to estimate damages wrought by poor-quality municipal water from the cost of illness, including medical care and income lost by sick leave,[1] but it is doubtful whether these losses represent the full willingness of individuals to pay for good health. A more reasonable method for calculating municipal water quality damages is determining how much it costs to treat the water to protect human health.

The relationship between water quality and the value of water in transit depends on effects on fish, recreation, and aesthetics. One might develop data to estimate the relationship between recreation visitation and poor water quality and convert visitation to benefit (Sec. 16-12). An analogous procedure might be based on the effect of water quality on fish population or fish catch. The purely aesthetic value is too intangible to approach directly (Sec. 5-5), but studies determining the cost of preserving alternative sets of aesthetic standards would prove helpful.

The alternative-cost approach has achieved widespread use in estimating water quality control benefits. Federal practice is to use as the alternative the least-expensive single-purpose reservoir providing dilution water.

15-12 BENEFIT MEASUREMENT   Engineering measures for water quality control modify the damage-concentration curve (Fig. 15-1), the concentration-flow curve (Fig. 15-2), or the flow-duration curve (Fig. 15-4). The damage inflicted by a given pollutant concentration may be varied by industrial process modification (Sec. 15-8) to change either the susceptibility of the process to damage or the amount of poor-quality water used. Economic analysis requires a damage-concentration curve with and without the process change.

The concentration-flow curve (Fig. 15-2) may be modified in three ways. Waste treatment changes the curve by reducing the quantity of

[1] Kneese, *op. cit.*, pp. 74–78.

waste discharged into the stream or by ameliorating the harmful properties of the waste which is discharged. Equation (15-1) may be used to adjust Fig. 15-2 for a given reduction in W to get a curve closer to the origin. A separate waste-water channel reduces W by diverting the waste load from the main channel, and Fig. 15-2 may be adjusted in the same way. Modification of the time pattern of waste discharge by waste storage or the rescheduling of industrial processes during low-flow periods steepens the concentration-flow curve with the ultimate line's being vertical if wastes are always discharged in proportion to flow. Low-flow augmentation alters the flow-duration curve (Fig. 15-4) by increasing the magnitude of low flows. The amount of augmentation may be expressed as the minimum flow allowed.

Once the physical effect of a proposed measure on one or more of the three curves has been determined, the damage-estimating process (Sec. 15-10) may be completed with and without the measure. Varying the measure over a range of possible sizes provides the basis for developing total- and marginal-benefit curves.

System Management

15-13 ECONOMIC OPTIMIZATION Water pollutants do not endanger health or produce other undesirable extramarket effects if their concentration is low enough. As concentrations increase, a point is eventually reached where extramarket consequences to public health, community development, or other intangible values become too severe to be permitted. This threshhold concentration defines a minimum socially acceptable water quality standard and must be selected by value judgments based on known qualitative factors. Economic damages are evaluated to determine whether a higher standard can be justified. Many nondegradable wastes are not detrimental in certain concentration ranges to health, wildlife, or aesthetics; but they may inflict an economic damage to industry or agriculture great enough to warrant water quality improvement measures.

Water quality standards determined by economic optimization display several characteristics. The optimum concentration of waste material increases with decreasing flow rate because of the increasing marginal cost of removal. As waste discharge which can be prevented at little cost is stopped, further prevention becomes increasingly costly. The optimum concentration rises downstream from each urban area because of the resulting demand for waste disposal. Optimum concentration also increases as the river proceeds downstream because fewer parties remain further downstream to be harmed.

15-14 *COORDINATED SYSTEM MANAGEMENT* The goal of river-system water quality management is to minimize the sum of the damages caused by poor water quality and the cost of water quality control measures. Difficulty in damage measurement has often caused substitution of the approximate goal of maintaining a set of water quality standards at least cost. Unless an economic analysis is performed to determine optimum standards, arbitrarily set standards may result in nonoptimum development. Some management alternatives (low-flow augmentation and a specialized waste channel) are accomplished by public agencies, but others (location adjustment, waste-water treatment, and modification of waste discharge patterns) require action by industries and municipalities. Successful water quality management must get all these diverse groups to work together efficiently through a combination of legal regulation and economic incentives.

A sound program of water quality management should (1) make those who discharge wastes responsible for the effects of their action; (2) consider the implications of extramarket values; (3) encourage a balance between the cost of measures employed and the gain in value achieved through higher water quality; (4) encourage economies of scale in pollution treatment through cooperation among industries, municipalities, and other parties; and (5) be flexible enough to adapt to local needs. Even where extramarket considerations determine the standards, economic efficiency requires the marginal cost of each water quality control effort to be equal. The greatest weakness of uniform water quality standards is the elimination of diversity, which should exist in order to reflect local conditions. Having some streams of very high and others of very low water quality may be better management than having every stream contain a standardized marginal-quality water. New York State has separate standards for seven different stream classifications according to water use.

Legal regulation, the most common method of enforcing water quality standards in the United States,[1] has numerous difficulties. If available data and methods of analysis permitted determination of truly optimum water quality standards, there would be no loss to economic efficiency in maintaining these standards by legal enforcement. However, reliable concentration-damage data are not yet available, and their collec-

---

[1] A more detailed discussion of the use of this method in the Ohio River valley is found in Kneese, *op cit.*, pp. 99–119.

tion is hampered by difficulty in determining the costs of alternative adjustments in industrial processes where competitive industries wish to protect production secrets. Even if reliable data were available, water quality systems are so complex as to be exceedingly difficult to analyze with even the most sophisticated systems analysis techniques, and a general analytic model for evaluating alternative water quality control measures is far from developed. In the meantime, there is no way to know the optimum division of the waste load among individual discharges. Legal enforcement adds the cost of monitoring waste discharge to ensure conformance to the required standards, does little to encourage the cooperation required to achieve economies of scale, and is not responsive to needed variations in standards with time or geography.

Legal enforcement is also limited by practical problems in enforcing any regulation to which those governed do not consent.[1] Consent is achieved through bargaining between the regulators and the regulated to define both the standards and the enforcement procedure. As long as damage quantification remains controversial, water quality regulation will remain a matter of mutual consent between potential polluters and those harmed.

The problem of data collection and analysis to determine what rules to enforce may be eased by using the market process to encourage the required marginal adjustments. The water quality management agency might pay each party discharging waste material into the stream to reduce his discharge rate. The optimum payment per pound of waste material not discharged would cause the various parties to cut their waste disposal just enough to reduce waste concentrations below the maximum allowable level. Distinct uniform unit payments would be established for each pollutant. Each party would reduce his waste discharge until the marginal value of further reduction equaled the marginal payment. The difficulties with the payment method are that it does not guide in establishing the standards, it requires a large expenditure of public funds, it does not seem equitable to pay someone to stop causing harm, and waste monitoring is required to determine payment amounts. What is worse, in cases where industry cost and revenue functions are subject to change, payments may actually effect an increase in waste discharge.[2]

The difficulties are reduced by using charges rather than payments. Each party would be charged in proportion to the waste he discharged into the stream at a rate high enough to reduce waste concentration to the required levels. The money collected can be used to finance large-scale

1   Matthew Holden, "Pollution Control as a Bargaining Process: An Essay on Regulatory Decision Making" (Ithaca, N.Y.: Cornell University, Water Resources Center Publication 9, October, 1966).
2   M. I. Kamien, N. D. Schwartz, and F. T. Dolbear, A Symmetry between Bribes and Charges, *Water Resources Res.*, vol. 2 (1st Quarter, 1966), pp. 147–157.

treatment, low-flow augmentation, specialized channels, or other water quality control measures too costly for individual dischargers to finance.[1] Three drawbacks to the charging system are the cost of monitoring waste discharges,[2] the lack of guidance in setting water quality standards, and the reluctance of industrial and governmental groups to accept a system of charges.

Theoretically it would be possible to establish water quality standards by a system in which new waste dischargers are required to pay those downstream the amount they are harmed and in which new water users are able to pay upstream waste dischargers to reduce their discharge rate.[3] The resulting standard could be constrained below the concentration levels required by extramarket effects. However, implementation difficulties and institutional inertia have thus far prevented any water quality management system from operating on this basis.

A major difficulty in using a system of payments or charges for water quality control is finding a suitable waste unit on which to base the payment or charge. Ideally, the unit should be linearly proportional to the amount of harm caused and vary with the stream hydrograph according to the amount of naturally available diluting water. A charge proportional to pounds per day of waste discharged is not satisfactory because some wastes are much more harmful than others and because a pound of a given waste is much more harmful during low- than during high-flow periods. The unit which has been successfully applied in the Ruhr is the amount of dilution water required to reduce waste concentrations to acceptable levels.[4] Dilution is not actually used; the amount of dilution water which would be required merely serves as a charging vehicle (Sec. 23-8).

15-15 ESTABLISHMENT OF A MANAGEMENT SYSTEM As urban and industrial growth impose a greater burden on the waste-carrying capacity of rivers and streams, increasing effort must be directed toward water quality management. The task of regional water quality management is to supplement projects constructed for water pollution control by measures which prevent the uninhibited discharge of wastes into streams from eliminating project benefits and to coordinate the planning of structural with the planning of other management measures. The task begins with the establishment of an agency with jurisdiction over the drainage basin and authority to enforce, finance, and operate an effective program.

---

[1] This method has been used for years in the Ruhr. See Kneese, *op. cit.*, pp. 160–187.

[2] Edward J. Cleary, An Electronic Monitor System for River-Quality Surveillance and Research, in B. A. Southgate (ed.), "Advances in Water Pollution Research" (New York: The Macmillan Company, 1964).

[3] The theory of this approach is presented in Kneese, *op. cit.*, pp. 54–85.

[4] *Ibid.*, pp. 172–76.

The agency must be institutionally free to explore and implement as necessary all management alternatives and technically capable of doing so. The agency must assemble regional concentration-damage, concentration-flow, and flow-duration data and analyze it to set regional water quality standards after giving due consideration to extramarket values. The agency must formulate an enforcement program combining legal regulation with the use of less costly and more efficient economic incentives. Finally, the program must be implemented and periodically modified to reflect changing conditions or advances in knowledge.

The water quality management agency should be free to select its standards according to conditions within its jurisdiction and vary its standards from stream to stream and point to point on the same stream. Within a large river basin, subbasin agencies must agree to mutually acceptable quality standards at the points where rivers flow from one jurisdiction to another. The water quality agencies must also coordinate their efforts with those of the water supply and other water resource agencies serving the same region. Coordination with agencies serving other areas or purposes is one of the most complicated but essential elements of water resources management.

SELECTED REFERENCES

Cleary, Edward J.: An Electronic Monitor System for River-quality Surveillance and Research, in B. A. Southgate (ed.), "Advances in Water Pollution Research" (New York: The Macmillan Company, 1964).

————: "The ORSANCO Story: Water Quality Management in the Ohio Valley under Interstate Compact" (Baltimore: The Johns Hopkins Press, 1967).

Davis, Robert K.: "The Range of Choice in Water Management" (Baltimore: The Johns Hopkins Press, 1968).

Elder, Rex A., et al.: Hydraulic Engineering Aspects of Water Quality Management, *Proc. ASCE*, vol. 92, no. HY 6 (November, 1966), pp. 61–80.

Eliassen, Rolf, and Walter Rowland: "Industrial Benefits Derived from Improved Raw Water Quality in the Contra Costa Canal" (Stanford, Calif.: Stanford University, Institute in Engineering Economic Systems, EEP-4, 1962).

Fair, Gordon M., John Charles Geyer, and Daniel A. Okun: "Water and Waste Water Engineering," 2 vols. (New York: John Wiley & Sons, Inc., 1966).

Federal Water Pollution Control Administration, "Water Quality Criteria: Report of the National Technical Committee to the Secretary of the Interior" (Washington: USGPO, 1968).

Frankel, Richard J.: Water Quality Management: Engineering-Economic Factors in Municipal Waste Disposal, *Water Resources Res.*, vol. 1 (2d Quarter, 1965), pp. 173–186.

Gloyna, Earnest F.: Major Research Problems in Water Quality, in A. V. Kneese and S. C. Smith (eds.), "Water Research" (Baltimore: The Johns Hopkins Press, 1966).

Hammond, R. J.: "Benefit-Cost Analysis and Water-pollution Control" (Stanford, Calif.: Stanford University Press, Food Research Institute, 1959).

Kneese, Allen V.: "The Economics of Regional Water Quality Management" (Baltimore: The Johns Hopkins Press, 1964).

Loucks, D. P., and Walter R. Lynn: Probabilistic Models for Predicting Stream Quality, *Water Resources Res.*, vol. 2 (3d Quarter, 1966), pp. 593–605.

Sobel, Mathew J.: Water Quality Improvement Programming Problems, *Water Resources Res.*, vol. 1 (4th Quarter, 1965), pp. 477–487.

Whipple, William: Economic Basis for Effluent Charges and Subsidies, *Water Resources Res.*, vol. 2 (1st Quarter, 1966), pp. 159–166.

PROBLEMS

15-1 Assume two large industrial plants are located on a stream having the flow-duration data given below. One plant has a threshold of chloride damage at 100 ppm and is damaged at a rate of $10 per ppm-year by concentrations above this amount. The second plant has values of 50 ppm and $8 respectively. Chlorides are being discharged into the stream upstream from the plants at a rate of 40,000 lb/day. Calculate annual damages for the wet year, dry year, and average year.

PERCENT OF TIME EXCEEDED

Flow, cfs	Dry year	Average year	Wet year
4.5	100.0	100.0	100.0
7.4	99.7	99.9	100.0
12.2	98.9	99.3	100.0
20.1	83.1	94.4	100.0
33.1	67.5	88.1	96.4
54.6	48.6	76.8	93.7
90.0	40.4	66.4	84.7
148.4	35.5	56.3	71.8
244.7	28.1	47.4	64.0
403.4	17.8	35.6	47.9
665.1	12.0	23.6	33.7
1,096.6	7.7	14.3	20.8

15-2 Forty industries of each of the two types indicated in Prob. 15-1 are located along a river where low-flow augmentation is proposed to reduce damages caused by poor water quality. Plot average annual damages vs. minimum flow allowed. Plot a marginal-benefit curve. Plot a curve of acre-feet of augmentation water required vs. minimum flow allowed. If water can be obtained for augmentation at $10 per acre-foot, what is the optimum minimum flow?

15-3 How much should each industrial plant in Prob. 15-1 be willing to pay to get those upstream to reduce their daily chloride discharge by 10,000 lb/day? How much could each one fairly charge a new upstream industry for discharging 10,000 lb/day and thus raising the total to 50,000?

15-4 The first of the two industries in Prob. 15-1 is considering conversion to a process having a threshold damage of 200 ppm and a damage rate of $6 per ppm-year. How much would the conversion save in average annual damage?

15-5 A method is available for disposing of chlorides underground at a cost of a penny a pound. How many pounds would have to be put underground in an average year to eliminate all damage to both industries of Prob. 15-1? What would be the benefit-cost ratio for doing this upstream of the reach of Prob. 15-2? Develop a marginal-benefit curve to determine the optimum average annual underground disposal.

15-6 The deteriorating water quality in many of our streams is becoming a major political issue. Many natural waters have deteriorated to the point where they can never recover. The people of Boston ask, "How long since you have seen a salmon in the Charles River?" The rebuttal has been, "How long since you have seen deer grazing along Boylston Street?" The only way to restore natural conditions is for man to leave, and such an alternative is simply not realistic.
  a What basic values (human needs) are achieved through improved water quality?
  b What kinds of sacrifices are required to accomplish this improvement?
  c What role does the engineer have in helping society resolve this issue?

CHAPTER
SIXTEEN

RECREATION

The Planning Context

16-1 DEFINITION   Recreation provides physical, mental, and emotional rejuvenation through the relaxation made possible by relieving the strain of doing what one has to do. The experience may be contrasted with activities undertaken to earn an income and such routine activities of life as eating and sleeping. The water resources planner is interested in outdoor recreation activities associated with the presence or proximity of water, particularly reservoirs. Activities which require direct use of water include boating, ice skating, swimming, water skiing, and fishing. Shoreline activities do not use the water directly, but the proximity of the water enhances the value of the activity to the participant or supplements the recreation experience for those not wishing to spend all their time in water-dependent activities. Included are picnicking, camping, and hiking. Water for fishing and hunting is closely related to recreation (Chap. 17).

16-2 HISTORICAL DEVELOPMENT   Lakes, rivers, and streams have always provided relaxation and enjoyment. However, increasing incomes have allowed people to spend more money on leisure-time activities, and shorter working hours have allowed them to spend more time. Modern transportation facilities have made recreation possible at more distant sites. Expanding urbanization has forced those who once enjoyed the open space of the farm to seek outdoor recreation away from home. Every forecast indicates the use of reservoirs for recreation will expand much faster than the total population. From 1953 to 1963, annual attendance at Corps of Engineers reservoirs increased an average of 13.6 percent,[1] while the annual rate of population growth was 1.7 percent.

Recreational features were not expressly incorporated into the older water resource projects, and recreation benefits were not counted. However, shortly after the completion of nearly every reservoir, recreation facilities appeared along the shorelines. As recreation became more important to the local economy, operating policies were often modified to enhance recreational attractiveness. As recreation became a factor in the planning and design of new reservoirs, it became necessary to include recreational benefits in project formulation and justification. The present status of recreation planning in the United States was clarified by the Federal Water Project Recreation Act of 1965, which stated:

> In investigating and planning any Federal . . . water resource project, full consideration shall be given to the opportunities, if any, which the project affords for outdoor recreation and for fish and wildlife enhancement and . . . it shall be constructed, operated, and maintained accordingly.[2]

Developing the Supply

16-3 FACILITY DESIGN   Recreation facilities are designed to provide an environment of sufficient quality to provide the desired relaxation and enjoyment. The key facility is the body of water, usually furnished by construction of a dam and reservoir. The reservoir is capital intensive or characterized by high construction and low operation and maintenance cost. Any body of water will attract visitors, but the experience can be enhanced by considering recreation in reservoir operation and site selection. Reservoir operation for recreation keeps the water surface as high as possible and minimizes water surface fluctuation. Excessive drawdown and large fluctuations disturb shoreline facilities and create an unattractive appearance. However, during the passage of floods, it is only necessary to protect shoreline facilities from damage because significant recreational use rarely occurs simultaneously with the intense storms. The reservoir must develop sufficient water to overcome net evaporation losses and to provide for the personal use of the recreational users.

Recreational use is a factor in reservoir site selection. Excessive shoreline slopes make walking difficult, restrict shallow-water swimming areas, and result in colder shoreline water temperatures. Sand for beach areas will have to be imported if not available naturally, and the finer the

---

[1]   William M. White, Evaluation of Recreation in Water Developments, *Proc. ASCE*, vol. 91, no. PO 1 (May 1965).

[2]   Public Law 89-72, 89th Cong., S. 1229, July 9, 1965.

grain size, the more will have to be imported because of erosion losses.[1] Clearing vegetation from the beaches and continued maintenance is required to control brush and weeds along the shoreline and nuisance plants (algae and other plants) within the reservoir. Mosquitos, gnats, and other insect pests as well as leeches and worms must be controlled. Sunshine is desirable along the shoreline, but a number of larger trees should be available to provide shade in the picnicking and camping areas. The optimum water temperature for swimming and water skiing is about 70°F.

Reservoir recreation also requires maintenance-intensive shoreline facilities; the annual cost of preserving their attractiveness is high compared with their first cost.[2] A cost analysis of recreation facilities at three Kentucky and Ohio reservoirs indicated average annual operation and maintenance cost to range from $0.066 to $0.132 per visitor day of use, while average annual amortized capital ranged from $0.046 to $0.237.[3] Total cost per marginal visitor averaged about $0.04.[4] The facilities have a much shorter life than the recreation reservoir and must normally be replaced several times during the project life.

Criteria have been published for the evaluation of existing or the design of new shoreline facilities to maximize the quality of the experience provided.[5] Parking areas must be provided, and observation points enhance the value of scenic spots. Small-craft launching and docking facilities are required to accommodate boaters and should provide mooring and fuel and repair service. Camping facilities may include tent and trailer sites, housekeeping cottages, tables, sanitary and waste-disposal systems, and a water supply. The camping and picnicking areas must be kept clean of undergrowth, trash, and refuse. Beach facilities include floats for swimmers, ropes separating boating from swimming areas, and a lifeguard during the swimming season. Attractive landscaping of the shoreline area is important, and plantings should screen nearby unattractive land use. The cleanliness of the site is a major factor determining its attractiveness. Designs and costs for features such as picnic tables, comfort stations, and parking areas have been largely standardized.[6]

[1] W. C. Krumbein and W. R. James, *A Log-normal Size Distribution Model for Estimating Stability of Beach Fill Material*, U.S. Army Coastal Eng. Res. Center, Tech. Mem. 16 (1965).

[2] The California Department of Water Resources estimates annual operation and maintenance cost for shoreline facilities at 30 cents per visitor day of use and annual replacement cost at 3.5 percent of capital investment. The Corps of Engineers uses 20 cents per visitor day.

[3] John E. Sirles, "Application of Marginal Economic Analysis to Reservoir Recreation Planning," (Lexington: University of Kentucky, Water Resources Institute Res. Rept. 12, 1968), pp. 30, 36.

[4] *Ibid.* p. 49.

[5] Charles C. Stott, "Evaluating Water Based Recreation Facilities and Areas" (Washington: National Recreation and Park Association, Bull. 70, 1967).

[6] U.S. Army Corps of Engineers, Project Operations: Recreation Facilities, in "Criteria for Design and Construction, Civil Works Projects," *Eng. Manual* EM 1130-2-312 (May 1, 1960).

Adequately signed access roads from nearby through highways are essential to full use of the reservoir recreation facilities. The cost of these roads should be considered in project evaluation; however, a portion of the cost may be attributed to nonrecreational users where their numbers are significant. Landscaping makes the road more attractive.

16-4   ESTIMATING RECREATION CAPACITY   The capacity of a recreation reservoir to provide outdoor leisure-time activity may be expressed as the number of visitors who can be accommodated simultaneously. However, two questions must be answered before a capacity can be determined. The first is: What activities should be provided and how should the total available space be divided among them (determining the activity composite)? The second is: How crowded should the activity space be before it is considered filled to capacity (establishing the capacity coefficients)?

There are six major recreation activities found at reservoirs: camping (including other overnight accommodations), picnicking, boating (including water skiing), swimming, fishing, and sightseeing. The capacity of a site for the first four depends on the maximum intensity of visitor use (say in campers per acre of camping area) which still provides a satisfying recreation experience. The capacity would be the product of the maximum use intensity and the acreage devoted to it. The capacity for fishing depends on the quantity of available fish (Sec. 17-8). Sightseers come to the reservoir not to take part in any particular activity but just to look around and to watch others. They do not congregate in a separate area but rather wander throughout the entire site to some extent restricting those engaged in the other activities. Therefore, it is better to consider sightseeing capacity included in the capacity for the first four activities rather than a separate capacity.

Some might wish to establish the activity composite by use of economic efficiency criteria. The efficient activity composite maximizes the total net benefit from the project or the sum of the areas between the activity-demand curves and their respective supply curves. At this point, the marginal rates of transformation among the various activities will be equal. Optimization thus requires data to estimate independent demand curves for each activity, but the demand for one activity depends on the availability of other activities. More campers will be attracted by improved swimming and boating facilities. The psychic interrelationship among demand curves violates the requirement of independent demand necessary for optimization based on economic efficiency (Sec.

4-16). Theoretically, it would be possible to select the activity composite maximizing the visitation provided by a given expenditure for recreation development or enjoyed within a given recreation area, but this would not be optimum because it would lead to overdevelopment of lower-valued at the expense of higher-valued activities. Picnicking and swimming would gain at the expense of camping and boating.

16-5   THE ACTIVITY COMPOSITE   While economic criteria cannot be used to select the optimum activity composite, the planner has other guidelines for designating the areas best assigned to specific activities. The most practical approach is to outline the gross area suitable for recreational use and appropriate for the total predicted number of visitors on topographic maps and then subdivide the total area among the designated activities. A number of guidelines for determining the suitability of an area for an activity have been published.[1] The planner must strive to provide the maximum quality recreation experience consistent with the availability of funds and the characteristics of the site as determined by consultation with experts in limnology, fish and game management, park and recreation planning, and related subjects. The intensity, relative to capacity, of the use in each area should be about the same. The success of existing patterns of development at reservoirs in similar environments provides additional guidance. The physical features of a site will make it more suitable for some and less suitable for other activities. A warmer climate favors activities for direct use of the water. Close proximity to a population center will favor day use with emphasis on short-duration activities, while greater distances favor vacation use and more camping facilities.

Facilities for indirect activities should be installed in areas of moderate slopes having a good view and in easy walking distance of the lake. Limits are arbitrary, but most recreation areas should be within 0.5 mile of the lake on slopes less than 20 percent and separated from through highways and other nonrecreational land use. Swimming should be concentrated in a few spots along the shoreline with ready access, sandy beaches, and some shallow water. Boating may be expected over the entire lake surface except for swimming, fishing, and other shallow shoreline areas and near the dam and spillway. Once the space dedicated to each activity is outlined on a map, the acreage by activity is readily tabulated.

[1]   California Committee on Planning for Recreation, "Guide for Planning Recreation Parks in California: A Basis for Determining Local Recreation Space Standards" (Sacramento, 1956); U.S. Army Corps of Engineers, *op. cit.*

16-6 THE CAPACITY COEFFICIENTS The attractiveness of a recreational activity to one user depends on the number of others who participate simultaneously.[1] This dependence also violates the independent demand requirement of marginal economic analysis and means that capacity coefficients must also be selected by other criteria. The desirability of a site generally increases with use by others up to the point where the user begins to feel crowded, and then it begins to decline. The crowding is usually psychological rather than physical. The optimum intensity is on the crowded side of the use having maximum attractiveness to the individual user because total value received is the product of individual value and the number of users. It is approximately the intensity at which significant numbers of people begin to leave or seek other recreation. Crowding will exist only during peak periods of use, which usually occur on summer Sundays and holidays.

The capacity coefficient is the number of visitors who can be accommodated per unit of area without excessive crowding. Individual participants require varying degrees of solitude during a satisfying recreation experience depending on various psychological and personality factors. The requirement of a given individual varies depending on whether he is seeking a summer afternoon of swimming or vacation camping. Capacity coefficients may be empirically determined by observing the density of activity participation during periods of peak use, but many individuals will feel too crowded and seek their recreation elsewhere before use density reaches a peak. Empirical observations typically give capacity coefficients about equal to those in Table 16-1. About 20 hikers/mile of trail may be used.

16-7 USER DAYS AND ACTIVITY DAYS Over a period of time, total visitation to a reservoir is less than the sum of those engaging in the

---

[1] Marion Clawson and Jack L. Knetsch, "Economics of Outdoor Recreation (Baltimore: The Johns Hopkins Press, 1966), pp. 167–170.

TABLE 16-1 Typical Capacity Coefficients

Activity	Users per acre
Picnicking	50
Camping	20
Boating (including water skiing)	0.5
Swimming	600

individual activities because many visitors take part in more than one activity during a day of reservoir recreation. A *user day* is 1 day all or part spent in recreational experience enjoyed at the site by one person. A visitor day comprises 12 visitor hr, but the term is often less precisely used interchangeably with user day. An *activity day* (alternatively called a *recreation day*) is 1 day during which an individual engages in a particular activity (boating, swimming, or hiking, for example). An activity day does not imply a whole day spent in the activity but only participation during a significant portion of the day.

On an annual basis,

$$U = f_a A_t \tag{16-1}$$

where U is the annual number of user days, A_t is the annual number of activity days, and f_a is the factor relating the two, which can never exceed 1. The value of f_a varies between 0.3 and 0.5 for a typical reservoir providing each of the basic activities. The Bureau of Outdoor Recreation has used 0.4 in one of its studies.[1] Data collected for Dewey Reservoir in Floyd County, Kentucky, revealed a value of 0.436 and a variation from 0.36 in July to about 0.93 in February. Summer visitors participate in many activities, while most winter visitors are sightseers. The value of f_a tends to be larger for sites primarily used for short-term visits from nearby communities and lower for more isolated sites visited primarily by vacationers. Records of total user days and total activity days can be used for estimating f_a under specified conditions.

At times of peak visitation to a total recreation area, f_a approaches 1.[2] Peak participation in the various activities tends to occur simultaneously. Movements of visitors among activities tend to compensate one another. As a result, total facility capacity is essentially equal to the sum of the activity capacities.

16-8   THE MARGINAL-COST CURVE   The marginal-cost curve for use in recreation facility optimization depends on the issue to be decided. Generally, reservoir size is determined by the requirements of other project purposes, and a procedure is needed to determine the marginal-cost curve for optimizing the degree of shoreline development. If the reservoir size is in question too, the process below can be repeated to determine the optimal shoreline development for each size of reservoir as a step in overall optimization (Sec. 16-17).

[1]   Ohio River Basin Comprehensive Survey, Appendix H, p. 3-6.
[2]   Sirles, *op. cit.*, p. 42.

The steps required to determine the optimum shoreline development include:

1 For each of a series of acreages devoted to shoreline recreation development covering the range within which the optimum size may potentially lie, the area is designated which would best be dedicated to each activity.

2 The capacity of each acreage to provide for each activity is estimated by multiplying the appropriate capacity coefficients by the designated areas.

3 The capacity of the facilities to accommodate visitors is computed by summing the activity capacities (Sec. 16-7).

4 The cost of developing each acreage with appropriate peripheral facilities is estimated. The cost in each case should be the sum of the installation, operation, and maintenance costs expressed as a discounted average annual value over the life of the project.

5 The total annual cost for each acreage is then plotted against the number of visitors which it can accommodate simultaneously to get the total-cost curve.

6 The marginal costs equal the slope of the total-cost curve and are plotted against the corresponding capacity.

Estimating the Demand

16-9 TIME DISTRIBUTION OF RESERVOIR VISITATION The number of visitors to a reservoir varies from practically zero during cold winter nights to near capacity during summer Sunday afternoons. In order to select a design capacity, it is necessary to estimate how often and how much a limited capacity will actually restrict visitation. The demand for a greater capacity is only significant when the available capacity is used. It is necessary to analyze the variation in reservoir utilization over the course of the year, the week, and the day.

During the year, visitation varies from summer highs to winter lows. Monthly visitor distribution by activity for Rough River Reservoir is shown in Table 16-2. Sightseeing is spread more evenly throughout the year than the other activities because it is least restricted by cold weather. At the opposite extreme, swimming is most highly concentrated in the summer. Table 16-3 indicates how fractions of total annual and peak monthly visitation vary from reservoir to reservoir. A colder climate or shorter summer season reduces the monthly utilization factor (0.345

TABLE 16-2 Monthly Distribution of Reservoir Visitation by Activity*

Month	Total	Sight-seeing	Fishing	Camping	Picnicking	Boating	Swimming
Jan.	0.021	0.016	0.021	0.000	0.000	0.017	0.000
Feb.	0.027	0.017	0.029	0.001	0.000	0.018	0.000
Mar.	0.027	0.026	0.035	0.025	0.020	0.021	0.000
Apr.	0.074	0.087	0.083	0.060	0.038	0.038	0.000
May	0.135	0.148	0.127	0.113	0.137	0.155	0.121
June	0.142	0.141	0.163	0.199	0.218	0.199	0.234
July	0.207	0.174	0.205	0.262	0.267	0.265	0.302
Aug.	0.194	0.173	0.185	0.233	0.259	0.228	0.278
Sept.	0.088	0.112	0.071	0.061	0.054	0.052	0.065
Oct.	0.057	0.082	0.050	0.037	0.004	0.004	0.000
Nov.	0.017	0.013	0.020	0.008	0.002	0.002	0.000
Dec.	0.011	0.011	0.011	0.001	0.001	0.001	0.000
$\dfrac{Average}{Peak}$	0.404	0.478	0.407	0.318	0.312	0.314	0.276

* Rough River Reservoir.
SOURCE: U.S. Army Corps of Engineers, Ohio River Division.

TABLE 16-3 Monthly Distribution of Reservoir Visitation for Selected Reservoir Sites

Month	ROUGH RIVER, KY.		DEWEY, KY.		TENN. AND KY. RESERVOIRS		INDIANA AND OHIO RESERVOIRS	
	A*	B†	A*	B†	A*	B†	A*	B†
Jan.	0.021	0.101	0.006	0.025	0.031	0.221	0.013	0.054
Feb.	0.027	0.130	0.008	0.033	0.028	0.200	0.012	0.050
Mar.	0.027	0.130	0.019	0.079	0.045	0.321	0.015	0.062
Apr.	0.074	0.357	0.056	0.231	0.085	0.607	0.036	0.149
May	0.135	0.652	0.125	0.517	0.109	0.779	0.122	0.506
June	0.142	0.686	0.178	0.736	0.130	0.929	0.178	0.739
July	0.207	1.000	0.242	1.000	0.140	1.000	0.241	1.000
Aug.	0.194	0.937	0.167	0.690	0.130	0.929	0.202	0.838
Sept.	0.088	0.449	0.106	0.438	0.110	0.786	0.089	0.369
Oct.	0.057	0.275	0.050	0.207	0.083	0.593	0.046	0.191
Nov.	0.017	0.082	0.029	0.120	0.064	0.457	0.025	0.104
Dec.	0.011	0.053	0.014	0.058	0.042	0.300	0.021	0.087
Average		0.404		0.345		0.594		0.346

* Taken as a fraction of the total annual visitation.
† Taken as a fraction of the maximum monthly visitation.
SOURCE: U.S. Army Corps of Engineers, Ohio River Division.

for Dewey Reservoir), which is defined as the average intensity of use over the year divided by the intensity of use in the peak month. The activity composite will also affect the total monthly utilization factor (Table 16-2). Those planning recreation facilities in climatic or activity situations substantially different from those illustrated should observe the local visitation time pattern to derive factors applicable to their area.

Reservoir visitation also varies from weekend highs to weekday lows. Kentucky and Indiana data (Table 16-4) revealed a weekly utilization factor of 0.288. The weekly utilization factor would be expected to be highest at remote locations primarily attracting vacationers.

The daily distribution of reservoir visitation varies from early afternoon highs to nighttime lows. Data collected for Dewey Reservoir revealed 8.7 percent of the daily visitors remained at the site overnight and a peak of 26.4 percent were simultaneously at the reservoir. Daily counts for several reservoirs showed visitation by hour listed in order of decreasing number of visitors to be as indicated on Table 16-5.

TABLE 16-4 Weekly Distribution of Reservoir Visitation*

	Sun.	Mon.	Tues.	Wed.	Thurs.	Fri.	Sat.
Distribution:	0.495	0.065	0.065	0.066	0.077	0.082	0.149
Fraction of peak day:	1.000	0.131	0.131	0.133	0.156	0.166	0.301

Average Weekly Utilization: 0.288

* Based on the average of four reservoirs in Kentucky and Indiana.

TABLE 16-5 Daily Distribution
of Reservoir Visitation

Hour	Fraction of peak hour
1	1.000
2	0.947
3	0.902
4	0.807
5	0.715
6	0.623
7	0.520
8	0.454
9	0.368
10	0.264
11	0.247
12	0.221

16-10 OVERALL UTILIZATION OF RESERVOIR CAPACITY
The data describing visitation variation over the year, week, and day
may be combined into a curve expressing the fraction of the annual
visitation vs. the fraction of the time that many or more visitors are
present (Fig. 16-1). The peak hourly visitation may be estimated as the
product of the fraction of the daily visitors present during the peak hour,
the fraction of the weekly visitors present during the peak day, the
fraction of the annual visitors present during the peak month, and the
fraction of a month present in a week. For the Dewey Reservoir data, the
peak hour was $0.264(0.495)(0.242)(7)(12)/365 = 0.00728$ or 0.728 percent
of the annual visitors. For the third highest hour on a Friday in August,
visitation would be $0.690(0.166)(0.902)$ or 0.104 times the peak hour or
0.076 percent of the annual total. Similar values may be readily calculated
for each hour of the year and sorted in order of magnitude. Figure 16-1
shows these points for Dewey Reservoir.

Sometimes more people wish to visit a reservoir than can be com-
fortably accommodated by the available facilities. Space limitations may
cause the potential visitation, by people who would like to participate
in reservoir recreation activities, to exceed the visitation which can
actually be accommodated. For a very large facility, the full potential
visitation can be accommodated. The data used to plot the time distribution of visitation in Fig. 16-1 were obtained at a reservoir capable of

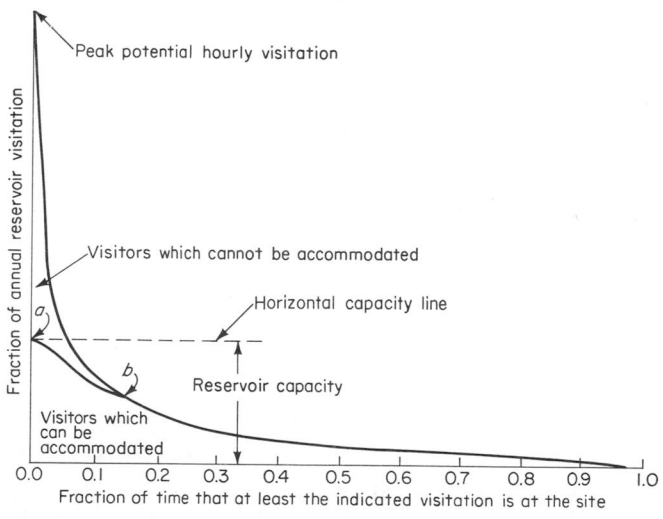

FIGURE 16-1   Time distribution of reservoir utilization.

accommodating full potential visitation. For progressively smaller facilities, actual visitation becomes a progressively smaller fraction of potential. Crowding would first begin to limit visitation during summer Sunday afternoons and then gradually extend over longer time periods.

If reservoir recreation capacity were plotted in Fig. 16-1, visitors represented by the area above the capacity line may go to the reservoir and then leave because of the crowding or may anticipate crowding and not go in the first place. The fraction of the total area below the horizontal, physically determined reservoir capacity line would represent the maximum fraction of the total potential visitors which a reservoir of the indicated capacity could accommodate.

However, even at times when the facilities are not crowded to their rated capacity, some visitors may not go to the reservoir because they are unwilling to take a chance of finding the facilities overcrowded. Others may not go because of a greater than average aversion to crowding. The result is an actual, psychologically determined reservoir capacity line of the general shape of Line *ab* in Fig. 16-1. Sirles collected empirical data verifying the downward slope in the capacity line by using data measuring how much visitation tends to concentrate during periods of peak use for sparsely used facilities and spread more evenly with time for heavily used facilities.[1]

The fraction of the total area below the capacity line (Fig. 16-1) represents the ratio of actual to potential visitors. Figure 16-2 is plotted

[1]   Sirles, *op. cit.*, pp. 62–73.

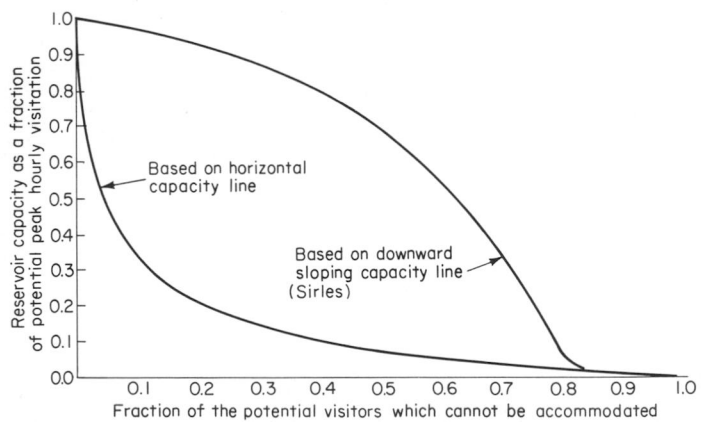

FIGURE 16-2   Relationship between reservoir recreation capacity and the fraction of the potential visitors who cannot be accommodated.

by measuring areas below a series of capacity lines and indicates the fraction of potential annual visitors who cannot be accommodated vs. reservoir capacity expressed as a fraction of the potential peak hourly visitation. One curve is based on the assumption of a physically determined horizontal capacity line, and the other is based on the psychologically determined downward-sloping line derived by Sirles.[1] This second line indicates that a psychological feeling of excessive crowding is more significant than physical capacity limitations in reducing visitation to intensively used facilities.

The procedure for estimating recreation benefit from a reservoir of specified size is thus to:

1 Estimate the total potential benefit (Fig. 16-4).
2 Estimate the reservoir recreation visitation capacity.
3 Estimate the fraction of the potential benefit accruing to visitors the reservoir can accommodate (Fig. 16-2).
4 Attribute the product of the last two numbers as recreation benefit from the reservoir.

Marginal benefits may be estimated from the change in area under the capacity line associated with a marginal change in capacity. The fraction of the potential benefits which can be attributed to the marginal capacity change is represented by the area bounded by the capacity lines with and without the change and the curve of Fig. 16-1.

16-11 FACTORS DETERMINING POTENTIAL VISITATION

Any reservoir will attract visitors. A more complete facility will attract more visitors. However, the geographical location limits the number of visitors conventional reservoir recreational facilities can attract to any site. A fully developed facility will attract this potential visitation. Lesser development will not. One might logically hypothesize potential recreation visitation to vary with:

1 *Accessibility of the site.* Accessibility factors (the travel distance, travel time, and the quality and attractiveness of the road) have been found statistically to be the primary determinants of recreation demand.
2 *The propensity of the surrounding population to engage in outdoor recreation.* People vary in their demand for outdoor recreation according to income, education, age, sex, cultural background, or occupation. Stevens has developed demand curves relating the demand

[1] Sirles, *op. cit.*, p. 80.

for recreation to the income of the participant and found demand to increase with income up to a maximum point at which it begins to decrease.[1]

3   *Recreational attractiveness of site development.* The greater the variety of the activities which are available, the higher is the quality of the environment provided by the space which is devoted to individual activities; and the higher the maintenance standards, the greater is the number of people to whom the site will appeal and thus the greater is the number of visitors who will be attracted from a given population.

4   *The competitive position of the site.* A large number of nearby reservoirs may reduce visitation. Complementary tourist attractions may bring additional recreationists into the area.

5   *The natural endowment of the site.* Some recreation spots are more attractive than others because of their climate, scenery, or terrain. Others possess unusual plant or animal life or a unique historical or cultural heritage.

16-12   ESTIMATING RECREATION BENEFITS   The refreshing coolness of a swim on a hot summer day, the spiritual renewal from a solitary walk along a secluded lakeshore, or the excitement of skimming across the water on skis add a quality to life whose value seems beyond measurement in dollars. The water resources planner is pressed to assign a value to such experiences. However, who can assign a value to the fear generated by an impending flood, the better diet made possible by increased production of fruits and vegetables, a well-lighted home not needing candles or kerosene lamps, or many other effects of water resources development? The planner has no way of assigning any values apart from the marketplace where the collective judgment of countless individuals weighs values achieved against expenses incurred. Recreation benefits are commensurate with other project purpose benefits only if both are evaluated through commensurate processes.

Six basic methods of recreation benefit evaluation have been proposed and used.

1   The oldest practice is to select a value per visitor day based on a judgment evaluation of the quality of the available recreation experience. By federal standards, appropriate values range between $0.50 and $2.50 per visitor day.[2] However, the procedure does not necessarily give benefits commensurate with those for other project purposes.

---

[1]   Joe B. Stevens, Recreation Benefits from Water Pollution Control, *Water Resources Res.*, vol. 2 (2d Quarter, 1966), pp. 167–182.

[2]   Senate Doc. 97, Suppl. 1.

2   Direct market analysis would derive a demand curve from the relationship between the admission fee charged to use existing recreational areas and the number of users who pay it. However, this approach is severely limited by the freedom of potential visitors to visit the many sites charging nominal fees. The public has become accustomed to free outdoor recreation. Demand curves from market analysis are more likely to measure the value placed on a high-quality experience in a limited access area above the value placed on a lower-quality experience in an area of free access.

3   Questionnaires can be designed to get the recreation user rather than the planner to assign the values. The questions may directly ask the value the user places on an experience. They may ask whether the user would still visit the reservoir were it located a stated additional distance from his home.[1] The doubt about how well questions can be used to measure desired values is because they necessarily contain an *if*. How much would you be willing to pay *if* you had to pay to enjoy the recreation experience? Most individuals do not know what they would do until confronted with an actual choice. Asking how much one would be willing to pay for a fresh, crunchy apple is not like asking whether one wants to buy a particular apple for a dime. Furthermore, questionnaires are costly and time consuming to compose, collect, and interpret.

4   Benefit analysis has also been approached by the alternative-cost or the requirements approach (Sec. 8-5).

5   Recreation benefits might be estimated from increases in the value of the land surrounding a recreation reservoir. The increase in land value caused by reservoir construction is a capitalization of the expenditures that would otherwise be incurred in travel to and from the site and thus represents the present worth of recreation benefits.[2] Difficulties with this approach include distinguishing gains in land values produced by a recreation facility from those resulting from other causes and predicting gains in land values in advance as is required for planning.

6   The most successful method for evaluating recreation benefits is based on demand curves imputed from the expenditures incurred to enjoy outdoor recreation. The incremental cost of a particular recreation experience is primarily for travel to and from the site, but also includes those expenses for food, lodging, clothing, and equipment

---

[1] Jack L. Knetsch and Robert K. Davis, Comparison of Methods for Recreation Evaluation, in Allen V. Kneese and Stephen C. Smith (eds.), "Water Research" (Baltimore: The Johns Hopkins Press, 1966), pp. 125–142.

[2] Jack L. Knetsch, The Influence of Reservoir Projects on Land Value, *J. Farm Economics*, vol. 46 (February, 1964).

which are required to participate in the recreation experience. This is the most widely used approach and is the one which will be expanded here.

16-13 RELATING RECREATION VISITATION TO TRAVEL DISTANCE   Logically, use of a fully developed recreation site by the people of a community should increase with community population and decrease with the distance to the site. The typical regression analysis of collected visitation data produces an equation of the form

$$U = \frac{KP}{D^n} \qquad (16\text{-}2)$$

where U is the annual visitation from an area having population P located D airline miles from the site, and K and n are constants determined from the regression. Total visitation to a reservoir may be estimated by using Eq. (16-2) to estimate community values and by summing over the surrounding communities. Total potential visitation is obtained if the regression is based on a large and essentially fully developed site. For this purpose, a fully developed site may be defined as one where further development of conventional facilities would not further increase visitation.

Ullman estimated mean values of 100,000 for K and 3 for n from studies on Missouri reservoirs.[1] Knetsch found K to be 8,000 and n to be 2.39 for Kerr reservoir along the Virginia–North Carolina border.[2] Tussey found K to be 2,577 and n to be 2.445 for Rough River in central Kentucky.[3] On the whole, the statistical evidence indicates a value of about 2.4 for n for the typical recreation reservoir.

Estimated values of K vary much more widely as it is affected more by the characteristics of the population, the characteristics of the route available to the population for going to the reservoir, the availability to the population of competing reservoir recreation sites, and the characteristics of the reservoir site. One approach to incorporating these additional factors into Eq. (16-2) is to include them in the multiple regression to predict visitation.[4] Another approach is to use a multiple regression between values of K, implied by substituting the basic visitation data into Eq. (16-2), and the additional factors.[5] A major problem in statistical

[1]   Edward L. Ullman, A Measure of Water Recreation Benefits: The Meramec Basin Example, "Water Resources Management for the Needs of an Expanding Society" (Seattle: University of Washington, Department of Civil Engineering, 1964).
[2]   Jack L. Knetsch, Economics of Including Recreation as a Purpose of Eastern Water Projects, *J. Farm Economics*, vol. 46 (December, 1964), pp. 1148–1157.
[3]   Robert C. Tussey, "Analysis of Reservoir Recreation Benefits" (Lexington: University of Kentucky, Water Resources Institute Res. Rept. 2, 1967).
[4]   Leonard Merewitz, Recreational Benefits of Water Resource Development, *Water Resources Res.*, vol. 2, no. 2 (4th Quarter 1966), pp. 1148–1157.
[5]   Tussey, *op. cit.*

derivation of visitation prediction relationships is the selection of criteria for evaluating goodness of fit. A correlation based on minimizing the sum of the squares of the departure of estimated from actual values of K would produce a different prediction equation than one based on minimizing the sum of the departures of estimated from actual values of benefit. The best correlation for predicting visitation is not necessarily the best for predicting benefit.

16-14   EXPRESSING TRAVEL DISTANCE IN ECONOMIC UNITS

A demand curve based on the visitation-distance relationship requires expression of the disutility of overcoming distance in money units. Knetsch and Davis have hypothesized the disutility as the sum of money cost (expense of making the trip), time cost (value of the time spent traveling), and the utility of the traveling experience (the pleasure or discomfort, whichever it may be, one gets from traveling).[1] The private automobile has a virtual monopoly as the mode of transport used to recreation reservoirs in the United States. As all the cost components are also considered in the economic analysis of alternative transportation plans, highway economy studies provide a valuable source of empirical data.

Collecting the various terms which compose travel cost leads to the equation

$$C = 2.42 \frac{(1 + a)m + t/v}{bp} \tag{16-3}$$

where C is the cost per mile in dollars per visitor day spent at the site; 2.42 is the product of 2.0, which accounts for round trips, and 1.21, an average ratio of road to air distance; a is the expense incurred for food and lodging above that spent at home, expressed as a fraction of vehicle operating cost; m is the variable vehicle operating cost in dollars per mile; t is the value of a vehicle hour of traveling time in dollars; v is the mean travel velocity in miles per hour; b is the number of days a visitor remains at the site; and p is the number of visitors per vehicle.

Values can be estimated for the variables in Eq. (16-3) either from the literature or from data specifically collected for a particular analysis. Ullman estimated b to be 2.0 and p to be 3.5 from Missouri data.[2] The University of Kentucky, Bureau of Business Research, found average values of 2.27 for b and 2.55 for p for Kentucky State Parks.[3] Wilbur Smith

---

[1] Knetsch and Davis, *loc. cit.*
[2] Ullman, *op. cit.*
[3] "Kentucky Tourist Preferences" (Lexington: University of Kentucky, Bureau of Business Research, 1962).

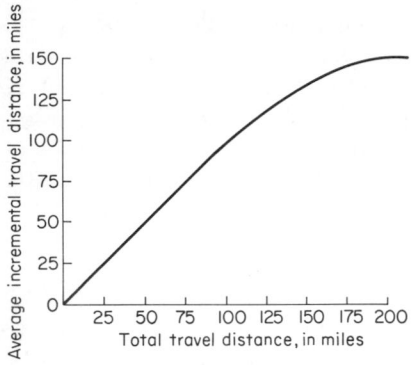

FIGURE 16-3 Relationship between total travel distance and incremental travel distance to a recreation reservoir.

and Associates have estimated a national average value for m of 0.053.[1] A typical value used for t is about $1.50,[2] but more recent research suggests a value of $2.82.[3] Values for v may be estimated from observed average travel speeds on roads near the reservoir or from average travel speeds by road type.[4] Typical travel budgets show values for a of over 1.0 for those on long trips, but the value will be close to 0.0 for those living nearby. A more refined analysis would make the value of C a function of distance traveled[5] because values of a, b, and p vary with the length of the trip.

Demand curve derivation also requires determination of the fraction of the total travel distance from the home to the reservoir which can be attributed to a particular recreation experience, the distance the visitor goes out of his way to reach the site. For the visitor living nearby, out-of-the-way distance equals total distance. For the visitor living several thousand miles away, out-of-the-way distance will equal only a small fraction of total distance. By questioning visitors to Dewey and Rough River Reservoirs, Tussey obtained the data used in Fig. 16-3 to relate the average distance traveled out of the way, ΔD, to the total distance from home to reservoir.[6]

16-15 DEVELOPING THE DEMAND CURVE Equation (16-2) allows one to estimate the annual user days from a community of population P for a recreation reservoir D miles away. If D were increased by δD, Eq. (16-2) could be used to calculate the number of these visitors

[1] "Future Highways and Urban Growth" (New Haven, Conn.: Wilbur Smith and Associates, 1961).
[2] Committee on Planning and Design Policies, American Association of State Highway Officials, "Road User Benefit Analyses for Highway Improvements" (Washington: AASHO, 1960).
[3] Dan G. Haney, "The Value of Time for Passenger Cars: A Theoretical Analysis and Description of Preliminary Experiments," vol. 1 (Menlo Park, Calif.: Stanford Research Institute, 1967), p. 134.
[4] David M. Winch, "The Economics of Highway Planning" (Toronto: University of Toronto Press, 1963).
[5] Knetsch and Davis, *op. cit.*, p. 137.
[6] Tussey, *op. cit.*, p. 79.

placing a value on the experience equal or greater than the disutility of δD. By repeating for a range of distance increases, demand can be estimated as a function of distance. Figure 16-3 may be used to estimate the portion of the total travel distance attributable to a given experience (obtain ΔD from δD). Equation (16-3) may then be used for placing a dollar value on ΔD. The procedure requires the following steps:

1   The reservoir is viewed as being at the middle of a target with the surrounding area divided into population centers. One approach would be to use distance zones based on concentric circles. However, data are more readily available for using such political subdivisions as counties and states.

2   The population for each center is estimated. Zone population is estimated by laying out the zones on a map and summing census data. Political subdivision population may be taken directly from census data.

3   A value of K must be selected for each center. The value found in deriving Eq. (16-2) may be used for each one. Regression analysis may be used to vary K with specific independent population or route characteristics. Socioeconomic conditions influence K more in the smaller centers than in centers containing larger populations where socioeconomic diversity balances out to an average value.

4   Equation (16-2) (taking D as the distance from the reservoir to the center of population) gives an estimate of the number of potential visitors to the reservoir from each center. Total visitation is the sum of the center visitations.

5   By adding a series of arbitrarily selected distances δD to the value of D for each center, the number of visitors willing to travel the extra distance can be calculated and the results summed in a series of progressively smaller totals.

6   Data can be collected to evaluate the variables in Eq. (16-3), and the unit cost per mile in dollars per visitor day can be calculated.

7   For each of the total distances δD in step 5, incremental distances ΔD can be read from Fig. 16-3.

The computational procedure is illustrated in Ex. 16-1.

EXAMPLE 16-1   SAMPLE CALCULATION OF POTENTIAL RECREATION BENEFIT

The following data are from Dewey Reservoir (Jenny Wiley State Park), Floyd County, Kentucky, and evaluation of K and n is according to the procedure suggested by Ullman. The calculations are intended to present the method of developing a marginal-benefit curve rather than portray the recreational benefits from the park in question.

1 The population within zones is estimated from 1960 census data and a map showing county boundaries to be:

Zone	Range, miles	Population	K
1	0–20	97,000	10,000
2	20–40	249,000	10,000
3	40–60	504,000	10,000
4	60–100	1,860,000	40,000
5	100–200	10,290,000	70,000
6	200–300	20,130,000	70,000
7	300–500	48,500,000	70,000

2 The values of K for the closer zones are low because the reservoir is located in an area populated mostly by low-income families, and low-income families tend to have a below-average inclination to partake of water-based recreation. The values for the more distant zones are lower than average because the reservoir is in an isolated area with few complementary attractions and poor access in three directions. Estimated values of K by zone for use with a value of 3 for n are shown above.

3 Computations to estimate total visitor days as a function of additional travel distance are provided in Table 16-6.

4 A value for C, the cost per additional mile per visitor day, may be estimated from Eq. (16-3) by using $b = 2.27$ days, $p = 2.55$ visitors per vehicle, $m = \$0.053$ per mile, $t = \$1.50$ per hour, $v = 40$ miles/hr, and $a = 0.50$. The result is

$$C = \frac{2.42[1.5(0.053) + 1.50/40]}{2.27(2.55)} = \$0.0489 \text{ per mile}$$

The cost of each travel distance is also shown in Table 16-6.

5 The demand curve is plotted in Fig. 16-4 from the data in Table 16-6. The area under the curve yields a potential annual benefit of $1,510,000 per year. Based on an annual total of 986,000 visitor days, this annual benefit implies an average benefit per visitor of $1.53.

At first inspection, some might want to convert the values of D, shown in Table 16-6 for zero additional miles, into travel cost and plot them against the value of U two rows down to get the demand curve. However, the cost of getting to the reservoir is not the full value of the recreation experience to those who would still visit even if the distance were much farther or if a user charge were initiated. The purpose of the analysis is to estimate the number of people who would still visit if additional costs were imposed upon them.

TABLE 16-6 Computations for Deriving the Marginal-benefit Curve

| ADDITIONAL COST | | | | ZONE | | | | | | | Total demand |
δD	ΔD	Dollars		1	2	3	4	5	6	7	
			Range	0–20	20–40	40–60	60–100	100–200	200–300	300–500	
			P	97,000	249,000	504,000	1,860,000	10,290,000	20,130,000	48,500,000	
			K	10,000	10,000	10,000	40,000	70,000	70,000	70,000	
0	0	0	D	14	30	50	80	150	250	400	
			$Q = K/D^3$	3.64	0.370	0.0800	0.0781	0.0207	0.00448	0.00109	
			$U = QP$	353,000	92,000	40,000	145,000	213,000	90,000	53,000	986,000
20	20	0.978	D	34	50	70	100	170	270	420	
			$Q = K/D^3$	0.254	0.0800	0.0292	0.0400	0.0142	0.00356	0.000945	
			$U = QP$	25,000	20,000	15,000	74,000	146,000	72,000	46,000	398,000
40	40	1.956	D	54	70	90	120	190	290	440	
			$Q = K/D^3$	0.0635	0.0292	0.0137	0.0231	0.0102	0.00287	0.000822	
			$U = QP$	6,200	7,300	6,900	43,000	105,000	57,800	39,900	266,100
60	59	2.885	D	74	90	110	140	210	310	460	
			$Q = K/D^3$	0.0247	0.0137	0.00751	0.0146	0.00756	0.00235	0.000719	
			$U = QP$	2,400	3,400	3,800	27,200	77,800	47,300	34,900	196,800
100	95	4.650	D	114	130	150	180	250	350	500	
			$Q = K/D^3$	0.00675	0.00455	0.00296	0.00686	0.00448	0.00163	0.000560	
			$U = QP$	700	1,100	1,500	12,800	46,100	32,800	27,200	122,200
150	133	6.504	D	164	180	200	230	300	400	550	
			$Q = K/D^3$	0.00227	0.00171	0.00125	0.00329	0.00259	0.00109	0.000421	
			$U = QP$	220	430	630	6,120	26,650	21,940	20,420	76,410
200*	150	7.340	D	214	230	250	280	350	450	600	
			$Q = K/D^3$	0.00102	0.000822	0.000640	0.00182	0.00163	0.000768	0.000324	
			$U = QP$	100	200	320	3,390	16,770	15,460	15,710	51,950

* The demand curves become horizontal for δD over 200 miles because ΔD becomes constant at 150 miles.

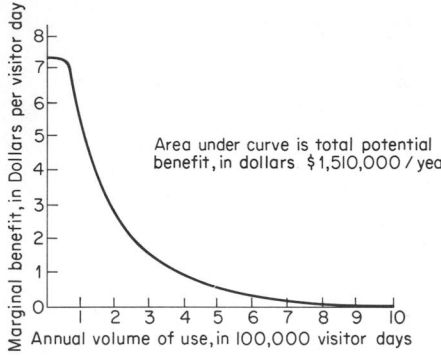

FIGURE 16-4 Dewey Reservoir's recreation-demand curve.

Statistically derived demand curves (Fig. 16-4) have been criticized because of the influence income distribution has on visitation. It is argued that the poor cannot afford to visit sites in cases where they would gain a greater utility value than those with greater incomes who do.[1] Before carrying this argument too far, one should remember that the diminishing marginal utility of money has an analogous effect on every market good. A poor man who likes watermelon is able to buy less than a rich man who likes them equally well. Both problems are solved only through improved income distribution (Sec. 8-10). Furthermore, the cost of getting to the reservoir includes the value of the time spent. The poor have as much total time as the rich, and may well have more, to devote to reservoir recreation.

16-16 TOTAL-BENEFIT CURVE For a given reservoir capacity, estimated from the sum of the products of areas and capacity coefficients, Fig. 16-2 is used to determine the fraction of the potential visitors who will visit the reservoir. The total benefits achieved by a reservoir of this capacity equals the product of this fraction and the benefits potentially produced by a very large reservoir and represented by the area under Fig. 16-4. The procedure can be repeated for as many capacities as needed to get the points necessary to develop a curve of total benefit as a function of reservoir capacity. The slope of such a total-benefit curve provides the benefit marginal to an increase in reservoir recreation capacity. Figure 16-4 shows benefit realized by a marginal visitor to a given facility having a fixed capacity. The two curves should not be confused. Total benefits are differentiated with respect to capacity in the first case and with respect to visitation in the second case.

---

[1] David W. Seckler, On the Uses and Abuses of Economic Science in Evaluating Public Outdoor Recreation, *Land Economics*, vol. 42 (November, 1966), pp. 485–494.

Project Feasibility

16-17 ECONOMIC FEASIBILITY Two levels of decision making may be involved in applying marginal economic analysis to reservoir recreation facilities. For a reservoir of given size, the optimum degree of shoreline development is needed. In order to determine optimum reservoir size, recreation benefits must be combined with other benefits before comparing them with reservoir cost. With the activity composite (Sec. 16-5) and the capacity coefficients (Sec. 16-6) fixed by considerations other than economic benefit, alternative facility design capacities or recreation acreages may be evaluated to determine the optimum development for a reservoir of given size (Sec. 16-8). The optimum development for reservoirs of a series of sizes may be used to compute the marginal recreation benefit realized from a larger reservoir. When added to the marginal benefit that the larger reservoir achieves with respect to other project purposes, the total may be used to select the optimum facility size. Typically, benefits achieved toward other purposes indicate an optimum reservoir size so large as to have a very low marginal recreation benefit. As a result, recreation may not be a significant factor in determining optimum size, and the optimization reduces to selecting the appropriate shoreline facilities. If land is available, these facilities may be expanded in stages to accommodate increasing usage.

16-18 FINANCIAL FEASIBILITY If the optimum-size project is provided without charge to those using the facilities, use will tend toward point F in Fig. 16-5. However, if only the optimum capacity (point D in

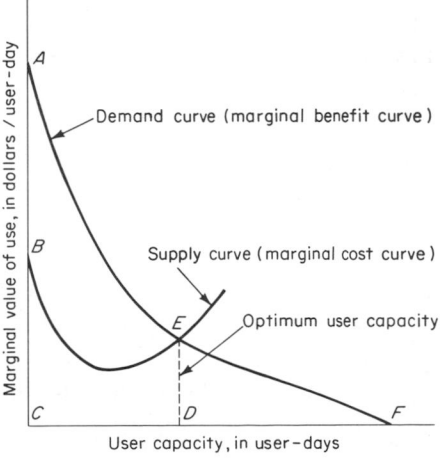

FIGURE 16-5 Optimum annual volume of recreation use; *BCDE*, total project cost; *ACDE*, gross project benefits; *ABE*, net project benefits.

Fig. 16-5) were provided, use would exceed the planning capacity coefficients and eventually be restricted by the capacity limitation to an equilibrium visitation between D and F. The crowding may cause many to believe that new facilities should be built even though they could not be economically justified. A charge of E (dollars) per user day would cause a market rather than a crowding mechanism to limit facility use. A third method of limiting facility use would be by rationing. For example, people might be allowed to use the facilities alternate weeks depending on the first letter of their name. Unless projects with negative net incremental benefits are built, one of the three methods must be used to allocate recreation space among users. Efficiency criteria do not help in the selection because of the psychological effect of crowding on the desirability of recreation space.

Charges function to raise revenue as well as allocate facility use. Congressman Aspinall pointed out, "Either we pay for the outdoors through taxes or we pay for it through direct fees."[1] A charge equal to the marginal cost of providing the facilities is unlikely to pay the full cost because of the decreasing marginal cost nature of recreational development (Sec. 24-2). The difficulty with allocation by charges is the potential for adverse effects on income distribution by exclusion of the poor. Allocation by rationing would overcome this difficulty but is fraught with numerous practical enforcement complications.

Additional recreation project revenue might be raised by allowing competitive bidding for concessions by entrepreneurs. This procedure might encourage a more efficient activity mix as those bidding would be very conscious of competing recreation forms. Its drawbacks are largely associated with extramarket effects and spillovers.

The financial practice in the United States is for federal interests to pay one-half the separable installation costs of the recreational features of a project and for local interests to pay the other half. Local interests may raise a portion of their required revenues by user charges. Management of the facilities may be incorporated in a state or local park system.

SELECTED REFERENCES
Boyet, Wayne E., and George S. Tolley: Recreation Projection Based on Demand Analysis, *J. Farm Economics*, vol. 48 (November, 1966), pp. 984–1001.
Clawson, Marion: "Land and Water for Recreation" (Chicago: Rand McNally & Company, 1963).
——, and Jack L. Knetsch: "Economics of Outdoor Recreation" (Baltimore: The Johns Hopkins Press, 1966).

[1] Wayne N. Aspinall, Should the Outdoors Be Free? *Am. Forests*, vol. 70 (1964), pp. 32–34, 59.

Knetsch, Jack L.: Economics of Including Recreation as a Purpose of Eastern Water Projects, *J. Farm Economics*, vol. 46 (December, 1964), pp. 1148–1157.

Lee, Ivan M.: Economic Analysis Bearing on Outdoor Recreation, "Economic Studies of Outdoor Recreation" (Washington: USGPO, Outdoor Recreation Review Research Commission Rept. 24, 1962).

Seckler, David W.: On the Uses and Abuses of Economic Science in Evaluating Public Outdoor Recreation, *Land Economics*, vol. 42 (November, 1966), pp. 485–494.

Stevens, Joe B.: Recreation Benefits from Water Pollution Control, *Water Resources Res.*, vol. 2 (2d Quarter, 1966), pp. 167–182.

PROBLEMS

16-1 A least-squares regression from historical visitation data has given values of $n = 2.5$ and $K = 8,000$ in Eq. (16-2); C equals 6 cents per mile per visitor day. Population by distance zone is as given in Ex. 16-1.

   a What are the potential benefits for recreation at the site?

   b What installed capacity would be required to realize this benefit?

   c Derive a marginal-benefit curve based on the downward-sloping capacity line of Fig. 16-2.

   d What marginal benefit would result from installing a capacity larger than that indicated in part *b*?

16-2 A certain reservoir provides 10 acres for picnicking, 25 acres for camping, 50 acres for boating, and 0.2 acres for swimming.

   a Estimate the capacity of the facility for simultaneous use.

   b If the area for each activity just equals capacity once a year, estimate annual visitation based on Table 16-2.

   c Estimate annual visitation if peak potential hourly use is 10 times capacity.

16-3 If *a*, *b*, and *p* of Eq. (16-3) were found to vary with *D* as shown below, estimate the potential benefits of Prob. 16-1.

D, miles	0	20	50	100	200
a	0	0.1	0.2	0.6	1.5
b	0.5	0.75	1.0	1.8	3.0
p	2.0	2.5	3.0	3.5	4.0

16-4 The project of Prob. 16-1 is being planned for a 50-year life. Assume the population in each distance zone is increasing at an annual rate of 2.0 percent.

a Answer parts *a*, *b*, and *c* of Prob. 16-1 for the last year of project life.

b Answer parts *a*, *b*, and *c* of Prob. 16-1 for average annual benefits discounted at a rate of 5.0 percent.

c Plot a curve of capacity for which marginal benefit is a minimum vs. year of project life.

d Recommend a stage construction schedule for recreation facilities which can be provided at an annual marginal cost of $250 per visitor day of installed capacity plus an annual fixed cost of $300.

CHAPTER SEVENTEEN

FISH AND WILDLIFE ENHANCEMENT

The Planning Context

17-1 DEFINITION   The effects of the development and management of water resources on the environment available to fish and wildlife need to be carefully weighed in water resources planning. Species are adversely affected by any change in the environment to which they have become accustomed. Each reservoir, channel improvement, diversion, or drained swamp harms species whose habitats are destroyed. However, each such change also creates new habitats, suited to different species. The planner must weight the values of the new habitats against the values of the old. Sometimes, a new habitat is developed as a form of compensation for one which has been destroyed. New fishing areas may be developed within a reservoir to compensate for losses to a downstream fishery caused by diverting or storing natural flows. However, there is no way to establish real equivalence between different habitats supporting different species.

Two basic types of fish habitat need to be distinguished. Cold-water fish inhabit rapidly flowing streams, particularly at higher elevations. Warm-water fish inhabit larger lakes or sluggishly flowing rivers. Reservoirs characteristically provide habitats for warm-water fish while destroying habitats for cold-water fish. Reservoirs may also flood the natural habitats of deer, bear, squirrels, pheasants, and other land-oriented wildlife.

Ducks and similar game birds require substantial shallow-water areas for feeding along migratory flight patterns or in seasonal resting areas. A number of small animals such as beaver or otter congregate along natural streams. Frogs prefer still water. The breeding of mosquitos and other harmful insects must be controlled by limiting areas of stagnant, shallow water, particularly in warmer climates.

17-2 HISTORICAL DEVELOPMENT Fish and wildlife were once too abundant for much thought to be given to their preservation; but as development of intensive agriculture and extensive urban areas threatened valuable species with extinction, society became more concerned. Its first step was to control destructive hunting and fishing. More recently, biological and ecological research and experience have greatly increased man's ability to implement positive measures to improve wildlife environment.

One of the earliest measures for fish enhancement was the stocking of reservoirs for fishing. Later, a growing conservation consciousness demanded protection for anadromous species blocked in their travel to spawning areas by reservoir construction. The problem became particularly acute for salmon and related species along the Pacific Coast of North America and in northern Europe.[1] When Grand Coulee Dam was constructed on the Columbia River in 1942, the importance of the anadromous fish runs was recognized, and bypass facilities were provided. However, the design used was ineffective in attracting fish, and as a consequence the dam severely impaired the fishery. Nevertheless, two good effects resulted. More intensive research was motivated to develop what have now become much more effective bypass facilities. Much more caution has been exercized in employing untried bypass approaches. For a time, the reaction was overly cautious, but a balanced perspective is gradually evolving.

The requirements approach has normally been followed in planning for fish and wildlife. Those constructing dams have been made financially responsible for installing bypass facilities. Water resources projects planned for other purposes were submitted to the fish and wildlife agency for approval. The agency would study project effects on various species and recommend changes needed to ameliorate harmful features and could sometimes delay construction until suitable changes were incorporated into the plans. In response to the Fish and Wildlife Coordination Act of 1959,[2] the recent trend has been toward the more positive approach of analyzing features for fish and wildlife in coordination with those for other project purposes from the beginning of project planning. The greatest benefit to fish and wildlife comes by considering the development

[1] C. H. Clay, "Design of Fishways and Other Fish Facilities" (Ottawa: Queen's Printer, 1961), p. 69.
[2] Public Law 85-624.

of new habitats as well as the preservation of the old as alternatives to be evaluated during project formulation.

The history of measures for wildlife enhancement and insect control has paralleled that for fish enhancement. The objectives of preserving unique or developing new wildlife habitats and controlling obnoxious insects were undertaken with minimal understanding of the biological interaction between the species and their environment. Research and experience has gradually increased measure effectiveness.

Developing the Supply

Measures for protecting and enhancing fish and wildlife achieve many varied objectives. Each must be evaluated independently on its own merits.

17-3 WARM-WATER FISH   While a few fish will live in almost any permanent pool, specific reservoir management practices can be used to maximize fish population and promote desirable species.[1] The aquatic plants providing the major food source for fish and waterfowl require light for photosynthesis. The intensity of light penetration and the length of daylight decrease with depth below the water surface. Food plants grow at a maximum depth of about 10 ft in muddy and 50 ft in clear water. Most plants are slow to adjust to major water-surface fluctuations. Fish species are least able to adjust to water-surface fluctuations during certain critical phases of their life cycle. However, the rate of adjustment and the density and speed of plant growth increase with temperature. Maximum fish populations are supported by stable, shallow, warm-water reservoirs; but because this condition also maximizes evaporation loss, compromise may be required to save the water for other uses.

Each fish species prefers a distinct environment. Propagation becomes increasingly successful as the environment more closely approaches the ideal. The most important environmental factors relate to water quality. Dissolved oxygen should remain above 85 percent of saturation. Hydrogen-ion concentration should be between 7.0 and 8.5. Specific electrical conductance at 77°F should range between 150 and

---

[1] For a more extended discussion, see Kenneth M. Mackenthun, William M. Ingram, and Ralph Porges, "Limnological Aspects of Recreational Lakes" (Washington: USGPO, Public Health Service Publ. 1167, 1964), pp. 9–30.

500 μmhos.[1] However, fish are repelled by environmental factors long before they are physically harmed.[2] Abandonment of slightly polluted waters is more prevalent than fish kills. The key to environmental analysis is establishment of the relationship between quality and fish and wildlife behavior.

The fish population a reservoir can support is largely determined by the temperature, availability of dissolved oxygen, and fish food in the minimum pool. Reservoirs support from 75 to over 600 lb of fish per acre of lake surface area. New reservoirs must be stocked with the desired species, and for the best fishing, the supply should be periodically replenished. Sometimes periodic drawdowns, chemical treatment, or netting operations are required to control undesirable fish species or animal life which destroys desired fish or their food supply.

17-4 COLD-WATER FISH Cold-water fish require cool, turbulent water. Populations may be increased by low-flow augmentation from reservoirs. The fish prefer releases of cold water from the depths of the reservoir, but water which has remained for long periods at the bottom of a reservoir may have lost most of its dissolved oxygen and require reaeration. Fish are also helped by reservoir control of rapid fluctuations in streamflow and elimination of high sediment content which harm fish during spawning and may upset the ecological environment of their food supply.

In the interest of preserving rare species or unique habitats, conservationists make a strong case for not building structures on the best fish streams. The argument becomes the more persuasive as fewer natural streams are left, but it is entirely unreasonable if carried to the extreme of saying that all streams are unique.

17-5 ANADROMOUS FISH The greatest expenditure for fish facilities has been for anadromous, or migrating, fish or eels (over \$150 million in the Columbia River basin).[3] Salmon and related species travel to mountain streams to have their young. Most species spawn in the late fall and winter. The eggs lodge in the interstices of the gravel and hatch in the early spring. The fingerlings or young fish remain in the general area

[1] "Branscomb Project Investigation" (Sacramento: Calif. Department of Water Resources, Bull. 92, 1965).
[2] Shinya Ishio, Behavior of Fish Exposed to Toxic Substances, in O. Jaag (ed.), "Advances in Water Pollution Research," vol. 1 (London: Pergamon Press, Ltd., 1965), pp. 19–40.
[3] Additional discussion of anadromous fish in the Columbia River is found in Richard S. Leavenworth, "Engineering-Economic Aspects of the Decision-Making Process in Municipal Electric Utilities" (Stanford, Calif.: Stanford University, Institute of Engineering Economic Systems, EEP-10, 1964), pp. 189–208.

of their birth for the first year or two, travel downstream to the ocean in the late spring, spend one or more years, and then return instinctively to their birthplace to lay and fertilize their eggs and die or, in some cases, return to the sea to complete another cycle. When a dam or other artificial obstruction blocks the river, the entire upstream fishery will be lost unless fish can bypass the structure or can be enticed to spawn in a substitute area. The fish swim upstream on a schedule allocating just enough time and physical strength to reach the spawning grounds before they lay and fertilize their eggs. Because excessive delays or exertion may cause the fish to die before they get there, bypass facilities, or any other measures affecting natural stream flow, must be designed so as to avoid prolonged delay or physical impairment to the fish.

The most common bypass device is a fishway through which the fish may swim under their own power[1] and consisting of water flowing through baffles or obstructions to reduce the flow velocity to about the 4 fps which a fish can easily navigate. The fishway must be designed to accommodate fish over the full range of probable headwater and tail-water elevations. The required fishway capacity depends on the number of fish wishing to travel upstream at the peak of the migration season. A design based on the peak hour is needed to save all the fish, but the cost should be balanced against the fish loss consequent to using average values for peak day or week based on the number of daylight hours. The capacity of a fishway may be estimated from the equation[2]

$$C = \frac{V}{v} 60r \tag{17-1}$$

where C is the capacity of the fishway in fish per hour, V is the fishway pool volume in cubic feet, v is the pool volume required per fish in cubic feet, and r is the rate of ascent in pools per minute. Clay recommends a design value for v/r of 15 for most species (4 cu ft/fish and 0.267 pools/min). Minimum pool size is about 2 ft deep, 6 ft wide, and 8 ft long; and dimensions where volumes in excess of 96 cu ft are required are determined by the configuration having least construction cost. A rough cost estimated from typical unit costs is illustrated in Ex. 17-1.

EXAMPLE 17-1
An 80-ft-high dam is under consideration at a sight having a maximum daily run of salmon of 80,000. What would be the approximate cost of installing a fishway if no powerhouse is involved?

[1] Clay, *op. cit.*
[2] *Ibid.*, pp. 109–110.

Volume per pool:

$$V = \frac{Cv}{60r} \tag{17-1}$$

$$C = \frac{80{,}000 \text{ fish}}{16 \text{ daylight hr/day}} = 5{,}000 \text{ fish/hr}$$

$$\frac{v}{r} = 15 \qquad \text{(design value from Clay)}$$

$$V = \frac{5{,}000}{60}\, 15 = 1{,}250 \text{ cu ft}$$

     (use this value as it is well in excess of the minimum of 96 cu ft)

Number of pools:

1 ft^{-1} of head $= 80$ pools

Cost of pools:	80(1,250)($6.50) =	$ 650,000
Cost of appurtenances:	0.30(650,000) =	195,000
Cost of auxiliary water:	0.50(650,000) =	325,000
(Use 1.00 with a powerhouse)		
Total cost:		$1,170,000
Annual operation and		
maintenance cost:	0.02(1,170,000) = $	23,400

    Because the fish must find the fishway quickly, the fish entrance is "the most important single part of any fishway."[1] Fish swim upstream into the current until they are stopped by high velocities below the dam. The ideal entrance emits sufficient flow to attract the fish at the point where the fish stop. If flow through the fishway is insufficient, auxiliary attraction water must be added. The fish exit is located in slack water upstream of any danger of the fish being swept back downstream by high currents. The fishway also needs to divert sufficient attraction water to entice the young fish coming downstream.

    Fishways are impractical for high dams and low fish counts. The fish may be lifted by locks or special elevators, but they are excited by mechanical handling and must not be deposited within areas of high velocity flows before they are sufficiently recovered to swim upstream at full strength. Trapping and trucking is the predominate way of getting annual runs of 20,000 fish or less past high dams in North America. The fish are enticed into a pool and then into a hopper by an attraction current, loaded into a tank truck, hauled upstream, and dumped back into the water at a point where the current is strong enough for the fish to know which way is upstream.

[1] *Ibid.*, p. 70.

If bypass is impractical or if it is necessary to accommodate fish whose spawning grounds are flooded by the reservoir, other measures must be used. Fish may be trapped, the eggs removed and fertilized, and the young fish raised in a hatchery.[1] Sometimes by planting the fish born in the hatchery, succeeding generations can be trained to shift their spawning grounds to a point to which their access is not obstructed by dams. Where such training fails, hatcheries are the only way that can be used to preserve the fish runs.

An artificial spawning area is a channel through which clear water flows at a mild velocity over a coarse gravel periphery. If practical, an artificial spawning area should be located outside the flood plain to avoid sediment deposition and other disturbance by high flows. The optimum velocity, channel depth, and area required per spawning pair depend on the species (Table 17-1). The coarse gravel should be 12 to 30 in. thick with a minimum grain size of 0.5 in. to allow free circulation of oxygen to fish eggs which have settled into the gravel. The spawning grounds should be raked annually during the off season, and the fines should be screened out about once in 5 years.

Protective screens are required to keep larger fish from entering turbines and to keep fish out of irrigation and municipal water supply and

[1] Earl Leitritz, "Trout and Salmon Culture" (Sacramento: California Department of Fish and Game, Fish Bull. 107, 1963).

TABLE 17-1 Approximate Average Weight and Recommended Area for Spawning per Spawning Pair for Artificial Spawning Channels for Several Species of Fish*

| | | | RECOMMENDED | |
| | Av wt, | Depth, | Velocity, | Area, |
Species	lb	ft	ft/sec	sq ft
Chinook salmon				
Summer and fall run	25	1.25	1.60	216
Spring run	15	1.70	2.00	144
Coho salmon	9	1.10	1.50	126
Chums salmon	10	†	†	99
Sockeye salmon	3	1.25	1.75	72
Pink salmon	5	†	†	6
Trout	1	†	†	18

* C. H. Clay, *Design of Fishways and Other Fish Facilities* (Ottawa: Queen's Printer, 1961), p. 237.
† No value given.

other diversions where the water is not directly returned to the stream. A bypass diverting 2 to 3 percent of the water should be constructed just upstream from a diversion screen to provide the fish with a continuous downstream path back to the river. Automatic cleaning is needed to keep screens from becoming clogged with trash.

Fishways may also be used to provide passage around low waterfalls, rapids, or other natural obstructions which restrict but do not prevent fish passage. Such facilities help the fish get upstream sooner so more fish reach the spawning area before they die. The fishways must be designed to accommodate a larger range of flows because flows at natural obstructions are not subject to the control they are at dams. The fishway is built from a point just below the obstruction, where large numbers of fish accumulate during upstream runs, to slack water sufficiently far upstream so the fish will not be swept back down.

17-6 WATERFOWL   Ducks, geese, and related fowl require the extensive shallow water areas in which their food plants thrive. Since most waterfowl migrate between summer nesting and winter feeding areas along fixed paths, major habitat developments are best located along established flyways or within established nesting areas. Draining or diverting water from habitat areas adversely affects many more fowl than are there at any one time. The cost of maintaining such areas includes the large amount of water lost by evapotranspiration from the continuously exposed water surface containing growing plants. Because most feed plants tolerate salinity up to about 8,000 ppm, irrigation return flows or other saline waters may be used for waterfowl provided ground-water aquifers are not contaminated and an outlet is provided to prevent excessive concentrations.

17-7 INSECT CONTROL   Insect control is an essential part of water resources development in areas where the climate is warm enough to support the insects which cause such diseases as yellow fever, malaria, and encephalitis. Stream water-surface fluctuations accomplished by systematic variation of reservoir releases to prevent breeding within shallow, stagnant areas along the banks is one of the most effective ways of controlling mosquitos and other obnoxious or disease-carrying insects. Mosquito larvae are destroyed by weekly fluctuations of about 1 ft, a variation too small to harm fish. However, the volumes of water involved in the cyclic fluctuation of water surface levels makes this method impractical for insect control in large reservoirs. It is necessary to spray shallow, stagnant areas along the reservoir shoreline with larvicides. Control is easier if the water surface level in the reservoir is kept below the elevation of dense shoreline vegetation during the mosquito breeding season because the vegetation shields the insects and provides shade and food for the larvae. Mosquito production has been found to be directly proportional to the water area covered by plants.[1] An alternate method is to build levees to prevent the water within the reservoir from inundating large shoreline swamp areas or to fill the shallow-water areas to elevations exceeding the high water level in the lake with material excavated from further out in the lake. The goal is to make the shoreline steep enough to prevent shallow water or stagnant pools from being left as the water level recedes. Measures to control tick-borne Rocky Mountain spotted fever may be necessary in some recreation areas.

17-8   THE SUPPLY CURVE   The yardstick best used to depict the degree of fish and wildlife enhancement varies with measure purpose. For fishing provided in a multiactivity recreational reservoir, fishing becomes one of the group of recreation activities which are so interrelated they must be evaluated together. Fishing areas within the lake are designated, their acreage determined, and user capacity found by applying a reasonable capacity coefficient. Most fishing occurs along shoreline area shallower than 20 ft, excluding areas used for swimming or some other incompatible purpose. The fishing area fluctuates with water surface elevation and may be expressed as an expected value by month. A capacity coefficient of 2.0 fishermen per acre is reasonable for a rough estimate. More precise analysis requires evaluation by fish biologists of the number of fish by species that the available habitat can support. Finally, the fishing capacity is added to those for the other recreational activities to estimate the annual user days that the reservoir can accommodate (Sec. 16-7), and the costs may be included in the recreation-supply curve.

The fishing capacity (fishermen per day) of a cold-water fishery may be estimated from a general relationship based on Horton's law of stream numbers, cubic feet per second per mile of streamflow, or the stream water-surface area; or it may be developed more precisely from an evaluation by fish biologists of the population that the particular stream can support. The recreational opportunity may be provided by increasing flows, preventing their reduction, or improving the temperature or quality of the water to increase fish population. The supply curve is developed from information on the cost of providing the facilities that will develop a range of fishing capacities.

The supply curve for providing for anadromous fish is best expressed by the design capacity of the bypass facilities. The design capacity may be expressed either as the quantity of fish using the facilities or as the

[1]   Mackenthun, Ingram, and Porges, *op. cit.*, p. 99.

net reduction in fish delay by the facilities made possible. Queuing theory may be used to calculate mean delay time.

The supply curve for wildlife enhancement measures may be based on the number of birds which can be accommodated or, more indirectly, on hunters per day. The degree of insect control is best measured by the reduction in insect numbers.

Estimating the Demand

The value realized from fish and wildlife enhancement measures may come either through harvesting the fish or game or through enjoying visits of observation. The benefit from sport hunting or fishing is recreational in character. In other cases, the harvest may have commercial value; or the preservation of rare species or unique habitats may have a large intangible value from environmental conservation (Sec. 9-5).

17-9   RECREATION DEMAND   If fishing is to be provided in a recreational reservoir, the best procedure is to include fishing as part of the total recreational activity composite, as there is no reliable way of separating visitors attracted by fishing from those attracted by other recreational activities. Many visitors or families are attracted by both types of facilities. The potential benefit (Ex. 16-1) of a recreation reservoir would be increased by providing for fishing because of the increased attraction to the surrounding population. The value of K [Eq. (16-2)] is increased by providing fishing opportunity, and quantitative estimates may be made by surveying visitation to existing facilities (Sec. 16-13). The increased capacity of the reservoir to accommodate visitors in the fishing areas increases the fraction of the potential benefit realized (Fig. 16-1). The balance of the benefit evaluation procedure then follows that used for recreation.

The same basic procedure also applies to developing a cold-water fishery. Statistical analysis of data showing number of visitors by place of residence collected for similar locations should be used to estimate K and n for determining potential benefits. The estimated visitation capacity (Sec. 17-8) then provides means for determining the fraction of the benefit potential realized. Values realized with and without an improvement in the fishery must both be estimated to determine net benefit for measure justification. Benefits lost by flooding a cold-water fishery through reservoir construction should also be estimated in this way and deducted from the benefits used in project justification.

The recreation approach also applies to wildlife areas. Potential benefit is found from analyzing K and n from records of visitation to existing areas. Benefits lost should again be deducted from projects adversely affecting wildlife.

17-10 COMMERCIAL DEMAND   The benefit realized through commercial harvest of fish and game may be estimated from a budget of operating cost and harvest values analogous to that used for estimating agricultural flood damage (Sec. 10-11). The total-benefit curve would be found from the net increase in harvest value resulting from low-flow augmentation, quicker fish passage past an obstruction, artificial spawning grounds, or protection of shellfish areas from pollution. The effect of the measures on harvest quantity must be determined from analysis of physical conditions on a with and without basis.

17-11 ENVIRONMENTAL CONSERVATION   The preservation of rare species of flora or fauna or of unique habitats is working toward an objective other than economic efficiency (Sec. 5-5, 9-5). Where the values realized cannot be measured in efficiency dollars, economic analysis can only be used to find the least costly method of achieving a legitimate nonefficiency objective. The best practice is to determine the cost of preservation as a function of some quantitative measure of the amount of resource conserved, such as numbers of fish or acreage of unique habitat. The total cost of preservation is the sum of the direct cost of the conservation measures and the benefits foregone by reducing other project output to provide fish and wildlife conservation. In each case, the marginal cost of preservation should be compared with the marginal resource conservation achieved to make sure the two are compatible. As an indication of the need for this type of analysis, costs of preservation exceeding $100 per fish have been noted.

17-12 INSECT CONTROL   The relationship between insect control and public health greatly restricts direct application of benefit maximizing rules. Efficiency-benefit evaluation is impractical even though attempts have been made to assign monetary values to good health based on medical costs and time lost from work.[1] The only reasonable approach is for health officials to set the levels of insect control required to preserve acceptable health standards. The planner can then provide the least expensive measures able to achieve the standard. However, the health official should weigh the costs of achieving alternative standards as

---

[1] Burton A. Weisbrod, "Economics of Public Health: Measuring the Economic Impact of Diseases" (Philadelphia: University of Pennsylvania Press, 1961).

he decides what degree of control can be justified in the context of current financial constraints. As a decision aid, the marginal disease incidence might be determined as a function of the marginal cost of insect control measures.

Many insects are more of a nuisance than a hazard to health. The marginal reduction in expected insect population is needed because the degree of nuisance should be roughly proportional to insect population. The approaches for evaluating nuisance damage were considered in the economic analysis of storm drainage (Sect. 11-6).

Project Feasibility

17-13 FINANCIAL FEASIBILITY   Features to ameliorate damages to fish and wildlife caused by the construction of water resource projects or features to compensate for such damages are normally financed from funds allotted for the other purposes of the project. The lack of financial responsibility of fish and wildlife interests for the suggested changes in water resource development plans has encouraged unrealistic demands. However, it is not unreasonable to expect the other project purposes to pay if the damage can be substantiated.

Measures to protect fish and wildlife are financed by cost sharing between federal and local funds with the percentage absorbed by the Federal government dependent on whether the facilities are judged part of a national program for fish and wildlife enhancement. Some states have programs which will absorb part or all of the local cost. Very few public projects receive a substantial financial contribution from users, but private developments by hunting or fishing clubs have been entirely financed by this means.

Other programs to enhance fish and wildlife are financed outside the general program for water resources development. Lands for waterfowl are purchased and developed from funds acquired through sale of duck stamps. Funds from the sale of fishing and hunting licenses are often used for similar purposes.

SELECTED REFERENCES
Clay, C. H.: "Design of Fishways and Other Fish Facilities" (Ottawa: Queen's Printer, 1961).
Crutchfield, James A.: Valuation of Fishery Resources, *Land Economics*, vol. 38 (May, 1962), pp. 145–54.

Ishio, Shinya: Behavior of Fish Exposed to Toxic Substances, in O. Jaag (ed.), "Advances in Water Pollution Research," vol. 1. (London: Pergamon Press, Ltd., 1965), pp. 19–40.

PROBLEMS

17-1 If critical depth occurs at the crest of a weir, having a coefficient of 2.5, what is the maximum head which can be allowed without exceeding a velocity of 4 fps in the flow over the weir? What would be the velocity over the weir if the head were 1 ft? What would be the flow rate over a 10-ft-long weir with 1-ft head? $Q = CLH^{1.5}$.

17-2 With a square-edged orifice $C_d = 0.62$ of 2-ft diameter, what would be the flow rate between pools of 1-ft difference in elevation? What would be the velocity of flow be through the orifice? What should the head be to have a velocity of exactly 4 fps?

$$Q = C_d A \sqrt{2gH}.$$

17-3 What pool size should be used in a fishway for a maximum daily run of 5,000 salmon? What is the approximate annual cost of the facility for a 30-ft-high dam with no powerhouse, assuming 4 percent interest and a 50-year life? If 8 percent of the annual run occurs during the peak day, what is the average cost per fish?

17-4 From the data of Prob. 17-3, above what value of the maximum daily run must the minimum pool size be exceeded? What is the marginal annual cost of enlarging the fishway to accommodate one additional fish per year once the minimum pool size is exceeded? How does the marginal cost per fish per year vary with the dam height?

17-5 Artificial spawning grounds are required to accommodate 10,000 sockeye salmon. How long must a 50-ft-wide channel be to provide adequate spawning area? Assuming a Manning n of 0.030, what should be the channel slope? What is the required flow rate?

17-6 If fishing could be provided in the reservoir of Prob. 16-1 at the marginal cost of $1.00 per user day of installed capacity and would in each case increase the value of K by 50 percent, what would the total annual benefits be? The net benefits? The benefit-cost ratio?

5
MULTIPURPOSE
WATER RESOURCES
DEVELOPMENT

Every water resources development project has a fixed cost, an amount which must be paid no matter how small the quantity of output produced. However, total project cost increases with the level of output. It is marginal cost, the rate of change of total cost, which is used in economic analysis to determine the optimum level of project development. However, only if benefits from optimum development exceed total cost, including fixed cost, is the project justified. As the ever-increasing pressure from population and economic growth increases competition for available water and development sites and necessitates larger and more expensive projects, the larger fixed cost makes it increasingly more difficult to justify any project built for but a single purpose. Multipurpose development provides an answer to the dilemma. The fixed cost can be shared. The physical facilities and the procedures for economic evaluation of specific outputs as described in Part 5 become the building blocks in overall resource development. The key to forming efficient systems from these blocks is the ability to recognize and take advantage of complementary physical and economic interdependencies, facilities producing more than one output (reservoirs) and outputs producing benefit in more than one way (low-flow augmentation).

The true multipurpose project must be planned, built, and operated to serve two or more purposes. An efficient multiproject system is a group of projects coordinated in planning, construction, and operation to serve a combination of purposes. Incidental use of an irrigation reservoir for swimming does not make a multipurpose project, nor does incidental downstream increase in hydroelectric generation capacity by upstream low-flow augmentation make a multiproject system.

The purpose of this section is to sketch the techniques by which multipurpose water resources development may be rationally formulated to achieve desired social objectives. Chapter 18 shows how manipulation of graphic demand and supply curves may be used to optimize simple projects. Chapter 19 surveys the more sophisticated analytical optimization techniques, such as linear programming and queuing theory, which are best adapted to specific components of the total system. Chapter 20 looks at simulation models, the one practical approach to optimizing complex water resources development systems. Chapter 21 turns to problems in organizing the planning team, achieving informed decision making, and implementing the selected course of action.

It is not the purpose of this discussion to provide a working knowledge of the techniques of hydrologic and hydraulic analysis required to model water resources systems or of the operations research algorithms required to work through to solutions. A number of other texts go into the methodology in detail.[1] The purpose here is rather to provide sufficient linkage between these tools and the economic building blocks presented in Part 4 to permit the planner to integrate the whole efficiently into a constructive planning effort.

[1]   Leading references include: Warren A. Hall and J. A. Dracup, "Water Resources Systems Engineering" (New York: McGraw-Hill Book Company, 1970); Russell F. Ackoff and Maurice W. Sasieni, "Fundamentals of Operations Research" (New York: John Wiley & Sons, Inc., 1968).

CHAPTER EIGHTEEN

GRAPHIC OPTIMIZATION TECHNIQUES

The Graphic Approach

18-1 THE METHOD The economic evaluation of multipurpose reservoirs may combine the purpose marginal-benefit curves to obtain an aggregate reservoir marginal-benefit curve by the same summation process used to combine consumer-demand curves to develop market-demand curves (Sec. 3-12). Likewise, the reservoir marginal-benefit curves may be combined to obtain the system marginal-benefit curve. The marginal-cost curve for a single reservoir may be determined from the relationship between reservoir cost and reservoir size. The system marginal-cost curve may be determined by combining reservoir marginal-cost curves to maximize storage for a given cost (Sec. 12-3). The optimum project or the optimum system may be determined from the point of intersection of corresponding marginal-benefit and -cost curves. The procedure described may be called *marginal analysis*.

Marginal analysis works best for individual multiple-purpose reservoirs or for simple water resource systems. Simplifying assumptions are required to condense all information determining the merit of a water resources project into two marginal curves. The more complex the prototype system is, the more restrictive the assumptions become. Nevertheless, marginal analysis provides valuable insight into the economic aspects of project development and in determining a starting point for simulation iteration.

The following example indicates how marginal analysis can be applied to a hypothetical project for a multiple-purpose reservoir, and an analogous analysis can be applied to any combination of project purposes or storage reservoirs. All the intermediate steps described are not essential to procuring the final result, but they do provide better understanding of the effectiveness of the method.

18-2   DATA FOR SAMPLE STUDY   A multipurpose reservoir for providing irrigation water, flood control, and low-flow augmentation for water quality control is under study for a particular site. The economic data required to optimize the reservoir have been collected and summarized in six curves by the following procedure:

1   By designing reservoirs of a number of different sizes for the site and estimating the total annual cost amortized over a 50-year life, a curve of annual reservoir cost as a function of active reservoir storage was developed (Fig. 18-1).
2   Reservoir operation studies were completed to determine the annual yield developed by a range of conservation storage volumes (Fig. 18-2).
3   Prospective crop patterns, crop water requirements, on-farm and distribution losses, and the other pertinent factors were analyzed to develop an irrigation-demand curve (Fig. 18-3). The curve expresses the value of water at the reservoir site as the distribution cost has been deducted from on-farm value. The 15,000 acre-ft/year of run-of-the-river yield (Fig. 18-2) will be used for irrigation independently of what happens with respect to constructing the multipurpose reservoir.

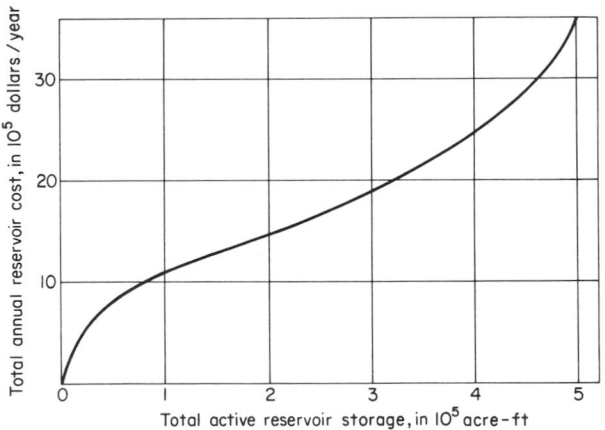

FIGURE 18-1   Reservoir-cost curve.

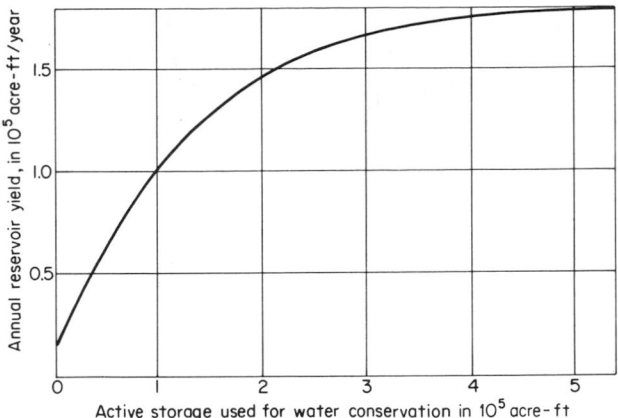

FIGURE 18-2 Reservoir-yield curve.

4 Flood damage as a function of flood flow was determined for the downstream flood plain. Based on a selected amount of flood control storage, floods covering a range of frequencies were routed through the reservoir and downstream to the flood plain to develop a curve of residual damage vs. frequency. The reduction in area under the damage-frequency curve provided the annual flood control benefit from the selected flood control storage. The procedure was repeated

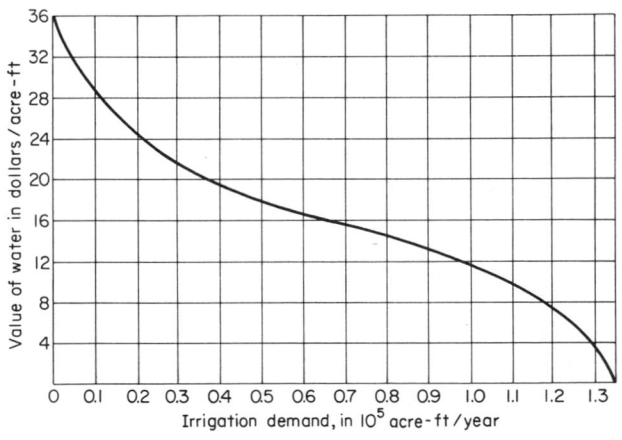

FIGURE 18-3 Annual irrigation demand.

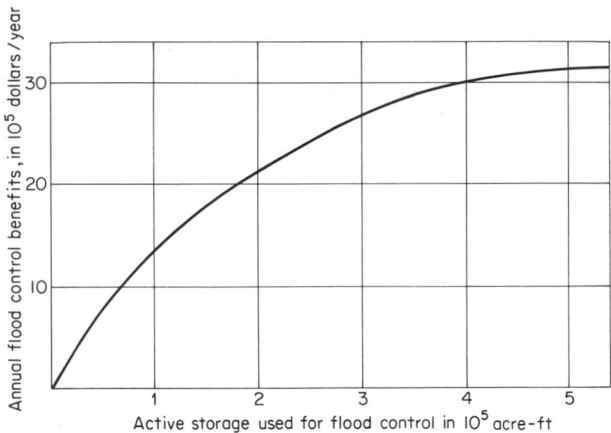

FIGURE 18-4   Annual flood control benefits.

for a number of storages to develop a curve of annual benefits vs. storage (Fig. 18-4).

5   Damage-concentration, flow-rate-concentration, and flow-duration curves were developed from a damage survey, a water quality sampling program, and stream-gage records respectively. The three curves were

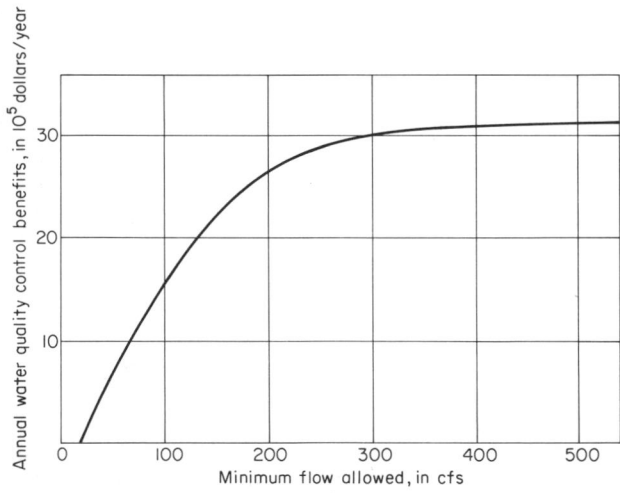

FIGURE 18-5   Water quality benefits from low-flow augmentation.

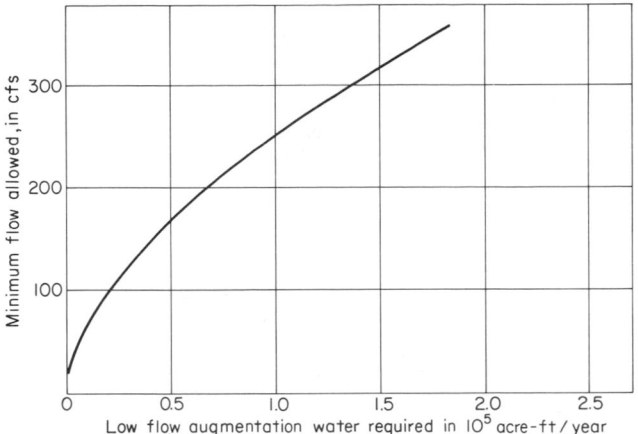

FIGURE 18-6 Water requirements of low-flow augmentation.

combined to estimate water quality damages without the project. By modifying the flow-duration curve by low-flow augmentation expressed in units of minimum flow allowed, residual damages were estimated as a function of minimum flow. Subtracting residual from initial damages produced a curve relating benefits to minimum flow (Fig. 18-5).

6   The flow-duration curve was analyzed to determine the amount of low-flow augmentation water required to prevent flows from falling below specified minimum values (Fig. 18-6). The curve gives augmentation required after 15,000 acre-ft/year run-of-the-river yield is withdrawn for irrigation, used, and returned to the stream.

Optimum Single-purpose Projects

18-3 IRRIGATION   Figures 18-1 and 18-2 can be combined by the computations in Table 18-1 to relate marginal cost to the annual reservoir yield (Fig. 18-7). The marginal-benefit curve (Fig. 18-3) is in the same units and may be directly transferred to Fig. 18-7.

Because 15,000 acre-ft/year of irrigation water may be supplied without any reservoir storage (Fig. 18-2), reservoir cost is zero up to an annual demand of 15,000 acre-ft. To increase the supply further, a reservoir must be built. Fixed cost is incremental to this enlargement so that marginal cost ascends vertically to a high value. It descends with further

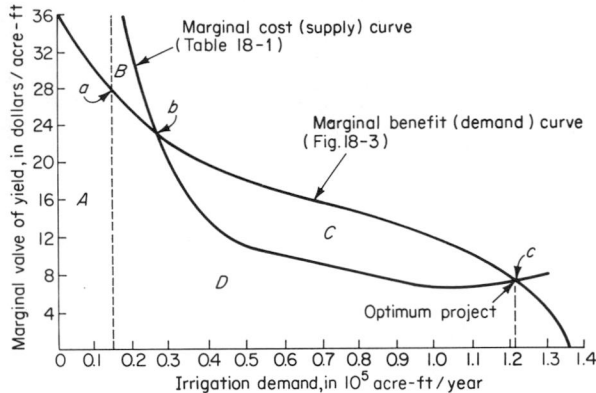

FIGURE 18-7 Single-purpose irrigation project optimization.

enlargement as calculated in Table 18-1. Thus, the supply and demand curves cross at points *a*, *b*, and *c* (Fig. 18-7). Point *b* cannot be optimum because the supply curve comes from above to intersect the demand curve. Point *a* represents a run-of-the-river irrigation project having a net benefit equal to area *A*. Point *c* represents the optimum reservoir if one is

TABLE 18-1 Calculating the Marginal Cost of Reservoir Yield

ANNUAL RESERVOIR COST		ANNUAL RESERVOIR YIELD		MARGINAL COST OF YIELD
Total cost Fig. 18-1, 10^5/year	Incremental cost 10^5/year	Total yield, Fig. 18-2, 10^5 acre-ft/year	Incremental yield, 10^5 acre-ft/year	Δ cost/Δ yield, $/acre-ft
0.0		0.15		
	5.0	0.25	0.20	25.0
5.0		0.35		
	3.0	0.49	0.27	11.1
8.0		0.62		
	2.0	0.74	0.23	8.7
10.0		0.85		
	2.0	1.00	0.30	6.7
12.0		1.15		
	2.0	1.28	0.25	8.0
14.0		1.40		
	2.0	1.48	0.15	13.3
16.0		1.55		
	2.0	1.59	0.08	25.0
18.0		1.63		

to be built. If area B exceeded area C, the project should not be built. However, because area C exceeds area B, point c is the optimum project. The benefits represented by area A will accrue without the reservoir and thus should not be counted in reservoir justification.

Point c reveals the optimum project to yield 121,000 acre-ft/year, of which 15,000 acre-ft/year comes from natural flow and 106,000 acre-ft/year is developed by the reservoir. Figure 18-2 reveals that 140,000 acre-ft of active reservoir storage is required to produce this yield. The annual cost of a reservoir providing this storage is $1,230,000 (Fig. 18-1). The annual benefit is the area under the demand curve between irrigation demands of 15,000 acre-ft/year and 121,000 acre-ft/year (Fig. 18-7, area $C + D$), or $1,680,000. Project benefit-cost ratio is 1.37.

18-4 FLOOD CONTROL The marginal cost and the marginal flood control benefit are derived from the slopes of the reservoir-cost curve (Fig. 18-1) and the annual-flood-control-benefit curve (Fig. 18-4) respectively. The marginal curves cross at a point indicating the optimum flood control storage to be 300,000 acre-ft (Fig. 18-8). The cost of the storage may be read directly (Fig. 18-1) as $1,880,000 per year. The benefit may be read directly (Fig. 18-4) as $2,620,000 per year. Benefit-cost ratio is 1.38.

18-5 WATER QUALITY CONTROL Low-flow augmentation for water quality control is supplied by reservoir yield, as is irrigation water.

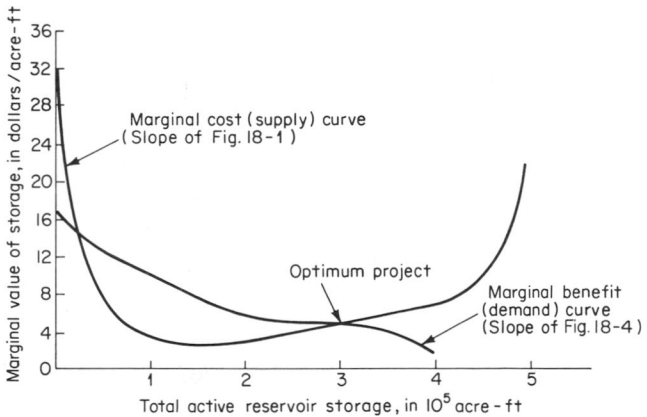

FIGURE 18-8 Single-purpose flood control project optimization.

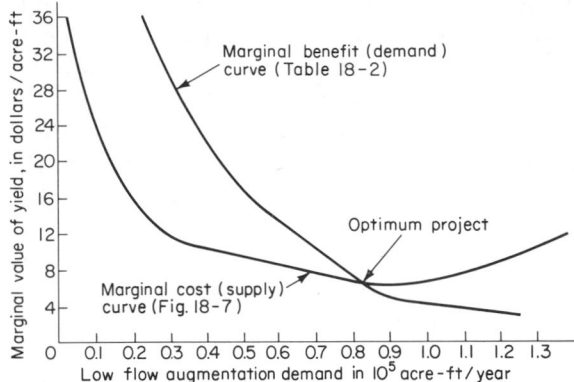

FIGURE 18-9   Single-purpose water quality control project optimization.

However, because the 15,000 acre-ft/year yield without the reservoir is not augmentation, the marginal-cost curve for water quality control (Fig. 18-9) is that for irrigation (Fig. 18-7) after a 15,000 acre-ft/year shift to the left. Strictly speaking, a further difference between the two marginal-cost curves is usually caused by a difference in demand pattern over the year, which affects the storage-yield relationship (Sec. 12-3).

The benefit resulting from a selected volume of low-flow augmentation water is found by reading the resulting minimum flow (Fig. 18-6) and using the minimum flow to read total annual benefits (Fig. 18-5). Marginal benefits are determined from incremental changes in total benefits (Table 18-2).

The point where the marginal curves cross designates an optimum low-flow augmentation yield of 83,000 acre-ft/year (98,000 acre-ft/year including natural yield). The storage required to produce this yield is 100,000 acre-ft (Fig. 18-2). The annual cost of providing this storage is $1,080,000 (Fig. 18-1). A yield of 83,000 acre-ft/year means a minimum flow of 222 cfs (Fig. 18-6) and benefits of $2,800,000 per year (Fig. 18-5). Benefit-cost ratio is 2.59.

Optimum Dual-purpose Projects

18-6   IRRIGATION AND FLOOD CONTROL   In order to combine the marginal-benefit curves for flood control and irrigation, both curves must be marginal to the same variable. The single-purpose curves for flood control were marginal to storage, while those for irrigation were marginal to yield. Storage is a better common denominator because it is required to produce both outputs. The marginal-cost curve for the dual-purpose project is identical with that for single-purpose flood control because the cost of storage does not depend on its use.

The dual-purpose marginal-benefit curve is the sum of the two single-purpose curves. Before combining, both axes of the marginal-benefit curve for irrigation must be converted into storage units. The abscissa (Fig. 18-7) is converted from yield to storage units by reading from Fig. 18-2 the storage required to supply the respective yields. The ordinate (Fig. 18-7), marginal benefit per unit of yield, is converted into marginal benefit per unit of storage by multiplication by the slope of corresponding points on the yield-storage curve (Fig. 18-2). The slope provides the incremental yield per incremental storage and, when multiplied by the benefits from incremental yield (Fig. 18-3), provides benefits from incremental storage. Results of computations converting the irrigation-marginal-benefit curve from a yield to a storage basis (Table 18-3) are plotted in Fig. 18-10. The flood-control-marginal benefit curve was already in storage units in Fig. 18-8 and remains unchanged. By assuming storage must be reserved either for flood control

TABLE 18-2 Calculating the Marginal Benefit of Water Quality Control

Annual augmentation water, 10^5 acre-ft/ year	Minimum flow, cfs Fig. 18-6	Annual benefits, Fig. 18-5, 10^5/year	Marginal benefit, Δ Benefit/ Δ Yield, $/acre-ft of yield	Yield, Av water req., 10^5 acre-ft/year
0.0	20.0	0.0		
0.1	66.0	10.0	100.0	0.05
0.2	98.0	16.0	60.0	0.15
0.3	123.0	19.5	35.0	0.25
0.4	145.0	22.0	25.0	0.35
0.5	167.0	24.0	20.0	0.45
0.6	185.0	25.5	15.0	0.55
0.7	202.0	26.7	12.0	0.65
0.8	218.0	27.6	9.0	0.75
0.9	233.0	28.2	6.0	0.85
1.0	246.0	28.7	5.0	0.95
1.5	315.0	30.3	3.2	1.25
2.0	380.0	30.9	1.2	1.75

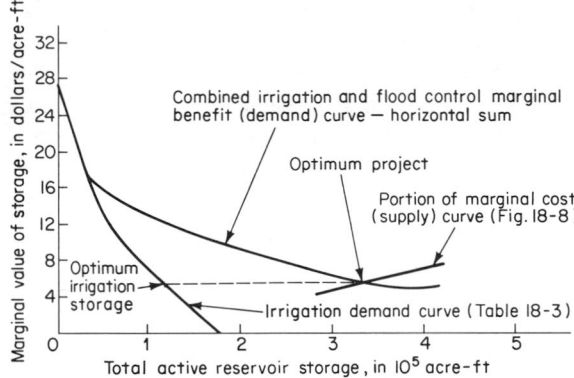

FIGURE 18-10 Dual-purpose flood control and irrigation project optimization.

or for irrigation, the two single-purpose-demand curves may be added
horizontally to get a combined-demand curve for storage (Fig. 18-10).
Actually, use of the same storage space sometimes for flood control and
other times for irrigation water increases the benefit from multipurpose
construction (Sec. 20-5).

The crossing of the supply and demand curves (Fig. 18-10) shows the
optimum total active storage to be 335,000 acre-ft. The optimum storage
by purpose produces a marginal benefit equal to the marginal cost of

TABLE 18-3 Calculating Marginal Irrigation Benefit in Storage Units

(1) Irrigation benefits, Fig. 18-3, $/acre-ft of yield	(2) Irrigation demand, Fig. 18-3, 10^5 acre-ft/ year	(3) Required storage (demand = yield) Fig. 18-2, 10^5 acre-ft	(4) Δ Yield/ Δ storage, dimensionless slope of Fig. 18-2	(5) Irrigation benefits (col. 1)(col. 4) $/acre-ft of storage
27.0	0.15	0.0	1.00	27.0
21.0	0.35	0.2	1.00	21.0
17.0	0.54	0.4	0.90	15.3
15.5	0.71	0.6	0.80	12.4
14.0	0.86	0.8	0.70	9.8
11.5	1.00	1.0	0.63	7.2
10.0	1.12	1.2	0.55	5.5
7.0	1.22	1.4	0.49	3.4
4.0	1.31	1.6	0.43	1.7
0.0	1.38	1.8	0.36	0.0

storage, \$5.50 per acre-ft. The division turns out to be 120,000 acre-ft for irrigation (Fig. 18-10) and 215,000 acre-ft for flood control (Fig. 18-9). The cost of 335,000 acre-ft of storage is \$2,050,000 per year (Fig. 18-1). This cost must be allocated between the two purposes (Sec. 23-1). A simple allocation proportional to storage gives \$1,316,000 per year for flood control and \$734,000 per year for irrigation. The irrigation storage of 120,000 acre-ft provides 112,000 acre-ft/year of gross yield (Fig. 18-2). Irrigation benefits equal the area under the demand curve (Fig. 18-3) between 15,000 acre-ft/year and 112,000 acre-ft/year, or \$1,590,000 per year. Flood control benefits from 215,000 acre-ft of storage equal \$2,160,000 per year (Fig. 18-4). Total project benefits are \$3,750,000 per year. Benefit-cost ratios are 1.64 for flood control, 2.17 for irrigation, and 1.83 for the overall project.

18-7 FLOOD CONTROL AND WATER QUALITY The marginal-benefit curve for water quality control (Fig. 18-9) must also be converted to a storage basis to be combined with flood control (Table 18-4). The differences between Tables 18-3 and 18-4 result from using augmented (that over 15,000 acre-ft/year) instead of total demand and the combined use of Table 18-2 and Fig. 18-9 to relate water quality benefit to augmented supply. The marginal water quality benefit per unit of storage is plotted in Fig. 18-11. The flood-control-marginal-benefit curve (Fig. 18-8) still remains unchanged. The demand curves for the two purposes may again be added horizontally to get a combined-demand curve for storage.

TABLE 18-4 Calculating Marginal Water Quality Control Benefit in Storage Units

(1)	(2)	(3)	(4)	(5)
Water quality benefit, Table 18-2, \$/acre-ft of yield	Augmented water quality demand, Fig. 18-9, 10^5 acre-ft/year	Required storage, Fig. 18-2, 10^5 acre-ft	Δ Yield/ Δ storage, dimensionless slope of Fig. 18-2	Water quality benefit (col. 1)(col. 4) \$/acre-ft of storage
150.0	0.00	0.0	1.00	150.0
45.0	0.20	0.2	1.00	45.0
23.0	0.39	0.4	0.90	20.7
15.0	0.56	0.6	0.80	12.0
10.5	0.71	0.8	0.70	7.4
6.0	0.85	1.0	0.63	3.8
4.65	0.97	1.2	0.55	2.56
4.25	1.07	1.4	0.49	2.08

The crossing of the supply and demand curves (Fig. 18-11) shows the optimum total active storage to be 325,000 acre-ft. By making the marginal benefits to each purpose equal to each other and to the marginal cost, the division comes out as 90,000 acre-ft of storage for water quality control and 235,000 acre-ft for flood control. The total cost is $2 million per year (Fig. 18-1) which when allocated proportional to storage turns out to be $550,000 per year for water quality control and $1,450,000 per year for flood control. Storage of 90,000 acre-ft augments flows by 78,000 acre-ft/year (Fig. 18-2). This means a minimum flow of 215 cfs (Fig. 18-6) and benefits of $2,760,000 per year (Fig. 18-5). Flood control benefits from 235,000 acre-ft of storage equal $2,280,000 per year (Fig. 18-4). Total project benefits are $5,040,000 per year. Benefit-cost ratios are 5.02 for water quality control, 1.57 for flood control, and 2.52 for the overall project.

18-8   IRRIGATION AND WATER QUALITY   The marginal curves for irrigation and water quality control are both already in demand units, and demands may be summed horizontally after the 15,000 acre-ft/year run-of-the-river yield has been deducted (Fig. 18-12). The supply curve for the dual-purpose project is identical with that for either single-purpose project.

The point where the two curves cross (Fig. 18-12) indicates an optimum yield of 142,000 acre-ft/year (157,000 acre-ft/year including run-of-the-river yield) and a marginal benefit of $12.50 per acre-ft of yield.

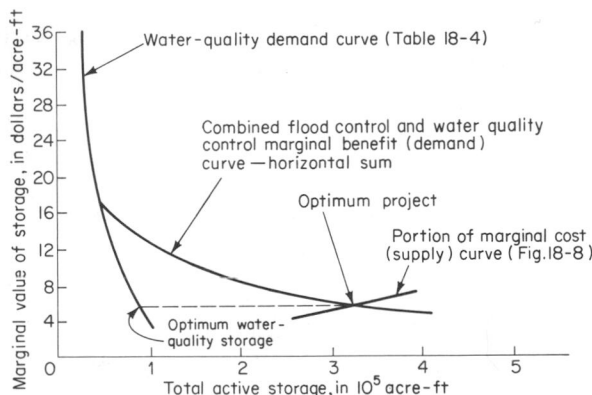

FIGURE 18-11   Dual-purpose flood control and water quality control project optimization.

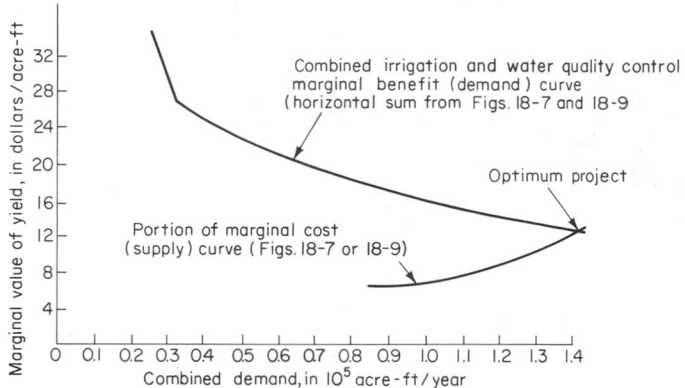

FIGURE 18-12   Dual-purpose irrigation and water quality control project optimization.

Thus, 79,000 acre-ft/year of net yield should be used for irrigation (Fig. 18-7) and 63,000 acre-ft/year should be used for water quality control (Fig. 18-9). Storage required to produce this yield is 250,000 acre-ft (Fig. 18-2). The cost of this amount of storage is \$1,650,000 per year. Storage is not a suitable allocation vehicle for this dual-purpose project because the same storage space is used for both purposes, but yield may be substituted. Prorating cost by yield gives \$920,000 per year for irrigation and \$730,000 per year for water quality control. Irrigation benefits equal the area under the demand curve (Fig. 18-3) between 15,000 acre-ft/year and 94,000 acre-ft/year, or \$1,415,000 per year. A low-flow augmentation yield of 63,000 acre-ft/year is sufficient to maintain a minimum flow of 190 cfs (Fig. 18-6). Benefits amount to \$2,610,000 per year for water quality control (Fig. 18-5). Total project benefit is \$4,025,000 per year. Benefit-cost ratios are 1.54 for irrigation, 3.58 for water quality control, and 2.44 for the total project.

Overall Evaluation

18-9 OPTIMUM TRIPLE–PURPOSE PROJECT   With flood control included, storage rather than yield units must be used for the marginal curves. The marginal-cost curve of Fig. 18-10 still applies. The combined-

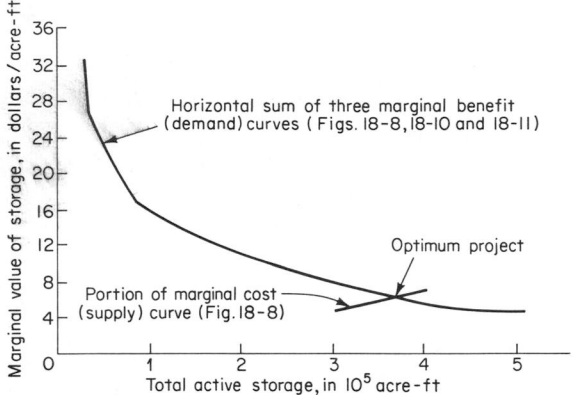

FIGURE 18-13　Triple-purpose project optimization.

marginal-benefit curve is the horizontal sum of the three individual curves. The marginal-benefit and marginal-cost curves cross (Fig. 18-13) at an optimum storage of 368,000 acre-ft and a marginal storage value of \$6.30 per acre-ft. This marginal value corresponds to 185,000 acre-ft of storage for flood control (Fig. 18-8), which leaves 183,000 acre-ft of storage for water conservation. This much water conservation yields 140,000 acre-ft/year, or 125,000 acre-ft/year net (Fig. 18-2). The marginal value at 125,000 acre-ft/year of yield is \$14/acre-ft (Fig. 18-12). Division at this marginal value gives 58,000 acre-ft/year for water quality control (Fig. 18-9) and 67,000 net acre-ft/year for irrigation (Fig. 18-7).

The total cost of the 368,000-acre-ft reservoir is \$2,250,000 per year (Fig. 18-1). Prorating cost between flood control and the other two purposes combined, proportional to storage, gives a cost of \$1,130,000 per year for the former and \$1,120,000 per year for the latter. Prorating their dual cost proportional to yield gives \$600,000 per year for irrigation and \$520,000 per year for water quality control.

Flood control benefits from 185,000 acre-ft storage are \$1,990,000 per year (Fig. 18-4). Irrigation benefits amount to the area under the demand curve (Fig. 18-3) between yields of 15,000 acre-ft/year and 82,000 acre-ft/year, \$1,230,000 per year. A water quality control yield of 58,000 acre-ft/year is sufficient to maintain a minimum flow of 180 cfs (Fig. 18-6). Benefits amount to \$2,540,000 per year (Fig. 18-5). Total project benefit is \$5,760,000 per year. Benefit-cost ratios are 2.05 for irrigation, 4.88 for water quality control, 1.76 for flood control, and 2.56 for the overall project.

TABLE 18-5 Summary of Results of Marginal Analysis

	Units	(1) Irrigation	(2) Flood control	(3) Water quality	(4) (1) and (2)	(5) (2) and (3)	(6) (1) and (3)	(7) (1), (2), and (3)
Net irrig. yield	Acre-ft/year	106,000			97,000		79,000	67,000
Irrig. storage	Acre-ft	140,000			120,000		920,000	600,000
Irrig. cost	$/year	1,230,000			734,000		920,000	600,000
Irrig. benefit,	$/year	1,680,000			1,590,000		1,415,000	1,230,000
B/C		1.37			2.17		1.54	2.05
Flood control storage	Acre-ft		300,000		215,000	235,000		185,000
Flood control cost	$/year		1,880,000		1,316,000	1,450,000		1,130,000
Flood control benefit	$/year		2,620,000		2,160,000	2,280,000		1,990,000
B/C			1.38		1.64	1.57		1.76
Water quality yield	Acre-ft/year			83,000		78,000	63,000	58,000
Water quality storage	Acre-ft			100,000		90,000		
Minimum flow	cfs			222		215	190	180
Water quality cost	$/year			1,080,000		550,000	730,000	520,000
Water quality benefit	$/year			2,800,000		2,760,000	2,610,000	2,540,000
B/C				2.59		5.02	3.58	4.88
Total storage	Acre-ft	140,000	300,000	100,000	335,000	325,000	250,000	368,000
Total cost	$/year	1,230,000	1,880,000	1,080,000	2,050,000	2,000,000	1,650,000	2,250,000
Total benefit	$/year	1,680,000	2,620,000	2,800,000	3,750,000	5,040,000	4,025,000	5,760,000
B/C		1.37	1.38	2.59	1.83	2.52	2.44	2.56

18-10 SUMMARY   The results of the seven optimization studies as summarized in Table 18-5 are typical of the situation where various project purposes compete for the same storage space. Each purpose uses less space when combined with other purposes because the space having lowest marginal value in the first use is converted to another use of higher marginal value. However, the optimum total storage increases with the number of purposes because the additional benefits justify additional storage. Purposes competing for storage space may reduce storage cost if the average cost per acre-foot of storage decreases with increasing reservoir size in the range of project optimization.

Marginal analysis is the best multipurpose project formulation method for providing insight into the required economic trade-offs. However, the method is severely limited by the approximations and simplifications required to develop supply and demand curves.

PROBLEMS

18-1 The multipurpose project being planned in the marginal analysis example could also be used to provide low-flow augmentation for navigation. Navigation is possible only if the flow is not allowed to fall below 250 cfs and when provided for, brings an annual benefit of $1 million.

  a Should navigation be provided for?

  b Develop all the information which would be required in an eighth column in Table 18-5 for a four-purpose project.

  c What would be the allocated cost and the benefits of the navigation features of the project?

18-2 Geological exploration of the dam site indicates such bad foundation conditions that all costs on the cost-storage curve of Fig. 18-1 will be increased by 50 percent. What will the optimum triple-purpose project now be?

CHAPTER
NINETEEN

ANALYTICAL
OPTIMIZATION TECHNIQUES

19-1   THE ANALYTIC APPROACH   The many complex production systems introduced by modern technology provide a major challenge in planning for optimum system design and operation. The disciplines of statistics, decision theory, and operations research have developed an increasingly sophisticated methodology to meet this need, and the advent of the digital computer has made possible the numerical work required in its execution. Water resources planning can benefit by applying these techniques to structure optimum policies.

The planner must decide what to do in a real world or prototype situation. The analytic approach requires the decision problem be converted to a standard mathematical model. The value to be gained depends on how closely the prototype can be modeled by a solvable algorithm. Structuring of the model begins with the selection of the physical variables for which an optimum quantity is desired (i.e., reservoir capacity, flood channel capacity, or power plant size). Equations are then developed to express the physical relationships among the variables and limit the range of values that given variables may assume (e.g., relate reservoir yield to storage and specify minimum water requirements of downstream users). The equations should describe the functioning of the prototype system as closely as possible within the limitations imposed by the ability of current analytic techniques to render optimal solutions.

Each analytic technique uses a specific sequence of mathematical operations to examine the model for the most desirable values for the physical variables according to an objective function (Secs. 4-3, 5-2).

The search for the optimum set of variables is structured to use the minimum computational effort to adjust the values systematically within the acceptable range until the optimum is found. A number of search operations have been developed and applied to specific types of problems. Detailed presentation of even the major techniques is beyond the scope of this discussion, but it will be useful to introduce the concepts and reference the details of the four techniques of greatest potential value to those engaged in planning public works projects: linear programming, dynamic programming, queuing theory, and the critical path method.[1]

19-2   LINEAR PROGRAMMING   Linear programming requires that the objective function and all the other equations in the mathematical model be linear. That is, no term in any equation can contain more than one variable and that variable must be to the first power. The three basic components of linear programming are the objective function, the constraint equations, and an iterative procedure for finding the optimum solution. As a very simple example, a production process might produce two outputs X and Y of equal value. The objective function would be to maximize $X + Y$. If 3 units of labor, 3 units of material, and 3 units of factory space are available for producing the two outputs, and producing X requires 2 units of labor, 1 unit of material, and 1 unit of factory space, while Y requires 1 unit of labor, 2 units of material, and 1 unit of factory space, the constraint equations would be $2X + Y = 3$, $X + 2Y = 3$, and $X + Y = 3$ (Fig. 19-1). Any amount of X and Y can be produced which does not exceed any of the three equations. The feasible region (see also Fig. 4-1) comprises the combinations of X and Y which can be physically produced. The upper limit is determined by the constraint equations; the lower limit is zero. Obviously, the factory space constraint is not critical. If the objective function is linear, production combinations having equal value will also plot as straight lines. Thus the optimum point must be at one of the corners (or possibly at two corners if the isovalue lines parallel one of the sides of the feasible region). In Fig. 19-1, the origin has a value of 0, the two other corners on axes have values of 1.5, and the interior corner is optimum with a value of 2.0.

While the solution to the two-dimensional illustrative graphic example is obvious, one can appreciate the complexity of a more realistic problem involving 15 or 20 variables. The required geometric figure would have 15 or 20 dimensions and contain a multitude of corners. A systematic,

[1] Application of the methods to water resources planning is summarized in Ven Te Chow, System Design by Operations Research, in Ven Te Chow (ed.), "Handbook of Applied Hydrology" (New York: McGraw-Hill Book Company, 1964).

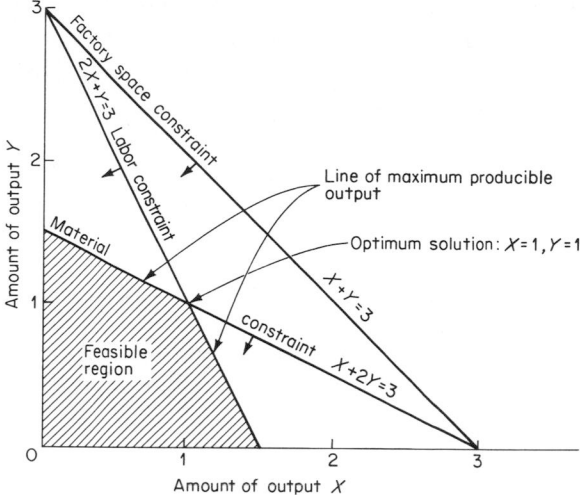

FIGURE 19-1   Geometry of linear programming example.

iterative, matematical search procedure is required. The one used is called the *simplex method*. The example may be expressed as

Maximize $X + Y$ Subject to

$$2X + Y \leq 3$$
$$X + 2Y \leq 3 \tag{19-1}$$
$$X + Y \leq 3$$

The objective function and constraint inequalities may be converted to equation form as

$$
\begin{aligned}
R - X - Y \qquad\qquad &= 0 \\
2X + Y + a \qquad\quad &= 3 \\
X + 2Y \qquad + b \quad &= 3 \\
X + Y \qquad\qquad + c &= 3
\end{aligned}
\tag{19-2}
$$

where R is the value of the objective function and a, b, and c are slack variables representing the amount of unused labor, materials, and factory space respectively. The simplex procedure systematically operates on Eq. (19-2) to convert it into a form indicating the solution. The operation may be executed manually[1] but more often is performed by digital

[1]   Harvey Wagner, The Simplex Method for Beginners. *Operations Res.*, vol. 5, no. 9 (March–April, 1958), pp. 190–199.

computer (library programs are readily available). For the sample problem, the solution would be

$$
\begin{aligned}
R &+ \tfrac{1}{3}a + \tfrac{1}{3}b && = 2 \\
X &+ \tfrac{2}{3}a - \tfrac{1}{3}b && = 1 \\
Y &- \tfrac{1}{3}a + \tfrac{2}{3}b && = 1 \\
& \tfrac{1}{3}a - \tfrac{1}{3}b + c && = 1
\end{aligned}
\tag{19-3}
$$

The optimum value of variables appearing in only one equation is given by the corresponding number on the right-hand side ($R = 2$, $X = 1$, $Y = 1$, $c = 1$). The optimum value of variables appearing in several equations is zero ($a = 0$, $b = 0$). The coefficients of the decision variables X and Y in the top row represent the amount the value of the item would have to increase to make some production of it optimal (0 for X and Y as some production already is optimal). The coefficients of the slack variables a, b, and c in the top row represent the increase in value of the objective function R which would be caused by a unit increase in the availability of the constrained resource ($\tfrac{1}{3}$ for a, $\tfrac{1}{3}$ for b, and 0 for c as enough is already available).

Linear programming has been used in formulating a hypothetical water resources project by a research group at Harvard.[1] A very useful application has been in optimizing the combination of generating capacity and interties in electric power systems.[2] Linear programming is used by the national electric system of France in formulating its expansion and operating policies. Other potential applications include allocating storage space in a reservoir among project purposes, determining from which reservoir in a system water should be released, and scheduling an activity sequence in a construction project.

Most linear programming models are deterministic in that the coefficients in the objective function are assumed to be known and fixed. Extensions can be made to the model by varying the coefficients in a preselected manner (parametric programming) or by recognizing them to be probability distributions (stochastic programming). Existing techniques provide much more freedom in varying coefficients in the objective function than in the restraint equations.

[1]   Robert Dorfman, Mathematical Models: The Multistructure Approach, in Arthur Maass et al., "Design of Water-resource Systems" (Cambridge, Mass.: Harvard University Press, 1962), pp. 494–539.
[2]   Joel Bergsman, "Economic Problems in Electric Power System Planning" (Stanford, Calif.: Stanford University, Institute in Engineering Economic Systems, EEP-6, 1963). Edouard Andre Sautter, "Studies in the Long-range Planning of Interties between Electric Power Systems" (Stanford, Calif.: Stanford University, Institute in Engineering Economic Systems, EEP-11, 1964).

19-3   DYNAMIC PROGRAMMING   Dynamic programming is distinguished by its way of viewing the problem.[1] As the word dynamic implies, the technique determines the optimum decision for each of a sequence of periods of time called *stages*. The mathematical model requires an objective function and a set of recurrence equations. A recurrence equation gives the value of a variable during a stage as a function of conditions during previous stages. The conditions within a stage are called the *state* and include all relevant information required to describe the nature of affairs during the stage. Example 19-1 illustrates each definition and the solution algorithm.

EXAMPLE 19-1

A traveler wants to go from A to J. He must travel by some combination of the available routes shown below. The cost of traveling between each pair of points is shown in the figure. What route should the traveler take if he wants to make the trip at least cost?

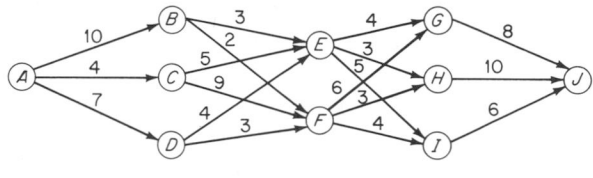

Stage: 1   2   3   4   5

State: Minimum cost of getting from A to point in question.

Recurrence equation:

$F = B + 2$ or $E = B + 3$ or 16 others

Sample calculation of state value at E

$B + 3 = 10 + 3 = 13$

$C + 5 = 4 + 5 = 9$ Select the minimum value, or 9

$D + 4 = 7 + 4 = 11$

State values at various points:

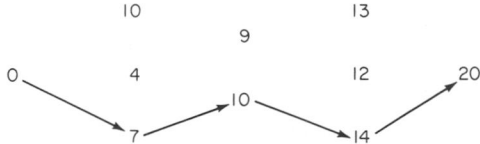

Minimum cost route shown by arrows.

---

[1]   The basic text is Richard Bellman, "Dynamic Programming" (Princeton, N.J.: Princeton University Press, 1957).

In solving the sample problem, it would be possible to tabulate the cost of all potential routes and pick the minimum. However, dynamic programming substantially reduces the work by making use of the fact that once the optimum state with a given stage is established, the optimal policy for the remaining stages is independent of the policy adopted in the previous stages. For example, once the optimum route from A to E is established, no other routes from A to E could appear in the optimum solution.

As is the case with all mathematical models, it is very easy to formulate a dynamic programming problem for which no practical iterative solution procedure has yet been devised. The difficulty is compounded when the state variables must be described by more than a single parameter (time and cost to get there in the example) because one is no longer able to identify the optimum state easily at intermediate stages. The least-cost route may take the longest time. Dynamic programming is most conveniently applied to multistage-decision-process problems in which the state at each stage can be defined with one parameter. Two parameters can be handled, but the solution algorithm gets out of hand with very many more.

Dynamic programming will be used more as water planners explore the economic advantage to be gained through better project timing.[1] Buras has used dynamic programming to pick the optimum design parameters and the optimum operating policy for the conjunctive operation of one surface reservoir and one aquifer.[2] Hall has used dynamic programming for multipurpose reservoir design based on mean inflows.[3] Hall and Roefs used the technique to optimize the operating policy for the hydroelectric power generating system of the California water project.[4] Liebman and Lynn used dynamic programming to determine the locations and degrees of waste treatment which minimize the cost of meeting specified stream dissolved-oxygen concentration standards.[5]

19-4   QUEUING THEORY   In dynamic programming models, the state changes at the discrete time periods, stages.[6] Queuing theory

[1]   Such problems are presented for the Columbia River in John Krutilla, Sequence and Timing in River Basin Development, (Washington: Resources for the Future, 1960).
[2]   Nathan Buras, Conjunctive Operation of Dams and Aquifers, *Proc. ASCE*, vol. 89, no. HY 6 (November, 1963).
[3]   Warren A. Hall, Optimum Design of a Multiple-purpose Reservoir, *Proc. ASCE*, vol. 90, no. HY 4 (July, 1964).
[4]   Warren A. Hall and Theodore F. Roefs, Hydroelectric Project Output Optimization, *Proc. ASCE*, vol. 92, no. PO 1 (January, 1966), pp. 67–79.
[5]   Jon C. Liebman and Walter R. Lynn, The Optimal Allocation of Stream Dissolved Oxygen, *Water Resources Res.*, vol. 2 (1966), pp. 581–591.
[6]   A basic text is Thomas L. Saaty, 'Elements of Queuing Theory" (New York: McGraw-Hill Book Company, 1961).

describes the state as a continuous function of time as units pass through a service facility. The function is determined by probability distributions which express the frequency at which units arrive to be served and the rate at which the facility can serve them. The analysis estimates probability distributions as well as expected values for the time a unit can expect to wait in queue, the expected number of units in queue at a given time, the chance that a unit arriving will not have to wait, and the percentage of the time the service facility is utilized.

The water resources planner must design many continuous time systems where queuing theory may help him reach the optimum decision. Examples would be the passage of water through a reservoir or a series of reservoirs, the arrival of visitors to use recreational facilities, or the arrival of ships at a harbor.[1]

19-5 CRITICAL–PATH METHOD   The critical-path method (CPM) or program evaluation research task (PERT) is an application of parametric linear programming to situations where time and cost must both be considered in selecting an optimum activity sequence.[2] The problem is formulated by representing the sequential relationships of the operations within the activity sequence with a network model. The activity sequence (construction of a dam, for example) is subdivided into a number of operations or tasks. Then, the operations are placed in a time sequence by determining which other operations must be completed before each operation can begin. Figure 19-2 illustrates a simple network model. The next step is to define the cost of completing each operation as a function of the time required to complete it. The normal time for an operation is that during which it can be completed at least cost. However, by

[1]   Robert Dorfman, Formal Models in the Design of Water Resource Systems, *Water Resources Res.*, vol. 1 (3d Quarter, 1965), pp. 329–336.
[2]   F. K. Levy, G. L. Thompson, and J. D. Wiest, The ABC's of the Critical Path Method, *Harvard Business Rev.*, vol. 41 (September–October, 1963), pp. 98–108.

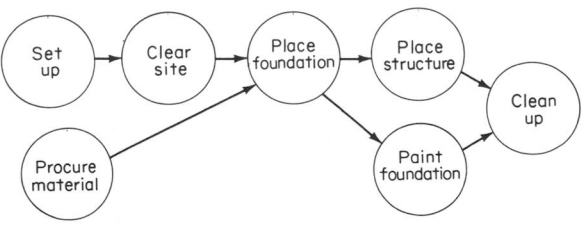

FIGURE 19-2   Simplified network model for critical-path method.

increasing the work force, using different equipment, or working overtime, most operations may be completed more quickly at extra cost. Cost continues to increase as time is reduced until the minimum possible, or crash time, is reached. The initial critical path is the route through the network model for which the sum of the operation normal times is greatest. The time of completing those operations on the critical path must be watched more closely than the time spent in other operations because they delay completion of the project as a whole. If the project must be accelerated to meet an earlier completion date, those operations on the critical path which can be accelerated at least cost should be shortened. As the operations on the critical path are shortened, they may be reduced to the sum of the normal times for an alternative path through the network model. Additional acceleration must consider time-cost relationships for operations along both paths. In a crash program, all operations on the critical path are shortened to the minimum possible time, and the other operations are shortened so that they will not hold up the sequence. The cost of imposing a required early completion date is the sum of the costs of accelerating the operations which must be completed more rapidly.

The critical-path method has become a working tool in planning the sequence of operations during project construction.[1] It has also been employed with some success in ordering the sequential steps in the planning process by the Corps of Engineers and the California Department of Water Resources.[2]

19-6 HARVARD STUDIES As part of a pioneering research program at Harvard University, seeking an improved methodology for the design of water resource systems, two linear programming models were developed.[3] The first model, called the *multistructure model,* sought optimum values for the decision variables of active and dead reservoir storage, power plant size, and target hydroelectric-energy and irrigation-water output from a hypothetical system of four reservoirs and two power plants. The model had three versions according to whether the optimum solution was based on the inflow to the reservoirs during a typical year in isolation, on the inflow during the entire critical dry period, or on a set of inflows drawn at random from an appropriate probability distribution. The first version was the simplest but the least accurate. The second version gave better results

---

[1] John W. Fondahl, "Methods for Extending the Range of Non-computer Critical Path Applications" (Stanford, Calif.: Stanford University, Department of Civil Engineering Tech. Rept. 47, 1964), pp. 3–7.

[2] Maynard F. Hufschmidt, Field Level Planning of Water Resource Systems, *Water Resources Res.*, vol. 1 (2d Quarter, 1965), p. 155.

[3] Arthur Maass et al., "Design of Water-resource Systems" (Cambridge, Mass.: Harvard University Press, 1962), pp. 257–261, 494–561.

because it made provision for water retained in the reservoir from one year to the next. The third version recognized that the reservoir operator never knows future streamflow in advance. All three versions were limited by the constricting approximations required to use the linear programming algorithm.

The second model, called the *stochastic sequential model,* sought to optimize reservoir capacity, target outputs, and operating procedure simultaneously. Using inflows drawn at random from a probability distribution based on historical flow records, the amount of reservoir yield was determined as a function of the fraction of the time it was available. The model optimized the target outputs and operating procedure for a given reservoir size by selecting the yield probability distribution with the highest expected value. However, the process had to be repeated by trial and adjustment for a series of reservoir sizes in order to optimize that variable. The second model was better able to handle overyear storage but was severely handicapped by the great number of other simplifying assumptions required.

19-7 SUMMARY   The simplification required to model a complex water resources system in a form amenable to optimization by the standardized analytic techniques severely limits their use for this purpose. The Harvard group concluded, "The mathematical models will probably continue to give only an approximate answer on a good first fit."[1] More recent applications to planning multipurpose water resources systems have offered little more encouragement. If one will eventually have to use simulation to complete the optimization, it is seldom worthwhile to structure a special mathematical model for analytic solution.

The situation is less gloomy for the many levels of suboptimization which must precede optimization of the overall system. Linear programming to optimize interties for electric power distribution, dynamic programming to optimize a stage construction sequence, and queuing theory to select the optimum number of berths in a ship harbor have all been successfully applied to practical problems. In summary, the standard analytic algorithms offer very little promise as a viable tool for the overall optimization of complex systems but are finding increased application in the optimization of system components.

SELECTED REFERENCES

Ackoff, Russell F., and Maurice W. Sasieni: "Fundamentals of Operations Research" (New York: John Wiley & Sons, Inc., 1968).

[1]   *Ibid.,* p. 261.

Bellman, Richard: "Dynamic Programming" (Princeton, N.J.: Princeton University Press, 1957).

Fondahl, John W.: "A Non-computer Approach to the Critical Path Method for the Construction Industry" (Stanford, Calif.: Stanford University, Department of Civil Engineering, Tech. Rept. 9, 1961).

Hall, Warren A., and J. A. Dracup: "Water Resources Systems Engineering" (New York: McGraw-Hill Book Company, 1970).

Maass, Arthur, et al.: "Design of Water-resource Systems" (Cambridge, Mass.: Harvard University Press, 1962).

Wagner, Harvey: The Simplex Method for Beginners, *Operations Res.*, vol. 5, no. 9 (March–April, 1958), pp. 190–199.

CHAPTER
TWENTY

OPTIMIZATION BY
SIMULATION

The Simulation Approach

20-1 SIMULATION MODELS Simulation is the most powerful tool available for establishing the optimum design for complex systems. Graphic optimization techniques are limited by the difficulty of condensing into two curves all the values gained and values sacrificed as a consequence of alternative project implementation choices. Analytical optimization is limited by difficulty in condensing equations describing the functioning of a real, physical system into a form solvable by available analytic models.

A simulation model attempts to represent the physical functioning and consequent economic effects of the prototype system by a computerized algorithm. The basic model is shown in Fig. 20-1. Hydrologic events produce runoff at different times and from different places in the watershed. The runoff subsequently flows downward through the watershed in a pattern determined by the nature of the currently existing channels and storage facilities as well as by the amount of runoff from previous hydrologic events still within the watershed. Standard flood-routing techniques can be used to calculate continuous runoff hydrographs or current storage volumes at any prescribed point.[1] Flood hydrographs must be routed with a fairly short time interval, but intervals up to a month can be used for low flows.

The economic effects of the way runoff moves through the watershed are determined by the state of simultaneous watershed economic

---

[1] See, for example, F. M. Henderson, "Open Channel Flow" (New York: The Macmillan Company, 1966), pp. 355–404.

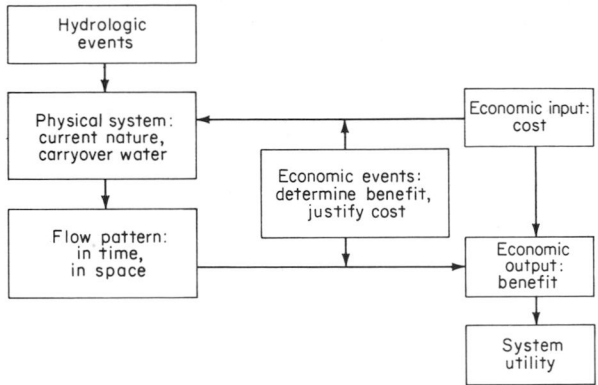

FIGURE 20-1 Schematic diagram for system simulation.

development. Flood-plain development, the extent of available uses for fresh water, and the number of participants in outdoor recreation translate the sequence of physical flow events into a time pattern of derived economic value. Structural measures can be used to alter the physical system and thereby the time and space pattern of flows and storage within the watershed. If the resulting increase in derived economic value (system utility) exceeds the cost of the structural measures, their installation is economically justified.

A simulation model has three kinds of input: the hydrologic events, the economic events, and the structural measures. The planner has no control over the magnitude and sequence of future hydrologic events. He is able to apply various combinations of structural measures and is trying to select the optimum. Often, he assumes future economic events are beyond his control. However, many nonstructural measures are available (Sec. 21-7) to control the demand for structural water resources development. Future studies are going to be forced by the physical constraints on maximum resource development to consider such alternatives more explicitly.

The uncontrolled inputs are normally brought into the model as a fixed set of values; however, the sensitivity of the optimum design to possible variation in these values can be studied by bringing in a series of value sets. The controlled inputs are varied by trial and error in an attempt to converge on the optimum design.

The model can be applied on either a long-run or a short-run basis. The long-run study evaluates the need for introducing new structural or nonstructural measures to increase system utility. The short-run study considers all such measures as fixed and seeks the best way to operate a given physical system. A short-run study is needed to determine the optimum operating policy for each combination of measures compared in the long-run study. Short-run studies are needed from time to time in the life of an installed system to determine how recent economic events may affect optimum operation. Occasionally, very short-run studies to determine the optimum disposal of currently stored water over the subsequent dry season are in order.

The key to successful simulation is a model algorithm which mathematically duplicates the response of the physical system and estimates the resulting economic benefit. The model builder must be careful to include all controlled variables which could be used to build a better system, to exclude controlled variables incapable of increasing system utility, to optimize only variables over which he indeed has a working control, and to structure his algorithm to portray the physical and economic functioning of the system adequately.[1] The model should be carefully tested against the functioning of the system during known historical events before it is used for planning purposes.

Simulation of a single-purpose flood control reservoir for a situation where no other structural or nonstructural measures are practical would require development of an algorithm relating storage to reservoir water surface elevation, the outflow resulting from various combinations of water surface elevation and gate opening, outflow to downstream flood peak, and downstream flood peak to flood damage. A promising value of the single controlled input, maximum flood storage, would be selected. Time sequences of inflows to the reservoir and flood-plain development would be forecast or represented by a trace generated by random processes. A short-run study would determine the best operating procedure to follow in opening and closing the gates. The algorithm would in the context of the selected maximum flood storage translate the inflows, economic development, and operating procedure into an average annual net benefit. Alternate traces could be used into estimate net benefit in different contexts. Other values of maximum flood storage could subsequently be picked to estimate other net benefits. An orderly selection of trial values of maximum flood storage will eventually converge on the optimum design.

This example illustrates the main components of a simulation model. Each value, representing a measurable physical or economic property of the system and brought into the simulation algorithm, may be called a simulation parameter. A parameter may either remain constant

[1] Russell F. Ackoff and Maurice W. Sasieni, "Fundamentals of Operations Research" (New York: John Wiley & Sons, Inc., 1968), pp. 384–408.

or vary with time according to a predetermined pattern. Physical factors tend to be in the first class, economic factors in the second. The operating procedure is a body of rules using current values of the simulation parameters, the state variables, and short-term inflow forecasts to decide whether inflow should be stored or released. The state variables, such as the amount of water in storage, define the state of the system at any given time. The inflow sequence and the demand pattern are time series of events to which the model is subjected. Finally, a systematic procedure must be developed for finding the set of controllable system parameters comprising the optimum system. Each component requires discussion in greater detail.

20-2 SIMULATION PARAMETERS The scope of a simulation study must be defined in time and space (Sec. 21-3.) The study must consider the influence of all significant factors, existing or predicted, within this boundary on the demand for and the ability to supply project output. The function of each physical entity within the system in contributing to system operation, and the physical interrelationships among these entities must be expressed within the simulation model by descriptive equations. The best way to begin modeling is to sketch the system, showing each structural and nonstructural measures to be evaluated. Figure 20-2 illustrates the system sketch for a hypothetical development used in the pioneering system design studies at Harvard.[1] The sketch can then be used to develop a schematic outline (Fig. 20-3) showing each path that water may follow within the system.[2]

Under natural conditions, water will travel downstream in a geographical pattern and time sequence predictable by hydraulic analysis of the channel system. Each structural measure functions by forcing the water to flow to different places (diversion for water supply), to flow in a different time pattern (flood control storage or low-flow augmentation), or to flow with a different quality. Each storage and conveyance facility can be analyzed to develop a set of equations and curves (input arrays with computerized interpolation) describing movement of water along each flow path under varying conditions of structural modification. Each nonstructural measure functions by varying the economic response to a given physical event. Economic analysis of each event can be used to evaluate the effects of specific proposals. The modeling must compromise by excluding minor flow paths and using approximate relationships to

---

[1] Arthur Maass et al., "Design of Water-resource Systems" (Cambridge, Mass.: Harvard University Press, 1962), p. 265, fig. 7.1. (Copyright in British Commonwealth excluding Canada by Macmillan & Co., Ltd., London.)

[2] *Ibid.*, p. 327, fig. 9.1.

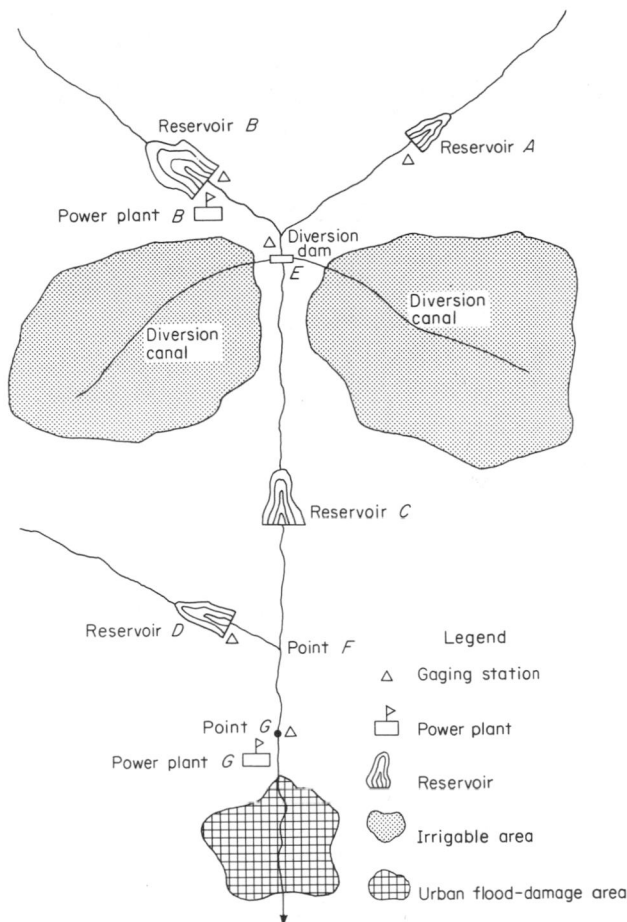

Reservoir *B*

Reservoir *A*

Power plant *B*

Diversion dam

E

Diversion canal

Diversion canal

Reservoir *C*

Reservoir *D*

Point *F*

Legend

△ Gaging station

Power plant

Reservoir

Irrigable area

Urban flood-damage area

Point *G*

Power plant *G*

FIGURE 20-2   Sketch of simplified river basin system.

produce acceptable results without excessive computational effort. Specific procedures apply the principles presented is most standard texts in hydrology and hydraulics in a manner described in much greater detail by Hall and Dracup.[1]

The performance of the system is determined by the interactions between its functioning parts and streamflow. The parameters and relationships required to model system performance depend on the

[1] Warren A. Hall and J. A. Dracup, "Water Resources Systems Engineering" (New York: McGraw-Hill Book Company, 1970), chap. 7.

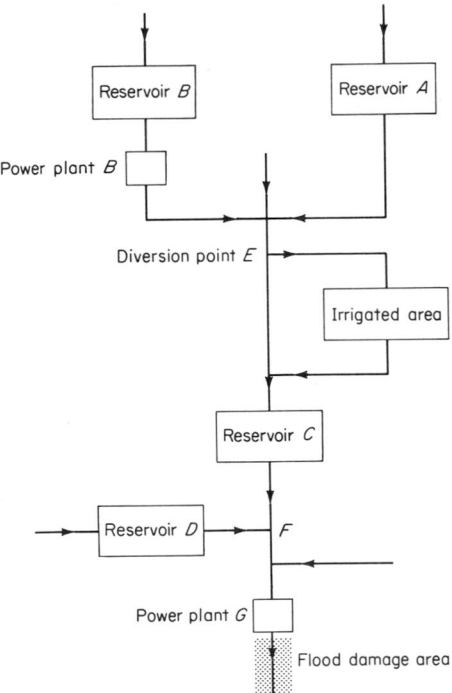

FIGURE 20-3 Schematic outline of river basin system.

nature of the reservoir-channel complex and the project purposes. Relationships may be expressed in equation form, but tabular form with computerized interpolation allows greater flexibility to represent the variability of real systems. Typical relationships include:[1]

1 *The relationship between water surface elevation and storage for each reservoir.* This relationship is necessary for hydrograph routing and for relating head to storage for power plants.

2 *The relationship between water surface elevation and outflow from each reservoir.* For gated spillways, the elevation-outflow relationship will depend on whether the gates are fully opened, fully closed, or partially opened.

3 *The relationship between inflow and outflow for each channel reach.* Streamflow routing is required to quantify the effects of channel storage on flood peaks and the time lag from the time water is released from reservoirs to when it reaches the point of use.

[1] A set of relationships developed for one study are found in Blair C. Bower, A Simplified River Basin System for Testing Methods and Techniques of Analysis, in Maass et al., *op. cit.*, 263–298.

4   *The costs of constructing and operating each component of the system.*
Where warranted, operating cost may be made to vary with the
inflow sequence.

5   *If the project is to provide irrigation water, the diversion requirements
by month of the year and by year of project life, from analysis of crop
needs and delivery losses.*   Monthly return flows as a function of
irrigation diversions need to be estimated. Irrigation benefits are
best expressed as a net amount if the full firm yield is supplied with
reductions in times of shortage and added benefits if secondary water
is available.

6   *If the project is to provide urban water supply, monthly diversion
requirements and quantities of flow returned to the stream as they
increase with calendar time for a growing community.* Benefits must be
related to water deliveries.

7   *If the project is to provide hydroelectric power, monthly energy requirements and load factors.* The plant should be integrated into the total
power supply network. Energy and peaking power benefit relationships must be determined from the power market.

8   *If flood control is to be provided, the relation between flow and damage.*

9   *If water is to be released for navigation, navigation flow requirements
and benefits as a function of the magnitude and duration of minimum
flow levels.*

10   *If the project is to provide water quality control, the amount of water
required to provide various amounts of low-flow augmentation and the
relationship between minimum flow and benefits.* The water quality
requirements and the effects on water quality of each project component must also be analyzed and incorporated into the model.

11   *If the project is to provide recreation or fishing, benefits as a function of
reservoir drawdown.*

The simulation parameters thus describe the physical properties
of the system, the amount of the benefit derived from the output, and the
cost of production.

Operating Procedure

20-3 DERIVING OPERATING RULES   The rules used to operate a
water resources system should be based on the economic trade-off among
the effects of alternative decision possibilities. However, the operator in
the field has neither the time nor the facts for economic analysis before

making individual operating decisions. The only practical approach is to analyze the various factors ahead of time to devise a body of rules which, when followed, will produce results as close to the economic optimum as possible. The rules must be expressed in a form which can be readily understood and followed by project operators and, for project formulation simulation studies, a form which can be readily incorporated into the simulation algorithm.

The operating rules tell the operator of each facility what to do in specific situations described by the current state of the system for reservoir storage, expected streamflows, demand for project output, and various other parameters. The rules must be made from information available to the operator at the time an operating decision has to be made and must be physically practicable for him to implement. Operating decisions must be made in the context of uncertainty about future flows and may not always be particularly efficient in hindsight. The operating rules for the simulation program strive to duplicate the consequences of the actions of operating personnel.

In practice, operating decisions related to the release of stored water for beneficial use are usually made weekly, but monthly decisions generally work satisfactorily in simulation studies. Whenever a flood occurs, the operating decisions must be made at intervals ranging from a few hours on smaller streams to daily on larger rivers.

Theoretically, a short-run simulation study should be used to find the operating procedure yielding the maximum net benefits from each proposed physical system. The optimum system operating procedure varies as structural or nonstructural measures are added or modified, and it changes with time for a fixed system in response to changes in the value of water in alternative uses. The necessary adjustments should be made by those actually operating a system and within the simulation models by making the operating rules functions of time. For simple systems, the optimum operating procedure may be determined by dynamic programming outside the simulation model.[1]

20-4 USE OF FLOOD STORAGE   The first of the six basic operating questions for which rules are needed is whether flood inflows should be stored to reduce current damages or released to provide additional storage space in case new rains produce even greater flows (Sec. 10-4). The principal situation parameters are the total available flood storage space, the amount of water currently stored in that space, the inflow forecast

---

[1] Warren A. Hall and Theodore F. Roefs, Hydroelectric Project Output Optimization, *Proc. ASCE*, vol. 92, no. PO 1 (January, 1966), pp. 67–69.

from available information on rainfall and upstream streamflow, the probability of continued rainfall by amount and duration by season, the way the reservoir combines with others in the overall system to reduce flood damages, and the relationship between release rate and downstream flood damages. The economic trade-off is between the increase in down-stream damages caused by larger releases and the increase in the expected value of future damages caused by having less storage space available to contain subsequent flows.

Operating procedures vary from the very simple but rigid to the very complex but much more flexible. Water might always be released at a rate equal to maximum downstream channel capacity as long as there is any water in flood storage. A more flexible rule would permit releases slightly exceeding downstream capacity in order to avoid much more severe subsequent flooding if a very large flood was expected shortly. The increased operating flexibility increases project benefits while making the operating procedure more complex. Flexibility is gained by incorporating more sophisticated expressions of the situation parameters into the operating decision. At some point, one reaches a trade-off between the marginal cost of executing a more complicated operating procedure and the marginal increase in benefit the operating procedure would produce. Normally a simpler operating procedure is used during project formulation simulation studies than when operating an actual system to save computer time and reduce the time spent in optimizing operating procedures for inefficient designs.

A typical operation schedule used to decide whether to release or store flood flows is shown in Fig. 20-4. The controlled discharge is given as a function of the elevation of the water within the reservoir and the rate the water surface elevation is rising.

20-5 USE OF TOTAL STORAGE The second operating question is whether storage space should be filled to save water for beneficial use or emptied to contain potential floods. The principal situation parameters are the amount of water currently stored in the reservoir, the amount of storage space currently available for flood control, the value of stored water in other uses, and the magnitude of the flood threat. The economic trade-off is between the value of the additional water stored within the reservoir and the additional flood damages if the storage space is not available when a flood occurs (Sec. 10-4). Most reservoirs follow a rule curve in which much more conservation storage is allowed in the dry than in the flood season (Fig. 20-5). The reservoir illustrated is kept quite empty from December through March because most floods occur during

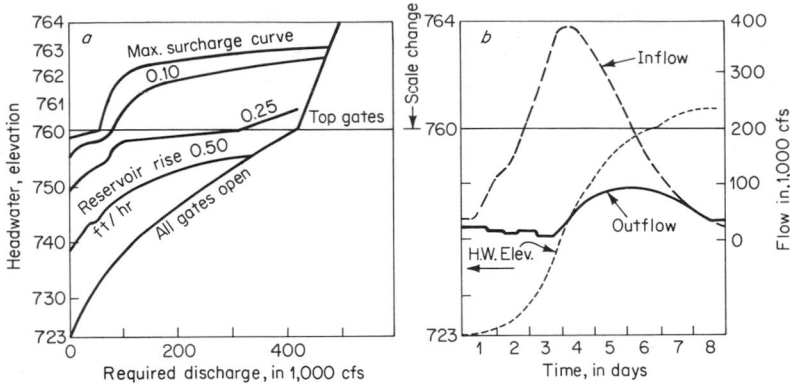

FIGURE 20-4 Operating schedule for flood flows (Wolf Creek Reservoir, Cumberland River): (*a*) emergency operation schedule; (*b*) operation in standard project flood. [*From Ven Te Chow* (*ed.*), *"Handbook of Applied Hydrology" (New York: McGraw-Hill Book Company, 1964), pp. 25–89, Fig. 25-III-22.*]

these months but is allowed nearly to fill during the summer when the flood threat is much less. The monthly probabilities of flood events and the monthly demands for water for conservation uses may be used to determine the optimum flood reservation by month.[1]

20-6   RELEASE OF STORED WATER   The third operating question is whether water stored within the reservoir should be released for present use or retained for use during possible future droughts. The main situation parameters are the quantity of water stored in the reservoir, the inflow which can be expected to enter the reservoir during the balance of the current drawdown period, and the value of water in alternative uses as a function of the quantity put to that use. The economic trade-off is between the value received from additional water when put to present use and its expected value in future use in the light of the probabilities of the water's being lost if the reservoir spills vs. the probabilities of severe drought's causing the value of the water saved to be extremely high.

The answer to this operating question is found by analysis of flow sequences. If the reservoir is so small as to provide only seasonal storage

---

[1]   Leo R. Beard, Flood Control Operations of Reservoirs, *Proc. ASCE*, vol. 89, no. HY 1 (January, 1963), pp. 1–24.
L. Douglas James, Economic Derivation of Reservoir Operating Rules, *Proc. ASCE*, vol. 94, no. HY 5 (September, 1968), pp. 1217–1230.

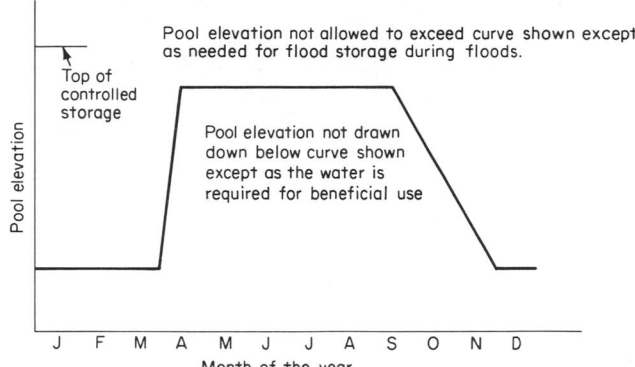

FIGURE 20-5 Typical rule curve for maintaining seasonal pool.

(i.e., it fills even during the driest wet season), historical flow sequences may be analyzed to determine the least amount of water contained in the reservoir on each date while providing the firm yield, and the results may be plotted as a function of the day of the year to produce the critical-rule curve of Fig. 20-6. A reservoir operator in possession of the critical-rule curve may release water for secondary use if the reservoir storage exceeds that shown for the current day of the year. If storage equals that shown

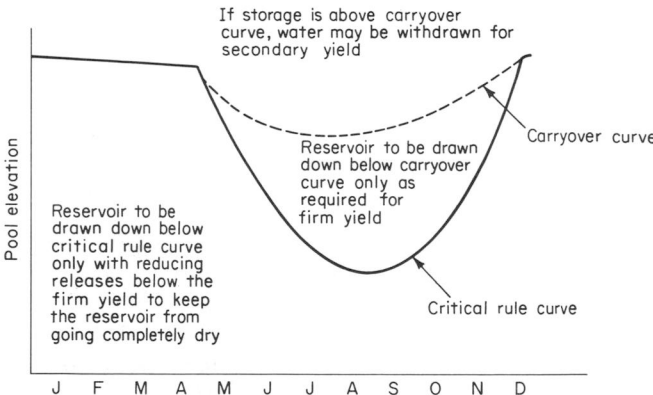

FIGURE 20-6 Typical rule curve for release of water from conservation storage.

by the curve, the reservoir is experiencing a drought more severe than that used to estimate the firm yield.

If the reservoir provides cyclic storage (i.e., water is stored for more than 1 year), releases for secondary yield cannot be allowed to draw the reservoir down to the critical-rule curve without depleting storage needed to provide firm yield in subsequent years. A carryover curve may be plotted from the results of a short-run simulation to show how low a water level can be allowed by date without depleting required carryover storage. At any given date, the reservoir may be drawn down to the carryover curve to provide secondary yield and down to the critical-rule curve to provide firm yield. The two curves are identical for a seasonal reservoir.

The marginal value of water stored in the reservoir depends on estimated future inflows. Future inflows may be predicted from the contents of a mountain snowpack or, less accurately, from soil-moisture conditions and expected rainfall. Firm runoff is that produced by the design-frequency rainfall (expected 49 out of 50 years for a 2 percent design for example) in conjunction with current known antecedent moisture conditions. The rainfall frequency analysis may be made from historical, recorded rainfall at corresponding times of the year.

Secondary water may be released if current storage is more than the minimum value indicated by the carryover curve. It should be released over a period and in a time pattern achieving maximum value in use. The length of the period (t months) depends on the volume of available water, the expected demand for secondary water, and the probability of the reservoir's filling and spilling within this interval. Alternate fixed values or relationships for functions for varying t with other variables should be tried during simulation to develop an optimum estimate. The amount of water available for secondary use within this period may be estimated as

$$R = (S_t + I_t) - (S_c + I_c) \tag{20-1}$$

where S_t is current storage, S_c is storage at the corresponding date on the carryover curve, I_t is the expected volume of inflow net of evaporation and seepage losses during the next t months, and I_c is the net inflow volume during the corresponding portion of the historical critical dry period.[1] The fraction of R which should be released for secondary use in the current month may be approximated as the ratio of the demand fraction (Ex. 12-1) for the current month to the sum of the demand fractions for the t months. A more refined estimate would be based on the month-by-month pattern of demand for secondary water. Releases for secondary use should be increased to supply the full secondary demand as the reservoir heads into periods where current runoff conditions indicate imminent spillage.

---

[1] Maass et al., *op. cit.*, pp. 443–458.

The reservoir level will fall below the critical-rule curve, even when water has been released only to satisfy firm yield, whenever the reservoir enters a period drier than the design drought. Benefit can be increased if releases are reduced before the reservoir runs dry so that some water is available for the highest valued uses throughout the dry spell. The release should be reduced whenever storage drops below the critical-rule curve by an amount which may be estimated from Eq. (20-1); R comes out negative if the yield must be reduced. The total R should be distributed over the t months predicted before minimum storage is reached, according to the same principles used to distribute secondary releases.

Whether viewed in the context of long-term system operation or a computer simulation algorithm, firm yield is not the maximum yield under the worst possible conditions. It is a target yield. If the reservoir is found to remain quite full, additional water can be released. If the reservoir is nearing empty, releases can be reduced. The target yield should be optimized in the operation studies.

20-7   RELEASE BY RESERVOIR   The fourth operating question is how much of the water to be released for beneficial use should come from each reservoir in which water is stored. The principal situation parameters are the amount of water stored in each reservoir, the inflows forecast to enter each reservoir, and the cost of transmitting the water from each reservoir to the point of use. The economic trade-off requires withdrawal of the water having the least value in storage, as determined by the probability of the reservoir spilling if additional storage space is not made available and the locational advantage of the reservoir for the various uses.

A simple but rigid rule is to divide withdrawal among the reservoirs by a fixed ratio proportional to reservoir capacity. A more flexible rule is to divide withdrawal in proportion to the quantity of water in the reservoir at the time. Still greater flexibility can be gained by making withdrawal proportional to current storage plus expected inflow during the balance of the dry season. If the system contains power plants, benefits might be increased by releasing water from reservoirs having power plants at times of power demand and from the other reservoirs at other times.

20-8   USE OF AVAILABLE WATER   The fifth operating question is how the water released from the reservoir should be divided among the various potential uses. The principal situation parameters are the demand curves for water in each of the uses. The economic trade-off is satisfied by dividing the water among the uses until its marginal value in each is equal. The most common practice in reservoir operation is to release to each use the amount of water specified by a requirements schedule. Such a schedule is the only practical way of telling the reservoir operator what to do, but a severe misallocation of water will result if the requirement schedule departs radically from equating marginal values in use.

20-9 RELEASE ELEVATION The sixth operating question is whether the released water should be taken from near the surface or from some elevation deeper within the reservoir.[1] The principal situation parameters are the temperature and quality of the water at various elevations at the outlet works and also over the lake as a whole, the rate of potential evaporation from the reservoir surface, the consequences of alternative levels of water quality in the lake, and the consequences of releasing waters of various temperatures or qualities to the downstream channel. The release of warm water reduces evaporation and hence increases reservoir yield, but it also increases downstream water temperature which may adversely affect some species of fish, the ability of the water to absorb waste effluent, and the usefulness of the water for industrial cooling. One economic trade-off between the value of the water lost due to the incremental increase in evaporation and the value of reducing stream water temperatures for downstream uses. Another trade-off may exist between water quality in the reservoir and that downstream as the operator must decide whether or not to release stagnant water with low oxygen content. The data required for economic analysis are sparse, and comprehensive operating rules have been slow to develop.

Specifying Uncontrolled Events

A water resources planner is interested in evaluating the benefits which a proposed combination of system components will produce in response to the future course of events. Two main types of future events must be predicted. The benefit per unit of project output is determined by the economic events which alter the demand curve for output. The quantity of project output is determined by hydrologic and climatological events.

---

[1] Norman H. Brooks and Robert C. Y. Koh, Selective Withdrawal from Density Stratified Reservoirs, *Proc. ASCE*, vol. 95, no. HY 4 (July, 1969), pp. 1369–1400.

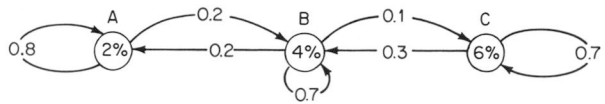

FIGURE 20-7   Growth-rate transition diagram.

20-10 *ECONOMIC EVENT SEQUENCES* The economic event sequences to which benefit projections are most sensitive are associated with economic development, population, and land use. The projections are sometimes synthesized as independent variables not influenced by project construction. However, economic growth really depends on the installation schedule of the water resource system. Land use in the flood plain depends on the degree of flood protection. Municipal growth depends on the water supply. Population increases rapidly with the installation of an irrigation project. In the most thorough analysis, the economic event sequence is made a function of both calendar time and the project installation schedule and includes a random component to provide for chance occurrences (Sec. 8-16).

The most powerful tool for explicitly recognizing the stochastic nature of future economic events is the use of Monte Carlo methods to develop Markov chains. As an oversimplified example for expository purposes, rates of economic growth might be segregated into class intervals having average annual values of 2, 4, or 6 percent. An analysis of historical growth rates might show that historical periods exhibiting a 2 percent growth rate were 80 percent of the time followed by a period exhibiting a 2 percent growth rate and 20 percent of the time followed by a period of growth at a 4 percent rate. Continuing the analysis might produce the information expressed in Table 20-1. This information may be expressed as a Markov chain in the form of either a transition diagram (Fig. 20-7) or a tree diagram (Fig. 20-8). From a known present growth rate as the initial state, one can calculate the probability of the growth rate's falling

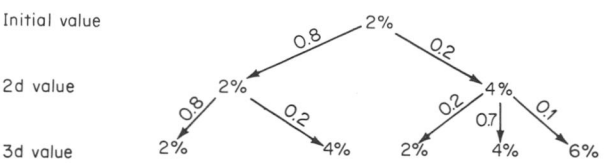

FIGURE 20-8   Growth-rate tree diagram.

in the respective class intervals during subsequent periods from the equations:

$$A_2 = 0.8A_1 + 0.2B_1$$
$$B_2 = 0.2A_1 + 0.7B_1 + 0.3C_1 \qquad (20\text{-}2)$$
$$C_2 = 0.1B_1 + 0.7C_1$$

where A refers to the probability of having a 2 percent growth rate, B to one of 4 percent, and C to one of 6 percent. The subscripts indicate consecutive periods, 2 following 1. The three equations are applied between consecutive periods beginning with an initial growth rate of 2 percent to develop the information summarized in Table 20-2.

The probabilities converge toward equilibrium values, which may be determined by noting that at equilibrium, changes from A to B must equal changes from B to A; and since Fig. 20-7 shows both changes to be

TABLE 20-1

FRACTION OF TIME THE FOLLOWING PERIOD
GROWTH RATE WAS THE INDICATED VALUE

Growth rate in period, %	2%	4%	6%
2	0.8	0.2	0.0
4	0.2	0.7	0.1
6	0.0	0.3	0.7

TABLE 20-2 Probability of Indicated Growth Rate
by Year if 2 Percent in Initial Year

Year	2%	4%	6%	Expected growth rate during year	Expected economic development at end of year
0					100.00
1	1.000			0.0200	102.00
2	0.800	0.200		0.0240	104.45
3	0.680	0.300	0.020	0.0268	107.25
4	0.604	0.352	0.044	0.0286	110.31
5	0.553	0.381	0.066	0.0301	113.63
6	0.519	0.397	0.084	0.0311	117.17
7	0.495	0.407	0.098	0.0319	120.91
8	0.478	0.413	0.109	0.0325	124.84
9	0.465	0.417	0.118	0.0329	128.94
10	0.456	0.420	0.124	0.0333	133.24
∞	0.4286	0.4286	0.1428		

the same fraction of the preceding probabilities, A_e (the equilibrium probability) must equal B_e. By similar reasoning, $B_e = 3C_e$. Since the sum of the three values must equal 1, $3C_e + 3C_e + C_e = 1$, or $A_e = B_e = \frac{3}{7}$, and $C_e = \frac{1}{7}$. The expected value of the growth rate is $2A + 4B + 6C$, or $3\frac{3}{7}$.

The above example is a first-order Markov process because the growth rate in a given period is assumed to depend only on the growth rate in the preceding period. A second-order process would use two preceding periods. An nth-order process would use n preceding periods.

Under the assumption that economic growth is independent of the project installation schedule, projections might be simulated in one of three ways.

1 The expected value of the growth rate in each year following an initial year of known growth rate could be calculated as the sum of the products of the column values in the row and the column headings (Table 20-2). The expected annual growth rates may be used to calculate expected states of economic development by year.

2 The state of economic development in any future year might be expressed as a probability distribution. By following through the tree diagram, a discrete probability distribution of potential states of economic development may be calculated for each year, as illustrated in Table 20-3. The economic development probability distribution may be translated into a benefit probability distribution by subjecting the simulation model to economic event sequences of varying probability.

3 The Monte Carlo technique of random number generation might be used to develop alternative growth rate sequences. For example, one of ten equally likely random numbers 0 through 9 may be generated. If a number in the range of 0 through 7 were selected, the growth rate in the second year would be taken as 2 percent; and if 8 or 9 were selected, the rate would be 4 percent. Another random number would be generated, and the growth rate in the third year would be selected by using the probabilities of Table 20-1 and the growth rate previously projected for the second year. The process could be repeated as many times as wanted to generate a trace of economic growth throughout any designated project life. Multiple traces may be generated to test sensitivity to benefits to alternative growth sequences. A typical trace is illustrated in Table 20-4.

If economic growth is expected to be influenced by project installation, one may modify any of the above three methods in one of several

TABLE 20-3   Probability Distribution of
Economic Development by Year

Year	Probability	Multipliers	Economic development
0			100.00
1	1.000	(1.02)	102.00
2	0.800	$(1.02)^2$	104.04
	0.200	(1.02)(1.04)	106.08
3	0.640	$(1.02)^3$	106.12
	0.200	$(1.02)^2(1.04)$	108.20
	0.140	$(1.02)(1.04)^2$	110.32
	0.020	(1.02)(1.04)(1.06)	112.44
4	0.512	$(1.02)^4$	108.24
	0.192	$(1.02)^3(1.04)$	110.36
	0.148	$(1.02)^2(1.04)^2$	112.52
	0.016	$(1.02)^2(1.04)(1.06)$	114.69
	0.098	$(1.02)(1.04)^3$	114.73
	0.028	$(1.02)(1.04)^2(1.06)$	116.93
	0.006	$(1.02)(1.04)(1.06)^2$	119.18

TABLE 20-4   Monte Carlo Trace of Economic Development

Year	Random number*	Growth rate†	Economic development	Year	Random number*	Growth rate†	Economic development
0			100.00	16	4	2	160.29
1		2	102.00	17	3	2	163.50
2	8	4	106.08	18	0	2	166.77
3	0	2	108.20	19	2	2	170.10
4	1	2	110.37	20	4	2	173.50
5	4	2	112.57	21	8	4	180.44
6	4	2	114.82	22	3	4	187.66
7	4	2	117.12	23	1	2	191.41
8	7	2	119.46	24	1	2	195.24
9	9	4	124.24	25	3	2	199.15
10	8	4	129.21	26	3	2	203.13
11	9	6	136.96	27	6	2	207.19
12	1	4	142.44	28	4	2	211.34
13	8	4	148.14	29	2	2	215.56
14	6	4	154.07	30	7	2	219.87
15	1	2	157.15	31	0	2	224.27

* Read from Table of random numbers.
† Taken from Fig. 20-5 and based on random number with the lowest numbers in each case associated with 2 percent, middle numbers with 4 percent, and highest numbers with 6 percent.

ways. One approach would be to modify the mean values of the class intervals or the probabilities of movement expressed in Table 20-1 according to data developed from the response to historical projects. The simulated economic development would then be based on one table if the project were installed and on the other table if it were not. An alternative approach would be to express a growth multiplier as a function of time since project construction and to take the growth rate in any year as the product of the time-dependent growth rate and the project multiplier. The simulation can be randomized by adding a random component $t_i\sigma$ to the mean value within each class interval, where σ is the standard deviation of values within the class interval and t_i is a value picked at random from a normal distribution of mean 0 and standard deviation 1.

Generated economic event sequences should be used whenever it is desired to test system performance in the context of sequences of future economic events. A design planned by testing a variety of economic growth traces is likely to be more effective in the long run than one based entirely on a single most probable sequence. Economic event sequences can also be translated to time patterns of unemployment and used to investigate project effectiveness in increasing economic stability.

20-11 HYDROLOGIC EVENT SEQUENCES A simulation model requires estimates of simultaneous local runoff as a function of time for a series of points throughout the study area. Streamflow pattern as well as magnitude determines reservoir yield because of the greater storage required to augment persistent low flows. Hydrograph shape as well as peak determines flood damage because of the effect of storage on flood routing. The water resources planner must try to estimate from historical records the magnitude and sequence of runoff expected during the project life. Basic strategies include:

1 If a long-term streamflow record is available, the flows used for project design have often been assumed to have exactly the same magnitude and to occur in exactly the same order as the historical flows did. While this technique is simple to execute and indicates system response to historical events with which the public is familiar, it is not quite realistic to expect the future to repeat historical sequences.
2 If a long-term streamflow record is unavailable, a synthetic record based on rainfall-runoff relationships[1] or correlations using regional streamflows may be substituted.

---

[1] Norman H. Crawford and Ray K. Linsley, "The Synthesis of Continuous Streamflow Hydrographs on a Digital Computer" (Stanford, Calif.: Stanford University, Department of Civil Engineering, Tech. Rept. 12, 1962).

3 If changes in land use or other watershed conditions are expected to alter the runoff regime during the project life, projected flows must be hydrologically adjusted with calendar time.

4 Historical flow magnitudes may be rearranged to determine the sensitivity of project benefit to flow sequence. A random order could be developed by a computer process, analogous to tabulating the historical flows on cards, shuffling, and tabulating the values of the cards in the order they appear in the deck.[1] A variation is to return each card to the deck and reshuffle before drawing the next one. Both methods eliminate the assumption that historical sequences will be repeated; however, they still assume that flows not occurring in the past will not occur in the future.

5 Flow magnitudes may be randomized by fitting a frequency distribution to the historical flow records. Values cannot be picked from the distribution at random because streamflows are serially correlated. High flows and low flows congregate because moisture which accumulates during one month drains in following months and also affects watershed response to precipitation. The lower the regression coefficient between successive flow periods, the less serial correlation is demonstrated and the closer the process comes to picking values at random from the distribution.

Recent development and refinement of the procedures of operational hydrology, first introduced in the Harvard studies,[2] is encouraging more and more planners to use the fifth strategy. The events are intended, not to duplicate any past or predict any future flow sequences, but rather to allow study of many possible inflow combinations. The approach begins by generating a long sequence of monthly flows at a selected point. The second step is to use this basic sequence to estimate compatible local runoff from other portions of the watershed. The third step is to synthesize flood hydrographs for the larger-flow months.

The flow during any month is estimated in a recursion equation as equal to the average flow for that month plus a component determined by the flow in the previous month plus a component of random variation, or

$$Q_i = \bar{Q}_j + b_j(Q_{i-1} - \bar{Q}_{j-1}) + T_i\sigma_j(1 - r_j^2)^{0.5} \tag{20-3}$$

where Q_i is the flow synthesized for the ith month in the sequence, $\bar{Q}^j$ is the average flow for the jth month of the year, Q_{i-1} is the flow synthesized for the previous month (or taken as initial conditions the first time the equation is applied), $\bar{Q}_{j-1}$ is the average flow for the previous

[1] W. Don Maughan and R. Y. Kawano, Project Yields by a Probability Method, *Proc. ASCE*, vol. 89, no. HY 3 (May, 1963), pp. 41–60.
[2] Maass et al., *op. cit.*, pp. 459–493.

month of the year, b_j is the regression coefficient (slope of the least-squares line) for estimating flow month-of-the-year j from the flow for month-of-the-year $j - 1$, σ_j is the standard deviation of flows during the jth month of the year, r_j is the correlation coefficient between flows for historical pairs of month j and month $j - 1$, and T_i is a value taken at random from a distribution of zero mean and unit variance and a shape representing the monthly flow population.

Random values following a normal distribution may be generated by applying the central-limit theorem, which states that the means of samples taken at random from any distribution tend to be normally distributed. The means, a series of sets of, say, 50 numbers taken at random from a uniform distribution, would be normally distributed. If the set means have a mean μ and standard deviation σ, any individual set mean x can be converted to a normal standard deviate K_i having a mean of 0 and standard deviation of 1 by multiplication by $(x - \mu)/\sigma$. K_i may be directly used for T_i in Eq. (20-3) if monthly flows are normally distributed. Because the distribution of flows for most months of the year is skewed to the right (low flows are more closely grouped than high flows), Fiering suggests that the random variate be taken from a gamma distribution.[1] The normal standard deviate may be transformed to a gamma random variate through the expression

$$T_i = \frac{2}{g_j}\left[1 + \frac{g_j K_i}{6} - \frac{g_j^2}{36}\right]^3 - \frac{2}{g_j} \tag{20-4}$$

where g_j is the coefficient of skewness of historical flows during the jth month of the year.[2] The skewness is calculated from N years of record by

$$g_j = \frac{N}{(N-1)(N-2)} \frac{1}{\sigma_j^3} \sum_{n=1}^{N} (Q_n - \bar{Q}_j)^3 \tag{20-5}$$

Application of the serial recursion equation (20-3) requires estimation of the 12 monthly values of $\bar{Q}$, σ, and g and of the 12 values of b and r, 1 between each pair of months. Longer records will give better estimates with at least 30 years' being desirable to avoid sequences of abnormally wet or dry years. Each time through the equation, a new random component T_i is generated, and the resulting Q_i is calculated. The process can be repeated to generate indefinitely long monthly flow sequences. Generated negative flows may be called zero or avoided by generating flow logarithms. This would require estimation of each of the five statistics from the logarithms of the historical flows.

[1] Myron B. Fiering, Multivariate Technique for Synthetic Hydrology, *Proc. ASCE*, vol. 90, no. HY 5 (September, 1964), p. 48.

[2] Myron B. Fiering, "Streamflow Synthesis" (Cambridge, Mass.: Harvard University Press, 1967), p. 35.

Once the basic monthly flow sequence has been generated, it is necessary to develop compatible monthly flow sequences for other points. The flow at a second point is assumed to equal the average flow for the calendar month, plus a component based on correlation with the base point plus a random component. Thus

$$Q_{yi} = \bar{Q}_{yj} + b_{yj}(Q_{xi} - \bar{Q}_{xj}) + T_i \sigma_{yj}(1 - r_{yj}^2)^{0.5} \qquad (20\text{-}6)$$

where the notation follows that of Eq. (20-3) with y the second and x the first point. The recursion uses an initial value of Q_y, the Q_x generated at the base point for each month over the long period, and the 12 values of $\bar{Q}_y$, $\bar{Q}_x$, σ_y, b_y, and r_y to generate a monthly flow sequence for the second point.

Fiering[1] has proposed using principal-component analysis to utilize historical serial correlation at the second as well as the first point by calculating

$$\pi = \frac{r_y - r_x r^2}{\sqrt{1 - r^2}} \qquad (20\text{-}7)$$

where r_y is the serial correlation coefficient between the month in question and the previous month at y, r_x is the serial correlation coefficient at x, and r is the cross correlation coefficient between the two points. The value of π is used in the equation

$$V_i = \frac{\pi}{\sigma_{yj}} (Q_{yi} - \bar{Q}_{yj}) + T_i(1 - \sigma)^{0.5} \qquad (20\text{-}8)$$

The value calculated for V_i replaces T_i in Eq. (20-6). Principal-component analysis may be extended to a general multivariate model to include the serial correlations at a number of points.

Generation of flood hydrographs compatible with the sequence of generated monthly flows requires determination of which months contain a flood and division of flood-month flows into periods of sufficiently short duration (say, 6 hr) to permit flood routing. Examining the historical record for monthly flows containing floods shows some months with a flood having a lower monthly flow than others without one. Nevertheless, a trigger value may be selected and used to pick enough flood months to generate floods about as often as the historical record shows them to occur. Where sharp-peaked hydrographs in a low-flow season produce higher peaks than broad-crested hydrographs associated with higher monthly flows, seasonal trigger values may be required. For each monthly flow in the synthesized sequence exceeding the trigger value, the peak flow for the

[1]   Fiering, Multivariate Technique.

month is generated from a linear regression between peak and monthly flows developed from the historical record plus a random component in the recursion

$$Q_p = a + bQ_x + T_i\sigma_p(1 - r^2)^{0.5} \tag{20-9}$$

where Q_p is the generated flood peak, Q_x is the average flow during the flood month, and a, b, and r are determined from a least-squares regression between historical values of Q_p and Q_x. The term σ_p is the standard deviation of the values of Q_p used in the correlation. The generated peak is then tested against known channel capacities to see if it is still large enough to cause flooding after the random component is added. If the peak is large enough, the monthly runoff volume is broken into short-duration flows based on the flow pattern in the historical month most like it in flood peak and monthly flow volume. Simulated flood control benefits have been found much more sensitive to streamflow sequence than other benefits.[1]

The Simulation Procedure

The heart of optimization by simulation is the procedure used to adjust system design to maximize net benefit. A model may duplicate the response of the prototype system to sequences of hydrologic and economic events. New sequence sets may be added indefinitely to test system response.[2] However, the real value from simulation is as a tool in the search for a better design.

20-12 STATE VARIABLES The state variables define the conditions existing within the system. Initial values are specified and subsequent values are computed within the computer simulation study in response to the time sequence of events as determined by the physical system and the operating procedures. A typical state variable is the amount of water stored for each purpose in each reservoir. In stage construction projects, the elements of the system in operation at any given time is a state variable. The simulation program keeps running tabulation of the state variables throughout the study.

[1] Maass et al., *op. cit.*, pp. 256–7.
[2] The Harvard simulation procedure is described by Deward F. Manzer and Michael P. Barnett, Analysis by Simulation: Programming Techniques for a High-speed Digital Computer, in Maass et al., *op cit.*, pp. 324–390.

20-13 SYSTEM YIELD   In order to determine the aggregate yield from controlled storage within a water resources system, eight factors must be introduced into the simulation study (Sec. 12-3).

1   The magnitude and sequence of streamflows must be generated for each reservoir in the system. The flow into downstream reservoirs must be modified according to the effect of upstream reservoirs.

2   The magnitude of the demand during each year must be estimated from projected or generated economic event sequences.

3   Evaporation may be taken as the mean value for the calendar month or estimated from an inverse correlation with streamflow.

4   Rainfall is best determined from correlation with streamflow.

5   Topographic maps must be analyzed to relate storage volume to surface area at each proposed reservoir site.

6   The prior water rights must be analyzed to determine which incoming flows can be stored and which must be released.

7   The reservoir operating rules must be selected to maximize benefits resulting from the physical system.

8   Reservoir yield is the net increase in system yield made possible by the reservoir. Thus, gross yield must be estimated with and without a contemplated reservoir in order to determine the net yield it produces.

20-14 SEARCHING FOR THE OPTIMUM SYSTEM   The search for the optimum system requires systematic adjustment of the system design until that having maximum net benefits is found. Variation of each controllable input should be considered. Typical variables include the size of each reservoir, the size of each flood control channel, the installed capacity of each power plant, the firm-water commitment to each project purpose, and the operating rules. Generally, one has to optimize n variables. Each possible combination of values for the n variables has a net benefit which may be plotted on an n-dimensional curve (called the *response surface*) for which each variable is one of the axes.

Five strategies for finding the response surface peak are:

1   *Uniform-grid method.*   Each of the n variables is divided into m equal increments. Net benefits are simulated for each of m^n points on the resulting uniform grid. The point on the surface with the highest net benefit is selected. The main disadvantage with the uniform-grid method is that too much time is spent examining areas of low net benefit instead of searching the higher areas for the peak.

2   *Random-sampling method.* Random values are generated for each of the n variables, and net benefits for the resulting random point on the response surface are calculated. Enough random points are generated and evaluated to determine the shape of the response surface, and the high point is selected. While random sampling still has the basic weakness of overemphasizing analysis of the lower portions of the response surface, the search may be discontinued before one is committed to such a large number of trials.

3   *Single-factor or univariate method.* Initial values are selected, and all the variables but one are held constant while the remaining variable is altered until maximum benefits are attained. The first variable is then held constant at the maximum benefit value while a second variable is altered in the same manner. After each variable has been individually optimized, the first variable must be reoptimized in the context of the new values for the other variables. The optimization cycle continues until the values of the respective variables stabilize. If the variables were independent, the optimum system would be determined at the end of the first cycle. The number of cycles may be greatly reduced by beginning with the best possible approximation of the system based on judgment gained from past experience and by first varying the variable to which net benefit is most sensitive.[1]

4   *Dual-factor method.* The cyclic procedure of the single-factor method is used but two variables instead of one are simultaneously released from their constant values. The procedure is needed when two variables are so interrelated that optimizing one produces a major change in the optimum value of the other.

5   *Steepest-ascent method.* A starting point on the response surface is selected (Sec. 4-2) and its net benefits are simulated. The process is repeated for enough nearby locations to define a plane in the n dimensions. The next point is then taken a preselected distance above the first point in the direction of greatest slope along the plane. The distance moved must not be so big that the response surface peak is missed or so small that it takes forever to climb it. A variation in the method is to proceed uphill in the direction of steepest slope from the starting point until a summit is reached before again defining a plane to pick a new direction. The method may lead to the top of a lesser peak in a multipeaked response surface and is unable to cross discontinuities in the surface.

The best overall strategy combines the individual strategies by first examining the total area which may potentially contain the optimum design and closing in on the peak by progressively more detailed

[1]   Leo R. Beard, Hydrologic Simulation in Water-yield Analysis, *Proc. ASCE*, vol. 93, no. IR 1 (March, 1967), pp. 33–42.

examination of the high spots. If the response surface might be irregular, multipeaked, or discontinuous, the analysis should begin with a study of its general shape. The uniform grid, based on large grid intervals, may be used if few variables are involved and points are easily computed. Random sampling should be used for many-variable or difficult-to-compute response surfaces. Once the highest mountain and the response surface discontinuities have been located, the method of steepest ascent is best for closing in on the peak. Single- or dual-factor analysis may be used to test a tentative peak or adjust an old one for changing conditions. The difficulty in examining a response surface containing major discontinuities indicates that continuous functions should be used wherever possible in the simulation model.

20-15 METHOD EVALUATION Optimization by simulation does not yield direct answers, may require a very large number of trials, and is influenced by the aptitude of the investigator for mathematical model building. Simulation is the most practical way for evaluating the many systems too complicated for direct optimization by other methods. However, it too has an upper limit. Recent experience indicated 45 development alternatives to be about the maximum which can be handled by computers available in 1965.[1]

SELECTED REFERENCES

Beard, Leo R.: Hydrologic Simulation in Water-yield Analysis, *Proc. ASCE*, vol. 93, no. IR 1 (March, 1967), pp. 33–42.

Dorfman, Robert: Formal Models in the Design of Water Resource Systems, *Water Resources Res.*, vol. 1, no. 3 (3d Quarter, 1965), pp. 329–336.

Fiering, Myron B.: "Streamflow Synthesis" (Cambridge, Mass.: Harvard University Press, 1967).

Hall, Warren A., and J. A. Dracup: "Water Resources Systems Engineering" (New York: McGraw-Hill Book Company, 1970).

Hufschmidt, Maynard F., and Myron B. Fiering: "Simulation Techniques for Design of Water-resource Systems" (Cambridge, Mass.: Harvard University Press, 1966).

Maass, Arthur, et al.: "Design of Water-resource Systems" (Cambridge, Mass.: Harvard University Press, 1962).

[1]   Maynard F. Hufschmidt, Field Level Planning of Water Resource Systems, *Water Resources Res.*, vol. 1 (2d Quarter, 1965), p. 161.

PROBLEMS

20-1 The following statistics have been computed for the sequential generation of synthetic streamflows:

	Mean flow	Standard deviation	Skew coefficient
July	286	355	2.13
August	155	200	1.39
Regression coefficient between the months			0.20
Correlation coefficient between the months			0.42

A flow of 250 cfs was generated for a particular July.

 a What flow would be generated for August if flows were assumed to be normally distributed and the random number of 0 were selected?

 b What flow would be generated for August if flows were assumed to follow a gamma distribution and the random number of 0 were selected?

 c What would be the chance of generating a zero flow for August by using the normal distribution?

 d What would be the chance of generating a zero flow for August by using the gamma distribution?

 e Does the chance of generating negative flows increase or decrease with:

　 i Larger mean flows

　 ii Larger standard deviations of flows

　 iii Larger regression coefficients

　 iv Larger correlation coefficients

20-2 A local economy may be in a state of decline (growth rate, -3 percent), static (0 percent), advancing ($+3$ percent), or rapidly advancing ($+6$ percent). The change of state probabilities from year to year are as given in the following table. In year 0, the local economy has an index value of 100.00 and is advancing.

FRACTION OF TIME FOLLOWING PERIOD
GROWTH RATE WAS INDICATED VALUE

Growth rate in period	-3	0	3	6
-3	0.6	0.3	0.1	0.0
0	0.3	0.4	0.2	0.1
3	0.1	0.3	0.4	0.2
6	0.0	0.0	0.3	0.7

Answer the following questions:

a What is the equilibrium expected growth rate?

b What is the expected growth rate in year 5?

c What is the expected economic index in year 5?

d What is the probability of the economic index being less than 100.00 in year 5?

e Use a table of one-digit random numbers to develop a trace of economic growth over the next 25 years.

20-3 Assume, with the data of Prob. 20-2, a current rate of full employment and the employable population increasing at a rate of 1.5 percent/year.

a What is the chance of there being some unemployment in year 5?

b What is the rate of unemployment in each year of your 25-year trace?

20-4 Select a gaging station for which over 30 years of monthly flow records are available, and beginning with the flow in the first October of record as the initial condition, generate and examine by use of a digital computer a long-term synthetic streamflow record by the following procedure:

a Develop, in a 12-by-M array, the recorded monthly flows (use average value in cubic feet per second for month).

b Develop, in a 2-by-100 array, all recorded flood peaks and their corresponding average monthly flows.

c Write a computer subroutine to compute from the 12-by-M array a 12-by-5 array containing, for each month of the year, the mean flow during the month, the standard deviation of the flow during the month, the skewness of the flow during the month, the regression coefficient between the flow in that and the flow in the succeeding month, and the correlation coefficient for flows between that and the succeeding month.

d Write a computer subroutine to compute, from the 2-by-100 array, the regression constant, the regression coefficient, the standard deviation of the flood peaks, and the correlation coefficient for a correlation between flood peaks and average monthly flows.

e Develop a subroutine for generating random variables of normal distribution having $\mu = 0$ and $\sigma = 1$. The same procedure can also be used to generate values following a log normal distribution.

f Incorporate Eq. (20-3) in a computer subroutine to generate a 12-by-N array containing synthesized flows for the N years from the 12-by-5 array.

g Write a computer subroutine based on a trigger value, equal to the minimum for any year of the maximum monthly flows, to generate a flood peak for the month; find the maximum of the flood peaks generated during the year; and store the results as a vector of N values.

h Examine the synthesized record and the recorded flows to find for both:
   i The minimum monthly flow
   ii The minimum average flow over 6 consecutive months
   iii The minimum average flow over 12 consecutive months
   iv The minimum average flow over 36 consecutive months
   v An estimate of the minimum instantaneous flow
   vi The maximum flood peak

i Estimate
   i The frequency of the minimum recorded flow
   ii The frequency of the maximum recorded flow

20-5 Select a simple water resources development scheme for simulation modeling. One approach would be to use this as a class project and model specific elements while discussing the specific-purpose project elements in Part 4.

CHAPTER
TWENTY-ONE

PLANNING
IMPLEMENTATION

Those responsible for the development and management of water resources to further human welfare find that correct application of the procedures for engineering and economic analysis is not sufficient to guarantee the implementation of sound projects. Some problems stem from difficulties in establishing public consensus on design objectives while preventing special interest groups or established institutional constraints from overriding the general welfare. Others are inherent in getting the planners as a group of people to work together effectively. Still others are associated with coordinating traditional water programs with land-use management, transportation planning, and other indirectly related programs.

The Planning Procedure

21-1 THE PLANNING IDEAL An expanding population has coupled with an even more rapidly expanding technology to concentrate people in large, industrialized urban centers. As a consequence, water resources planning has been revolutionized. Bigger projects must be planned to meet bigger needs. Projects must be multipurpose to avoid the duplication inherent in solving each problem individually. Project planning must be comprehensive because each activity profoundly affects the ability of society to accomplish many diverse objectives. A freeway constructed the length of the flood plain can force construction of structural flood control measures to protect resultant development. A comprehensive plan must analyze all such interactions as they currently exist, while at the same time leaving sufficient flexibility to adjust for changing conditions in a dynamic interaction process.

The planner needs a strategy for pursuing this task. The popular conception of an ideal planning procedure may be divided into four parts.[1]

1 The objectives and criteria to be followed are specified by legislative action or group consensus prior to the commencement of planning.
2 The professional personnel prepare a single best plan by producing a conclusive analysis based on all relevant data in accordance with the objectives and criteria.
3 Conflicts among project purposes and between project purposes and the balance of the economy are resolved by an integrated planning group able to utilize professional experts efficiently in all relevant disciplines and in a manner in keeping with the best interest of all concerned.
4 In order for each planning proposal to receive equal treatment, standardized planning procedures are developed and used.

The planner who sets out to achieve an ideal, comprehensive, multipurpose plan soon realizes that his is an impossible task.

1 He has no objective means for weighing extramarket values or noneconomic goals.
2 The objectives of water resources planning are too complex to be specified by political and administrative processes without feedback to make sure the consequences of the selected objectives are really in the popular will.[2] Various pressures often force the planner to make new decisions before the feedback from previous ones has crystalized.
3 The planner can never get the data needed to substantiate conclusively every necessary design decision.
4 Regional differences must be reflected in design where local needs contrast with national or professional norms. The "Ugly American" provides a lesson to planners.
5 Real instutional and financial constraints may preclude implementation or even objective analysis of certain alternatives (particularly unconventional ones).[3]

1 Irving Fox, "Basin Planning: Past Experience and Current Problems," paper presented at a joint meeting of the Columbia Basin and the Missouri Basin Inter-Agency Committees, Jackson Hole, Wyo., June 19, 1963.
2 C. E. Lindblom, The Science of Muddling Through, *Public Admin. Rev.*, vol. 19 (Spring, 1959), pp. 79–88.
3 Robert K. Davis, "The Range of Choice in Water Management" (Baltimore: The Johns Hopkins Press, 1968), pp. 30–33, 124–128.

The water resources planner must recognize that he can never develop a perfect plan. He must use fragmentary data and limited analytic procedures to strive for hazily defined objectives. He cannot hope to produce the optimum expansion path of social welfare; he can only strive to make the expansion path better than it would have been without him.

21-2 LEVELS OF DECISION MAKING   The planning, design, and implementation of water resources development programs entail many kinds of decision making. Planning decisions are made by the community, by the electorate, by legislative bodies, and by administrative agencies. Each level plays its own role in resource development. Each is best adapted to specific decision types.

The community consensus, which determines social feasibility, often develops outside formal decision-making procedures. Community opinion on specific questions is expressed at public meetings and through letters, petitions, or other communications to appropriate public officials. Excessive opposition expressed through any of these vehicles suggests that design modifications to meet community needs better may be in order.

The electorate may be asked to vote. Electoral decisions are only structured to accept or reject specific proposed plans. A legislative body may ask for an advisory referendum on a controversial proposal. An affirmative vote is often required by law in order to sell bonds or levy local taxes. Certain candidates may take strong stands on water-related issues. When elections are held, the planner is responsible for presenting all aspects of the issue clearly and to provide the public with sufficient information to make an informed decision.

Traditionally, legislative bodies have tried to analyze the merits of individual water resources projects in order to try to allocate funds more wisely. Because legislators lack the time and experience to do this job adequately, they too often agree to support projects in each other's districts after only minimal examination. More effective planning could be achieved if the legislature were instead to concentrate on defining the performance objectives desired from water resources development and on periodically revising them in a feedback process. Legislatures are best suited to resolve broad policy issues.

The task of the administrative agencies is to translate the goals chosen by laymen through the other three decision-making processes into concrete proposals for specific structural and nonstructural measures for water resources development.[1] The process is illustrated by Fig. 21-1.

---

[1]   Maynard F. Hufschmidt, Field Level Planning of Water Resources Systems, *Water Resources Res.*, vol. 1 (2d Quarter, 1965), pp. 150–151.

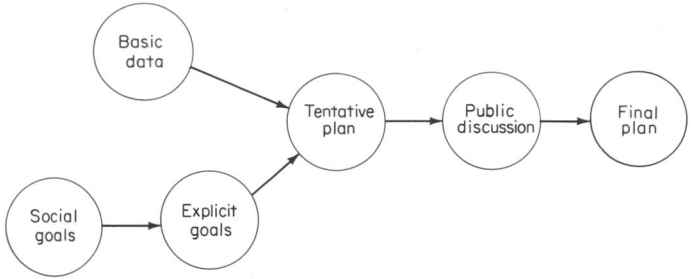

FIGURE 21-1   Steps in planning by administrative agencies.

The social goals such as economic efficiency, regional development, and environmental quality must be translated from the language of laymen to more explicit or precise goals which can be used quantitatively to judge the relative worth of available alternatives. Specific methods are needed for assigning a relative weight to diverse goals; picking a planning discount rate; evaluating intangibles; handling uncertainty; establishing and ascertaining the flexibility of political, institutional, financial, and technical constraints; and bounding the study problem in time and space. Basic physical and economic data must be collected and evaluated and used to develop a tentative plan. A period of public discussion is then needed to make sure the tentative plan is acceptable. The public at large can react on whether the administrative agency has properly interpreted social goals. Some individuals may provide previously overlooked information to supplement the basic data. The technical or academic communities may be able to suggest promising but overlooked alternatives. Special interest groups will be able to state their positions. Afterward, the administrative agency can aggregate these comments and incorporate them as warranted into a final plan. If needs be, additional periods of public discussion and plan adjustment can follow until a satisfactory plan is formulated. It is helpful for the administrative agency to conceive of this process as a search for the best solution to a problem rather than a defense of a specific dam or other structural measure. The public must rely on the integrity of the professional experts to ensure planning conformance to consensus criteria.

Engineers have an important role in each level of decision making. Those in responsible positions in the planning agencies should do their best to create a better-informed public opinion by presenting the factors for and against each proposal and should not be afraid to take a definite stand where they believe it to be in the public interest. They should advise legislators on the technical implications of alternative criteria for project evaluation. They should do their best to be objective in using the criteria to evaluate specific projects. Engineers not personally involved in the planning process should assume active leadership in the community when it is considering issues which their training gives them an advantage in understanding.

21-3   THE TOTAL WATER RESOURCES PROGRAM   The planner must coordinate his work with the total water resources program. Resource development requires research, data collection, project formulation, design, construction, and operation and maintenance. The major challenge to program administration lies in how best to organize these groups to get the total job done. Because of a rapidly expanding technology and the fact that many water resources planning techniques are still in their formative stages, planning agencies must act regularly without adequate background theory or information for normative decision making. Research may be required; however, planning agencies cannot afford a staff qualified to research every planning problem and should normally contract research problems to a research-oriented group.

While data are essential to planning, the traditional government organization separates data-collecting from planning agencies (Sec. 7-1). However, the planning agency seldom finds all the data it needs available and must gather additional information. Data gathering is economical whenever the cost of getting the data will be less than the value of the data in improving the plan.

Projections are estimates of future data. A planning agency can often adapt regional projections by other agencies for application to its particular study. The planning agency should consider the effect of planned decisions on economic growth and the sensitivity of the optimum plan to uncontrollable future events.

The most critical phase in planning is project formulation. The planning staff must include experts qualified in engineering, economics, geology, hydrology, ecology, and a number of other disciplines working closely together in evaluating alternatives. In project formulation, it is necessary to:[1]

1   *Bound the analysis.* Because comprehensive examination of every effect of project development is impossible, "optimum decision making

---

[1]   Ray K. Linsley and Joseph B. Franzini, "Water-Resources Engineering" (New York: McGraw-Hill Book Company, 1964), chap. 21.
J. W. Dixon, Water Resources, in Ven Te Chow (ed.), "Handbook of Applied Hydrology" (New York: McGraw-Hill Book Company, 1964).

is a planned series of suboptimizations."[1] The limits of each suboptimization should be chosen so that the neglected factors will not invalidate the conclusions of the analysis and the work required does not exceed the capacity of the agency, but the selection of the exact limits is a matter of judgment, experience, sensitivity analysis, and compromise. The boundaries selected should define the geographical area, the planning horizon, the types of problems, and the types of effects to be considered.

2 Inventory the possible land-use plans, and evaluate their demand for project output under present and future conditions.

3 Inventory the development and management alternatives capable of meeting the water requirements of the projected land-use patterns. Special effort is required to make sure that extraordinary alternatives such as nonstructural measures for flood control, recirculation of the water supply, and artificial fish spawning are considered.

4 Prepare preliminary designs and cost estimates as required for marginal-cost curves (Sec. 4-16). As soon as the cost of one alternative is found to exceed that of another doing an equivalent job, analysis of the first alternative should be dropped so no time is wasted evaluating manifestly inferior alternatives.

5 Prepare preliminary benefit estimates to determine the marginal-benefit curve and optimum project scale.

6 Place project components in every conceivable combination and total combined benefits and costs after accounting for project interdependencies. Include combinations which allow for alternative construction sequences and stage construction.

7 Reject all projects which cannot be economically justified individually or when combined with complementary projects.

8 Select the two or three alternative combinations having maximum excess of benefits over costs, and make additional cost and benefit estimates until the best alternative is established. If the extramarket consequences vary greatly among projects of comparable economic advantage, such consequences should be defined as clearly as possible and the final selection left to the public.

9 Prepare the reports required to define the problem clearly, and describe the nature, benefits, and costs of the optimum project, the optimum project timing and staging, and the suggested financial arrangement.

After the optimum project has been formulated, implementation may proceed through the remaining steps (Sec. 7-5). Whenever new

---

[1] C. West Churchman, Decision and Value Theory, in Russell F. Ackoff (ed.), "Progress in Operations Research" (New York: John Wiley & Sons, Inc., 1961), p. 46.

information indicates either benefits or costs will substantially depart from project formulation estimates, the project should be reviewed and if necessary reformulated.

21-4 PROGRAM COORDINATION Intensive coordinating effort is required in order to keep all those participating in the total water resources program working together efficiently. Coordination is required among the staff of a planning unit, among the units of the agency, among the agencies within a governmental jurisdiction, and among comparable agencies in various jurisdictions. The planners should be aware of the research in progress which will improve their ability to serve the public, and the research group should be aware of the problems which baffle planners. The planning agencies should be aware of the available data, and the data-collecting agencies should concentrate on gathering the most useful data. Planning should be based on current design practice so substantial changes will not be required during final design, and the design agencies should consult with the planners to better understand the reasoning used in project formulation. Planning should be based on current construction practice in order to formulate plans which can be built economically, and the construction supervision should have in mind the functional requirements of each project component. The planner should be aware of maintenance practice and costs so as to make the proper trade-offs between capital and annual cost, and the operation and maintenance group should keep its program flexible enough to adjust for changing demand for project output.

21-5 HUMAN FACTORS IN PLANNING Planning is done by men. All men have feelings, opinions, and bias. They have a degree of loyalty to their agency, their home area, their personal ideology, and their profession. They tend to favor decisions which will increase their power, prestige, or the security of their job. All these, even if only subconsciously, influence judgment.[1] The planning organization must consciously strive to minimize the influence of these subjective factors and encourage objective analysis.

The two basic approaches to greater objectivity are a bias balance and outside review. A bias balance requires a planning staff of diverse background with respect to home, profession, and ideology and an outside review to combat agency loyalty. The best review comes from a group with enough counterbias to force give and take in seeking more

---

[1] Hubert Marshall, Politics and Efficiency in Water Development, in Allen V. Kneese and Stephen C. Smith (eds.), "Water Research" (Baltimore: The Johns Hopkins Press, 1966), pp. 291–310.

generally acceptable solutions. Water resources development has suffered from the absence of a powerful antidevelopment group. Private power lobbies, railroads, and conservationist organizations sometimes fulfill this function, but projects receiving universal support often are poorly planned.

Planning agencies must continuously combat the tendency of many to rank planning accomplishment according to the number and size of projects constructed. For example, a comparison of alternative flood control projects might find the best alternative to be to build a dam, build an improved channel, restrict new development from the flood plain, or take no preventive measures at all. The resulting prestige drops progressively as one proceeds through these alternatives, and yet each finding may be of equal service to the public. A water resources planner naturally takes pride in an imposing structure, but the public interest demands that each alternative be considered without prejudice.

The water resources planner must also consider the human relations aspect of presenting his findings. Public acceptance of a project is not directly proportional to the benefit-cost ratio. Important human factors include:

1 Ability to communicate with the local citizens and willingness to give friendly consideration to local opinion and advice.
2 A consistent effort to keep those most directly affected informed so that they are not suddenly confronted with the loss of homes and lands.
3 Avoidance of the appearance of siding with a particular local faction.
4 The reasonableness of the plan and the estimated costs and benefits. Many local people are better acquainted with many aspects of the local economy than the planners are. Benefit and cost estimates must make sense to these people before they will accept them.
5 The development of a design which blends in with the area and avoids appearances which are esthetically displeasing.

Human relations must also be considered in the internal organization of the planning staff.[1] Creative planning requires that each individual feel he is making a meaningful contribution to the total effort. The organization must satisfy the need of the individual for self-fulfillment even as the individual works to satisfy organization goals. Individuals whose needs are not met become less creative as they retreat through one or

---

[1] Basic references are:
M. Haire (ed.), "Modern Organization Theory" (New York: John Wiley & Sons, Inc., 1959).
Harvey Leibenstein, "Economic Theory and Organizational Analysis" (New York: Harper & Brothers, 1960).
Richard F. Neuschel, "Management by System," 2d ed. (New York: McGraw-Hill Book Company, 1960).

more of the various possible defense mechanisms into stagnation.[1] Communications within the planning agency should be free and open. Psychological barriers should not be allowed to develop among functional specialties. The leadership must remain receptive to ideas developing within the ranks. There should be group participation in decision making in order for all employees to have a clear understanding of organizational goals. Supervision should emphasize objectives and goals and give the individual a maximum of freedom in action. Psychologists have found the common goal of a united group to be one of the strongest possible incentives for individual achievement and morale.

Interactions with Other Resources

The interactions among the patterns in time and space of land use, population growth, transportation facilities, and water development are continually discussed by political leaders, research personnel, and planners. They are too complex to allow rigorous analysis, but they do require thoughtful consideration in every planning effort.

21-6 LAND USE AND PROJECT OUTPUT   Land use affects project output in many ways.

1 Land use affects precipitation. Forests increase precipitation by about 6 percent.[2] Urban areas generate suspended material, water vapor, and air turbulence to increase precipitation from 5 to 10 percent.[3]

2 Land use has a much larger effect on soil moisture conditions. Less incoming radiation and lower wind speeds preserve soil moisture and snow packs much longer in forests than in open spaces. Urban drainage has a reverse effect, which may be offset by yard watering in drier climates.

3 Urbanization affects runoff in a number of ways. The runoff volume for drier climates and smaller storms is increased up to severalfold. The annual pattern of runoff tends to follow the annual pattern of precipitation and snowmelt more closely. Storm runoff begins much sooner after rainfall commences. Peak runoff volumes are substantially larger, and flood peaks will be made relatively even larger if channel

[1] Chris Argyris, "Personality and Organization" (New York: Harper & Brothers, 1957).

[2] Helmut Landsburg, "Physical Climatology" (DuBois, Pa.: Gray Printing Company, Inc., 1962), pp. 307–308.

[3] *Ibid.*, pp. 317–326.

improvements substantially reduce the time of concentration. Minor flood peaks may be multiplied severalfold, while major peaks increase less than 50 percent as the watershed changes from entirely rural to entirely urban.[1] Urbanization affects watershed yield by decreasing low flows and increasing surface runoff from the small storms which occur from time to time during the dry period.

4 Forests or other dense vegetation reduce flood peaks, eliminate surface runoff from small storms, and increase base flow.[2] However, denser vegetation is unlikely to effect a significant reduction in the rare flood peaks usually used in designing structural measures for flood control. Additional transpiration reduces total runoff; however, slower runoff may make more water available for diversion or ground-water recharge.

5 Improper conservation practice increases erosion and deposition. Flood damages are multiplied by high sediment content, and reservoir life may be substantially shortened. Reforestation and soil conservation measures are much more effective for sediment than for flood control.

6 Land use also affects water quality. Storm runoff from urban areas acquires waste material left on streets and other exposed locations. Rural runoff accumulates agricultural chemicals and animal wastes. Return flows from upstream irrigators increase downstream salinity.

7 Land use near a recreational facility may substantially alter site attractiveness. Woods and well-maintained farms are much more attractive than intensive summer-cabin development or unkept rural land.

21-7 LAND USE AND PROJECT DEMAND The demand for the output from water resources projects depends on land use. Some issues are nationwide in scope. Should water be transported long distances at greater cost, or should population growth concentrate closer to the source locations? Should large sums of money be spent to irrigate new areas when the marginal cost of increased agricultural production is lower for humid areas than for arid ones?[3] Should planners continue to assume an ever-expanding population, or think in terms of an upper limit at which population will stabilze?[4]

---

[1] L. Douglas James, Using A Digital Computer to Estimate the Effects of Urban Development on Flood Peaks, *Water Resources Res.*, vol. 1 (2d Quarter, 1965), pp. 223–234.

[2] For approximate quantitative evaluation of these effects, see Herbert C. Storey, Robert L. Hobba, and J. Marvin Rosa, Hydrology of Forest Lands and Rangelands, Ven Te Chow (ed.), "Handbook of Applied Hydrology" (New York: McGraw-Hill Book Company, 1964).

[3] Rudolph Ulrich, Relative Costs and Benefits of Land Reclamation in the Humid Southeast and the Semiarid West, *J. Farm Economics*, vol. 35 (February, 1953).

[4] George Macinko, Saturation: A Problem Evaded in Planning Land Use, *Science*, vol. 149 (July 30, 1965), pp. 516–521.

Historically, public support has favored bringing water to the desert so that farms and cities might be established, but those living in humid areas are beginning to worry that the water exports will unduly restrict local economic growth. The most equitable water policy is to charge all water users according to the cost (adjusted in recognition of extraeconomic goals) of supplying their water. If arid areas offer enough advantages so that those living there are willing to pay the cost of importing additional water, then they would continue to develop. Otherwise, growth would shift to regions where water is more readily available.

Both the demand for water and land use depend on population. The recent expansion of world population has made many pessimistic about how or even whether it will be possible to supply everyone with needed food, clothing, and water. The supply of water and land has an absolute upper limit. As the death rate declines, the planner must give serious consideration to the issues involved in reducing the birth rate to avoid severe overpopulation as an alternative to stricter rationing of limited natural resources.

Comprehensive water resources planning requires examination of the relationship between the demand for each type of water-related output and land use. An important planning alternative is to vary the land use to adjust the demand to match the supply rather than to rely solely on structural measures to meet a fixed demand. On the other hand, land-use adjustment has its own cost and should be used only when it costs less than the structural measures. Examples of land-use adjustment alternatives include:

1   Restricting land use in flood plains to those types less susceptible to damage when floods do occur
2   Restricting new land developments in arid areas to those for which the marginal physical product of water has a high value, while encouraging industry and crops requiring large volumes of low-cost water to locate in humid areas
3   Requiring industry needing to dispose of large quantities of waste material to locate in areas where such disposal can be accomplished at low social cost, and confining development in other areas to industries having minor waste-disposal problems
4   Building plants requiring large amounts of heavy bulk transport near existing navigation facilities, rather than building them inland and then building waterways to them.

21-8   URBAN LAND USE PLANNING   In addition to estimating total demand for water resource project output from large areas, the water resources planner needs a detailed breakdown of local land use by time to optimize project timing. He needs a breakdown by location to bound the area of benefit and design distribution systems.

One may optimize land use within the flood plain by a trade-off between the value of the location and the damage potential (Sec. 10-7). More generally, the land should transfer from agricultural to urban use when its value in the former no longer exceeds that in the latter. The economic justification of new irrigation measures depends on whether the benefit required for their justification will be reaped before the land will be converted to urban uses. If the pattern of urban growth were determined by marginal trade-offs in land (or more properly location) values, the following characteristics could be expected:

1   The city would grow faster in the directions in which the farm land was less productive.
2   Growth into areas having flooding, drainage, or water supply problems would be slower than growth into otherwise equivalent locations.
3   Because location value is partially determined by travel times, growth would accelerate adjacent to major transportation arteries and thus give the developed area a star-shaped pattern.

The methods developed for predicting urban growth patterns have been formulated on a predictive rather than an optimizing basis. The older methods used historical trends to forecast urban expansion around the existing city nucleus or nuclei.[1] The recent trend has been toward using an input-output analysis (Sec. 9-3). Digital computer models have been used to predict urban growth as a series of individual location decisions by countless industries, businesses, and families to develop a projected pattern of land development extending to the planning time horizon.[2] The best models provide for alternative government policies with respect to flood-plain restrictions, highway improvement and location, or water supply service and compare the consequences of alternative resulting growth patterns.

21-9   WATER AND TRANSPORTATION PLANNING   Water resources development needs to be coordinated with transportation planning in a number of ways.

---

[1]   Orris C. Herfindahl and Allen V. Kneese, "Quality of the Environment" (Baltimore: The Johns Hopkins Press, 1965), pp. 55–56.
[2]   Britton Harris, Experiments in Projection of Transportation and Land Use, *Traffic Quart.*, vol. 16 (April, 1962).
    J. F. Kain and J. R. Meyer, "A First Approximation to a Rand Model for Study of Urban Transportation" (Santa Monica, Calif.: Rand Corporation, RM-28878-FF, November, 1961).

1   It is necessary to analyze whether the effects of new transportation facilities on the urban growth pattern will entice development into the flood plain or have any other adverse consequences.

2   Navigation facilities should be closely coordinated with other transportation facilities to speed the transfer of goods between navigation and the other transportation modes and avoid unnecessary overcapacity for hauling bulk goods. The benefit derived by navigation in opening draw bridges should be weighed against the loss suffered by surface-transport delay.

3   The effects of temporary closure by flooding should be considered in highway location studies. Occasional short-term closure of a highway by flooding is not unreasonable unless damages exceed the cost of preventing the flooding or relocating the highway.

4   Where transportation facilities are displaced by a reservoir or other structural measures for water resource development, one must make (a) the economic decision of whether the facilities should be abandoned or replaced and (b) the financial decision of whether costs should be allocated to the water resources project or the transportation facilities. The decision to replace should be based on demonstrated transportation benefits exceeding replacement cost. The question in providing roads for land access is whether it costs less to provide minimum access facilities or to buy the land. The optimum level of replaced transportation facility has marginal benefit equal to marginal cost. However, the common practice is to replace the previously existing facility in kind or as modified to meet more recent design standards. The most practical rule for allocating the cost of transportation facilities is to ascribe the amount required to replace the facilities in kind to the water resources project and any amount for facility improvement to transportation. If a facility is abandoned, losses to the previous users are a project economic cost.

21-10   WATER AND WEATHER PLANNING   Weather can be changed.[1] Recent advances in the understanding of the dynamics and thermodynamics of atmospheric processes have brought attempts to dissipate fog, increase precipitation, suppress hail and lightning, reduce hurricane and tornado severity, and even effect purposeful large-scale climate modification. Only cold fog dissipation was operational in 1966, but other modifications may soon be successful. Techniques to increase precipitation have received the greatest attention. Some increases of 10 to 15 percent have been observed, but it is yet to be shown that such

---

[1]   Donald L. Gilman, James R. Hibbs, and Paul L. Laskin, "Weather and Climate Modification" (Washington: USGPO, Weather Bureau, U.S. Department of Commerce, 1965).

an increase can be maintained on a long-term basis without a corresponding decrease somewhere else. Chances for achieving reductions in the severity of extreme storms are much higher than those for achieving more general climatological changes.

The basic problem in economic evaluation of weather modification is that the weather changes help some and harm others. The same hurricane which inflicts severe damage near its center may bring drought-relieving rain at its fringes. The economic cost of increased drought severity may well exceed the benefit of reduced storm damage. Too little is known about the magnitude of these effects to quantify them to the extent required to properly analyze the economic trade-offs. As physical science provides new operational techniques for weather modification, increased research will be needed into the interactions between weather and the biotic system. The power to modify weather and climate has far-reaching implications. If it is not wisely used, disaster will result.[1]

SELECTED REFERENCES

Argyris, Chris: "Personality and Organization" (New York: Harper & Brothers, 1957).

Chapin, F. Stewart: "Urban Land Use Planning" (New York: Harper & Brothers, 1957).

Dunham, Allison: City Planning: An Analysis of the Content of the Master Plan, *J. Law and Economics*, vol. 1 (October, 1958), pp. 170–186.

Lindblom, C. E.: The Science of Muddling Through, *Public Admin. Rev.*, vol. 19 (Spring, 1959), pp. 79–88.

Sewell, W. R. Derrick: "Human Dimensions of Weather Modification" (Chicago: The University of Chicago Press, Department of Geography, Res. Paper 105, 1966).

PROBLEMS

21-1 Agencies responsible for water resources development have been criticized for building large and imposing structures instead of using nonstructural measures to accomplish the same objectives.

a Tabulate the nonstructural measures (including land-use options) which might potentially be used for flood control, for irrigation, for water quality control, for recreation.

b Evaluate the relative effectiveness from the economic, financial, social, and political viewpoints of these possibilities.

---

[1] W. R. Derrick Sewell, "Human Dimensions of Weather Modification" (Chicago: The University of Chicago Press, Department of Geography, Res. Paper 105, 1966).

21-2 State and local governments are becoming more and more involved
in water resources planning in recent years. The Federal government has a much larger and more experienced staff and many
more financial resources to perform this task.

a Do you believe this state and local involvement wise? Does it
represent an overlapping of jurisdictions with all levels doing
the same thing? Are there any tasks or functions that the state
and local governments can perform best?

b What considerations should determine the order of priorities in
deciding what tasks the new agencies should do first?

6
FINANCIAL ANALYSIS

The emphasis to this point has been on economic analysis, using economic criteria to determine the best project design. However, no matter how many benefits are expected, a project will not be built unless someone is found who is willing and financially able to pay for it. Financial analysis is the search for that person. Equity suggests beneficiaries be responsible for raising the necessary funds, but income redistribution and other noneconomic goals may be advanced by shifting some of the burden to others.

It is important to recognize the difference between economic analysis and financial analysis (Sec. 8-1). Confusion can lead to a serious misallocation of funds. The fact that a community has the financial resources to pay for a suggested water supply project (financial feasibility) does not mean that it is the best of available alternatives.

An economic analysis helps answer the questions: Should the project be built at all, should it be built this way, and should it be built now? However, the financial analysis comes after the economic analysis and helps answer the questions: Who should repay the project costs? Are they able to meet the repayment obligations? Unfortunately financial analyses prepared by municipal investment counseling firms are often viewed by the public as serving the function of economic analyses. Data from an economic analysis are useful in the financial analysis and economic analysis can help evaluate financing plans, but the two types of studies are conceptually different.

Financial analysis has both short-term and long-term aspects. Most water resources projects require a large inital capital expenditure. This first cost must be raised to pay the installation bills. Alternative funding possibilities are described in Chap. 22. As project benefits are realized, beneficiaries may be charged to recover or pay off loans covering the initial cost. Chapter 23 describes procedures used to allocate total cost among beneficiary groups. Chapter 24 describes procedures for charging individual beneficiaries for project output used.

CHAPTER
TWENTY-TWO

FINANCIAL
FEASIBILITY

Financial Studies

22-1   THE ROLE OF FINANCIAL ANALYSIS   The test of financial feasibility is passed by a project if the funds needed for project construction can be raised. Only a few basic approaches to fund raising are possible; however, the details of the fund-raising procedures and the legal technicalities involved in borrowing add a complexity to financial analysis which often obscures the goal of seeking the best source of funds for achieving project objectives. The purpose of this chapter is to concentrate on the goal rather than the details. Federal financing is covered briefly, but because federal funding procedures are largely fixed by law, greater emphasis is given to state and local financing where many more funding possibilities must be considered.

Analysis of financing alternatives must distinguish between financing initial construction and repayment by the beneficiaries. State and local projects may be financed by loans repaid from charges to project beneficiaries. Federal financing requires beneficiaries to repay a portion of the cost specified according to type of benefit. A large project typically utilizes many sources of funds and repayment procedures. The overall financial structure must be formulated in financial analysis.

22-2   DISTINCTIONS FROM ECONOMIC ANALYSIS   A water supply project may be financially feasible in that funds can be generated to pay for it through water charges and taxes. However, this does not mean that the project is the best of available alternatives or that present construction is appropriate. On the other hand, a project may be economically feasible even though it cannot be financed. The debt limit of a political jurisdiction may prohibit borrowing additional funds to finance a project whose benefits exceed its cost. For example, city officials may wish to construct a multipurpose water project which is economically feasible only to find that a legally prescribed maximum debt limit precludes the undertaking. Current fiscal policy at times precludes federal funding to start new projects. In other instances, the beneficiaries may be so widespread that no institutional framework exists to set charges and collect funds for project repayment.

Another difference between the analyses is in the treatment of inflation (Sec. 9-8). Only differential inflation should be included in an economic analysis. However, general price inflation must be considered in the financial analysis since a bond issue or appropriation based on current prices may not be adequate at the time funds are expended.

Finally, the degree to which they must bear the burden of project repayment affects the beneficiaries' private calculations of benefits and costs. If the beneficiaries are required to repay very little of the project costs, they have every incentive to argue for a project though it may not pass the test of economic feasibility. For example, a federal flood control project may have an overall benefit-cost ratio of 0.8. If local interests are required to pay only 5 percent of the costs, the project has benefit-cost ratio of 16 from the local viewpoint. Financial incentives work against planning from the overall viewpoint when those benefiting are required to pay so little of the costs.

Federal Financing

Funds for financing the initial construction of federal projects are appropriated from the general budget (Sec. 7-5) and ultimately come from tax revenues or borrowing, adding to the national debt (Sec. 8-10). Federal cost-sharing practice divides the burden for this cost between the beneficiaries and a subsidy from the taxpayers. The portion of the funds which must be repaid by the beneficiaries depends on the agency constructing the project and the type of benefit received. Repayment requires allocation of total project cost among project purposes (Chap. 23) and setting specific charges from allocated costs (Chap. 24).

22-3 SMALL PROJECTS Specific details of cost-sharing arrangements are continually changing so that the following discussion must concentrate on examples of how federal funding is used to assist small project development.

The Watershed and Flood Protection Act of 1954 (Public Law 566) is administered by the Soil Conservation Service to encourage the construction of relatively small water resources development projects.[1] A project cannot have more than 250,000 acres in its watershed, and reservoirs can have no more than 25,000 acre-ft storage, of which no more than 12,500 acre-ft can be for flood control. If a project costs less than $250,000 and stores less than 2,500 acre-ft of water, it can be approved administratively without specific congressional authorization. For larger projects, congressional approval must be obtained before funds can be expended. Under this program, Soil Conservation Service engineers, sometimes assisted by state funds or personnel, prepare the planning studies. All costs associated with flood control, except rights-of-way and maintenance, are nonreimbursable by local beneficiaries; 50 percent of the costs allocated to recreation are nonreimbursable; and up to 50 percent of the costs allocated to irrigation may be nonreimbursable. All costs allocated to municipal and industrial water supply or water quality control and the reimbursable portion of other costs must be borne by local or state entities. In many states, it has been difficult to obtain funds to repay the reimbursable portion of costs allocated to flood control, recreation, and fish and wildlife enhancement. California has a system of grants for these purposes in recognition of the public benefits derived from flood control and recreation. Table 22-1 shows the cost-sharing arrangements for a typical Public Law 566 project for the purposes of flood control and irrigation.

The Small Reclamation Projects Act of 1956 (Public Law 984) is administered by the U.S. Bureau of Reclamation and assists the construction of small multipurpose reclamation projects through a loan and grant program.[2] Following are some of the features of this program:

1 Total project cost cannot exceed $10 million.

2 The upper limit of federal funds that may be provided is $6,500,000 for a combination of a loan and a grant or for either.

3 Grants may be made for flood control, recreation, and fish and wildlife purposes.

[1] See "Watershed Protection Handbook," U.S. Dept. Agr., Soil Conservation Service (August, 1967), for details of the Public Law 566 program.

[2] For details, see "Loans under the Small Reclamation Projects Act of 1956," U.S. Dept. Int., Bureau of Reclamation (January, 1967).

TABLE 22-1 Cost Sharing in a Typical Public Law 566 Project*

ESTIMATED COST, DOLLARS

Item	Unit	NUMBER TO BE APPLIED			PUBLIC LAW 566 FUNDS			OTHER			TOTAL
		Federal land	Nonfed land	Total	Federal land	Nonfed land	Total	Federal land	Nonfed land	Total	
Structural Measures:											
Dam, multiple-purpose	No.	1		1	758,420		758,420	235,580		235,580	994,000
Channel, multiple-purpose											
North canal	ft		15,770	15,770		19,135	19,135		10,495	10,495	29,630
North drain	ft		18,725	18,725		50,290	50,290		3,710	3,710	54,000
Diversion	ft		6,000	6,000		4,140	4,140				4,140
Irrigation canal	ft		8,500	8,500		9,935	9,935		9,935	9,935	19,870
Debris basin	No.		1	1		14,150	14,150				14,150
Stream channel improvement (pipeline)	ft		4,800	4,800		93,800	93,800				93,800
SCS, Subtotal construction					758,420	191,450	949,870	235,580	24,140	259,720	1,209,590
Installation Services:											
Engineering					163,800	32,310	196,110				196,110
Other					99,200	21,720	120,920				120,920
SCS, Subtotal installation services					243,000	54,030	317,030				317,030
Other Costs:											
Land, easements, and R/W								60,000	29,680	89,680	89,680
Adm. of contracts								20,000	4,375	24,375	24,375
Water rights								1,000	1,000	2,000	2,000
Subtotal, other								81,000	35,055	116,055	116,055
TOTAL STRUCTURAL MEASURES					1,021,420	245,480	1,266,900	316,580	59,195	375,775	1,642,675

* Montpelier Creek Watershed, Bear Lake County, Idaho.

4 The substantial cost of making the necessary investigations and in preparing the application report is borne by the applicant.

5 The portion of the project costs allocated to irrigation of lands not in excess of 160 acres in a single ownership is free of interest charges. Interest must be charged on the reimbursable portion of the project costs chargeable to providing irrigation to lands in excess of 160 acres in single ownership, to the production of commercial power, or to furnishing water for domestic, industrial, or municipal use.

6 The repayment period may be less than, but cannot exceed, 50 years. The payout schedule followed for a specific project depends on anticipated conditions and is negotiated between the Bureau of Reclamation and the applicant. The interest rate in 1969 was 3.5 percent.

7 The eligible applying organizations include a state or a department, agency, or political subdivision thereof; a conservancy district; irrigation district; or water users' association.

8 Proposals must receive approval of the Bureau of Reclamation, Secretary of Interior, Bureau of the Budget, and must be before two committees of Congress for 60 days before funds can be appropriated.

The 160-acre limitation, the lack of provision for basin account financing of part of the costs allocated to irrigation (Sec. 12-20), and the fact that local entities must pay for all of the investigations and other costs incurred in the preparation of the application report have limited program utilization. Federal funds for resource development seldom come without strings attached. Table 22-2 shows the repayment schedule for a typical small reclamation project.

22-4 LARGE PROJECTS Projects constructed by the Bureau of Reclamation and the Corps of Engineers must go through a series of time-consuming coordinating and review steps before being submitted to Congress and eventually funded (Sec. 7-5). A period of 25 years may lapse from the inception of planning to completion of the project. However, financial constraints limiting the ability of local groups to obtain sufficient funds from other sources, and the hope that federal cost sharing will substantially reduce local repayment, make federal funding highly desirable from the local point of view.

The Flood Control Act of 1936 requires that beneficiaries (1) secure and pay all costs for lands, easements, and rights-of-way; (2) relocate or reconstruct all bridges, structures, and utilities; (3) assume certain responsibilities for operation and maintenance of the project; and (4) hold the government free from damage claims. All other costs are non-

TABLE 22-2 Cost Sharing in a Typical Public Law 984 Project*

Beginning of year	Revenue total assessments	TOTAL OBLIGATIONS			PAYMENTS				
		Small projects loan	Other†	Total	Annual O&M	Operating reserve	Other	Small projects loan	Total
1	69,470	2,351,600	289,470	2,641,070	22,000		47,470	0	69,470
2	72,000	2,351,600	242,000	2,593,600	22,000	2,000	48,000	0	72,000
3	72,000	2,351,600	194,000	2,545,600	22,000	2,000	48,000	0	72,000
4	72,000	2,351,600	146,000	2,497,600	22,000	2,000	48,000	0	72,000
5	73,000	2,351,600	98,000	2,449,600	22,000	2,000	49,000	0	73,000
6	73,000	2,351,600	49,000	2,400,600	22,000	2,000	49,000	0	73,000
7	75,500	2,351,600	0	2,351,600	22,000	0	0	53,500	75,500
8	75,500	2,298,100	0	2,298,100	22,000	0	0	53,500	75,500
49	75,000	104,600		104,600	22,000			53,500	75,500
50	73,100	51,100		51,100	22,000			51,100	73,100

* Cassia Creek Reservoir Project, $2,641,070.

† The first item of $289,470 includes the following: $189,000 for channel improvement, collected by assessment, needed; $87,000 right-of-way costs amortized over 5 years at 5 percent; $13,470 interest on $87,000. Remainder of district contribution amounting to $55,000 is assumed available from sale of stock in reservoir company.

reimbursable. Similar policies are applied by the Corps of Engineers to navigation costs. Costs allocated to power and municipal and industrial water supply must be paid in full with interest. Local interests must repay 50 percent of all costs allocated to water quality control and recreation. Table 22-3 shows a breakdown of cost repayment requirements by project purpose for a typical multipurpose Corps of Engineers project.

The U.S. Bureau of Reclamation has repayment requirements for irrigation features which vary from those for other project purposes. Interest is not required on costs allocated to irrigation. This results in a subsidy of about 50 percent of the total cost over the lifetime of the project. The subsidy is even larger to the degree the interest rate charged falls short of the optimum planning discount rate. Another subsidy is granted through the write-off of a portion of the irrigation capital costs which are deemed to exceed the users "ability to pay." The remaining costs are paid from surplus power revenues (Sec. 13-18), from postamortization revenues from the sale of municipal and industrial water supply, and in some instances from a portion of power revenues equivalent to the interest repayment on costs allocated to the power purpose. Many projects being submitted to Congress require only 20 percent repayment by water users of the costs allocated to irrigation. Table 22-4 shows the cost-sharing arrangements for a typical multipurpose Bureau of Reclamation project.

State and Local Financing

22-5 FUNDING OPTIONS Local areas desiring to raise funds for water resources development may apply for federal grants or loans, seek aid through state appropriations, or sell bonds supported by project charges or local taxes. Several states, such as Utah, Wyoming, Kentucky, New York, and Montana, have appropriated funds for small project development programs. The state of California's mammoth water project is being financed mainly by general obligation bonds backed up by the taxing power of the state but largely repaid from project revenues.

A local government seeking financial backing for a small water resources project characteristically raises the first cost by a combination of loans and grants from the Federal (or sometimes the state) government and by funds obtained from the sale of bonds. After the project is completed, it will gradually over the years pay off the loans and incurred bonded indebtedness. Federal loans and grants are obtainable through a

TABLE 22-3 Cost Sharing in a Typical Corps of Engineers Project*†

Item	FUNCTION				Total
	Flood control	Irrigation	Water supply	Recreation	
1 Allocation of annual costs:					
a Average annual benefits	200.0	125.0	73.0	80.0	478.0
b Alternate costs	229.0	107.0	73.0	107.0	516.0
c Limited benefits	200.0	107.0	73.0	80.0	460.0
d Separable costs	133.0	0.0	2.0	17.0	152.0
e Remaining benefits					
i Amount	67.0	107.0	71.0	63.0	308.0
ii Percent	21.75	34.75	23.05	20.45	100.0
f Allocated joint costs	21.0	33.0	22.0	19.0	95.0
g Total allocation	154.0	33.0	24.0	36.0	247.0
2 Allocation of O, M, and R costs:					
a Separable costs	19.0	0.0	1.0	7.0	27.0
b Allocated joint costs	3.0	5.0	3.0	3.0	14.0
c Total allocation	22.0	5.0	4.0	10.0	41.0
3 Allocation of investment:					
a Annual investment cost	132.0	28.0	20.0	26.0	206.0
b Allocated investment	4,635.0	987.0	704.0	920.0	7,246.0
4 Allocation of construction costs:					
a Specific investment	1,635.0	504.0	49.0	339.0	2,527.0
b Investment in joint use	3,000.0	483.0	655.0	581.0	4,719.0
c Int. due const., joint-use facs (proportionate to b)	76.2	12.3	16.7	14.8	120.0
d Const. cost, joint-use facs. (b − c)					
i Amount	2,923.8	470.7	638.3	566.2	4,599.0
ii Percent	63.57	10.24	13.88	12.31	100.0
e Const. cost of specific facs	1,593.0	491.0	48.0	330.0	2,462.0
f Allocated construction cost	4,516.8	961.7	686.3	896.2	7,061.0

* Ririe Dam and Reservoir.
† All amounts in thousands of dollars.

multitude of programs with each having specific cost-sharing requirements.[1] Communities in an area of substantial unemployment and having
a coordinated program of economic development may obtain funds through

[1] The Office of Economic Opportunity periodically publishes the "Catalog of Federal Assistance
Programs" (Washington, USGPO), which gives details on the wide variety of federal programs
available to help finance water resource development.

TABLE 22-4   Cost Sharing in a Typical Bureau of
Reclamation Project*

Item	Amount
Total allocated division construction costs	$156,333,000
Nonreimbursable construction costs:	
Recreation	1,096,000
Fish and wildlife enhancement	8,925,000
Flood control	476,000
Subtotal	$ 10,497,000
Reimbursable construction costs:	
Irrigation	$127,330,000
Commercial power	17,640,000
Recreation	462,000
Fish and wildlife enhancement	25,000
Municipal and industrial water	379,000
Subtotal	$145,836,000
Total construction costs	$156,333,000
Reimbursable interest during construction:	
Commercial power	$ 1,306,000
Municipal and industrial water	34,000
Recreation	
Fish and wildlife enhancement	1,200
Total	$ 1,341,200
Total reimbursable investment costs	$147,177,200
Repayment of Reimbursable Costs:	
Irrigation allocation	$127,330,000
By irrigators	24,355,000
Percent payout	(19)
By power revenues	$102,975,000
Commercial power investment	18,946,000
Recreation	462,000
By nonfederal public body	462,000
Fish and wildlife enhancement	26,200
By nonfederal public body	26,200
Municipal and industrial water	413,000
By municipal and industrial water users	413,000
Total reimbursable costs	$147,177,200

* Mountain Home Division, Southwest Idaho Water Development
Project.

the Economic Development Administration. Funds to assist urban areas
may be obtained through the Department of Housing and Urban Development, and for small rural communities through the Farmer's Home
Administration. Grants for waste-treatment facilities may be obtained
through the Federal Water Pollution Control Act (Public Law 660).
The local government should evaluate the available options for loans
and grants and turn to its own sources for raising the balance of the
required funds.

22-6 BOND FINANCING   In the early history of our country, canals,
dams, and water supply facilities were largely financed by the states.
However, depression periods near the middle of the nineteenth century
coupled with the decline of navigation in favor of railroad transportation
to cause some of the state governments to default on bonds sold to
finance navigation improvement (Sec. 14-2). The public reacted by
inserting provisions in many state constitutions prohibiting borrowing by
state governments or restricting the issuance of additional bonds. Only
in recent years has the role of the states in financing water resource
development rejuvenated. For example, California spent $300 million
for water resource development in fiscal year 1969 compared with $100
million by federal agencies in that state. Texas has passed a $400 million
general obligation bond issue to finance water resource development.

The underlying motivation for bond financing is to "buy now, pay
later." This enables the public to obtain money for project construction
and repay the costs while the benefits are being enjoyed. The bond
issuer promises to repay the specified principal at a prescribed date and
to pay the stated interest rate in the meantime.

There are three main types of bonds—general obligation bonds,
revenue bonds, and assessment bonds. These are collectively termed
municipal bonds even though states, counties, school districts, public
authorities, and other entities besides municipalities may issue the bonds.

An attractive feature favoring the sale of municipal bonds is that
the interest on them is exempt from federal income taxes and usually
exempt from state income taxes in the state of the issuer. This tax-free
provision means that the interest rate to be paid on borrowed money is
substantially less compared with financing the same project with private
utility bonds.

The interest rate an agency must pay on a particular bond issue
is determined by competitive bidding. The prospective issue is a promise
to repay a fixed sum of money on a fixed schedule. Interested buyers bid
the amount they are willing to pay to secure this income. The agency
accepts the highest bid. The interest rate is calculated as the rate of

return obtained by the investors on the money loaned and deviates from the nominal rate based on the face value of the bonds because the high bid never exactly equals the face value of the issue. The bidding is usually done by large banks or related financial institutions who in turn sell the bonds at a slight profit to individual clients. Bidding practices have been institutionalized to the point where individual bids are all generally quite close.

If a local group finds a project to be economically feasible and needs money to finance the project, it should hire a financial consultant. The financial consultant will prepare a study of financial feasibility, recommend the type of bond to use and repayment schedules, make certain that all legal requirements are met, and prepare material which will help sell the bonds at the lowest possible interest rate. In addition, a competent bond attorney should be employed to ensure that all steps are authorized to guarantee that the bonds are negotiable instruments, and to furnish an unqualified approving legal opinion to those who will bid on the bonds. It is important that the legal opinion be given by a recognized firm of bond attorneys whose opinion is marketable in order to get the lowest possible interest rate. The reputation of the consulting engineer can also affect the interest rate on bonds. This is especially true with bonds that cannot be absorbed by the local bond market.

22-7   GENERAL OBLIGATION BONDS   General obligation bonds are secured by the issuer's pledge of its full faith, credit, and taxing power. If necessary, the issuer will raise taxes to cover bond service (payment of interest and principal). If the issuer is reluctant to do so, the bondholders can go to court and force payment. In many instances, revenues from user charges are actually used to cover bond payments, but the taxing pledge is made to reduce the risk to the bondholder and thus lower the interest rate. General obligation bonds offer the buyer the greatest security and thus sell at lowest interest rates. Despite this financial advantage for the seller, it is sometimes advantageous to use another type of bonds. Since general obligation bonding capability is characteristically limited to a legally fixed percent of assessed valuation, there may be a need to conserve bonding capacity. Since these bonds must be approved by the voters, usually by a two-thirds majority, rejection at the polls means some other type of bond will have to be used.

Any history of defaults on payments of interest or principal on its bonds is sure to make it more difficult for a general purpose government (state, county, or city) and almost impossible for a special district to later sell more bonds. However, few defaults have occurred in recent years. Other factors are used by bond buyers as indices of default probability in setting the relative interest rate an agency must pay on new bond issues. An important index is the tax-supported debt in relation to assessed valuation. The buyer looks not only at the issuer's own debt but also at the debt of other agencies taxing the same property. An entity may employ sound financial policies and be conservative in incurring debt but have its credit adversely affected by the debt of school districts, recreation districts, or other groups serving a common clientele. The record of tax rates and deliquencies is also important. The economic characteristics of the community or state are also important. Very rapid growth or one-industry economies tend to frighten some buyers. Eastern bond-rating agencies evaluate such factors for each entity selling municipal bonds and have enormous influence on municipal bond sales.

State general obligation bonds are backed up by taxes from sources other than real estate. Since in most states the state cannot be sued for payment of debt by any individual without consent (Sec. 7-13), the holder of a state bond must have confidence in the good faith of the state.

22-8 REVENUE BONDS   Revenue bonds are payable from revenues collected from project beneficiaries. They are used when it is inadvisable or impossible to sell general obligation bonds. In some cases, no vote is required, while in others, a simple majority vote is necessary for authorization. Revenue bonds are outside the statutory debt limit placed on state and most local governments. They can be used by agencies that have no power of taxation or when there are prohibitions against the extension of state credit.

The distinctive characteristic of revenue bonds is that, instead of being secured by the full faith and credit of the issuer, they are supported only by a pledge of gross or net revenues from a specific enterprise such as a hydropower facility or a municipal water supply. This feature limits the use of revenue bonds to revenue-producing projects. When benefits are widespread such as from flood or water quality control, revenue bonds cannot be used. Since revenue bond security is less than that of general obligation bonds for a comparable project, the interest rate paid on revenue bonds is higher.

Coverage is an essential measure of bond quality. It is defined as the ratio of pledged revenues to annual bond service requirements. The specified minimum ratio will depend on the certainty with which benefits can be forecast for a particular type of project, but most often net coverage of between 1.25 and 1.50 times annual bond service is required.

A bond reserve fund is usually created in connection with the sale of revenue bonds. Excess revenues are accumulated to provide for payment of interest and principal when due in the event that pledged revenues temporarily are insufficient. Common practice is to require that the reserve fund be equal to at least 1 year's total requirements of interest and principal. The reserve may be initially funded as the bonds are sold.

The issuer of revenue bonds must give legal assurance that the project will be maintained in good operating condition and run efficiently so that its annual earnings will not diminish during the life of the bond issue. He must promise not to build competing facilities which will reduce operating revenue.

22-9 ASSESSMENT BONDS   Assessment bonds are backed by liens against specific real property. After the project is constructed, its total cost is apportioned among benefiting property owners proportional to some index of benefit received (area, assessed value, foot frontage, etc.). Upon receiving his bill the individual property owner may either pay immediately or agree to an assessment bond's being sold which he will pay off over the next 10 to 20 years. Refusal to pay on schedule gives the bond owner right to compensation through sale of the property.

Assessment bonds are best suited for small drainage, water supply, or waste-water-treatment projects serving limited areas. The project may not be revenue producing by nature or may be too small to make the more formal revenue bonds worthwhile. The project may serve such a small portion of a total jurisdiction that the voters as a whole are unwilling to place their full faith and credit behind it. The local area may not wish to form a local government and consequently may use assessment bonds as a means of still obtaining limited services.

Planning the Debt Structure

Borrowing to finance water resources development must be coordinated with the overall financial capabilities of the supporting agencies. Each agency must schedule its debt service obligations to provide coverage from expected income sources. Groups of agencies may join to share the financial burden of projects too large for anyone to support alone or to realize the benefits of its multipurpose project development.

22-10 COORDINATING THE DEBT SERVICE   The debt service for each new bond issue should be coordinated with previous debt service commitments in order to have the maturity schedule coincide as closely as possible with expected revenues or tax receipts. This flexibility is gained through choices among serials and sinking-fund bonds, different types of serials, callable and noncallable bonds, and different maturity lengths.

Sinking-fund and serial bonds differ by method of redemption. *Sinking-fund bonds* (sometimes called *term bonds*) are so called because all principal becomes due in a lump sum at maturity. In order to accumulate sufficient funds to redeem sinking-fund bonds, annual payments must be made to a sinking fund which, when invested at compound interest, will produce the required amount of principal when it becomes due. However, individual bonds within an issue of *serial bonds* have different maturity dates so that the bonds may be retired in more uniform annual installments.

There are advantages and disadvantages in both sinking-fund and serial bonds, but the disadvantages usually outweigh the advantages for sinking-fund bonds. These disadvantages are:

1   The temptation to divert sinking-fund moneys to other purposes or to fail to make necessary assessments in order that taxes may be kept low.
2   Sinking-fund administration requires expert investment of accumulated funds and bookkeeping not available to smaller local governments. It is often difficult to find sound investments which will mature prior to the bonds for which the fund was created.
3   The single maturity does not appeal to many purchasers, hence sinking funds are often not popular with the dealers.

Nevertheless, sinking-fund bonds have some advantages for larger local governments. When the general bond market is unsatisfactory, the sinking fund may be used as a source of funds to accelerate construction before bonds can be sold, or it may be used as a source of short-term loans when interest rates on other funds are unfavorable. Moreover, failure to make a sinking-fund contribution does not injure the credit of the issuing agency, whereas failure to meet serial maturity causes the issuing agency to go into default.

Some of the advantages of the serial bonds are:

1   A periodic reduction of debt guarantees regular retirement.
2   Administrative costs are reduced through avoiding the task of investing and accounting for sinking-fund moneys.
3   The appeal to financial institutions bidding for the bonds is greater since the single bond issue will include a wide range of maturities and thus meet the investment needs of a wider spectrum of clients.
4   Quicker debt retirement allows borrowing for other needed capital improvements while staying within the statutory bond limit.

There are, however, some disadvantages in using serial bonds. Some public officials assume that serial bonds will provide uniform annual debt service without properly integrating new issues into the existing debt structure. If serial bonds are used indiscriminately, it may be that debt service requirements will vary widely from year to year and cause great fluctuations in the tax levy. Another disadvantage is the rigidity of the serial method of retirements, which may cause an issuing agency to go into default if a serial payment is not made.

Serial-bond maturities may be arranged to achieve nearly uniform annual debt service or uniform annual repayment of principal or to follow some more irregular pattern to match expected revenues or integrate with other debts. Bond issues may be made *callable* so that they can be paid off before maturity; however, a higher interest rate will often result. The maturity length of individual issues may be varied up to a maximum of about 50 years.

22-11   *JOINT-VENTURE FINANCING* The fierce competition for federal funds has caused states and local entities to seek new approaches to financing water resource development. For example, Oroville Dam is being financed primarily by the state of California, but in excess of $60 million was contributed by the Federal government in recognition of the flood control benefits provided. In other instances, county water agencies or irrigation districts have joined with private power utilities in joint ventures to construct multipurpose hydropower and irrigation projects. The private utilities have underwritten the power costs through contracts to purchase the power output. In some instances federal appropriations have been received to cover nonreimbursable costs for flood control and recreation. Some irrigation districts have even obtained water at essentially no cost through a favorable financing arrangement made possible by their ability to borrow at a lower interest rate than private utilities can.

The California experience also gives us an example of state-federal cooperation in the construction of San Luis Dam. This is an offstream storage facility which was originally planned by the Federal government as part of its Central Valley Project. However, the state of California needed a similar offstream storage site for its California water project. Therefore, a jointly financed structure was in the interest of both the state and the Federal government.

In the Pacific Northwest, there have been several instances of non-federal and private joint ventures in the construction of multipurpose projects. In one instance, the United States joined with Canada in working out a plan by which public and private utilities in the United States helped finance construction of dams in Canada to provide downstream benefits for power and flood control. This arrangement required the creation of a nonprofit corporation, the Columbia Storage Power Exchange, which acted as an intermediary to coordinate power generation and revenue bond financing. These bonds were secured with contracts for sale of the power between Bonneville Power Administration, private utilities, and public utilities. A similar arrangement was used to fund the Hanford Nuclear Electric Plant.

A proposal for joint financing of the proposed Appaloosa Project on the Middle Snake River was considered by the Department of Interior, private utilities, and public utilities. Under this proposal, public and private power agencies in the Northwest would contract with the Bonneville Power Administration to receive power from the Bonneville Power Administration system at the Administration's rates for a period of 40 to 50 years. These contracts would be the security for raising $300 million through the sale of tax-exempt revenue bonds by an appropriate financial intermediary. The remainder of the $429 million project would be financed through appropriations from Congress.

SELECTED REFERENCES

Investment Banker Association of America, "Fundamentals of Municipal Bonds" (Washington: French-Brag Printing Company, 1968).

Porter, Carley V.: "Handbook of Federal and State Programs of Financial Assistance for Water Development" (Sacramento: California State Printing Office, 1968).

Stanford Research Institute, "Economic Considerations in the Formulation and Repayment of California Water Plan Projects" (Los Angeles, Calif.: Haynes Foundation, 1958).

U.S. Office of Economic Opportunity: "Catalog of Federal Assistance Programs" (Washington: USGPO, 1966).

PROBLEMS

22-1 A bond issue of $1 million comprises one thousand $1,000 bonds. The issue is sold at an interest rate of 5 percent and has a maturity length of 20 years. Develop a repayment schedule showing the principal and interest to be paid each of the 20 years, assuming:

a Debt service from year to year is to be kept as equal as possible.

b Increasing revenues permit payment of debt service in a pattern which increases at a uniform gradient to become twice as high in the last year as in the first.

c The agency already has a debt service obligation of $50,000 annually for the first 10 years and wants to keep its total debt service payments as equal as possible in each of the 20 years.

CHAPTER
TWENTY-THREE

COST
ALLOCATION

23-1   THE NEED FOR COST ALLOCATION   Whenever the financial responsibility for a project is divided, its total cost must be distributed among the responsible groups. For example, it is necessary to divide the cost of a multipurpose water resources project among the respective project purposes. Costs for flood control must be distinguished from those for irrigation. Often, the cost of a single project purpose must also be divided among financially responsible groups. For example, towns which obtain water from a common reservoir must divide the cost among them.

The procedure for dividing total financial cost among the responsible parties is called *cost allocation*. Once a formula for allocating costs is established, it needs to be incorporated into a legally binding *cost-sharing* agreement. In projects which involve the United States government, cost allocation refers to the division of total project cost among project purposes; and cost sharing refers to the division of purpose cost between the government and local interests according to established federal law (Sec. 22-4).

Since cost allocation determines how much each party should pay, it is part of financial analysis. It is never part of economic analysis. Fixed costs which cannot be directly attributed to any project purpose are not marginal and thus have no influence on optimum design (they may affect economic justification), but since they must be paid, financial analysis is required to assign them to someone.

23-2   SEPARABLE AND NONSEPARABLE COSTS   Cost allocation requires assignment of total cost among project purposes and division of purpose cost among user groups. Each group assigned a cost is called a *cost center*. Each distinct physical portion of the project such as power-house, canal, or fish ladder is called a *project element*. *Direct costs* are the costs of project elements serving only one cost center. If an element serves more than one cost center, the difference in its cost with and without serving a center is the separable cost of that element with respect to that cost center and is determined from project designs with and without the cost center's being served. For example, the *separable cost* of flood control in a dual-purpose flood control and irrigation project is the cost of the dual-purpose project less the cost of a single-purpose irrigation project. Conversely, the separable cost of irrigation is the cost of the dual-purpose project less the cost of a single-purpose flood control project. Economies of scale and complementarity among project purposes will normally cause the sum of the separable costs to be less than the total cost. The difference between total project cost and the sum of the separable costs is the *non-separable cost*.

Nonseparable costs include joint costs and common costs. *Joint costs* occur when a project element contributes to the production of more than one output. For example, the water released from a reservoir for low-flow augmentation may enhance both water quality and navigation. *Common costs* are indirect or other fixed costs which must be paid but cannot be associated with any production operation. An example is the salary of a supervisor in charge of operating a multipurpose water project.

The costs of some project elements may be separable with respect to a group of cost centers but not with respect to any individual cost center. For example, a main canal leaving a multipurpose reservoir may benefit irrigation and municipal water supply but not recreation. Its total cost is separable to the two purposes combined, but part of its cost may not specifically be separable to either one. Costs nonseparable to any single or group of cost centers must be allocated among all centers; and costs separable to a group but not to a single cost center must be allocated among the centers composing that group.

23-3 ALLOCATION RULES The very proposal that costs be allocated implies that it is impossible to say who caused them to be incurred. All possible costs are assigned to the cost center responsible for their expenditure and those remaining are allocated. While it is rare for those who make cost allocations to admit that allocation problems have no correct answer, engineers in public planning nevertheless should be aware of this fact. Any procedure which directly affects the pocket book is always controversial, and the fundamentally indeterminate nature of cost allocation intensifies the controversy. Each party tends to favor the allocation shifting the largest share of the joint costs to others. The essence of cost allocation is successful resolution of the conflicting interests among these parties.

Even though there is no correct method of cost allocation, eight guiding rules are available:

1   The allocation to any cost center should never be less than the additional cost of including that center in the plan nor more than the total benefits provided the center. The cost allocated to a center which receives a benefit of 3 and adds 2 to project cost, should be between 2 and 3.

2   The sum of the allocations to all the cost centers should equal the total project cost.

3   The allocation method should avoid costly data and complex computations that have no other use. Complex allocation methods are no more correct than simple ones.

4   The allocation process should be straightforward and simple enough to be easily understood. Conflicting interests are more likely to accept compromises they can understand.

5   The amount allocated to each cost center determines the price charged within the center for project services. The cost allocated to an irrigation district will determine how much the district must charge individual irrigators. If the allocation to the irrigation district results in a charge to the individual irrigator approximately equaling the marginal cost of serving him, the irrigator is encouraged to use the economically optimum amount of water.

6   The charges resulting from the allocation should be fairly constant with time in order to provide stability to the market for project goods and services.

7   As cost allocation helps determine user charges, it affects income distribution. Where those comprising one cost center are relatively more well to do than those comprising another, the equity of the resulting income distribution is an important component in evaluating the allocation.

8   Joint facilities should be operated in accordance with the cost allocation. It is not equitable to allocate most of the cost to a center having a low service priority in facility operation.

23-4 ALLOCATION CONSEQUENCES   Cost allocation serves two major functions. One is the revenue function. If an investment is made, the money must be raised. Private industry has developed cost-accounting procedures for allocating nonseparable costs among the various goods produced. Every manufacturing concern must include its overhead and other nonseparable costs in setting product prices in order for it to make a profit. In fact, accounting procedures developed in private industry provide a starting point in the development of methods for cost allocation of public works.

The second function of cost allocation in public works is to encourage economic efficiency. The optimum use of a good or service requires that its price equal its marginal cost. This equality is achieved automatically by interaction of supply and demand in private industry with perfect competition, and there is at least a tendency in this direction in real world competitive conditions. However, because no economic force serves this purpose for public works, cost allocation must be deliberately made with economic efficiency in mind to encourage optimum use of project output.

In summary, cost allocation affects price, and price affects use. Use affects the production functions of industries throughout the economy. Therefore, one way to judge the merit of a cost allocation is by evaluating its effect on the decisions it influences. The decisions need to be studied with respect to their effects on economic efficiency, income distribution, institutional stability, and each of the other social goals.

23-5 COST CENTER CLASSIFICATION Every cost allocation requires selection of the centers among which the cost is to be distributed. In water resources planning, each project purpose (flood control, irrigation, etc.) has come by law to have distinct procedures for cost sharing among the several levels of government. Thus each purpose serves as a cost center or as a combination of cost centers defined by location. This distinction produces a two-step process of first allocating the total cost among project purposes and then allocating the cost for each purpose among the location centers. Sometimes a third step is added of allocating the location center cost among types of users. Total project cost may be divided between flood control and water supply. The water supply allocation may be divided between two water districts. Within a water district, agricultural and municipal water supply may be charged different rates.

23-6 DEFINITION OF COST The total economic cost of a project includes the cost of project planning; the cost of project installation; operation, maintenance, and replacement costs; interest costs; the cost of external project diseconomies; and the associated cost that private parties must spend to realize project benefits. Additional social costs arise from differences between the true social value of project input and output and the market values used in project evaluation. The costs selected for allocation may affect the magnitude of the obligation placed on a cost center more than does the method of dividing the nonseparable costs.

Because cost allocation is part of financial analysis, the total financial cost must be explicitly allocated (Sec. 24-4). Financial cost differs from economic cost for a number of reasons. Certain planning and overhead costs may be borne by agencies not requiring reimbursement by project sponsors. The project may not be legally required to reimburse those suffering from project-caused external diseconomies or may be legally unable to collect from beneficiaries of project-caused external economies. Financial cost may be required for the benefit of others than project sponsors, such as when a low-quality road through a reservoir site must be replaced with a high-quality one around it. The associated costs borne by private parties are not the financial responsibility of the sponsoring agencies. All economic costs must be considered while calculating marginal values for economic evaluation and optimization. Only financial costs must be considered when determining how much money each sponsoring agency must raise. However, it is important to recognize that the difference between the two represents an implicit cost allocation to the one bearing the economic cost.

Installation cost may be allocated separately from annual upkeep cost. Federal agencies may participate less fully in annual than in installation cost. The allocation of installation cost is normally incorporated in cost-sharing agreements prior to project construction according to predicted project output. The allocation of annual cost may be adjusted from time to time during the life of the project as required by changing conditions.

23-7 SEPARABLE COST IDENTIFICATION   Before nonseparable costs can be allocated, the separable costs must be identified and assigned to the appropriate cost center. While the correct procedure for identifying separable cost is a "with and without" analysis, the determination of incremental quantities may not be so simple. As an example, in the allocation of highway costs between passenger cars and trucks, the incremental cost of providing for trucks must be based on the cost for facilities designed only for cars. A vast disparity exists among the design standards suggested for highways built for cars only. Thus one criterion for evaluating a given cost allocation is the reasonableness of the design standards used in computing separable costs.

Separable costs are determined in two steps. First, the costs separable to individual cost centers are determined. Second, the costs separable to combinations of but not to individual cost centers are determined. Costs in this second group must be allocated among the cost centers within the group. Since the ordering of the allocation will affect the results in the case of multiple groups, as an arbitrary rule costs may be allocated in the order of increasing number of cost centers within the group and in the order of decreasing nonseparable cost to be allocated among groups of equal size.

23-8 ALLOCATION VEHICLE All methods of cost allocation require selection of a measureable unit that is reasonably indicative of cost-center responsibility for the nonseparable costs. When the non-separable costs are allocated in proportion to the measured quantity associated with the respective cost centers, this item is called the *cost allocation vehicle*. Different vehicles may be selected for allocating different kinds of nonseparable cost. In manufacturing, direct labor and direct material costs are the most common vehicles. In public works cost allocation, some other suitable vehicle must be found.

Six principal vehicles have been used for allocating joint costs of public works projects. The nonseparable costs may be divided:

1 Equally among the cost centers
2 Proportionally to the quantity of use the center makes of the facilities as expressed in units such as volume or flow rate
3 Entirely to the highest-priority cost center within the limit of the benefit the center receives
4 Proportionally to the benefit in excess of assigned separable cost derived by the given cost center
5 Proportionally to the excess cost required to provide the service by some alternate means
6 Proportionally to the smaller of the excess benefit or the excess cost of the alternative project

23-9 METHOD MATRIX A method of cost allocation is identified by the definition of cost used, the amount of cost directly assigned to the respective cost centers, and the allocation vehicle. If only financial costs figured at the planning discount rate are to be explicitly repaid, the remaining methods can be identified by their position within the two-dimensional matrix of Table 23-1. The alternative amounts to be allocated in the matrix are total financial cost, total financial cost less direct costs which are assigned to the cost center, or total financial cost less separable costs which are assigned to the cost center.

Common usage has named various points in the definition matrix. The Green Book recommends use of the separable-cost remaining-benefits method, Fc.[1] Where separable costs are difficult to evaluate, it recommends the alternative justifiable expenditure method Fb. The California Department of Water Resources recommends the use-of-facilities method, Bb, for conveyance facilities. Other names have been suggested for other matrix points, but more precise definitions can be obtained by using the definition matrix rather than names which may be unique to a given author.

23-10 EVALUATION OF ALTERNATIVE METHODS The alternative allocation methods may be evaluated from the eight guiding rules (Sec. 23-3).

The methods in column a use the vehicle to distribute total project cost. These methods are the simplest and avoid computational work. However, they provide no check that assigned cost exceeds separable cost. A cost center may be assigned less than its separable cost and charge the user less than marginal cost. Since direct costs are so easy to estimate, little reason exists for not using the slightly more complex methods of column b.

The methods in column b subtract direct costs from total costs before using the vehicle to complete the allocation. Their principal

[1] Inter-Agency Committee on Water Resources, Subcommittee on Evaluation Standards, "Proposed Practices for Economic Analysis of River Basin Projects" (Washington, Inter-Agency Committee on Water Resources, 1958), pp. 47–51.

TABLE 23-1 Cost Allocation Matrix

| | AMOUNT TO BE ALLOCATED | | |
Vehicle	a Total cost	b Direct cost excluded	c Separable cost excluded
A Equal	Aa	Ab	Ac
B Unit of use	Ba	Bb	Bc
C Priority of use	Ca	Cb	Cc
D Net benefit	Da	Db	Dc
E Alternative cost	Ea	Eb	Ec
F Smaller of benefit or alternative cost	Fa	Fb	Fc

advantage over the methods in column c is that they do not require the complex and often controversial computational process required to estimate separable costs. If separable costs have not been calculated for economic analysis, their calculation is not worthwhile for cost allocation. The methods in column b are favorable to cost centers having large separable and small direct costs. Assigned costs may still not exceed separable costs.

The methods in column c subtract the full separable cost from total cost. This is the ideal position on this dimension of the matrix because theoretically a vehicle is not needed to allocate separable costs. Because proper project economic analysis requires that separable costs be calculated in order to equate incremental costs to incremental benefits, separable cost should be available before financial analysis begins. Occasionally, there may be grounds for not deducting calculated separable costs during cost allocation on the basis of difficulty in presenting the complex computations to the public in accordance with rule 4.

The methods in row A divide residual cost equally among cost centers. Dividing equally is very simple, but it would shift a large share of the financial burden to minor cost centers. It should be used only when the service provided each cost center is about equal in scope.

The methods in row B use a vehicle measuring the amount of facility use and require finding an acceptable unit of use. Within a reservoir, storage capacity has the disadvantage that it does not measure head for power users or that the duration storage is required for other users. Channel use may be measured either in terms of volume of water carried or of peak flow rate. Units of use may be weighted less heavily during slack periods. A multiple-purpose river basin project includes many facilities whose use is expressed in different units. A metering system can seldom be justified for cost allocation alone, but it is often required to collect user charges. The methods in row B will not necessarily limit the cost allocated to a given center to the benefit it receives. Use of facilities is often used because of its appeal to fairness in making payment proportional to use and the resulting ease in gaining public acceptance. The vehicle is a visible physical quantity and not a vague and somewhat theoretical concept, as is benefit.

The methods in row C allocate the entire nonseparable cost to the cost center given highest priority. Priority of use implies a single major center and one or more incidental centers. It is used when a private power company pays the full cost of a reservoir also used for recreation. Priority of use makes little sense in multipurpose projects based on comprehensive planning where design and operations must represent a workable compromise among competing interests. Normally, there is no reasonable way to establish priorities, and it is hardly fair to make one cost center pay the whole cost.

The methods in row D allocate the residual cost proportionally to the net benefits derived by the respective cost centers. The net benefits equal the gross benefits a center receives less the cost assigned to the center previous to the allocation (including assigned separable or direct costs). Allocation by benefits has great appeal because of the inherent fairness in making each center pay in proportion to the benefit it derives. It conforms with each of the basic rules, providing benefits can be calculated in a clear and concise manner. However, benefit as an allocation vehicle poses several knotty problems. Should all benefits be used or just direct benefits? Secondary benefits accrue to the general public rather than the cost centers. Is it fair to make those directly served pay for benefits they do not receive? On the other hand, if secondary or indirect benefits provide the margin of project justification, allocation proportional to direct benefit may exceed the direct benefit. The imprecision in benefit calculation means benefits will vary widely according to the method of benefit evaluation used by the estimating agency. To some extent, benefit estimate may be manipulated to fit the desires of the planning agency, and this possibility causes suspicion of the whole allocation process. Many benefits are based on long-term projections: Should the allocation be made proportional to the discounted average annual benefit over project life, the predicted benefit during a given year, or the benefit actually realized as estimated after the year is over? Difficulties arise if the method allocates a large cost in a year few benefits are realized. For project elements having nonseparable costs assigned to varying combinations of cost centers, the allocation varies with the order in which group nonseparable costs are distributed. This difficulty makes the use-of-facilities method desirable in circumstances such as a canal delivering water to a number of cost centers.

The methods in row E allocate cost proportional to the excess cost of the cheapest alternative project which can provide the same service. The primary advantage of the method is that it avoids the calculation of benefits which cannot be adequately defined or which are largely intangible in nature. Where the alternative is seriously being considered a means of supplying project output, the alternative cost serves as an upper limit to the amount a cost center will pay to participate in a project. However, difficulty in defining proper alternatives makes the method subject to severe abuse (Sec. 8-5).

The methods in row F allocate by the smaller of excess benefits or excess alternative cost. This procedure thus combines the best features and eliminates some of the worst features of the methods in rows D and E.

For this reason, it is the most widely used allocation method for public works planning. However, it is by no means the final answer to all cost allocation problems.

One may be tempted to average the results of several methods to combine their advantages or minimize their disadvantages. However, this procedure complicates the cost-allocation calculations and multiplies the difficulty in explaining them. Since there is no unique solution, it does not really provide a better result. Example 23-1 illustrates the mathematical procedure followed in cost allocation.

EXAMPLE 23-1

The Orchard and the Grainlands Irrigation Districts joined forces to construct a water supply reservoir. By enlarging the reservoir, the two districts were also able to provide flood control for the downstream town of Centerville, having an average annual benefit of $400,000. The Orchard Irrigation District requires 50,000 acre-ft of water per year and receives a unit benefit of $15 per acre-ft. The Grainlands Irrigation District requires 200,000 acre-ft of water per year but, because of the lower-value crops grown, receives a unit benefit of only $2 per acre-ft. The project has a first cost of $15 million which must be divided among the two irrigation districts and the Federal government, which will pay for flood control. Of the project first cost, 80 percent is for the reservoir and 20 percent is for a canal from the reservoir to the point where the water going to the two districts separates. The unit benefit figures given above for irrigation water are net of district distribution and on-farm costs. The costs are allocated in the following steps:

1 The three cost centers are the Orchard Irrigation District, the Grainland Irrigation District, and the Federal government.
2 Alternative designs reveal the reservoir to cost $10 million if it provides only irrigation water, $10,500,000 if no water is delivered to the Orchard Irrigation District and $8,500,000 if no water is delivered to the Grainlands Irrigation District. Alternative designs reveal that a canal serving only the Orchard Irrigation District would cost $1,500,000 and that a canal serving only the Grainlands Irrigation District would cost $2,500,000. From these figures, total project cost may be divided as follows:

	Sep. to OID	Sep. to GID	Sep. to flood control	Nonseparable
Reservoir:	1,500,000	3,500,000	2,000,000	5,000,000
Canal:	500,000	1,500,000	0	1,000,000

3 Method *Fc* on the matrix is selected for the allocation. Thus, benefits received by, and alternative cost of supply to, each cost center must be estimated.

4 The present worth of the benefits is found by multiplying the average annual value times the uniform-annual-series present-worth factor. For $i = 3$ percent, $N = 50$ years, $(P/A, i\%, N) = 25.73$.

	OID	GID	Flood control
Annual benefit:	\$ 750,000	\$ 400,000	\$ 400,000
Capitalized benefit:	19,275,000	10,280,000	10,280,000

5 Costs of alternative projects serving each center are determined. Flood control can be provided by channel improvement costing \$7 million. The Orchard Irrigation District can be served by water from a different river at a cost of \$9,500,000. The Grainlands Irrigation District can be supplied for \$20 million.

6 Cost allocation is carried out as shown on the following table. Each allocation is proportional to the remaining benefits in the row above it.

	OID	GID	Flood control	Total
Benefits	\$19,275,000	\$10,280,000	\$10,280,000	\$39,835,000
Alternative cost	9,500,000	20,000,000	7,000,000	36,500,000
Smaller of two	9,500,000	10,280,000	7,000,000	26,780,000
Reservoir separable cost	1,500,000	3,500,000	2,000,000	7,000,000
Remaining benefits	8,000,000	6,780,000	5,000,000	19,780,000
Canal separable cost	500,000	1,500,000		2,000,000
Remaining benefits	7,500,000	5,280,000	5,000,000	17,780,000
Allocated canal nonseparable cost	590,000	410,000		1,000,000
Remaining benefits	6,910,000	4,870,000	5,000,000	16,780,000
Allocated reservoir nonseparable cost	2,060,000	1,450,000	1,490,000	5,000,000
Total cost to center	4,650,000	6,860,000	3,490,000	15,000,000
Annual cost to center	181,000	266,000	136,000	583,000
Irrigation water delivered, acre-ft	50,000	200,000		250,000
Unit charge for water*	\$3.62	\$1.33		\$1.79

* In some areas, it is possible to get the Federal government to sponsor the project and subsidize part of the cost of irrigation.

23-11 SUMMARY No matter which allocation method is used, problems develop in timing. If allocation is proportional to benefit, two cost centers may have different benefit time streams. A center which receives most of its benefit in the later years of project life may end up paying an amount well in excess of benefits derived in early years. If the use-of-facility method is used, use may vary over project life. Projects often have excess capacity during early years. As projects approach full capacity use, the allocation per unit of use may decline. The effects of timing problems on project repayment should be explicitly analyzed.

A discussion of cost allocation theory always shows that there is no unique correct method. A look at current practice shows further that there is no standardized method either, but method Fc is gaining predominance. Nevertheless, the basic goal of public works projects is improved social (or economic) efficiency. Cost allocation affects the price of project output. Price affects use. Efficient use occurs when price equals marginal cost. Charges affect income distribution. Thus, because cost allocation directly affects economic and social efficiency, the allocation method should be used which does the most to promote the desired social goals.

SELECTED REFERENCES

Bonbright, James C.: "Principles of Public Utility Rates" (New York: Columbia University Press, 1961).

Eckstein, Otto: "Water Resource Development" (Cambridge, Mass.: Harvard University Press, 1958), pp. 259–272.

Parker, Theodore B: Allocation of the Tennessee Valley Authority Projects, *Trans. Am. Soc. Civil Eng.*, vol. 108 (1943).

"Proposed Practices for Economic Analysis of River Basin Projects" (Washington: Inter-Agency Committee on Water Resources, May, 1958), chap. 6.

PROBLEMS

23-1   A multipurpose water resources project costs $12 million including capitalized operation, maintenance, and replacement. It provides 80,000 acre-ft/year of water to irrigation district *A* and 120,000 acre-ft/year to irrigation district *B*. It also provides flood control having $250,000 average annual benefit. The irrigation benefit is $2 per acre-foot of water in district *A*, but $4 in district *B* because higher-valued crops are grown there. Both districts get water at a common head gate. Of the project cost, 30 percent is for a canal from the reservoir to the head gate. The canal cost is separable to irrigation but only 30 percent of the canal cost is separable to district *A* and 40 percent to district *B*. Of the 70 percent of the project cost spent on the reservoir, 25 percent is separable to flood control and 50 percent is separable to irrigation. Of the separable reservoir irrigation cost, 30 percent is separable to district A, 40 percent is separable to district B, and 30 percent is separable to both districts jointly. The project is to be analyzed for a 50-year life at $i = 3$ percent. Irrigation water use and its benefit and flood control benefit are projected to remain constant throughout this time.

a What is the project benefit-cost ratio?

b What separable cost can be assigned to each of the three cost centers?

c Allocate all the joint cost by the remaining-benefits method Dc. What will the price of irrigation water be in each district?

d If the nonseparable canal cost were instead allocated by the use-of-facilities Bc method, what would the price be in each district?

CHAPTER
TWENTY-FOUR

WATER RESOURCES
PRICING

Part of the responsibility of those managing water resources projects is to determine charges for project output. The general public may not fully appreciate the abstract principles of economic evaluation, but individuals are intimately concerned with the bill they must pay for goods and services received. For many people, the substance of project evaluation is contained in the answer to the question, How much will it cost me? The project manager needs guidelines to select a fair price and persuasive reasons to justify his decision to those required to pay.

24-1 CHARGING FUNCTIONS Prices are charged for two reasons. One is financial. Enough money must be raised to pay the cost incurred in providing a good or service. The other is economic. The quantity of goods people buy depends on the price. If the price exceeds the marginal cost, full economic utilization will be prevented. If the price is less than the marginal cost, an apparent demand will suggest an expansion which cannot be justified on economic grounds. Only if price equals marginal cost will market forces encourage the economic level of production.

In a broader sense, pricing also has a social function related to the multidimensional nature of social welfare.[1] In addition to affecting economic efficiency, price levels influence income distribution, economic stability, the foreign trade balance, and other social goals. Prices can be reduced to effect income redistribution, encourage more rapid utilization of project output during the buildup period, encourage substitution

[1] Stephen A. Marglin, "Public Investment Criteria" (Cambridge, Mass.: The M.I.T. Press, 1966), pp. 88–92.

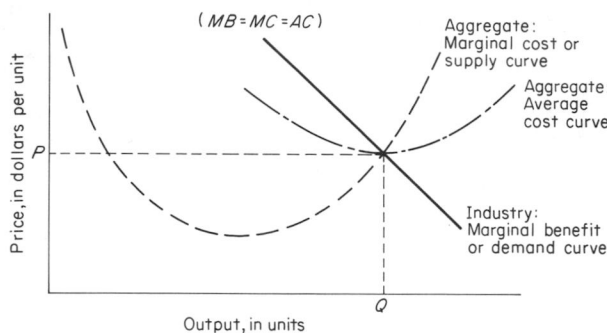

Output, in units

FIGURE 24-1 Selection of price under pure competitoin.

of project output for imports to improve the trade balance, and encourage reinvestment by project beneficiaries. A conflict exists between making prices flexible so as to be able to respond quickly to changing conditions and maintaining stable prices to provide increased certainty to planning by project users. These broader functions of pricing cannot be readily quantified but must be considered in deriving a pricing policy.

24-2 CHARGING DILEMMA The financial and the economic. functions of charges are satisfied simultaneously under pure competition. The market reaches an equilibrium point where the long-run marginal cost equals the marginal benefit (Sec. 4-15), as shown in Fig. 24-1 to fix the price P and the output Q. Because at this intersection marginal cost equals average cost, the product of P and Q equals the total cost and the financial requirement is satisfied. Because the marginal cost equals the price, the economic requirement is also satisfied.

Where the economies of large-scale production are large or total demand is small, the optimum scale of plant (Sec. 4-15) may be almost as large as total market demand (Fig. 24-2). The optimum Q is still determined by the point where marginal costs equal marginal benefits. The price satisfying the economic requirement is P_1. However, only the average cost P_2 of producing Q need be charged to satisfy the financial requirement. Marginal-cost pricing will produce a profit equal to $(P_1 - P_2)Q$, which if large enough, may justify an additional production unit. If demand is smaller than the optimum production-unit size (Sec. 5-11), the marginal-cost curve intersects the demand curve at an output level where average cost exceeds marginal cost (Fig. 24-3). The price P_1 will satisfy the economic requirement. However, the price

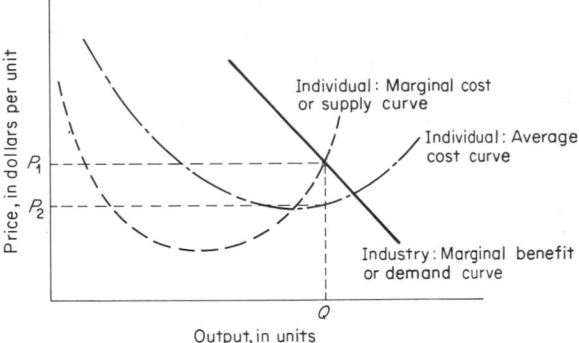

FIGURE 24-2   Selection of price for large, optimum production units (increasing average costs).

would have to be P_2, or the average cost, for the financial requirement
to be satisfied.

Under conditions of increasing average cost (at the market-deter-
mined level of production), a charge fixed by the economic requirement
more than satisfies the financial requirement. Under conditions of
decreasing average cost, there is a dilemma. Marginal-cost pricing P_1
does not raise enough revenue, and average-cost pricing P_2 restricts
economic use. Some compromise between the conflicting requirements
is required.[1]

[1]   Jack Hirshleifer, James C. DeHaven, and Jerome W. Milliman, "Water Supply: Economics, Technology, and Policy" (Chicago: The University of Chicago Press, 1960), pp. 88–93.

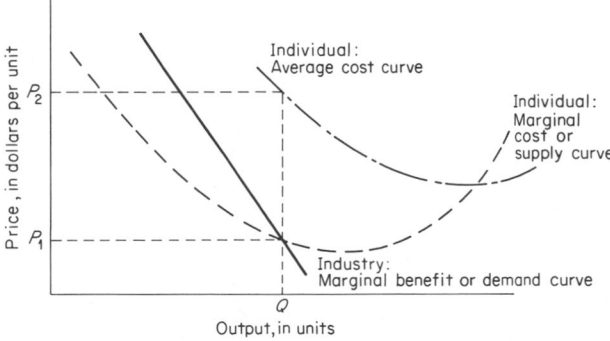

FIGURE 24-3   Selection of price under natural monopoly
(decreasing average costs).

*24-3 RECONCILING ECONOMIC AND FINANCIAL REQUIRE-
MENTS* Three alternative approaches are available for reconciling
economic and financial requirements. One possibility is to employ price
discrimination to capture some of the consumer's surplus (Sec. 4-16).
Under conditions of decreasing average cost (Fig. 24-3), the total benefit
may exceed the total cost P_2Q even though only P_1Q can be recovered by
marginal-cost pricing. The goal in price discrimination is that those
benefiting by an amount exceeding P_1 be charged an extra fee in order to
satisfy the revenue requirement. The result is a marginal-cost fee plus a
surplus fee which varies with the value the consumer derives from use of
the output. In practice, it is difficult to discriminate among individual
users, and the result is price discrimination by user group. A typical price
discrimination is to charge industrial users more for water than agricultural
users. Although such price discrimination produces economic inefficiency
by restricting economic marginal industrial development while permitting
full economic agricultural development, it is a reasonable compromise
between the economic and the financial requirements. Application of
price discrimination requires division of the users into the groups by
benefit received, selection of a fair price for each user group, and administration and enforcement of the selected price.

The second approach is to find an outside benefactor willing to
subsidize the project by the amount $(P_1 - P_2)Q$. In water resources
planning, the benefactor is usually the Federal government. While this
approach satisfies the revenue requirement, it distorts economic resource
allocation by diverting, to the project, tax funds which have greater
value in other uses. It redistributes income from those paying the taxes
to those receiving the subsidy. Whether a particular redistribution is
warranted or not is basically a value judgment, but the strongest case
can be made where the income of those receiving the subsidy is much
lower than the income of those paying the taxes.

The third approach used to raise the revenue $(P_1 - P_2)Q$ while
maintaining marginal-cost pricing is to levy a nonmarginal charge or
tax on those using the output. Each user would pay a flat fee independent
of the quantity used plus a charge per unit of use. The unit charge would
equal the marginal cost, while the flat fee would be set to raise the balance
of the required revenue. The nonmarginal levy may be assessed in various
ways. For the example of irrigation water, an equal sum could be charged
to each user, a charge could be made proportional to farm size, or a
charge could be made proportional to farm value. The last of the three
is the fairest because it considers both the size of the farm and the
quality of the land.

Use of a nonmarginal charge requires both user benefit and ability to pay to exceed the levy. If most benefits accrue to output users, price discrimination works best where users can be grouped by unit benefit received and a nonmarginal charge works best where users receive approximately equal unit benefits. Where substantial indirect benefits are dispersed over the community, a community-wide tax has advantages A mixture of the approaches may be used for a large project producing diverse kinds of output.

24-4 TOTAL CHARGES Simultaneous satisfaction of the financial and the economic requirements of pricing is further complicated by differences between the economic cost used in project evaluation and the financial cost that the constructing agency will actually have to pay. According to the financial requirement, only the cost legally obligated during project construction and operation need be recovered. However, according to the requirement of economic efficiency, all costs should be paid by the beneficiaries even if they result from economic or physical linkages where no legal obligation is involved. The merits of doing otherwise must be evaluated according to the merits of income redistribution from those paying the bill to the beneficiaries.

The maximum sum that charges could possibly recover would be the aggregate value in use, or the total gross benefit. Charges set at this level would avoid all income redistribution to the users and may thus be suggested to avoid the unjust enrichment of an especially wealthy group of beneficiaries. However, few seriously advocate such high charges because they would eliminate all incentive for beneficiaries to participate in project realization, the amount of money raised would substantially exceed that spent, and no practical way exists either for determining total benefit or collecting the full value of the consumer's surplus.

The total economic or opportunity cost equals the benefit foregone by diverting capital from the way it would otherwise be invested to the project at hand. Economic cost includes the value of project-created external diseconomies net of external economies. Under ideal conditions, marginal trade-offs would equate the marginal cost of investments foregone with the marginal value of investments made, and financial compensation would accompany all external effects. Economic cost would equal financial cost. Under real conditions, economic cost will not equal financial cost. If economic cost exceeds financial cost, the injustice of not compensating those harmed by project construction is not made right by requiring the beneficiaries to pay while the project management keeps the funds. If financial cost exceeds economic cost, the beneficiaries are still legally obligated to collect sufficient charges to pay financial cost. In both cases, the total financial cost must be recovered.

The time pattern of project expenditure normally begins with a large outlay followed by a much lower continuing cost. The time pattern of revenues collected varies with output used at a gradually changing rate. Because the time patterns differ, an interest rate must be used in fixing charges. For economic efficiency through marginal-cost pricing, a normative discount rate should be used. For revenue requirement, the borrowing interest rate must be paid. The ideal reconciliation of the economic and financial requirements would be for government action to bring interest rates in line with normative discount rates (Sec. 6-7); but as long as this is not done, it is the interest rate which must be paid.

Prevailing federal practice has used an interest rate less than the average interest rate paid on long-term government bonds sold within the year to figure the base cost for setting charges. This policy has resulted in a government subsidy of a part of the interest cost because this interest rate is too low to cover the cost of current borrowing. Those served by federal water resources projects (users of hydroelectric power or agricultural or municipal water) pay less than the full marginal cost. Uneconomic use of output is encouraged.

Theoretical support for the interest subsidy is based on a large indirect benefit distributed throughout the community or the nation, on the macroeconomic advantage to the national economy of developing remote regions, on the need to redistribute income to those financially unable to pay, or on the need for forced savings to increase capital for future generations. However worthy these objectives may be, it is better to calculate the total project cost and explicitly allocate a portion to the general treasury to achieve specific objectives than to implicitly allocate the same cost by omitting it from the analysis. To do otherwise is to conceal the full magnitude of the subsidy.

24-5 CHARGING VEHICLE   The charges for use of a good or service must be proportional to some measurable item called a charging vehicle. The amount spent on apples is determined by the number of apples purchased. The amount spent on water can be determined by the volume of water used.

Ability to pay is one possible vehicle. The charge an individual pays for a service received would depend on his income. Medical and legal fees are common examples. The policy objective of income redistribution may dictate reducing charges to low-income groups and offsetting the loss by increasing charges to high-income groups.

Benefit received is another possible vehicle. An industry for whom the marginal value in use of water is $1,000 per acre-foot would pay more than a farmer for whom the marginal value is only $10. The practical difficulty with this charging vehicle is the problem of basing precise charges on often nebulous benefits. The theoretical difficulty centers on the fairness of charging two parties receiving an identical service different amounts. The benefit vehicle is used to greatest advantage in supplementing marginal-cost pricing to meet a financial obligation.

Quantity of output used is a third possible vehicle. All those using identical quantities of water would pay an identical cost. Each user would pay the average cost of serving everyone. This has been called *postage stamp pricing* because a letter is taken across town for the same charge as a letter is taken across the country. The economic difficulty with average cost pricing is that it costs more to serve remote areas than it does to serve points near the supply. If all are charged equally, remote users will be encouraged to use more water than economically warranted, and nearby users will be discouraged from using the economic optimum amount. Delivery of the extra water to the remote users will require distribution facilities more costly than can be justified by marginal economic analysis.

The ideal charging system from the viewpoint of economic efficiency is based on quantity of output and figured according to the marginal cost of service. Deliveries to more remote locations would command a greater charge than shorter distance deliveries. However, it is not practical to charge every individual a slightly different rate even though service to each user has a slightly different marginal cost. The reasonable compromise is to charge all those within a preselected marginal-cost range a uniform rate. The more complicated the rate structure, the closer the charges can be kept to marginal cost, but the more costly the billing and collection process becomes.

24-6 UTILITY RATES The variety of charging schemes used by electric utilities gives a prime example of the practical alternatives for establishing charges. The ideal rate schedule for electrical service raises sufficient revenue to pay costs, apportions charges according to responsibility for cost, encourages the economic optimum use of the service by consumers, is simple enough to be understood and accepted by the public, produces a fairly uniform rate of cash inflow with time, and does not require constant revision. The cost of providing electric service may be divided among capacity cost, commodity cost, and customer cost. The *capacity cost* provides generation, transmission, and distribution facilities large enough to meet the peak power requirement of the customer whenever he elects to use it. The *commodity cost* is the cost of generating the energy the customer actually uses. The *customer cost* is the cost of meter reading, billing, and related items not dependent on the quantity of electricity used. While some cost items do not fit neatly into any of the three, the division is useful in rate structure analysis.

The rate structures used may be classified into nine categories.

1   *Uniform rate per customer.* Each customer or each customer within a customer class (apartment dwellers or single-family residences, for example) is charged the same fixed fee. Severe overuse often results because the customer pays the same fee no matter how much he uses.

2   *Uniform rate per energy unit.* The charge is equal for each kilowatthour of energy. A high cost to the utility for providing peaking capacity often results because there is no penalty for using power during peak demand periods.

3   *Uniform rate per unit of readiness to serve.* The charge is equal for each kilowatt of connected load. The load in kilowatts is measured by summing the power rating of all connected electricity-using apparatus. The rate penalizes the customer even if he does not use all his additional electrical machinery during periods of peak demand.

4   *Uniform rate per unit of maximum demand.* The charge is equal for each kilowatt of metered maximum use. This rate structure provides no incentive for the customer to economize during off-peak periods and may thus result in excessive commodity use.

5   *Step rate.* The unit charge per each kilowatt of energy depends on the number of kilowatts used. It is analogous to selling eggs for a nickel each and 50 cents a dozen. Step rates may be used to approximate an average commodity-cost curve, but they do not reflect capacity or consumer costs.

6   *Block rate.* The incremental charge per each kilowatt of energy depends on the number of kilowatts used. It is analogous to selling the first dozen eggs for 50 cents and all additional dozens for 30 cents. Block rates are widely used by many kinds of utilities for residential service. They may be used to approximate a marginal-cost curve. The Water Rates Committee of the American Water Works Association recommends a fixed charge per customer plus a schedule of declining block prices for actual deliveries.[1] Capacity and consumer costs are not reflected in the rate.

---

[1]   Hirshleifer, DeHaven, and Milliman, *op. cit.*, p. 99.

7 Hopkinson type of demand rate. An equal charge for each kilowatthour of energy is added to an equal charge for each kilowatt of metered peak demand.

8 Wright type of demand rate. Energy is paid for in blocks sized according to metered peak demand. A typical rate would be 8 cents per kilowatthour up to a monthly energy use in kilowatthours equal to 100 times the peak monthly demand in kilowatts and 5 cents per each additional kilowatthour.

9 Off-peak rate. A Hopkinson type of demand rate is used, but the energy charge is reduced if the metered peak occurs at specified off-peak times. On a daily basis, a 3:00 A.M. demand peak would be charged much less than a 6:00 P.M. demand peak. On a seasonal basis, a premium might be charged for water used in the summer.

Many electric utilities combine the above rate structures. Different schedules may be used for different customer groups. The rate schedule selected for a specific situation should be the one which comes closest to satisfying simultaneously the financial and the economic requirements of user charges. The economic requirement is best satisfied when the amount each customer pays equals the sum of the marginal cost of providing the commodity, the marginal cost of the service capacity he requires, and the marginal customer cost.

SELECTED REFERENCES
Hirshleifer, Jack, James C. DeHaven, and Jerome W. Milliman: "Water Supply: Economics, Technology, and Policy" (Chicago: The University of Chicago Press, 1960).

Marglin, Stephen A.: "Public Investment Criteria" (Cambridge, Mass.: The M.I.T. Press, 1966), pp. 88–92.

PROBLEMS
24-1 The short-run average-cost and marginal-cost curves for the optimum scale of plant in a given industry are those of Prob. 4-1.

   a Find the marginal-cost price, the total revenue, and the total cost if industry-demand curve is $69P + Q = 524$.

   b Find the marginal-cost price, the total revenue, and the total cost if there is only one production unit and the industry-demand curve is $80P + Q = 1,000$.

   c How many production units could economically exist under the conditions of part *b*?

   d Find the marginal-cost price, the total revenue, and the total cost if the industry-demand curve is $8P + Q = 100$.

    e What is the total benefit under conditions of part *d*?

    f What fraction of the consumers' surplus in part *d* would have to be captured by price discrimination to make the project financially feasible?

24-2 If the industry-demand curve in Prob. 24-1 is $0.08KP + Q = K$:

    a For what value of K would marginal-cost pricing just satisfy the financial requirement based on one production unit?

    b For what value of K would marginal-cost pricing just satisfy the financial requirement based on two production units?

    c For what value of K would it be economical to shift from one to two equally sized production units? A project becomes economical when total benefits surpass total cost.

    d What is the implication of the findings in part C on marginal-cost pricing?

APPENDIX A

COMPOUND-INTEREST FACTORS

TABLE A-1 2.000 Percent Compound-interest Factors

N	F/P,2.000%,N	P/F,2.000%,N	A/F,2.000%,N	A/P,2.000%,N	F/A,2.000%,N	P/A,2.000%,N	N
1	1.0200	0.980392	1.000000	1.020000	1.0000	0.9804	1
2	1.0404	0.961169	0.495050	0.515050	2.0200	1.9416	2
4	1.0824	0.923845	0.242624	0.262624	4.1216	3.8077	4
6	1.1262	0.887971	0.158526	0.178526	6.3081	5.6014	6
8	1.1717	0.853490	0.116510	0.136510	8.5830	7.3255	8
10	1.2190	0.820348	0.091327	0.111327	10.9497	8.9826	10
12	1.2682	0.788493	0.074560	0.094560	13.4121	10.5753	12
15	1.3459	0.743015	0.057825	0.077825	17.2934	12.8493	15
20	1.4859	0.672971	0.041157	0.061157	24.2974	16.3514	20
25	1.6406	0.609531	0.031220	0.051220	32.0303	19.5235	25
30	1.8114	0.552071	0.024650	0.044650	40.5681	22.3965	30
35	1.9999	0.500028	0.020002	0.040002	49.9945	24.9986	35
40	2.2080	0.452890	0.016556	0.036556	60.4020	27.3555	40
45	2.4379	0.410197	0.013910	0.033910	71.8927	29.4902	45
50	2.6916	0.371528	0.011823	0.031823	84.5794	31.4236	50
60	3.2810	0.304782	0.008768	0.028768	114.0515	34.7609	60
70	3.9996	0.250028	0.006668	0.026668	149.9779	37.4986	70
80	4.8754	0.205110	0.005161	0.025161	193.7720	39.7445	80
90	5.9431	0.168261	0.004046	0.024046	247.1567	41.5869	90
100	7.2446	0.138033	0.003203	0.023203	312.2323	43.0984	100
INF	INF	0.0	0.0	0.020000	INF	50.0000	INF

TABLE A-2 3.000 Percent Compound-interest Factors

N	F/P,3.000%,N	P/F,3.000%,N	A/F,3.000%,N	A/P,3.000%,N	F/A,3.000%,N	P/A,3.000%,N
1	1.0300	0.970874	1.000000	1.030000	1.0000	0.9709
2	1.0609	0.942596	0.492611	0.522611	2.0300	1.9135
4	1.1255	0.888487	0.239027	0.269027	4.1836	3.7171
6	1.1941	0.837484	0.154598	0.184597	6.4684	5.4172
8	1.2668	0.789409	0.112456	0.142456	8.8923	7.0197
10	1.3439	0.744094	0.087231	0.117231	11.4639	8.5302
12	1.4258	0.701380	0.070462	0.100462	14.1920	9.9540
15	1.5580	0.641862	0.053767	0.083767	18.5989	11.9379
20	1.8061	0.553676	0.037216	0.067216	26.8704	14.8775
25	2.0938	0.477606	0.027428	0.057428	36.4593	17.4131
30	2.4273	0.411987	0.021019	0.051019	47.5754	19.6004
35	2.8139	0.355383	0.016539	0.046539	60.4621	21.4872
40	3.2620	0.306557	0.013262	0.043262	75.4013	23.1148
45	3.7816	0.264439	0.010785	0.040785	92.7199	24.5187
50	4.3839	0.228107	0.008865	0.038865	112.7969	25.7298
60	5.8916	0.169733	0.006133	0.036133	163.0534	27.6755
70	7.9178	0.126297	0.004337	0.034337	230.5940	29.1234
80	10.6409	0.093977	0.003112	0.033112	321.3630	30.2008
90	14.3005	0.069928	0.002256	0.032256	443.3488	31.0024
100	19.2186	0.052033	0.001647	0.031647	607.2876	31.5989
INF	INF	0.0	0.0	0.030000	INF	33.3333

TABLE A-3 3.500 Percent Compound-interest Factors

N	F/P,3.500%,N	P/F,3.500%,N	A/F,3.500%,N	A/P,3.500%,N	F/A,3.500%,N	P/A,3.500%,N
1	1.0350	0.966184	1.000000	1.035000	1.0000	0.9662
2	1.0712	0.933511	0.491400	0.526400	2.0350	1.8997
4	1.1475	0.871442	0.237251	0.272251	4.2149	3.6731
6	1.2293	0.813501	0.152668	0.187668	6.5502	5.3286
8	1.3168	0.759412	0.110477	0.145477	9.0517	6.8740
10	1.4106	0.708919	0.085241	0.120241	11.7314	8.3166
12	1.5111	0.661783	0.068484	0.103484	14.6020	9.6633
15	1.6753	0.596891	0.051825	0.086825	19.2957	11.5174
20	1.9898	0.502566	0.035361	0.070361	28.2797	14.2124
25	2.3632	0.423147	0.025674	0.060674	38.9499	16.4815
30	2.8068	0.356278	0.019371	0.054371	51.6227	18.3920
35	3.3336	0.299977	0.014998	0.049998	66.6740	20.0007
40	3.9593	0.252573	0.011827	0.046827	84.5503	21.3551
45	4.7024	0.212659	0.009453	0.044453	105.7817	22.4955
50	5.5849	0.179053	0.007634	0.042634	130.9979	23.4556
60	7.8781	0.126934	0.005089	0.040089	196.5169	24.9447
70	11.1128	0.089986	0.003461	0.038461	288.9378	26.0004
80	15.6757	0.063793	0.002385	0.037385	419.3067	26.7488
90	22.1122	0.045224	0.001658	0.036658	603.2049	27.2793
100	31.1914	0.032060	0.001159	0.036159	862.6114	27.6554
INF	INF	0.0	0.0	0.035000	INF	28.5714

TABLE A-4 4.000 Percent Compound-interest Factors

N	F/P,4.000%,N	P/F,4.000%,N	A/F,4.000%,N	A/P,4.000%,N	F/A,4.000%,N	P/A,4.000%,N
1	1.0400	0.961538	1.000000	1.040000	1.0000	0.9615
2	1.0816	0.924556	0.490196	0.530196	2.0400	1.8861
4	1.1699	0.854804	0.235490	0.275490	4.2465	3.6299
6	1.2653	0.790315	0.150762	0.190762	6.6330	5.2421
8	1.3686	0.730690	0.108528	0.148528	9.2142	6.7327
10	1.4802	0.675564	0.083291	0.123291	12.0061	8.1109
12	1.6010	0.624597	0.066552	0.106552	15.0258	9.3851
15	1.8009	0.555265	0.049941	0.089941	20.0236	11.1184
20	2.1911	0.456387	0.033582	0.073582	29.7781	13.5903
25	2.6658	0.375117	0.024012	0.064012	41.6459	15.6221
30	3.2434	0.308319	0.017830	0.057830	56.0849	17.2920
35	3.9461	0.253415	0.013577	0.053577	73.6522	18.6645
40	4.8010	0.208289	0.010523	0.050523	95.0255	19.7923
45	5.8412	0.171198	0.008262	0.048262	121.0294	20.7200
50	7.1067	0.140713	0.006550	0.046550	152.6671	21.4822
60	10.5196	0.095060	0.004202	0.044202	237.9907	22.6235
70	15.5716	0.064219	0.002745	0.042745	364.2904	23.3945
80	23.0498	0.043384	0.001814	0.041814	551.2449	23.9154
90	34.1193	0.029309	0.001208	0.041208	827.9833	24.2673
100	50.5049	0.019800	0.000808	0.040808	1237.6236	24.5050
INF	INF	0.0	0.0	0.040000	INF	25.0000

TABLE A-5   4.250 Percent Compound-interest Factors

N	F/P,4.250%,N	P/F,4.250%,N	A/F,4.250%,N	A/P,4.250%,N	F/A,4.250%,N	P/A,4.250%,N	N
1	1.0425	0.959233	1.000000	1.042500	1.0000	0.9592	1
2	1.0868	0.920127	0.489596	0.532096	2.0425	1.8794	2
4	1.1811	0.846634	0.234615	0.277115	4.2623	3.6086	4
6	1.2837	0.779011	0.149817	0.192317	6.6748	5.1997	6
8	1.3951	0.716789	0.107565	0.150065	9.2967	6.6638	8
10	1.5162	0.659537	0.082330	0.124830	12.1462	8.0109	10
12	1.6478	0.606858	0.065603	0.108103	15.2431	9.2504	12
15	1.8670	0.535623	0.049020	0.091520	20.3997	10.9265	15
20	2.2989	0.434989	0.032720	0.075220	30.5625	13.2944	20
25	2.8308	0.353263	0.023215	0.065715	43.0765	15.2173	25
30	3.4856	0.286892	0.017098	0.059598	58.4855	16.7790	30
35	4.2920	0.232990	0.012910	0.055410	77.4594	18.0473	35
40	5.2850	0.189216	0.009918	0.052418	100.8228	19.0773	40
45	6.5076	0.153666	0.007717	0.050217	129.5913	19.9137	45
50	8.0131	0.124795	0.006060	0.048560	165.0152	20.5931	50
60	12.1496	0.082307	0.003812	0.046312	262.3447	21.5928	60
70	18.4215	0.054284	0.002440	0.044940	409.9170	22.2521	70
80	27.9309	0.035803	0.001578	0.044078	633.6684	22.6870	80
90	42.3492	0.023613	0.001028	0.043528	972.9233	22.9738	90
100	64.2105	0.015574	0.000672	0.043172	1487.3066	23.1630	100
INF	INF	0.0	0.0	0.042500	INF	23.5294	INF

TABLE A-6 4.500 Percent Compound-interest Factors

N	F/P,4.500%,N	P/F,4.500%,N	A/F,4.500%,N	A/P,4.500%,N	F/A,4.500%,N	P/A,4.500%,N	N
1	1.0450	0.956938	1.000000	1.045000	1.0000	0.9569	1
2	1.0920	0.915730	0.488998	0.533998	2.0450	1.8727	2
4	1.1925	0.838561	0.233744	0.278744	4.2782	3.5875	4
6	1.3023	0.767896	0.148878	0.193878	6.7169	5.1579	6
8	1.4221	0.703185	0.106610	0.151610	9.3800	6.5959	8
10	1.5530	0.643928	0.081379	0.126379	12.2882	7.9127	10
12	1.6959	0.589664	0.064666	0.109666	15.4640	9.1186	12
15	1.9353	0.516720	0.048114	0.093114	20.7841	10.7395	15
20	2.4117	0.414643	0.031876	0.076876	31.3714	13.0079	20
25	3.0054	0.332731	0.022439	0.067439	44.5652	14.8282	25
30	3.7453	0.267000	0.016392	0.061392	61.0071	16.2889	30
35	4.6673	0.214254	0.012270	0.057270	81.4966	17.4610	35
40	5.8164	0.171929	0.009343	0.054343	107.0303	18.4016	40
45	7.2482	0.137964	0.007202	0.052202	138.8500	19.1563	45
50	9.0326	0.110710	0.005602	0.050602	178.5030	19.7620	50
60	14.0274	0.071289	0.003454	0.048454	289.4979	20.6380	60
70	21.7841	0.045905	0.002165	0.047165	461.8696	21.2021	70
80	33.8301	0.029559	0.001371	0.046371	729.5576	21.5653	80
90	52.5371	0.019034	0.000873	0.045873	1145.2689	21.7992	90
100	81.5885	0.012257	0.000558	0.045558	1790.8557	21.9499	100
INF	INF	0.0	0.0	0.045000	INF	22.2222	INF

TABLE A-7 4.625 Percent Compound-interest Factors

N	F/P,4.625%,N	P/F,4.625%,N	A/F,4.625%,N	A/P,4.625%,N	F/A,4.625%,N	P/A,4.625%,N	N
1	1.0462	0.955795	1.000000	1.046250	1.0000	0.9558	1
2	1.0946	0.913543	0.488699	0.534949	2.0462	1.8693	2
4	1.1982	0.834561	0.233309	0.279559	4.2862	3.5771	4
6	1.3116	0.762408	0.148411	0.194661	6.7380	5.1371	6
8	1.4358	0.696492	0.106135	0.152385	9.4220	6.5623	8
10	1.5716	0.636276	0.080907	0.127157	12.3599	7.8643	10
12	1.7204	0.581265	0.064202	0.110452	15.5759	9.0537	12
15	1.9703	0.507537	0.047666	0.093916	20.9794	10.6478	15
20	2.4701	0.404847	0.031461	0.077711	31.7853	12.8682	20
25	3.0966	0.322934	0.022059	0.068309	45.3321	14.6393	25
30	3.8821	0.257594	0.016047	0.062297	62.3152	16.0520	30
35	4.8668	0.205475	0.011961	0.058211	83.6060	17.1789	35
40	6.1012	0.163901	0.009066	0.055316	110.2973	18.0778	40
45	7.6488	0.130739	0.006956	0.053206	143.7589	18.7948	45
50	9.5890	0.104286	0.005385	0.051635	185.7082	19.3668	50
60	15.0705	0.066355	0.003287	0.049537	304.2274	20.1869	60
70	23.6855	0.042220	0.002039	0.048289	490.4977	20.7088	70
80	37.2252	0.026863	0.001277	0.047527	783.2486	21.0408	80
90	58.5049	0.017093	0.000804	0.047054	1243.3494	21.2521	90
100	91.9490	0.010876	0.000509	0.046759	1966.4648	21.3865	100
INF	INF	0.0	0.0	0.046250	INF	21.6216	INF

TABLE A-8 4.750 Percent Compound-interest Factors

N	F/P,4.750%,N	P/F,4.750%,N	A/F,4.750%,N	A/P,4.750%,N	F/A,4.750%,N	P/A,4.750%,N	N
1	1.0475	0.954654	1.000000	1.047500	1.0000	0.9547	1
2	1.0973	0.911364	0.488400	0.535900	2.0475	1.8660	2
4	1.2040	0.830585	0.232876	0.280376	4.2941	3.5666	4
6	1.3211	0.756965	0.147945	0.195445	6.7593	5.1165	6
8	1.4495	0.689871	0.105662	0.153162	9.4641	6.5290	8
10	1.5905	0.628723	0.080437	0.127937	12.4321	7.8163	10
12	1.7452	0.572996	0.063740	0.111240	15.6887	8.9896	12
15	2.0059	0.498528	0.047221	0.094721	21.1770	10.5573	15
20	2.5298	0.395293	0.031050	0.078550	32.2056	12.7307	20
25	3.1904	0.313436	0.021685	0.069185	46.1146	14.4540	25
30	4.0237	0.248530	0.015709	0.063209	63.6559	15.8204	30
35	5.0745	0.197065	0.011658	0.059158	85.7784	16.9039	35
40	6.3997	0.156257	0.008797	0.056297	113.6784	17.7630	40
45	8.0711	0.123899	0.006718	0.054218	148.8648	18.4442	45
50	10.1789	0.098242	0.005175	0.052675	193.2404	18.9844	50
60	16.1898	0.061767	0.003127	0.050627	319.7856	19.7523	60
70	25.7503	0.038835	0.001919	0.049419	521.0588	20.2351	70
80	40.9565	0.024416	0.001189	0.048689	841.1888	20.5386	80
90	65.1423	0.015351	0.000741	0.048241	1350.3634	20.7295	90
100	103.6103	0.009652	0.000463	0.047963	2160.2179	20.8494	100
INF	INF	0.0	0.0	0.047500	INF	21.0526	INF

TABLE A-9   4.875 Percent Compound-interest Factors

N	F/P,4.875%,N	P/F,4.875%,N	A/F,4.875%,N	A/P,4.875%,N	F/A,4.875%,N	P/A,4.875%,N	N
1	1.0487	0.953516	1.000000	1.048750	1.0000	0.9535	1
2	1.0999	0.909193	0.488103	0.536853	2.0487	1.8627	2
4	1.2097	0.826632	0.232443	0.281193	4.3021	3.5563	4
6	1.3306	0.751568	0.147481	0.196231	6.7806	5.0960	6
8	1.4634	0.683320	0.105191	0.153941	9.5065	6.4960	8
10	1.6096	0.621270	0.079970	0.128720	12.5048	7.7688	10
12	1.7704	0.564854	0.063281	0.112031	15.8024	8.9261	12
15	2.0421	0.489689	0.046780	0.095530	21.3767	10.4679	15
20	2.5908	0.385976	0.030644	0.079394	32.6325	12.5954	20
25	3.2870	0.304229	0.021316	0.070066	46.9128	14.2722	25
30	4.1702	0.239795	0.015377	0.064127	65.0302	15.5939	30
35	5.2908	0.189008	0.011362	0.060112	88.0158	16.6357	35
40	6.7124	0.148978	0.008534	0.057284	117.1778	17.4569	40
45	8.5161	0.117425	0.006486	0.055236	154.1756	18.1041	45
50	10.8044	0.092555	0.004972	0.053722	201.1149	18.6143	50
60	17.3908	0.057502	0.002974	0.051724	336.2206	19.3333	60
70	27.9923	0.035724	0.001806	0.050556	553.6876	19.7800	70
80	45.0565	0.022194	0.001107	0.049857	903.7240	20.0576	80
90	72.5233	0.013789	0.000682	0.049432	1467.1447	20.2300	90
100	116.7340	0.008566	0.000421	0.049171	2374.0305	20.3371	100
INF	INF	0.0	0.0	0.048750	INF	20.5128	INF

TABLE A-10 5.000 Percent Compound-interest Factors

N	F/P,5.000%,N	P/F,5.000%,N	A/F,5.000%,N	A/P,5.000%,N	F/A,5.000%,N	P/A,5.000%,N	N
1	1.0500	0.952381	1.000000	1.050000	1.0000	0.9524	1
2	1.1025	0.907029	0.487805	0.537805	2.0500	1.8594	2
4	1.2155	0.822702	0.232012	0.282012	4.3101	3.5460	4
6	1.3401	0.746215	0.147017	0.197017	6.8019	5.0757	6
8	1.4775	0.676839	0.104722	0.154722	9.5491	6.4632	8
10	1.6289	0.613913	0.079505	0.129505	12.5779	7.7217	10
12	1.7959	0.556837	0.062825	0.112825	15.9171	8.8633	12
15	2.0789	0.481017	0.046342	0.096342	21.5786	10.3797	15
20	2.6533	0.376890	0.030243	0.080243	33.0660	12.4622	20
25	3.3864	0.295303	0.020952	0.070952	47.7271	14.0939	25
30	4.3219	0.231377	0.015051	0.065051	66.4388	15.3725	30
35	5.5160	0.181290	0.011072	0.061072	90.3203	16.3742	35
40	7.0400	0.142046	0.008278	0.058278	120.7998	17.1591	40
45	8.9850	0.111297	0.006262	0.056262	159.7001	17.7741	45
50	11.4674	0.087204	0.004777	0.054777	209.3480	18.2559	50
60	18.6792	0.053536	0.002828	0.052828	353.5837	18.9293	60
70	30.4264	0.032866	0.001699	0.051699	588.5284	19.3427	70
80	49.5614	0.020177	0.001030	0.051030	971.2287	19.5965	80
90	80.7303	0.012387	0.000627	0.050627	1594.6070	19.7523	90
100	131.5012	0.007604	0.000383	0.050383	2610.0246	19.8479	100
INF	INF	0.0	0.0	0.050000	INF	20.0000	INF

TABLE A-11 5.125 Percent Compound-interest Factors

N	F/P,5.125%,N	P/F,5.125%,N	A/F,5.125%,N	A/P,5.125%,N	F/A,5.125%,N	P/A,5.125%,N	N
1	1.0512	0.951249	1.000000	1.051250	1.0000	0.9512	1
2	1.1051	0.904874	0.487508	0.538758	2.0512	1.8561	2
4	1.2213	0.818796	0.231581	0.282831	4.3181	3.5357	4
6	1.3497	0.740907	0.146556	0.197806	6.8233	5.0555	6
8	1.4916	0.670428	0.104255	0.155505	9.5919	6.4307	8
10	1.6484	0.606652	0.079042	0.130292	12.6515	7.6751	10
12	1.8217	0.548944	0.062372	0.113622	16.0328	8.8011	12
15	2.1164	0.472509	0.045908	0.097158	21.7827	10.2925	15
20	2.7172	0.368027	0.029845	0.081095	33.5062	12.3312	20
25	3.4886	0.286649	0.020594	0.071844	48.5579	13.9191	25
30	4.4790	0.223265	0.014731	0.065981	67.8828	15.1558	30
35	5.7506	0.173896	0.010788	0.062038	92.6939	16.1191	35
40	7.3831	0.135444	0.008029	0.059279	124.5488	16.8694	40
45	9.4792	0.105494	0.006044	0.057294	165.4473	17.4538	45
50	12.1703	0.082167	0.004588	0.055838	217.9566	17.9089	50
60	20.0614	0.049847	0.002689	0.053939	371.9291	18.5396	60
70	33.0690	0.030240	0.001598	0.052848	625.7359	18.9221	70
80	54.5106	0.018345	0.000958	0.052208	1044.1086	19.1542	80
90	89.8547	0.011129	0.000577	0.051827	1733.7502	19.2950	90
100	148.1156	0.006751	0.000348	0.051598	2870.5487	19.3805	100
INF	INF	0.0	0.0	0.051250	INF	19.5122	INF

TABLE A-12 5.250 Percent Compound-interest Factors

N	F/P,5.250%,N	P/F,5.250%,N	A/F,5.250%,N	A/P,5.250%,N	F/A,5.250%,N	P/A,5.250%,N	N
1	1.0525	0.950119	1.000000	1.052500	1.0000	0.9501	1
2	1.1078	0.902726	0.487211	0.539711	2.0525	1.8528	2
4	1.2271	0.814914	0.231151	0.283651	4.3262	3.5255	4
6	1.3594	0.735643	0.146095	0.198595	6.8448	5.0354	6
8	1.5058	0.664084	0.103789	0.156289	9.6349	6.3984	8
10	1.6681	0.599486	0.078582	0.131082	12.7256	7.6288	10
12	1.8478	0.541171	0.061922	0.114422	16.1494	8.7396	12
15	2.1544	0.464161	0.045477	0.097977	21.9891	10.2065	15
20	2.7825	0.359383	0.029452	0.081952	33.9532	12.2022	20
25	3.5938	0.278258	0.020241	0.072741	49.4055	13.7475	25
30	4.6416	0.215445	0.014417	0.066917	69.3629	14.9439	30
35	5.9948	0.166812	0.010511	0.063011	95.1388	15.8703	35
40	7.7426	0.129156	0.007786	0.060286	128.4296	16.5875	40
45	9.9999	0.100001	0.005833	0.058333	171.4262	17.1428	45
50	12.9153	0.077427	0.004406	0.056906	226.9585	17.5728	50
60	21.5440	0.046417	0.002555	0.055055	391.3142	18.1635	60
70	35.9375	0.027826	0.001503	0.054003	665.4753	18.5176	70
80	59.9471	0.016681	0.000891	0.053391	1122.8023	18.7299	80
90	99.9975	0.010000	0.000530	0.053030	1885.6676	18.8571	90
100	166.8055	0.005995	0.000317	0.052817	3158.2002	18.9334	100
INF	INF	0.0	0.0	0.052500	INF	19.0476	INF

TABLE A-13 5.500 Percent Compound-interest Factors

N	F/P,5.500%,N	P/F,5.500%,N	A/F,5.500%,N	A/P,5.500%,N	F/A,5.500%,N	P/A,5.500%,N	N
1	1.0550	0.947867	1.000000	1.055000	1.0000	0.9479	1
2	1.1130	0.898452	0.486618	0.541618	2.0550	1.8463	2
4	1.2388	0.807217	0.230294	0.285294	4.3423	3.5052	4
6	1.3788	0.725246	0.145179	0.200179	6.8881	4.9955	6
8	1.5347	0.651599	0.102864	0.157864	9.7216	6.3346	8
10	1.7081	0.585431	0.077668	0.132668	12.8754	7.5376	10
12	1.9012	0.525982	0.061029	0.116029	16.3856	8.6185	12
15	2.2325	0.447933	0.044626	0.099626	22.4087	10.0376	15
20	2.9178	0.342729	0.028679	0.083679	34.8683	11.9504	20
25	3.8134	0.262234	0.019549	0.074549	51.1526	13.4139	25
30	4.9840	0.200644	0.013805	0.068805	72.4355	14.5337	30
35	6.5138	0.153520	0.009975	0.064975	100.2514	15.3906	35
40	8.5133	0.117463	0.007320	0.062320	136.6056	16.0461	40
45	11.1266	0.089875	0.005431	0.060431	184.1192	16.5477	45
50	14.5420	0.068767	0.004061	0.059061	246.2175	16.9315	50
60	24.8398	0.040258	0.002307	0.057307	433.4504	17.4499	60
70	42.4299	0.023568	0.001328	0.056328	753.2712	17.7533	70
80	72.4764	0.013798	0.000769	0.055769	1299.5714	17.9310	80
90	123.8002	0.008078	0.000448	0.055448	2232.7310	18.0350	90
100	211.4686	0.004729	0.000261	0.055261	3826.7024	18.0958	100
INF	INF	0.0	0.0	0.055000	INF	18.1818	INF

TABLE A-14 5.750 Percent Compound-interest Factors

N	F/P,5.750%,N	P/F,5.750%,N	A/F,5.750%,N	A/P,5.750%,N	F/A,5.750%,N	P/A,5.750%,N	N
1	1.0575	0.945626	1.000000	1.057500	1.0000	0.9456	1
2	1.1183	0.894209	0.486027	0.543527	2.0575	1.8398	2
4	1.2506	0.799611	0.229441	0.286941	4.3584	3.4850	4
6	1.3986	0.715019	0.144268	0.201768	6.9315	4.9562	6
8	1.5640	0.639377	0.101946	0.159446	9.8091	6.2717	8
10	1.7491	0.571737	0.076763	0.134263	13.0271	7.4481	10
12	1.9560	0.511253	0.060148	0.117648	16.6257	8.5000	12
15	2.3132	0.432309	0.043788	0.101288	22.8376	9.8729	15
20	3.0592	0.326883	0.027923	0.085423	35.8121	11.7064	20
25	4.0458	0.247167	0.018878	0.076378	52.9712	13.0927	25
30	5.3507	0.186891	0.013216	0.070716	75.6645	14.1410	30
35	7.0764	0.141315	0.009463	0.066963	105.6767	14.9337	35
40	9.3587	0.106853	0.006879	0.064379	145.3685	15.5330	40
45	12.3770	0.080795	0.005054	0.062554	197.8616	15.9862	45
50	16.3689	0.061092	0.003741	0.061241	267.2847	16.3288	50
60	28.6301	0.034928	0.002081	0.059581	480.5231	16.7839	60
70	50.0756	0.019970	0.001172	0.058672	853.4889	17.0440	70
80	87.5851	0.011417	0.000664	0.058164	1505.8271	17.1927	80
90	153.1912	0.006528	0.000378	0.057878	2646.8032	17.2778	90
100	267.9400	0.003732	0.000215	0.057715	4642.4344	17.3264	100
INF	INF	0.0	0.0	0.057500	INF	17.3913	INF

TABLE A-15 6.000 Percent Compound-interest Factors

N	F/P,6.000%,N	P/F,6.000%,N	A/F,6.000%,N	A/P,6.000%,N	F/A,6.000%,N	P/A,6.000%,N	N
1	1.0600	0.943396	1.000000	1.060000	1.0000	0.9434	1
2	1.1236	0.889996	0.485437	0.545437	2.0600	1.8334	2
4	1.2625	0.792094	0.228591	0.288591	4.3746	3.4651	4
6	1.4185	0.704961	0.143363	0.203363	6.9753	4.9173	6
8	1.5938	0.627412	0.101036	0.161036	9.8975	6.2098	8
10	1.7908	0.558395	0.075868	0.135868	13.1808	7.3601	10
12	2.0122	0.496969	0.059277	0.119277	16.8699	8.3838	12
15	2.3966	0.417265	0.042963	0.102963	23.2760	9.7122	15
20	3.2071	0.311805	0.027185	0.087185	36.7856	11.4699	20
25	4.2919	0.232999	0.018227	0.078227	54.8645	12.7834	25
30	5.7435	0.174110	0.012649	0.072649	79.0582	13.7648	30
35	7.6861	0.130105	0.008974	0.068974	111.4348	14.4982	35
40	10.2857	0.097222	0.006462	0.066462	154.7620	15.0463	40
45	13.7646	0.072650	0.004700	0.064700	212.7435	15.4558	45
50	18.4202	0.054288	0.003444	0.063444	290.3359	15.7619	50
60	32.9877	0.030314	0.001876	0.061876	533.1282	16.1614	60
70	59.0759	0.016927	0.001033	0.061033	967.9321	16.3845	70
80	105.7960	0.009452	0.000573	0.060573	1746.5998	16.5091	80
90	189.4645	0.005278	0.000318	0.060318	3141.0749	16.5787	90
100	339.3020	0.002947	0.000177	0.060177	5638.3675	16.6175	100
INF	INF	0.0	0.0	0.060000	INF	16.6667	INF

TABLE A-16 7.000 Percent Compound-interest Factors

N	F/P,7.000%,N	P/F,7.000%,N	A/F,7.000%,N	A/P,7.000%,N	F/A,7.000%,N	P/A,7.000%,N	N
1	1.0700	0.934579	1.000000	1.070000	1.0000	0.9346	1
2	1.1449	0.873439	0.483092	0.553092	2.0700	1.8080	2
4	1.3108	0.762895	0.225228	0.295228	4.4399	3.3872	4
6	1.5007	0.666342	0.139796	0.209796	7.1533	4.7665	6
8	1.7182	0.582009	0.097468	0.167468	10.2598	5.9713	8
10	1.9672	0.508349	0.072378	0.142377	13.8164	7.0236	10
12	2.2522	0.444012	0.055902	0.125902	17.8885	7.9427	12
15	2.7590	0.362446	0.039795	0.109795	25.1290	9.1079	15
20	3.8697	0.258419	0.024393	0.094393	40.9955	10.5940	20
25	5.4274	0.184249	0.015811	0.085811	63.2490	11.6536	25
30	7.6123	0.131367	0.010586	0.080586	94.4608	12.4090	30
35	10.6766	0.093663	0.007234	0.077234	138.2369	12.9477	35
40	14.9745	0.066780	0.005009	0.075009	199.6351	13.3317	40
45	21.0024	0.047614	0.003500	0.073500	285.7492	13.6055	45
50	29.4570	0.033948	0.002460	0.072460	406.5288	13.8007	50
60	57.9464	0.017257	0.001229	0.071229	813.5201	14.0392	60
70	113.9893	0.008773	0.000620	0.070620	1614.1336	14.1604	70
80	224.2343	0.004460	0.000314	0.070314	3189.0613	14.2220	80
90	441.1027	0.002267	0.000159	0.070159	6287.1823	14.2533	90
100	867.7157	0.001152	0.000081	0.070081	12381.6548	14.2693	100
INF	INF	0.0	0.0	0.070000	INF	14.2857	INF

TABLE A-17 8.000 Percent Compound-interest Factors

N	F/P,8.000%,N	P/F,8.000%,N	A/F,8.000%,N	A/P,8.000%,N	F/A,8.000%,N	P/A,8.000%,N	N
1	1.0800	0.925926	1.000000	1.080000	1.0000	0.9259	1
2	1.1664	0.857339	0.480769	0.560769	2.0800	1.7833	2
4	1.3605	0.735030	0.221921	0.301921	4.5061	3.3121	4
6	1.5869	0.630170	0.136315	0.216315	7.3359	4.6229	6
8	1.8509	0.540269	0.094015	0.174015	10.6366	5.7466	8
10	2.1589	0.463194	0.069029	0.149029	14.4866	6.7101	10
12	2.5182	0.397114	0.052695	0.132695	18.9771	7.5361	12
15	3.1722	0.315242	0.036830	0.116830	27.1521	8.5595	15
20	4.6610	0.214548	0.021852	0.101852	45.7620	9.8181	20
25	6.8485	0.146018	0.013679	0.093679	73.1059	10.6748	25
30	10.0627	0.099377	0.008827	0.088827	113.2832	11.2578	30
35	14.7853	0.067635	0.005803	0.085803	172.3167	11.6546	35
40	21.7245	0.046031	0.003860	0.083860	259.0564	11.9246	40
45	31.9204	0.031328	0.002587	0.082587	386.5054	12.1084	45
50	46.9016	0.021321	0.001743	0.081743	573.7698	12.2335	50
60	101.2570	0.009876	0.000798	0.080798	1253.2124	12.3766	60
70	218.6062	0.004574	0.000368	0.080368	2720.0777	12.4428	70
80	471.9543	0.002119	0.000170	0.080170	5886.9294	12.4735	80
90	1018.9137	0.000981	0.000079	0.080079	12723.9236	12.4877	90
100	2199.7579	0.000455	0.000036	0.080036	27484.4789	12.4943	100
INF	INF	0.0	0.0	0.080000	INF	12.5000	INF

TABLE A-18 10.00 Percent Compound-interest Factors

N	F/P,10.00%,N	P/F,10.00%,N	A/F,10.00%,N	A/P,10.00%,N	F/A,10.00%,N	P/A,10.00%,N	N
1	1.1000	0.909091	1.000000	1.100000	1.0000	0.9091	1
2	1.2100	0.826446	0.476190	0.576190	2.1000	1.7355	2
4	1.4641	0.683014	0.215471	0.315471	4.6410	3.1699	4
6	1.7716	0.564474	0.129607	0.229607	7.7156	4.3553	6
8	2.1436	0.466508	0.087444	0.187444	11.4359	5.3349	8
10	2.5937	0.385543	0.062745	0.162745	15.9374	6.1446	10
12	3.1384	0.318631	0.046763	0.146763	21.3843	6.8137	12
15	4.1772	0.239392	0.031474	0.131474	31.7725	7.6061	15
20	6.7275	0.148644	0.017460	0.117460	57.2750	8.5136	20
25	10.8347	0.092296	0.010168	0.110168	98.3470	9.0770	25
30	17.4494	0.057309	0.006079	0.106079	164.4939	9.4269	30
35	28.1024	0.035584	0.003690	0.103690	271.0241	9.6442	35
40	45.2592	0.022095	0.002259	0.102259	442.5921	9.7791	40
45	72.8904	0.013719	0.001391	0.101391	718.9040	9.8628	45
50	117.3907	0.008519	0.000859	0.100859	1163.9070	9.9148	50
60	304.4810	0.003284	0.000330	0.100329	3034.8115	9.9672	60
70	789.7452	0.001266	0.000127	0.100127	7887.4544	9.9873	70
80	2048.3949	0.000488	0.000049	0.100049	20473.9562	9.9951	80
90	5313.0071	0.000188	0.000019	0.100019	53120.0897	9.9981	90
100	13780.5675	0.000073	0.000007	0.100007	137795.7246	9.9993	100
INF	INF	0.0	0.0	0.100000	INF	10.0000	INF

TABLE A-19 12.00 Percent Compound-interest Factors

N	F/P,12.00%,N	P/F,12.00%,N	A/F,12.00%,N	A/P,12.00%,N	F/A,12.00%,N	P/A,12.00%,N
1	1.1200	0.892857	1.000000	1.120000	1.0000	0.8929
2	1.2544	0.797194	0.471698	0.591698	2.1200	1.6901
4	1.5735	0.635518	0.209234	0.329234	4.7793	3.0373
6	1.9738	0.506631	0.123226	0.243226	8.1152	4.1114
8	2.4760	0.403883	0.081303	0.201303	12.2997	4.9676
10	3.1058	0.321973	0.056984	0.176984	17.5487	5.6502
12	3.8960	0.256675	0.041437	0.161437	24.1331	6.1944
15	5.4736	0.182696	0.026824	0.146824	37.2797	6.8109
20	9.6463	0.103667	0.013879	0.133879	72.0524	7.4694
25	17.0000	0.058823	0.007500	0.127500	133.3338	7.8431
30	29.9599	0.033378	0.004144	0.124144	241.3324	8.0552
35	52.7995	0.018940	0.002317	0.122317	431.6629	8.1755
40	93.0508	0.010747	0.001304	0.121304	767.0903	8.2438
45	163.9872	0.006098	0.000736	0.120736	1358.2276	8.2825
50	289.0015	0.003460	0.000417	0.120417	2400.0134	8.3045
60	897.5943	0.001114	0.000134	0.120134	7471.6226	8.3241
70	2787.7903	0.000359	0.000043	0.120043	23223.2629	8.3303
80	8658.4492	0.000115	0.000014	0.120014	72145.4429	8.3324
90	26891.8157	0.000037	0.000004	0.120004	224090.2334	8.3330
100	83521.8568	0.000012	0.000001	0.120001	696007.4580	8.3332
INF	INF	0.0	0.0	0.120000	INF	8.3333

TABLE A-20 15.00 Percent Compound-interest Factors

N	F/P,15.00%,N	P/F,15.00%,N	A/F,15.00%,N	A/P,15.00%,N	F/A,15.00%,N	P/A,15.00%,N	N
1	1.1500	0.869565	1.000000	1.150000	1.0000	0.8696	1
2	1.3225	0.756144	0.465116	0.615116	2.1500	1.6257	2
4	1.7490	0.571753	0.200265	0.350265	4.9934	2.8550	4
6	2.3131	0.432328	0.114237	0.264237	8.7537	3.7845	6
8	3.0590	0.326902	0.072850	0.222850	13.7268	4.4873	8
10	4.0456	0.247185	0.049252	0.199252	20.3037	5.0188	10
12	5.3502	0.186907	0.034481	0.184481	29.0017	5.4206	12
15	8.1371	0.122895	0.021017	0.171017	47.5804	5.8474	15
20	16.3665	0.061100	0.009761	0.159761	102.4436	6.2593	20
25	32.9189	0.030378	0.004699	0.154699	212.7929	6.4642	25
30	66.2117	0.015103	0.002300	0.152300	434.7449	6.5660	30
35	133.1754	0.007509	0.001135	0.151135	881.1697	6.6166	35
40	267.8633	0.003733	0.000562	0.150562	1779.0891	6.6418	40
45	538.7688	0.001856	0.000279	0.150279	3585.1257	6.6543	45
50	1083.6563	0.000923	0.000139	0.150139	7217.7099	6.6605	50
60	4383.9933	0.000228	0.000034	0.150034	29219.9599	6.6651	60
70	17735.6943	0.000056	0.000008	0.150008	118231.3141	6.6663	70
80	71750.7604	0.000014	0.000002	0.150002	478331.8120	6.6666	80
90	290271.7836	0.000003	0.000001	0.150000	1935138.8649	6.6666	90
100	1174311.0161	0.000001	0.000000	0.150000	7828734.6851	6.6667	100
INF	INF	0.0	0.0	0.150000	INF	6.6667	INF

APPENDIX
B

GRADIENT-SERIES
FACTORS

TABLE B-1 2.000 Percent Gradient-series Factors

	Uniform gradient			Uniform percentage gradients				
N	P/G,2.000%,N	P 1,2.000%,N	P 2,2.000%,N	P 3,2.000%,N	P 5,2.000%,N	P 7,2.000%,N	P10,2.000%,N	N
1	0.98039	0.98039	0.98039	0.98039	0.98039	0.98039	0.98039	1
2	2.90273	1.95117	1.96078	1.97040	1.98962	2.00884	2.03768	2
4	9.42508	3.86427	3.92157	3.97962	4.09800	4.21946	4.40753	4
6	19.28156	5.74005	5.88235	6.02843	6.33222	6.65211	7.16369	6
8	32.20341	7.57922	7.84314	8.11761	8.69980	9.32911	10.36915	8
10	47.93769	9.38251	9.80392	10.24795	11.20870	12.27499	14.09715	10
12	66.24650	11.15062	11.76471	12.42027	13.86735	15.51675	18.43286	12
15	98.05139	13.73830	14.70588	15.75927	18.15581	21.00002	26.29695	15
20	160.95177	17.88471	19.60784	21.54611	26.18644	32.08373	44.09267	20
25	233.78269	21.83181	24.50980	27.62223	35.46959	46.16375	70.05106	25
30	314.11290	25.58918	29.41176	34.00209	46.20062	64.05008	107.91627	30
35	399.88127	29.16595	34.31373	40.70089	58.60533	86.77170	163.14981	35
40	489.34862	32.57079	39.21569	47.73456	72.94478	115.63575	243.71832	40
45	581.05536	35.81196	44.11765	55.11985	89.52071	152.30274	361.24266	45
50	673.78420	38.89734	49.01961	62.87433	108.68195	198.88208	532.67405	50
60	858.45343	44.63030	58.82353	79.56561	156.43614	333.22078	1147.50583	60
70	1037.33295	49.82537	68.62745	97.96740	220.24820	550.00974	2455.72738	70
80	1206.53130	54.53301	78.43137	118.25501	305.51775	899.85275	5239.32398	80
90	1363.75704	58.79896	88.23529	140.62167	419.46012	1464.41161	11162.18157	90
100	1507.95113	62.66465	98.03922	165.28046	571.71686	2375.46800	23764.66937	100

TABLE B-2 3.000 Percent Gradient-series Factors

	Uniform gradient	Uniform percentage gradients						
N	P/G,3.000%,N	P 1,3.000%,N	P 2,3.000%,N	P 3,3.000%,N	P 5,3.000%,N	P 7,3.000%,N	P10,3.000%,N	N
1	0.97087	0.97087	0.97087	0.97087	0.97087	0.97087	0.97087	1
2	2.85607	1.92290	1.93232	1.94175	1.96060	1.97945	2.00773	2
4	9.15544	3.77184	3.82730	3.88350	3.99808	4.11563	4.29763	4
6	18.49339	5.54968	5.68567	5.82524	6.11545	6.42095	6.90935	6
8	30.50030	7.25915	7.50813	7.76699	8.31585	8.90880	9.88812	8
10	44.83899	8.90287	9.29537	9.70874	10.60253	11.59363	13.28554	10
12	61.20219	10.48338	11.04807	11.65049	12.97887	14.49105	17.16043	12
15	88.93813	12.74091	13.61383	14.56311	16.71924	19.27293	24.01737	15
20	141.67614	16.22052	17.72670	19.41748	23.45333	28.56376	38.92647	20
25	199.84677	19.37517	21.64374	24.27184	30.86710	39.80430	59.63877	25
30	260.96174	22.23520	25.37430	29.12621	39.02915	53.40370	88.41313	30
35	323.11394	24.82815	28.92725	33.98058	48.01501	69.85699	128.38762	35
40	384.86474	27.17893	32.31103	38.83495	57.90783	89.76305	183.92177	40
45	445.15122	29.31018	35.53372	43.68932	68.79915	113.84647	261.07203	45
50	503.21013	31.24239	38.60297	48.54369	80.78975	142.98388	368.25224	50
60	610.72822	34.58232	44.31005	58.25243	108.52380	220.88562	724.00772	60
70	705.21036	37.32755	49.48664	67.96117	142.13886	334.91391	1410.61132	70
80	786.28737	39.58398	54.18204	77.66990	182.88201	501.82230	2735.74761	80
90	854.63272	41.43863	58.44099	87.37864	232.26478	746.13366	5293.24397	90
100	911.45306	42.96304	62.30405	97.08738	292.11919	1103.74327	10229.17971	100

TABLE B-3   3.500 Percent Gradient-series Factors

	Uniform gradient			Uniform percentage gradients			
N	P/G,3.500%,N	P 1,3.500%,N	P 2,3.500%,N	P 3,3.500%,N	P 5,3.500%,N	P 7,3.500%,N	P10,3.500%,N
1	0.96618	0.96618	0.96618	0.96618	0.96618	0.96618	0.96618
2	2.83320	1.90903	1.91836	1.92770	1.94637	1.96504	1.99305
4	9.02480	3.72695	3.78153	3.83682	3.94956	4.06523	4.24429
6	18.11567	5.45811	5.59108	5.72754	6.01124	6.30986	6.78717
8	29.69290	7.10664	7.34856	7.60003	8.13312	8.70887	9.65948
10	43.38567	8.67650	9.05546	9.45448	10.31694	11.27287	12.90389
12	58.86147	10.17144	10.71325	11.29105	12.56451	14.01322	16.56860
15	84.77603	12.28114	13.11092	14.01277	16.05952	18.48114	22.97477
20	133.10057	15.47096	16.88090	18.46202	22.23046	26.99347	36.63094
25	185.13409	18.29371	20.38550	22.80483	28.86173	37.04576	55.14879
30	238.49758	20.79162	23.64340	27.04376	35.98765	48.91663	80.25911
35	291.47128	23.00208	26.67196	31.18127	43.64513	62.93506	114.30886
40	342.84577	24.95816	29.48733	35.21981	51.87382	79.48959	160.48052
45	391.80361	26.68914	32.10452	39.16174	60.71633	99.03900	223.08957
50	437.82564	28.22093	34.53747	43.00937	70.21844	122.12512	307.98781
60	520.04981	30.77596	38.90165	50.43069	91.40197	181.58253	579.21718
70	588.89671	32.77677	42.67302	57.50119	115.86373	264.49890	1077.94081
80	645.18737	34.34358	45.93213	64.23745	144.11105	380.12996	1994.97002
90	690.39827	35.57053	48.74854	70.65527	176.72975	541.38333	3681.15959
100	726.21023	36.53134	51.18240	76.76971	214.39634	766.25930	6781.64454

TABLE B-4 4.000 Percent Gradient-series Factors

	Uniform gradient	Uniform percentage gradients							
N	P/G,4.000%,N	P 1,4.000%,N	P 2,4.000%,N	P 3,4.000%,N	P 5,4.000%,N	P 7,4.000%,N	P10,4.000%,N	N
1	0.96154	0.96154	0.96154	0.96154	0.96154	0.96154	0.96154	1
2	2.81065	1.89534	1.90459	1.91383	1.93232	1.95081	1.97855	2
4	8.89686	3.68291	3.73662	3.79104	3.90198	4.01580	4.19198	4
6	17.74838	5.36884	5.49887	5.63231	5.90971	6.20163	6.66817	6
8	28.91333	6.95891	7.19400	7.43835	7.95622	8.51539	9.43832	8
10	41.99225	8.45856	8.82455	9.20982	10.04228	10.96457	12.53732	10
12	56.63280	9.87295	10.39300	10.94740	12.16866	13.55707	16.00422	12
15	80.85389	11.84517	12.63435	13.49160	15.43550	17.73308	21.99129	15
20	125.15501	14.77071	16.09165	17.57144	21.09304	25.53578	34.50571	20
25	171.72608	17.29794	19.22906	21.45887	27.02786	34.53070	51.07131	25
30	218.35387	19.48110	22.07617	25.16297	33.25355	44.90001	72.99957	30
35	263.54141	21.36703	24.65985	28.69237	39.78436	56.85369	102.02647	35
40	306.32308	22.99620	27.00448	32.05533	46.63525	70.63384	140.45000	40
45	346.12283	24.40356	29.13216	35.25968	53.82190	86.51953	191.31207	45
50	382.64604	25.61932	31.06298	38.31291	61.36078	104.83248	258.63928	50
60	445.62015	27.57680	34.40520	43.99418	77.56509	150.28032	465.73513	60
70	495.87345	29.03756	37.15754	49.15222	95.39667	210.67763	828.61655	70
80	535.03155	30.12764	39.42412	53.83521	115.01896	290.94184	1464.47148	80
90	565.00422	30.94111	41.29061	58.08691	136.61178	397.60791	2578.64124	90
100	587.62990	31.54815	42.82779	61.94703	160.37300	539.36038	4530.93286	100

TABLE B-5 4.250 Percent Gradient-series Factors

N	Uniform gradient	Uniform percentage gradients						N
	P/G,4.250%,N	P 1,4.250%,N	P 2,4.250%,N	P 3,4.250%,N	P 5,4.250%,N	P 7,4.250%,N	P10,4.250%,N	
1	0.95923	0.95923	0.95923	0.95923	0.95923	0.95923	0.95923	1
2	2.79949	1.88856	1.89776	1.90696	1.92537	1.94377	1.97137	2
4	8.83387	3.66121	3.71449	3.76847	3.87854	3.99144	4.16621	4
6	17.56853	5.32505	5.45365	5.58561	5.85991	6.14856	6.60984	6
8	28.53362	6.88677	7.11854	7.35942	7.86989	8.42100	9.33046	8
10	41.31710	8.35263	8.71234	9.09096	9.90890	10.81490	12.35947	10
12	55.55854	9.72852	10.23809	10.78122	11.97736	13.33676	15.73184	12
15	78.97784	11.63565	12.40543	13.24137	15.13617	17.37455	21.52050	15
20	121.40206	14.43785	15.71683	17.14885	20.55420	24.84625	33.50245	20
25	165.47043	16.82966	18.68597	20.82762	26.16995	33.35681	49.17394	25
30	209.06759	18.87118	21.34823	24.29107	31.99063	43.05066	69.67109	30
35	250.81504	20.61370	23.73534	27.55180	38.02372	54.09234	96.47984	35
40	289.86887	22.10103	25.87573	30.62167	44.27697	66.66925	131.54368	40
45	325.76758	23.37053	27.79490	33.51185	50.75842	80.99483	177.40458	45
50	358.31819	24.45410	29.51572	36.23287	57.47639	97.31222	237.38722	50
60	413.46025	26.16841	32.44216	41.20644	71.65676	137.06871	418.45053	60
70	456.42201	27.41735	34.79494	45.61482	86.89096	188.64917	728.19000	70
80	489.10557	28.32726	36.68651	49.52225	103.25731	255.57015	1258.05182	80
90	513.52970	28.99016	38.20728	52.98565	120.83997	342.39408	2164.47024	90
100	531.52995	29.47310	39.42994	56.05548	139.72931	455.04028	3715.05248	100

TABLE B-6 4.500 Percent Gradient-series Factors

| | Uniform gradient | | | Uniform percentage gradients | | | | |
N	P/G,4.500%,N	P 1,4.500%,N	P 2,4.500%,N	P 3,4.500%,N	P 5,4.500%,N	P 7,4.500%,N	P10,4.500%,N	N
1	0.95694	0.95694	0.95694	0.95694	0.95694	0.95694	0.95694	1
2	2.78840	1.88183	1.89098	1.90014	1.91845	1.93677	1.96424	2
4	8.77153	3.63971	3.69257	3.74612	3.85531	3.96731	4.14068	4
6	17.39116	5.28181	5.40899	5.53949	5.81075	6.09618	6.55226	6
8	28.16044	6.81575	7.04426	7.28174	7.78494	8.32812	9.22436	8
10	40.65586	8.24866	8.60223	8.97434	9.77807	10.66813	12.18514	10
12	54.51001	9.58720	10.08655	10.61869	11.79032	13.12144	15.46578	12
15	77.15597	11.43153	12.18249	12.99776	14.84494	17.02592	21.06308	15
20	117.78748	14.11591	15.35450	16.74059	20.03419	24.18148	32.53653	20
25	159.49364	16.37988	18.16481	20.22240	25.34878	32.23491	47.36431	25
30	200.26419	18.28927	20.65466	23.46139	30.79174	41.29889	66.52707	30
35	238.84118	19.89962	22.86059	26.47450	36.36616	51.50020	91.29216	35
40	274.50018	21.25776	24.81498	29.27747	42.07522	62.98156	123.29745	40
45	306.88860	22.40320	26.54652	31.88497	47.92218	75.90359	164.65966	45
50	335.90703	23.36924	28.08061	34.31062	53.91036	90.44706	218.11432	50
60	384.20874	24.87113	30.64394	38.66623	66.32413	125.23771	376.47576	60
70	420.95245	25.93947	32.65602	42.43551	79.34480	169.30713	640.96820	70
80	448.24508	26.69929	34.23538	45.69739	93.00206	225.13000	1082.71872	80
90	468.15851	27.23978	35.47510	48.52017	107.32703	295.84101	1820.52252	90
100	482.48745	27.62423	36.44820	50.96296	122.35236	385.41087	3052.78918	100

TABLE B-7 4.625 Percent Gradient-series Factors

	Uniform gradient		Uniform percentage gradients					
N	P/G,4.625%,N	P 1,4.625%,N	P 2,4.625%,N	P 3,4.625%,N	P 5,4.625%,N	P 7,4.625%,N	P10,4.625%,N	N
1	0.95579	0.95579	0.95579	0.95579	0.95579	0.95579	0.95579	1
2	2.78288	1.87847	1.88761	1.89674	1.91501	1.93329	1.96069	2
4	8.74060	3.62903	3.68169	3.73503	3.84378	3.95534	4.12802	4
6	17.30339	5.26039	5.38687	5.51665	5.78640	6.07024	6.52375	6
8	27.97627	6.78066	7.00756	7.24336	7.74297	8.28224	9.17196	8
10	40.33035	8.19740	8.54795	8.91685	9.71359	10.59581	12.09926	10
12	53.99517	9.51768	10.01201	10.53875	11.69836	13.01561	15.33505	12
15	76.26480	11.33145	12.07321	12.87837	14.70227	16.85521	20.83923	15
20	116.03027	13.95890	15.17787	16.54165	19.78100	23.85806	32.06708	20
25	156.60542	16.16165	17.91212	19.92916	24.95141	31.69264	46.49097	25
30	196.03468	18.00833	20.32015	23.06164	30.21513	40.45776	65.02067	30
35	233.12070	19.55652	22.44088	25.95829	35.57387	50.26392	88.82491	35
40	267.19755	20.85446	24.30859	28.63688	41.02934	61.23478	119.40511	40
45	297.96469	21.94259	25.95346	31.11381	46.58327	73.50867	158.69008	45
50	325.36642	22.85483	27.40209	33.40428	52.23746	87.24035	209.15765	50
60	370.57923	24.26079	29.80146	37.48089	63.85385	119.79022	357.27937	60
70	404.56539	25.24896	31.66244	40.96680	75.89337	160.53129	601.72977	70
80	429.51026	25.94348	33.10586	43.94761	88.37145	211.52487	1005.15474	80
90	447.49470	26.43163	34.22539	46.49650	101.30405	275.35101	1670.94093	90
100	460.28198	26.77472	35.09372	48.67606	114.70774	355.23901	2769.71094	100

TABLE B-8 4.750 Percent Gradient-series Factors

	Uniform gradient		Uniform percentage gradients						
N	P/G,4.750%,N	P 1,4.750%,N	P 2,4.750%,N	P 3,4.750%,N	P 5,4.750%,N	P 7,4.750%,N	P10,4.750%,N	N
1	0.95465	0.95465	0.95465	0.95465	0.95465	0.95465	0.95465	1
2	2.77738	1.87513	1.88425	1.89336	1.91159	1.92981	1.95715	2
4	8.70983	3.61841	3.67086	3.72398	3.83231	3.94342	4.11541	4
6	17.21623	5.23910	5.36489	5.49395	5.76221	6.04446	6.49542	6
8	27.79367	6.74583	6.97114	7.20528	7.70133	8.23673	9.11999	8
10	40.00820	8.14662	8.49417	8.85990	9.64972	10.52419	12.01422	10
12	53.48650	9.44890	9.93827	10.45969	11.60742	12.91097	15.20585	12
15	75.38650	11.23265	11.96535	12.76055	14.56153	16.68686	20.61857	15
20	114.30550	13.80446	15.00413	16.34608	19.53224	23.54044	31.60637	20
25	153.78172	15.94772	17.66453	19.64195	24.56254	31.16240	45.63787	25
30	191.91546	17.73384	19.99353	22.67155	29.65316	39.63887	63.55620	30
35	227.56991	19.22233	22.03245	25.45640	34.80482	49.06567	86.43802	35
40	260.13664	20.46280	23.81742	28.01626	40.01825	59.54932	115.65825	40
45	289.36554	21.49656	25.38006	30.36933	45.29418	71.20832	152.97270	45
50	315.24247	22.35807	26.74808	32.53229	50.63338	84.17444	200.62349	50
60	357.56776	23.67434	28.99418	36.34811	61.50460	114.63065	339.18023	60
70	389.00660	24.58849	30.71560	39.57230	72.63808	152.29870	565.13113	70
80	411.80838	25.22337	32.03493	42.29658	84.04014	198.88634	933.59971	80
90	428.05285	25.66429	33.04607	44.59847	95.71727	256.50566	1534.47847	90
100	439.46601	25.97052	33.82102	46.54345	107.67611	327.76889	2514.35929	100

TABLE B-9 4.875 Percent Gradient-series Factors

	Uniform gradient	Uniform percentage gradients						
N	P/G,4.875%,N	P 1,4.875%,N	P 2,4.875%,N	P 3,4.875%,N	P 5,4.875%,N	P 7,4.875%,N	P10,4.875%,N	N
1	0.95352	0.95352	0.95352	0.95352	0.95352	0.95352	0.95352	1
2	2.77190	1.87180	1.88089	1.88998	1.90817	1.92635	1.95363	2
4	8.67922	3.60784	3.66008	3.71299	3.82089	3.93156	4.10286	4
6	17.12966	5.21795	5.34305	5.47140	5.73817	6.01885	6.46728	6
8	27.61264	6.71128	6.93501	7.16749	7.66003	8.19159	9.06844	8
10	39.68935	8.09630	8.44089	8.80348	9.58647	10.45326	11.93003	10
12	52.98390	9.38086	9.86533	10.38150	11.51750	12.80752	15.07813	12
15	74.52087	11.13513	11.85889	12.64429	14.42269	16.52082	20.40102	15
20	112.61251	13.65253	14.83338	16.15382	19.28781	23.22852	31.15423	20
25	151.02093	15.73799	17.42191	19.36064	24.18199	30.64388	44.80451	25
30	187.90329	17.46560	19.67457	22.29086	29.10540	38.84157	62.13237	30
35	222.18313	18.89678	21.63493	24.96835	34.05823	47.90412	84.12861	35
40	253.30845	20.08239	23.34092	27.41490	39.04064	57.92278	112.05096	40
45	281.07779	21.06456	24.82555	29.65043	44.05281	68.99841	147.49600	45
50	305.51652	21.87821	26.11754	31.69313	49.09493	81.24252	192.49045	50
60	345.14228	23.11062	28.22034	35.26518	59.26970	109.74233	322.11173	60
70	374.22778	23.95639	29.81284	38.24760	69.56640	144.57284	530.98519	70
80	395.07307	24.53681	31.01888	40.73773	79.98649	187.14031	867.56670	80
90	409.74786	24.93514	31.93225	42.81683	90.53144	239.16337	1409.93866	90
100	419.93609	25.20850	32.62396	44.55274	101.20275	302.74240	2283.92412	100

TABLE B-10 5.000 Percent Gradient-series Factors

N	Uniform gradient P/G,5.000%,N	Uniform percentage gradients P 1,5.000%,N	P 2,5.000%,N	P 3,5.000%,N	P 5,5.000%,N	P 7,5.000%,N	P 10,5.000%,N	N
1	0.95238	0.95238	0.95238	0.95238	0.95238	0.95238	0.95238	1
2	2.76644	1.86848	1.87755	1.88662	1.90476	1.92290	1.95011	2
4	8.64876	3.59731	3.64935	3.70206	3.80952	3.91976	4.09037	4
6	17.04369	5.19693	5.32134	5.44899	5.71429	5.99340	6.43932	6
8	27.43317	6.67700	6.99916	7.13001	7.61905	8.14680	9.01730	8
10	39.37378	8.04645	8.38811	8.74760	9.52381	10.38301	11.84666	10
12	52.48731	9.31354	9.79318	10.30415	11.42857	12.70523	14.95188	12
15	73.66769	11.03885	11.75381	12.52955	14.28571	16.35707	20.18655	15
20	110.95063	13.50308	14.66540	15.96478	19.04762	22.92217	30.71047	20
25	148.32146	15.53236	17.18415	19.08508	23.80952	30.13679	43.99036	25
30	183.99501	17.20345	19.36306	21.91931	28.57143	38.06521	60.74793	30
35	216.95489	18.57959	21.24798	24.49370	33.33333	46.77802	81.89392	35
40	246.70428	19.71283	22.87858	26.83208	38.09524	56.35285	108.57756	40
45	272.08863	20.64605	24.28918	28.95608	42.85714	66.87497	142.24900	45
50	296.17073	21.41455	25.50945	30.88535	47.61905	78.43811	184.73822	50
60	333.27248	22.56856	27.47828	34.22950	57.14286	105.10960	306.01130	60
70	360.18361	23.35113	28.95166	36.98858	66.66667	137.31970	499.11837	70
80	379.24255	23.88184	30.05428	39.26495	76.19048	176.21856	806.60900	80
90	392.50109	24.24173	30.87943	41.14307	85.71429	223.19516	1296.23630	90
100	401.59718	24.48578	31.49694	42.69261	95.23810	279.92694	2075.88572	100

TABLE B-11 5.125 Percent Gradient-series Factors

	Uniform gradient	Uniform percentage gradients						
N	P/G, 5.125%, N	P 1, 5.125%, N	P 2, 5.125%, N	P 3, 5.125%, N	P 5, 5.125%, N	P 7, 5.125%, N	P 10, 5.125%, N	N
1	0.95125	0.95125	0.95125	0.95125	0.95125	0.95125	0.95125	1
2	2.76100	1.86517	1.87422	1.88327	1.90137	1.91946	1.94661	2
4	8.61846	3.58684	3.63867	3.69117	3.79821	3.90801	4.07795	4
6	16.95830	5.17604	5.29977	5.42672	5.69055	5.96812	6.41154	6
8	27.25573	6.64298	6.86359	7.09281	7.57839	8.10238	8.96659	8
10	39.06145	7.99705	8.33581	8.69223	9.46175	10.31344	11.76410	10
12	51.99662	9.24694	9.72181	10.22764	11.34063	12.60409	14.82709	12
15	72.82677	10.94381	11.65009	12.41632	14.15057	16.19555	19.97510	15
20	109.31919	13.35605	14.50019	15.77892	18.81159	22.62127	30.27491	20
25	145.68175	15.33073	16.95112	18.81513	23.44496	29.64084	43.19491	25
30	180.18758	16.94723	19.05879	21.55663	28.05085	37.30915	59.40166	30
35	211.87989	18.27051	20.87127	24.03202	32.62942	45.68614	79.73128	35
40	240.31578	19.35375	22.42990	26.26714	37.18083	54.83732	105.23259	40
45	265.38580	20.24051	23.77024	28.28530	41.70525	64.83423	137.22123	45
50	287.18812	20.96642	24.92285	30.10757	46.20283	75.75504	177.34753	50
60	321.92975	22.04710	26.76641	33.23863	55.11813	100.71777	290.82037	60
70	346.83164	22.77129	28.12973	35.79136	63.92798	130.50771	469.36982	70
80	364.25937	23.25659	29.13791	37.87257	72.63364	166.05834	750.31731	80
90	376.23993	23.58179	29.88347	39.56936	81.23633	208.48364	1192.38805	90
100	384.36214	23.79972	30.43481	40.95274	89.73728	259.11303	1887.98616	100

TABLE B-12 5.250 Percent Gradient-series Factors

	Uniform gradient		Uniform percentage gradients					
N	P/G,5.250%,N	P 1,5.250%,N	P 2,5.250%,N	P 3,5.250%,N	P 5,5.250%,N	P 7,5.250%,N	P 10,5.250%,N	N
1	0.95012	0.95012	0.95012	0.95012	0.95012	0.95012	0.95012	1
2	2.75557	1.86187	1.87090	1.87993	1.89798	1.91604	1.94312	2
4	8.58831	3.57641	3.62804	3.68033	3.78696	3.89632	4.06558	4
6	16.87350	5.15529	5.27834	5.40459	5.66697	5.94300	6.38394	6
8	27.07881	6.60922	6.82829	7.05591	7.53806	8.05830	8.91628	8
10	38.75230	7.94811	8.28400	8.63738	9.40027	10.24454	11.68236	10
12	51.51177	9.18105	9.65120	10.15196	11.25365	12.50408	14.70373	12
15	71.99789	10.84997	11.54771	12.30456	14.01724	16.03624	19.76662	15
20	107.71758	13.21139	14.33770	15.59617	18.57963	22.32571	29.84738	20
25	143.10032	15.13302	16.72272	18.55066	23.08809	29.15575	42.41770	25
30	176.47808	16.69676	18.76156	21.20257	27.54327	36.57280	58.09240	30
35	206.95307	17.96927	20.50447	23.58289	31.94578	44.62731	77.63813	35
40	234.13499	19.00479	21.99439	25.71942	36.29625	53.37408	102.01089	40
45	257.95768	19.84746	23.26805	27.63715	40.59530	62.87261	132.40277	45
50	278.55648	20.53319	24.35684	29.35847	44.84354	73.18750	170.30026	50
60	311.08720	21.54529	26.08325	32.29029	53.18996	96.55305	276.48419	60
70	334.13226	22.21552	27.34485	34.65234	61.34023	124.10756	441.59079	70
80	350.07027	22.65934	28.26680	36.55535	69.29896	156.60203	698.31695	80
90	360.89747	22.95325	28.94053	38.08853	77.07066	194.92208	1097.50340	90
100	368.15112	23.14787	29.43287	39.32374	84.65972	240.11213	1718.20300	100

TABLE B-13 5.500 Percent Gradient-series Factors

N	Uniform gradient P/G,5.500%,N	Uniform percentage gradients P 1,5.500%,N	P 2,5.500%,N	P 3,5.500%,N	P 5,5.500%,N	P 7,5.500%,N	P10,5.500%,N	N
1	0.94787	0.94787	0.94787	0.94787	0.94787	0.94787	0.94787	1
2	2.74477	1.85530	1.86429	1.87327	1.89124	1.90921	1.93616	2
4	8.52848	3.55571	3.60693	3.65882	3.76460	3.87310	4.04102	4
6	16.70563	5.11415	5.23587	5.36074	5.62024	5.89323	6.32927	6
8	26.73048	6.54248	6.75852	6.98296	7.45834	7.97121	8.81689	8
10	38.14344	7.85157	8.18181	8.52921	9.27905	10.10870	11.52125	10
12	50.55924	9.05135	9.51224	10.00304	11.08255	12.30741	14.46123	12
15	70.37549	10.66586	11.34689	12.08540	13.75587	15.72409	19.35838	15
20	104.60135	12.92901	14.02065	15.23973	18.12761	21.75019	29.01575	20
25	138.10648	14.74896	16.27937	18.03763	22.39672	28.21705	40.91609	25
30	169.34147	16.21249	18.18746	20.51937	26.56562	35.15689	55.58037	30
35	197.52447	17.38941	19.79936	22.72067	30.63667	42.60432	73.65052	35
40	222.36611	18.33585	21.16105	24.67323	34.61216	50.59645	95.91758	40
45	243.88131	19.09694	22.31136	26.40515	38.49433	59.17313	123.35630	45
50	262.26229	19.70899	23.28311	27.94136	42.28537	68.37712	157.16783	50
60	290.80209	20.59696	24.79749	30.51263	49.60258	88.85388	250.17363	60
70	310.54466	21.17120	25.87821	32.53562	56.58031	112.43554	391.39881	70
80	323.87906	21.54255	26.64945	34.12725	63.23431	139.59290	605.84299	80
90	332.72543	21.78269	27.19983	35.37950	69.57959	170.86814	931.46696	90
100	338.51322	21.93799	27.59261	36.36473	75.63048	206.88566	1425.91253	100

TABLE B-14 5.750 Percent Gradient-series Factors

	Uniform gradient	Uniform percentage gradients					
N	P/G, 5.750%, N	P 1, 5.750%, N	P 2, 5.750%, N	P 3, 5.750%, N	P 5, 5.750%, N	P 7, 5.750%, N	P10, 5.750%, N
1	0.94563	0.94563	0.94563	0.94563	0.94563	0.94563	0.94563
2	2.73405	1.84878	1.85772	1.86666	1.88455	1.90243	1.92926
4	8.46925	3.53520	3.58602	3.63750	3.74246	3.85010	4.01670
6	16.54003	5.07353	5.19392	5.31744	5.57411	5.84409	6.27530
8	26.38904	6.47677	6.68981	6.91114	7.37987	7.88549	8.71909
10	37.54691	7.75677	8.08149	8.42303	9.16011	9.97544	11.36325
12	49.62909	8.92438	9.37622	9.85731	10.91518	12.11510	14.22422
15	68.79896	10.48637	11.15117	11.87187	13.50140	15.42035	18.96146
20	101.59714	12.65559	13.71384	14.89501	17.69091	21.19476	28.21425
25	133.32875	14.37947	15.85323	17.54498	21.73395	27.31861	39.48192
30	162.56345	15.74945	17.63927	19.86786	25.63563	33.81304	53.20324
35	188.63196	16.83818	19.13031	21.90401	29.40091	40.70049	69.91249
40	211.33990	17.70339	20.37508	23.68883	33.03455	48.00474	90.26035
45	230.77602	18.39098	21.41425	25.25334	36.54115	55.75100	115.03914
50	247.18563	18.93741	22.28178	26.62474	39.92516	63.96604	145.21374
60	272.23010	19.71676	23.61065	28.88059	46.34237	81.91760	226.70622
70	289.15042	20.20895	24.53679	30.61392	52.31872	102.10760	347.55449
80	300.31175	20.51980	25.18226	31.94574	57.88449	124.81515	526.76497
90	307.54348	20.71612	25.63212	32.96907	63.06789	150.35417	792.52299
100	312.16432	20.84011	25.94565	33.75537	67.89518	179.07773	1186.62562

TABLE B-15 6.000 Percent Gradient-series Factors

N	Uniform gradient P/G,6.000%,N	P 1,6.000%,N	Uniform percentage gradients P 2,6.000%,N	P 3,6.000%,N	P 5,6.000%,N	P 7,6.000%,N	P10,6.000%,N	N
1	0.94340	0.94340	0.94340	0.94340	0.94340	0.94340	0.94340	1
2	2.72339	1.84229	1.85119	1.86009	1.87789	1.89569	1.92239	2
4	8.41062	3.51488	3.56531	3.61639	3.72052	3.82732	3.99261	4
6	16.37668	5.03340	5.15250	5.27467	5.52855	5.79557	6.22201	6
8	26.05137	6.41205	6.62216	6.84043	7.30262	7.80113	8.62285	8
10	36.96241	7.66370	7.98300	8.31880	9.04337	9.84470	11.20830	10
12	48.72070	8.80005	9.24307	9.71468	10.75144	11.92702	13.92257	12
15	67.26680	10.31136	10.96040	11.66382	13.25359	15.12475	18.57549	15
20	98.70037	12.39078	13.41686	14.56153	17.26892	20.65859	27.44165	20
25	128.75653	14.02390	15.44353	17.07175	21.09839	26.45844	38.11177	25
30	156.12362	15.30652	17.11559	19.24630	24.75060	32.53707	50.95292	30
35	180.24098	16.31385	18.49510	21.13006	28.23376	38.90789	66.40680	35
40	201.00312	17.10499	19.63324	22.76192	31.55569	45.58495	85.00503	40
45	218.56548	17.72633	20.57224	24.17556	34.72385	52.58296	107.38738	45
50	233.21924	18.21431	21.34695	25.40016	37.74536	59.91735	134.32379	50
60	255.20423	18.89856	22.51344	27.38000	43.37528	75.66074	205.75373	60
70	269.71169	19.32062	23.30745	28.86574	48.49607	92.95402	309.20797	70
80	279.05845	19.58095	23.84792	29.98069	53.15376	111.94976	459.04403	80
90	284.97332	19.74152	24.21580	30.81739	57.39024	132.81559	676.05637	90
100	288.66462	19.84057	24.46621	31.44528	61.24360	155.73558	990.36223	100

TABLE B-16 7.000 Percent Gradient-series Factors

	Uniform gradient		Uniform percentage gradients					
N	P/G,7.000%,N	P 1,7.000%,N	P 2,7.000%,N	P 3,7.000%,N	P 5,7.000%,N	P 7,7.000%,N	P10,7.000%,N	N
1	0.93458	0.93458	0.93458	0.93458	0.93458	0.93458	0.93458	1
2	2.68146	1.81675	1.82549	1.83422	1.85169	1.86916	1.89536	2
4	8.18193	3.43547	3.48435	3.53387	3.63481	3.73832	3.89850	4
6	15.74492	4.87774	4.99181	5.10881	5.35188	5.60748	6.01553	6
8	24.76024	6.16279	6.36167	6.56821	7.00537	7.47664	8.25294	8
10	34.73913	7.30777	7.60650	7.92053	8.59763	9.34579	10.61757	10
12	45.29330	8.32794	8.73771	9.17363	10.13092	11.21495	13.11666	12
15	61.55397	9.65352	10.24391	10.88302	12.32504	14.01869	17.13423	15
20	88.10308	11.41133	12.32006	13.33166	15.71687	18.69159	24.61712	20
25	112.33008	12.72855	13.95439	15.35558	18.80335	23.36449	33.20951	25
30	133.38088	13.71562	15.24093	17.02844	21.61195	28.03738	43.07590	30
35	151.08297	14.45528	16.25369	18.41114	24.16769	32.71028	54.40520	35
40	165.62450	15.00955	17.05093	19.55400	26.49335	37.38318	67.41430	40
45	177.36147	15.42490	17.67851	20.49863	28.60962	42.05608	82.35228	45
50	186.70589	15.73614	18.17253	21.27941	30.53538	46.72897	99.50514	50
60	199.80696	16.14415	18.86757	22.45817	33.88237	56.07477	141.81776	60
70	207.67896	16.37325	19.29826	23.26348	36.65384	65.42056	197.60809	70
80	212.79684	16.50191	19.56515	23.81364	38.94875	74.76636	271.16913	80
90	214.95757	16.57415	19.73054	24.18951	40.84904	84.11215	368.16134	90
100	216.46937	16.61472	19.83302	24.44629	42.42257	93.45794	496.04817	100

TABLE B-17 8.000 Percent Gradient-series Factors

N	Uniform gradient	Uniform percentage gradients						N
	P/G,8.000%,N	P 1,8.000%,N	P 2,8.000%,N	P 3,8.000%,N	P 5,8.000%,N	P 7,8.000%,N	P10,8.000%,N	
1	0.92593	0.92593	0.92593	0.92593	0.92593	0.92593	0.92593	1
2	2.64060	1.79184	1.80041	1.80898	1.82613	1.84328	1.86900	2
4	7.96222	3.35893	3.40633	3.45435	3.55222	3.65258	3.80786	4
6	15.14615	4.72946	4.83878	4.95089	5.18375	5.42853	5.81920	6
8	23.55774	5.92809	6.11648	6.31207	6.72589	7.17175	7.90572	8
10	32.68692	6.97638	7.25616	7.55013	8.18355	8.88283	10.07023	10
12	42.16999	7.89318	8.27273	8.67622	9.56136	10.56237	12.31565	12
15	56.44515	9.05735	9.59544	10.17727	11.48784	13.02382	15.84214	15
20	78.90795	10.54586	11.35321	12.25004	14.35799	16.97662	22.16865	20
25	98.47890	11.61060	12.67404	13.88542	16.85105	20.74977	29.10305	25
30	114.71360	12.37221	13.66653	15.17571	19.01657	24.35144	36.70374	30
35	127.74659	12.91698	14.41231	16.19372	20.89756	27.78943	45.03476	35
40	137.96685	13.30666	14.97270	16.99691	22.53143	31.07118	54.16627	40
45	145.84153	13.58540	15.39379	17.63062	23.95063	34.20378	64.17519	45
50	151.82633	13.78478	15.71020	18.13060	25.18337	37.19401	75.14583	50
60	159.67662	14.02941	16.12662	18.83631	27.18424	42.77296	100.35076	60
70	163.97550	14.15458	16.36174	19.27561	28.69389	47.85635	130.63207	70
80	166.27366	14.21862	16.49450	19.54908	29.83291	52.48818	167.01218	80
90	167.48033	14.25139	16.56946	19.71931	30.69229	56.70858	210.71940	90
100	168.10511	14.26815	16.61178	19.82527	31.34069	60.55409	263.22944	100

TABLE B-18 10.00 Percent Gradient-series Factors

Uniform percentage gradients

	Uniform gradient								
N	P/G,10.00%,N	P 1,10.00%,N	P 2,10.00%,N	P 3,10.00%,N	P 5,10.00%,N	P 7,10.00%,N	P10,10.00%,N	N
1	0.90909	0.90909	0.90909	0.90909	0.90909	0.90909	0.90909	1
2	2.56198	1.74380	1.75207	1.76033	1.77686	1.79339	1.81818	2
4	7.54798	3.21393	3.25855	3.30375	3.39586	3.49029	3.63636	4
6	14.03943	4.45333	4.55388	4.65698	4.87102	5.09590	5.45455	6
8	21.36360	5.49822	5.66765	5.84346	6.21512	6.61512	7.27273	8
10	29.03592	6.37912	6.62531	6.88374	7.43981	8.05260	9.09091	10
12	36.71492	7.12177	7.44874	7.79584	8.55570	9.41275	10.90909	12
15	47.75808	8.02304	8.47262	8.95764	10.04642	11.31700	13.63636	15
20	63.92050	9.09585	9.73904	10.45048	12.11209	14.15987	18.18182	20
25	76.77347	9.79597	10.60724	11.52504	13.74906	16.63566	22.72727	25
30	86.50353	10.25286	11.20242	12.29853	15.04632	18.79176	27.27273	30
35	93.63136	10.55102	11.61045	12.85531	15.07436	20.66946	31.81818	35
40	98.73164	10.74560	11.89017	13.25608	16.88905	22.30469	36.36364	40
45	102.31730	10.87258	12.08194	13.54457	17.53466	23.72878	40.90909	45
50	104.80375	10.95545	12.21340	13.75223	18.04630	24.96897	45.45455	50
60	107.66824	11.04482	12.36531	14.00930	18.77306	26.98962	54.54546	60
70	108.97443	11.08288	12.43670	14.14250	19.22947	28.52213	63.63637	70
80	109.55582	11.09909	12.47025	14.21151	19.51611	29.68442	72.72728	80
90	109.80998	11.10599	12.48602	14.24727	19.69612	30.56592	81.81818	90
100	109.91953	11.10893	12.49343	14.26580	19.80916	31.23448	90.90909	100

TABLE B-19 12.00 Percent Gradient-series Factors

	Uniform gradient		Uniform percentage gradients					
N	P/G,12.00%,N	P 1,12.00%,N	P 2,12.00%,N	P 3,12.00%,N	P 5,12.00%,N	P 7,12.00%,N	P10,12.00%,N	N
1	0.89286	0.89286	0.89286	0.89286	0.89286	0.89286	0.89286	1
2	2.48725	1.69802	1.70600	1.71397	1.72991	1.74585	1.76977	2
4	7.16466	3.07889	3.12095	3.16354	3.25034	3.33931	3.47690	4
6	13.04158	4.20183	4.29451	4.38951	4.58666	4.79367	5.12360	6
8	19.43909	5.11502	5.26787	5.42637	5.76115	6.12107	6.71202	8
10	25.90432	5.85765	6.07517	6.30328	6.79342	7.33260	8.24422	10
12	32.14666	6.46157	6.74474	7.04492	7.70069	8.43837	9.72218	12
15	40.73105	7.16269	7.54115	7.94850	8.85983	9.91871	11.84162	15
20	52.43704	7.94097	8.45957	9.03074	10.35631	11.97685	15.12910	20
25	60.94781	8.40512	9.03495	9.74264	11.44005	13.61482	18.13334	25
30	66.83728	8.68193	9.39541	10.21093	12.22490	14.91838	20.87876	30
35	70.78072	8.84701	9.62123	10.51897	12.79328	15.95582	23.38766	35
40	73.35971	8.94545	9.76271	10.72160	13.20490	16.78146	25.68040	40
45	75.01679	9.00417	9.85134	10.85489	13.50300	17.43854	27.77562	45
50	76.06697	9.03918	9.90687	10.94257	13.71888	17.96148	29.69033	50
60	77.13415	9.07251	9.96345	11.03819	13.98844	18.70887	33.03908	60
70	77.54070	9.08437	9.98566	11.07956	14.12981	19.18224	35.83568	70
80	77.69187	9.08859	9.99437	11.09746	14.20395	19.48206	38.17116	80
90	77.74706	9.09009	9.99780	11.10521	14.24284	19.67196	40.12155	90
100	77.76694	9.09062	9.99914	11.10856	14.26323	19.79224	41.75036	100

TABLE B-20 15.00 Percent Gradient-series Factors

	Uniform gradient				Uniform percentage gradients			
N	P/G,15.00%,N	P 1,15.00%,N	P 2,15.00%,N	P 3,15.00%,N	P 5,15.00%,N	P 7,15.00%,N	P10,15.00%,N	N
1	0.86957	0.86957	0.86957	0.86957	0.86957	0.86957	0.86957	1
2	2.38185	1.63327	1.64083	1.64839	1.66352	1.67864	1.70132	2
4	6.64141	2.89308	2.93166	2.97072	3.05030	3.13185	3.25792	4
6	11.72126	3.86483	3.94715	4.03149	4.20640	4.38991	4.68211	6
8	16.96804	4.61437	4.74602	4.88242	5.17017	5.47902	5.98514	8
10	21.99825	5.19253	5.37449	5.56504	5.97362	6.42188	7.17733	10
12	26.60551	5.63849	5.86890	6.11263	6.64342	7.23812	8.26811	12
15	32.54039	6.12374	6.42000	6.73779	7.44511	8.26163	9.73278	15
20	39.84151	6.61033	6.99391	7.41372	8.37883	9.54452	11.77896	20
25	44.49555	6.86459	7.30894	7.80330	8.97131	10.43909	13.41734	25
30	47.31858	6.99745	7.48187	8.02784	9.34726	11.06290	14.72921	30
35	48.97526	7.06688	7.57679	8.15726	9.58581	11.49789	15.77964	35
40	49.92478	7.10316	7.62890	8.23185	9.73718	11.80121	16.62072	40
45	50.45943	7.12211	7.65750	8.27484	9.83323	12.01272	17.29418	45
50	50.75636	7.13202	7.67320	8.29962	9.89418	12.16022	17.83343	50
60	51.00823	7.13990	7.68655	8.32214	9.95739	12.33478	18.61094	60
70	51.08193	7.14205	7.69057	8.32961	9.98285	12.41966	19.10942	70
80	51.10298	7.14264	7.69179	8.33210	9.99309	12.46094	19.42902	80
90	51.10888	7.14280	7.69215	8.33292	9.99722	12.48101	19.63392	90
100	51.11052	7.14284	7.69226	8.33320	9.99888	12.49077	19.76529	100

APPENDIX
C

ACCELERATED-, NORMAL-, DEFERRED-SERIES FACTORS

TABLE C-1 Accelerated-, Normal-, Deferred-series Factors; 2.000 and 3.000 Percent

N	$P/F_a, 2.000\%, N$	$P/F_n, 2.000\%, N$	$P/F_d, 2.000\%, N$	$P/F_a, 3.000\%, N$	$P/F_n, 3.000\%, N$	$P/F_d, 3.000\%, N$	N
1	0.17283	0.00116	0.00039	0.17116	0.00115	0.00039	1
2	0.44140	0.00565	0.00193	0.43453	0.00555	0.00190	2
4	1.15181	0.03221	0.01123	1.12088	0.03119	0.01088	4
6	2.00402	0.09287	0.03308	1.92846	0.08863	0.03156	6
8	2.94140	0.19783	0.07199	2.79963	0.18614	0.06771	8
10	3.93173	0.35472	0.13192	3.70226	0.32908	0.12230	10
12	4.95440	0.56882	0.21626	4.61638	0.52040	0.19767	12
15	6.51919	1.00389	0.39481	5.98140	0.89967	0.35330	15
20	9.13753	2.03727	0.84949	8.17833	1.76545	0.73412	20
25	11.69870	3.43024	1.52092	10.22517	2.87750	1.26994	25
30	14.15733	5.11988	2.42164	12.09661	4.16261	1.95473	30
35	16.48980	7.01940	3.55451	13.78757	5.53893	2.77517	35
40	18.68484	9.02917	4.91488	15.30317	6.92610	3.71363	40
45	20.73860	11.04514	6.49249	16.65373	8.25158	4.75025	45
50	22.65177	12.96494	8.27296	17.85196	9.45397	5.86458	50

TABLE C-2 Accelerated-, Normal-, Deferred-series Factors; 3.500 and 4.000 Percent

N	P/F_a,3.500%,N	P/F_n,3.500%,N	P/F_d,3.500%,N	P/F_a,4.000%,N	P/F_n,4.000%,N	P/F_d,4.000%,N	N
1	0.17033	0.00114	0.00039	0.16951	0.00114	0.00038	1
2	0.43117	0.00551	0.00188	0.42785	0.00546	0.00186	2
4	1.10599	0.03070	0.01070	1.09119	0.03021	0.01054	4
6	1.89219	0.08660	0.03084	1.85689	0.08464	0.03013	6
8	2.73226	0.18061	0.06568	2.66712	0.17528	0.06373	8
10	3.59430	0.31710	0.11781	3.49058	0.30564	0.11352	10
12	4.45891	0.49802	0.18908	4.30857	0.47678	0.18094	12
15	5.73448	0.85232	0.33446	5.50097	0.80787	0.31678	15
20	7.74829	1.64536	0.68322	7.34778	1.53462	0.63634	20
25	9.57972	2.63985	1.16231	8.98743	2.42450	1.06495	25
30	11.21421	3.76181	1.76004	10.41596	3.40471	1.58705	30
35	12.65575	4.93480	2.45912	11.64588	4.40523	2.18321	35
40	13.91692	6.08889	3.23968	12.69630	5.36629	2.83305	40
45	15.01387	7.16538	4.08132	13.58821	6.24147	3.51710	45
50	15.96382	8.11864	4.96444	14.34220	6.99810	4.21781	50

TABLE C-3 Accelerated-, Normal-, Deferred-series Factors; 4.250 and 4.500 Percent

N	P/F$_a$,4.250%,N	P/F$_n$,4.250%,N	P/F$_d$,4.250%,N	P/F$_a$,4.500%,N	P/F$_n$,4.500%,N	P/F$_d$,4.500%,N
1	0.16910	0.00114	0.00038	0.16870	0.00113	0.00038
2	0.42620	0.00543	0.00186	0.42457	0.00541	0.00185
4	1.08395	0.02997	0.01045	1.07679	0.02974	0.01037
6	1.83958	0.08367	0.02979	1.82251	0.08273	0.02945
8	2.63535	0.17269	0.06279	2.60410	0.17015	0.06186
10	3.44024	0.30009	0.11145	3.39089	0.29467	0.10941
12	4.23596	0.46657	0.17702	4.16499	0.45661	0.17320
15	5.38897	0.78667	0.30836	5.28001	0.76612	0.30019
20	7.15786	1.48250	0.61429	6.97446	1.43242	0.59311
25	8.70962	2.32446	1.01979	8.44326	2.22916	0.97680
30	10.04546	3.24089	1.50787	9.69264	3.08612	1.43316
35	11.18188	4.16522	2.05856	10.74286	3.94021	1.94195
40	12.14085	5.04254	2.65170	11.61856	4.74128	2.48346
45	12.94540	5.83197	3.26863	12.34450	5.45354	3.04001
50	13.61744	6.50635	3.89306	12.94366	6.05479	3.59662

TABLE C-4 Accelerated-, Normal-, Deferred-series Factors; 4.625 and 4.750 Percent

N	P/F$_a$,4.625%,N	P/F$_n$,4.625%,N	P/F$_d$,4.625%,N	P/F$_a$,4.750%,N	P/F$_n$,4.750%,N	P/F$_d$,4.750%,N	N
1	0.16850	0.00113	0.00038	0.16830	0.00113	0.00038	1
2	0.42376	0.00540	0.00184	0.42295	0.00539	0.00184	2
4	1.07323	0.02962	0.01033	1.06969	0.02951	0.01029	4
6	1.81406	0.08226	0.02928	1.80566	0.08179	0.02912	6
8	2.58867	0.16889	0.06140	2.57337	0.16765	0.06094	8
10	3.36657	0.29201	0.10842	3.34249	0.28937	0.10743	10
12	4.13011	0.45173	0.17133	4.09562	0.44691	0.16948	12
15	5.22664	0.75608	0.29620	5.17400	0.74619	0.29227	15
20	6.88513	1.40812	0.58284	6.79732	1.38430	0.57278	20
25	8.31420	2.18321	0.95608	8.18779	2.13835	0.93587	25
30	9.52255	3.01194	1.39739	9.35651	2.93983	1.36264	30
35	10.53223	3.83302	1.88649	10.32727	3.72919	1.83282	35
40	11.36912	4.59854	2.40394	11.12710	4.46080	2.32731	40
45	12.05874	5.27516	2.93259	11.78228	5.10360	2.82951	45
50	12.62454	5.84294	3.45817	12.31661	5.63980	3.32582	50

TABLE C-5 Accelerated-, Normal-, Deferred-series Factors; 4.875 and 5.000 Percent

N	P/F_a, 4.875%, N	P/F_n, 4.875%, N	P/F_d, 4.875%, N	P/F_a, 5.000%, N	P/F_n, 5.000%, N	P/F_d, 5.000%, N	N
1	0.16810	0.00113	0.00038	0.16790	0.00113	0.00038	1
2	0.42214	0.00538	0.00184	0.42133	0.00537	0.00183	2
4	1.06617	0.02939	0.01025	1.06267	0.02927	0.01021	4
6	1.79732	0.08133	0.02895	1.78904	0.08087	0.02879	6
8	2.55819	0.16642	0.06049	2.54314	0.16520	0.06004	8
10	3.31865	0.28676	0.10645	3.29504	0.28418	0.10549	10
12	4.06153	0.44215	0.16766	4.02782	0.43745	0.16586	12
15	5.12206	0.73646	0.28840	5.07083	0.72687	0.28460	15
20	6.71102	1.36094	0.56291	6.62619	1.33804	0.55324	20
25	8.06398	2.09455	0.91615	7.94269	2.05180	0.89690	25
30	9.19442	2.86971	1.32888	9.03615	2.80152	1.29607	30
35	10.12780	3.67862	1.78090	9.93364	3.53121	1.73065	35
40	10.89226	4.32785	2.25347	10.66434	4.19952	2.18231	40
45	11.51475	4.93857	2.73057	11.25581	4.77979	2.63558	45
50	12.01940	5.44499	3.19927	11.73247	5.25811	3.07824	50

TABLE C-6   Accelerated-, Normal-, Deferred-series Factors; 5.125 and 5.250 Percent

N	P/F_a,5.125%,N	P/F_n,5.125%,N	P/F_d,5.125%,N	P/F_a,5.250%,N	P/F_n,5.250%,N	P/F_d,5.250%,N	N
1	0.16770	0.00113	0.00038	0.16750	0.00112	0.00038	1
2	0.42053	0.00535	0.00183	0.41973	0.00534	0.00182	2
4	1.05918	0.02916	0.01017	1.05571	0.02905	0.01013	4
6	1.78081	0.08042	0.02863	1.77263	0.07996	0.02846	6
8	2.52821	0.16399	0.05960	2.51340	0.16279	0.05916	8
10	3.27166	0.28163	0.10453	3.24851	0.27910	0.10359	10
12	3.99448	0.43281	0.16408	3.96152	0.42823	0.16233	12
15	5.02029	0.71744	0.28085	4.97042	0.70814	0.27716	15
20	6.54281	1.31559	0.54376	6.46084	1.29358	0.53447	20
25	7.82388	2.01005	0.87811	7.70748	1.96928	0.85978	25
30	8.88161	2.73520	1.26418	8.73069	2.67071	1.23320	30
35	9.74463	3.43682	1.69203	9.56060	3.34536	1.63496	35
40	10.44310	4.07562	2.11371	10.22831	3.95600	2.04758	40
45	11.00513	4.62700	2.54438	10.76239	4.47995	2.45680	45
50	11.45537	5.07882	2.96248	11.18772	4.90677	2.85173	50

TABLE C-7 Accelerated-, Normal-, Deferred-series Factors; 5.500 and 5.750 Percent

N	P/Fa, 5.500%, N	P/Fn, 5.500%, N	P/Fd, 5.500%, N	P/Fa, 5.750%, N	P/Fn, 5.750%, N	P/Fd, 5.750%, N	N
1	0.16710	0.00112	0.00038	0.16671	0.00112	0.00038	1
2	0.41814	0.00532	0.00182	0.41656	0.00530	0.00181	2
4	1.04883	0.02882	0.01005	1.04201	0.02860	0.00997	4
6	1.75644	0.07907	0.02814	1.74046	0.07819	0.02783	6
8	2.48414	0.16042	0.05830	2.45535	0.15810	0.05745	8
10	3.20287	0.27414	0.10173	3.15811	0.26928	0.09991	10
12	3.89670	0.41924	0.15888	3.83332	0.41048	0.15552	12
15	4.87269	0.68998	0.26995	4.77754	0.67236	0.26295	15
20	6.30103	1.25083	0.51643	6.14654	1.20972	0.49910	20
25	7.48169	1.89060	0.82441	7.26487	1.81556	0.79071	25
30	8.43933	2.54695	1.17380	8.16129	2.42983	1.11767	30
35	9.20690	3.17085	1.54529	8.87135	3.00690	1.46124	35
40	9.81717	3.72891	1.92235	9.42926	3.51703	1.80587	40
45	10.29956	4.20213	2.29189	9.86507	3.94454	2.13966	45
50	10.67920	4.58310	2.64432	10.20401	4.28467	2.45427	50

TABLE C-8 Accelerated-, Normal,- Deferred-series Factors; 6.000 and 7.000 Percent

N	P/F_a,6.000%,N	P/F_n,6.000%,N	P/F_d,6.000%,N	P/F_a,7.000%,N	P/F_n,7.000%,N	P/F_d,7.000%,N	N
1	0.16631	0.00112	0.00028	0.16476	0.00111	0.00037	1
2	0.41499	0.00528	0.00180	0.40881	0.00519	0.00177	2
4	1.03526	0.02838	0.00989	1.00890	0.02752	0.00959	4
6	1.72468	0.07732	0.02752	1.66360	0.07396	0.02632	6
8	2.42703	0.15582	0.05661	2.31820	0.14709	0.05342	8
10	3.11421	0.26452	0.09813	2.94676	0.24649	0.09138	10
12	3.77134	0.40193	0.15225	3.53668	0.36980	0.13995	12
15	4.68490	0.65527	0.25617	4.33789	0.59185	0.23103	15
20	5.99718	1.17018	0.48243	5.44704	1.02644	0.42193	20
25	7.05661	1.74396	0.75860	6.30149	1.48873	0.64435	25
30	7.89586	2.31896	1.06461	6.94736	1.93089	0.87958	30
35	8.55284	2.85282	1.38242	7.42978	2.32270	1.11272	35
40	9.06299	3.31924	1.69748	7.78721	2.64938	1.33327	40
45	9.45682	3.70555	1.99906	8.05049	2.90759	1.53473	45
50	9.75952	4.00931	2.27997	8.24357	3.10135	1.71380	50

TABLE C-9 Accelerated-, Normal-, Deferred-series Factors; 8.000 and 10.00 Percent

N	P/F$_a$,8.000%,N	P/F$_n$,8.000%,N	P/F$_d$,8.000%,N	P/F$_a$,10.00%,N	P/F$_n$,10.00%,N	P/F$_d$,10.00%,N	N
1	0.16323	0.00110	0.00037	0.16026	0.00108	0.00036	1
2	0.40279	0.00510	0.00174	0.39119	0.00494	0.00169	2
4	0.98355	0.02669	0.00930	0.93567	0.02514	0.00876	4
6	1.60558	0.07079	0.02518	1.49799	0.06496	0.02310	6
8	2.21609	0.13897	0.05045	2.03009	0.12433	0.04510	8
10	2.79153	0.22993	0.08519	2.51358	0.20070	0.07426	10
12	3.32165	0.34071	0.12882	2.94295	0.29038	0.10958	12
15	4.02524	0.53558	0.20874	3.48756	0.44102	0.17135	15
20	4.96433	0.90301	0.37009	4.16419	0.70503	0.28721	20
25	5.65496	1.27629	0.54962	4.61825	0.94996	0.40493	25
30	6.15329	1.61721	0.73092	4.91720	1.15417	0.51344	30
35	6.50861	1.90563	0.90247	5.11168	1.31188	0.60716	35
40	6.75992	2.13524	1.05740	5.23718	1.42646	0.68440	40
45	6.93662	2.30850	1.19251	5.31769	1.50538	0.74587	45
50	7.06031	2.43264	1.30715	5.36911	1.55698	0.79346	50

TABLE C-10   Accelerated-, Normal-, Deferred-series Factors; 12.00 and 15.00 Percent

N	P/F$_a$,12.00%,N	P/F$_n$,12.00%,N	P/F$_d$,12.00%,N	P/F$_a$,15.00%,N	P/F$_n$,15.00%,N	P/F$_d$,15.00%,N	N
1	0.15740	0.00106	0.00036	0.15330	0.00103	0.00035	1
2	0.38015	0.00478	0.00163	0.36457	0.00456	0.00156	2
4	0.89125	0.02371	0.00826	0.83044	0.02177	0.00758	4
6	1.40057	0.05974	0.02123	1.27097	0.05287	0.01878	6
8	1.86551	0.11156	0.04044	1.65248	0.09534	0.03452	8
10	2.27305	0.17589	0.05500	1.96970	0.14537	0.05362	10
12	2.62218	0.24877	0.09370	2.22747	0.19913	0.07478	12
15	3.04577	0.36579	0.14168	2.52056	0.27996	0.10791	15
20	3.53649	0.55675	0.22542	2.82724	0.39882	0.15999	20
25	3.83749	0.71879	0.30325	2.99210	0.48731	0.20245	25
30	4.01860	0.84233	0.35385	3.07903	0.54649	0.23384	30
35	4.12628	0.92956	0.42064	3.12432	0.58312	0.25556	35
40	4.18979	0.98750	0.45966	3.14772	0.60445	0.26991	40
45	4.22702	1.02398	0.48304	3.15975	0.61623	0.27906	45
50	4.24875	1.04579	0.50313	3.16590	0.62240	0.28473	50

INDEX

INDEX